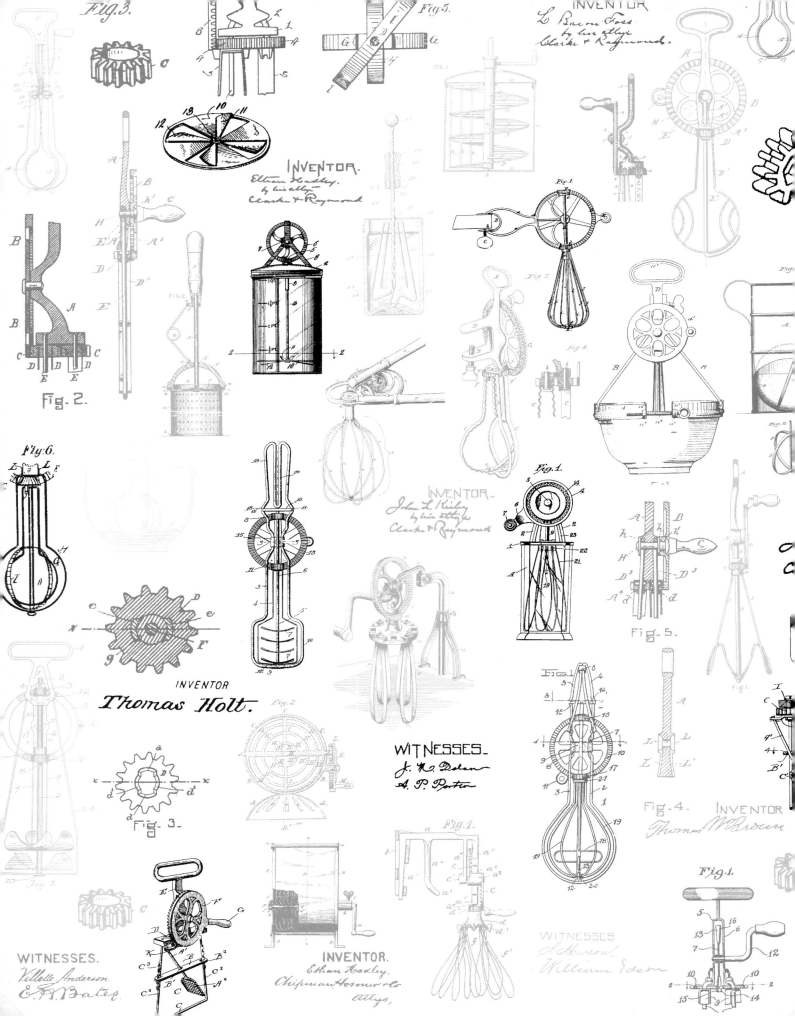

The Eggbeater Chronicles

SECOND EDITION

The Eggbeater Chronicles

THE STIRRING STORY OF AMERICA'S GREATEST INVENTION

Don Thornton

PHOTOGRAPHS BY
DONALD G. SIMONS and ROBERT S. ARNOLD

Thornton House
Sunnyvale, California

THE EGGBEATER CHRONICLES

Second Edition

© 1999 by Donald D. Thornton
Photographs © 1999 by Robert S. Arnold, Sturbridge, MA;
Diane S. Thornton, Sunnyvale, California

Cover & interior design by Diane Thornton, Sunnyvale, CA
This book has been set in Adobe's Minion and Univers families,
Digital Typeface Corp.'s Arsis, and ITC Isadora.

For information, address publisher at:
Thornton House
1345 Poplar Avenue
Sunnyvale, CA 94087-3770
Phone: (408) 737-0434
Fax: (408) 737-0191
email: info@thorntonhouse.com

www.thorntonhouse.com/publishing.html

Library of Congress Catalog Card Number 98-066124

ISBN 0-9641243-4-3

Printed in the United States of America

5 4 3 2 1

To Donald G. Simons
1926 – 1996

Put all your eggs in one basket
and —
watch that basket.

—MARK TWAIN, *PUDD'NHEAD WILSON*

Contents

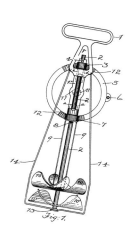

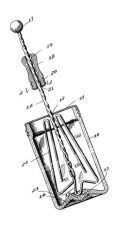

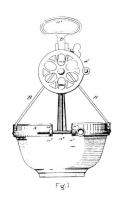

Fig.1.

Foreword

*By Linda Campbell Franklin, author, **300 Years of Kitchen Collectibles***

Dear Don & Diane,

It's hard to believe you've had to do this new edition because of so many new discoveries! A few years ago, I wrote the Foreword in your *nonpareil, acme, ace, non-plus-ultra, AAA, can't **Beat This!**,* and relived my early kinetic feelings about eggbeaters. At the time of your book, 1994, it had only been about 25 years since we few collectors of kitchen antiques thought that there were — tops — about 40 or 50 eggbeaters in all. To most of us, including me in 1974 when I wrote my first book, "old eggbeater" meant iron Dovers in diverse sizes and shapes. We included some 20th century A&Js and a few others, especially the Aluminum Beauty, and we happily didn't know what we were missing until many years later.

Your *Beat This* showed longtime collectors that diligent searching of patent records, flea markets and kitchen drawers, by you and a dozen or so other collectors around the country, had resulted in hundreds of more beaters coming to light. Your book shared quite a few rarities, and everybody smiled, sighed, and assumed that the catalog was now complete. I bet it wasn't but a few weeks after publication that you began hearing about even more new beaters. And now you've added over 300 more! Congratulations to everyone involved.

Those Yolk Folks, introduced in your first book, have been lying around waiting for another chance to show you a page in their Albumen. So, Don and Diane, I give you:

Those Yolk Folks & the Family Albumen, Part 2

Psychiatrist (Ingrid Bergman)
to her patient (Gregory Peck) in
Spellbound, 1945:

"I'm glad you didn't dream of me as an eggbeater
as one of my patients did."

Acknowledgments

Many thanks to those who shared their collections, research and ephemera and took the time to make this book possible.

Butch & Dea Allen
Robert S. Arnold
Chuck & Bonnie Badger
Ralph & Faye Beckwith
Ed Boedecker
Carol & Jim Bohn
Dell & Marcia Breon
Diane M. Calkins of the Free Library
    of Philadelphia
Erwin & Glenda Clark
Reid Cooper
Jack P. Dazey
Guy & Sheila DiAmbrosio
Mary Faria
Patricia Feeley of the Boston Public
    Library
Jack & Marty Ford
Linda Campbell Franklin
George Gaspari
Robert Gilson
John Gray
Carroll & Bill Griffiths
Bob & Kaaren Grossman
Tim & Sandy Gruender
Suzanne Dazey
Jack & Judy Howe
Janet & Dale Hoy
Bruce Johnson
Betty & Frederick Johnson
Steve Kehrer
Rob Roy Kelly
Mark & Sharon Kempfer

Nancy Kosiewski
Barbara Kraus
Charlie & Donna Krebs
Lyle Krug
Brian Mair
Bill & Lois Maloney
Carole & Larry Meeker
Diane & Jerry Mertz
Jim & Phyllis Moffet
Keith & Jeanne Monnier
Terry Olivares
Arlene C. Palmer of the New Britain
    (Connecticut) Public Library
Robert Rauhauser
Sunny Scharnhorst
Gale & Billie Scarborough
Trish & Ed Seidel
Paul Smith
Steve Smith
George & Helen Storey
Sunnyvale Center for Innovation,
    Invention & Ideas
Rosella Tinsley
Randy & Phyllis Tompkins
Dennis Traverso
Rosemary & Bill Ulmer
Margaret Upchurch & Kyle Goad
Bob & Phyllis Van Buiten
Doris Willis
Anne & Doug Young
Jackie & Joe Young

And a very *special* thank you to Cherie and Reid Cooper, Bob and Susan Arnold, Butch and Dea Allen, Terry Olivares, and, of course, Jim and Phyllis Moffet.

Introduction

*I*t's been five years since we published *Beat This, The Eggbeater Chronicles*. *Beat This* sold out in three quick years — at least they were quick for Diane and me. Encouraged by author Linda Campbell Franklin and fellow collectors Jim and Phyllis Moffet, we had taken a big gamble — we self-published a major book, on eggbeaters no less, and marketed it and sold it ourselves.

Beat This was a family affair: I did the research and writing, Diane's father, Don Simons, took the photos, and Diane put it all together in an easy-to-use book that many say set a new standard for quality collector books.

We took a loan and had 3,000 copies printed. The books ended up in boxes stacked in corners and hallways throughout our home. Part of our marketing approach was that there were only 3,000 copies — that the book itself would become collectible. And it has.

Following *Beat This,* we did a second major book, this one on another true Americana collectible, the apple parer. We published *Apple Parers* in 1997 and sales since then have been brisk.

What was next? I wanted to do a book on can openers and jumped headfirst into patent research. But then something strange occurred. It was as if the collectible world had rediscovered *Beat This.* What had been a trickle of orders grew into a steady stream. And they just kept coming in. With no books to fill the orders, we were sending back checks with notes of apology. Finally, we realized it was time to do a new, updated eggbeater book.

I had never stopped gathering beater patents and other ephemera. We also had been lucky to add some astounding, unknown beaters to our collection. And our network of collector friends always kept us posted on new discoveries.

Mixing the old photos and text with new photos and new text proved to be a monumental, but very rewarding, task.

Don Simons succumbed to ALS in 1996 and photographer Bob Arnold (whose work graces *Apple Parers)* took over for him, shooting nearly 200 photos of newly-discovered mixers. A corresponding amount of work went into patent and manufacturer research. As work progressed, several chapters were reorganized, a new chapter was added, and nearly all the chapters were expanded, with the churn chapter jumping from 10 to 26 pages.

Now two years after we launched work on it, we present *The Eggbeater Chronicles, Second Edition.* It features our trademark in-depth research, beautiful photos and a design and layout unmatched by any other collectors' book.

All of this for America's greatest invention!

We gave that lofty title to the eggbeater in the introduction to *Beat This,* and although five years have passed since *Beat This* first appeared, that introduction is still a grand tribute worth repeating:

Without a doubt, it's America's greatest invention.

Forget the wheel, forget the water closet, forget the auto, forget television, radio, and the telephone. Forget the computer, the VCR and MTV.

The eggbeater has had more impact than all of them put together. And impact where it counts — in the kitchen.

The rotary crank eggbeater revolutionized cooking in America. It took the deadly drudgery out of mixing food ingredients. And that was a big mix, ranging from scrambled eggs, to cream, to batters, to cakes and scores of other deserts, breads, sauces. You name it.

Mixing became an art — and the variation of eggbeaters vying for attention on the marketplace told a true American success story.

For decades, the eggbeater's utilitarian beauty graced every kitchen in the USA. It's impact on the stomachs of America,

Eggbeater ephemera is unbeatable!

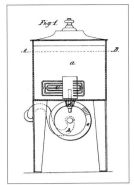

Ralph Collier patent
Dec. 23, 1856
Pat. No. 16,267

and the world for that matter, cannot be measured — but obviously it is monumental.

The patent for the first rotary crank in America was granted Dec. 23, 1856 to Ralph Collier of Baltimore, who in promoting his device said:

"Eggs prepared by beating are thoroughly charged with atmospheric air, and would on account of their comparative easy digestion in this form, be used so much more than they are, were it not for the laborious and fatiguing operation of beating eggs by hand." (must run collier patent drawing here)

It was the beginning of the beater revolution. Collier's device apparently never was manufactured — but it set the stage for a century of mixing ideas.

There were more than 1,000 patents granted and of those, several hundred different mixers made it to the marketplace. They range from the handheld, to the Archimedes, the rotary, the ratchet, the rope powered, the water powered and the squeeze.

But then came the electric powered mixer. Laziness took over. Mixing became boring. And slowly it all came full circle — with unimaginative electric motors replacing rotary cranks

the drudgery returned. The soul of mixing was gone.

And with it the popularity of America's greatest invention.

In recent years, there has been one brief moment of recognition. In late 1992 the Smithsonian Institution featured an early Dover eggbeater in its Hands on History exhibit at the National Museum of American Art.

But for decades the hand-held rotary eggbeater has been ignored. Forgotten.

Until now. In *Beat This* and its moving sequel, *The Eggbeater Chronicles, Second Edition,* the glory continues to return.

—Don Thornton,
Sunnyvale, California, 1999

More unbeatable eggbeater ephemera

A Guide to Using This Book

Beater Identification

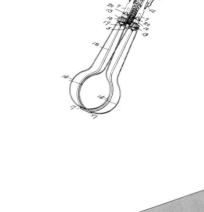

The names on the beaters will be listed as they actually appear in **bold face** type in the photo captions.

If the beater has no markings, but can be identified through an advertisement or other means, the name will appear in *CAPS*. This is to provide the reader with a quick means of identification.

Price guide

The values listed here are based on surveys of collectors, dealers, and Internet auctions. They are highly subjective and are listed only as a guide — there are no fixed prices in the mixed up eggbeater field.

Prices vary from region to region, buyer to buyer and in the past three years have been turned upside down by Internet sales. Internet auctions have leveled the playing field for many collectors — insuring everyone gets a chance at a rare mixer.

In such auctions, it usually comes down to two collectors competing for a prized beater and both willing to pay an astounding amount to add the item to their collections.

Do the results of Internet auctions set the price standard? No, because there is no standard. For example, when two people are competing for something they really want, the price is going to reflect how much one of them is willing to pay more than the other — and it can cause longtime collectors to shake their heads in disbelief. Use this book, and Internet auction prices, as a guide and not an absolute.

Here's an item that doesn't fit in any of the 27 chapters. Call it beater objet d'art. This mixer-in-motion was purchased at the 1999 KOOKS convention auction by Mark and Sharon Kempfer.

Beater Placement

There are eggbeaters in this book that fit in two or three different chapters. We put the beaters where we thought they fit best. For example, there will be foreign Archimedes in *Chapter 12, Archimedes,* and not in *Chapter 26, International Mix.* Another example is small churns. Several jar churns — because of their small size — are featured in *Chapter 18, Rotary Beaters With Containers,* instead of *Chapter 13, Dazey and Other Churns.*

One Word or Two?

You may notice the two spellings: Before the turn of the century, it was "egg beater," two words, and as such graced all early mixers. Some time after 1900, it ended up one word, "eggbeater."

Beater sizes

The measurements listed were made with a ruler by human hands and may be off one- or two-eighths of an inch either way. And some of the devices themselves may have been altered over the years by heavy use. It's best to use the listed sizes as a general guide, not as an absolute.

Patent clues

French:
> BTE — abbreviation for *breveteor* or patentee.
> SGDG — *sans garante de gouvernement,* or registered, but without warranty by the government.
> *Brevete en Franco* — patented in France.
> *Depose* — registered.

German:
> DRGM — *Deutsches Reichs GebrawchsMuster* (pre-1918)
> DRP — *Deutshces Reichspatent*
> *Ges Gesch,* or *Gesetzlich Geschutzt* — legally patented or registered, used after 1899.

Danish:
> *Eneret* — registered in Denmark

English:
> *R. D.* or *Reg. Des. No.* — Registered Design

Conversation between Leonard Vole (Tyrone Power)
and Sir Wilfrid (Charles Laughton) in
Witness for the Prosecution, 1957:

VOLE

I'm a bit of an inventor. Nothing big, just household things — pocket pencil sharpeners, keychains, flashlights and that sort of thing. But my best is really this eggbeater. You see, it not only beats the egg, but it also separates the yolk from the white.

SIR WILFRID

Is that desirable?

VOLE

If you were a housewife, Sir Wilfrid, you'd see it right away.

....

LATER,
SIR WILFRID
TO THE POLICE

This is the dangerous Leonard Vole. You better search him — he might be armed with an eggbeater.

Chapter 1

Dover

"Beats the whites of two eggs in ten seconds."

The Dover is unbeatable. The simple but beautiful hand crank mixer was one of the first mechanical eggbeaters mass produced in the world.

Horace Whitney was the man who initially marketed the eggbeater, or any kitchen utensil for that matter. He purchased the patents and exclusive rights for the production of the hand crank rotary beater and named it after the hometown of his business — Dover — a name that is even today associated with the most popular collectible of cast-iron eggbeaters.

But the Dover name didn't evolve from the eggbeater. It has deep and proud New England roots. It all started in 1833 when Whitney, of Kennebunk, Maine, opened a general store and tinware business in Dover, New Hampshire. Under the name Horace Whitney & Company, the combination factory and retail store was in a red brick building on Main Street.

The business puttered along, with tinware and a line of cooking stoves — very fine cooking stoves — that brought fame to the city of Dover. Whitney realized the name recognition and changed the name of the business to the Dover Stove Factory.

In 1857 the name was changed again, to the Dover Stamping Company, and a very important corporate move was made: The opening of a Boston office at 67 Blackstone Street.

During the Civil War, the firm provided the Union army tin cups, canteens, knives, forks and lanterns. By the end of the war, Dover was in position to launch an American first — mass production with a marketing plan of a fleet of traveling salesmen.

But its namesake was about to fall by the wayside. The main market was Boston, and in 1865 Whitney initiated work on a new factory in Cambridgeport (later Cambridge). The factory opened June 16, 1866 and the move from Dover was complete.

The firm maintained its stove market and successfully went after sales in the domestic housewares field. In 1869 it moved its sales office to 88-90 North Street in Boston *(fig. 1-1)*, offering a full line of tin housewares, including pans, tea and coffee pots and stove ornaments.

The firm also offered two eggbeaters *(fig. 1-2)* prior to its own trade name DOVER model.

FIG. 1-1

The 1869 Dover catalog cover featured the North Street Dover sales office.

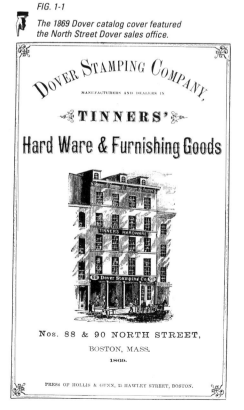

DOVER STAMPING COMPANY,

MANUFACTURERS AND DEALERS IN

TINNERS'

Hard Ware & Furnishing Goods

Nos. 88 & 90 NORTH STREET,

BOSTON, MASS.

1869.

PRESS OF HOLLIS & GUNN, 25 HAWLEY STREET, BOSTON.

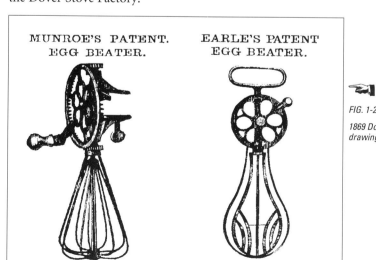

MUNROE'S PATENT. EGG BEATER.

EARLE'S PATENT EGG BEATER.

FIG. 1-2

1869 Dover catalog drawings

The first was the table-mount EP MONROE PATENTED APRIL 19, 1859 (*fig. 1-3*). The 1869 Dover Stamping Company catalog said of the MONROE:

"This beater is too well known to the public to need our commendation." Although it was offered in the Dover catalog (even misspelled as "Munroe's"), Dover did not manufacture the MONROE. This beater and others were made by Monroe Manufacturing Company of Fitchburg, Massachusetts (*See Chapter 6, Monroe Brothers, page 59*).

The second was EARL'S PAT JULY 7 1863 (*fig. 1-4*), by Timothy Earle, a prolific inventor from Smithfield, Rhode Island. (Although Earle spelled his name, "Earle," the beater is embossed EARL'S.)

Said the same catalog about the EARL'S: "This, while it is the simplest, is the most effective Egg Beater made. Held in the hand with an immovable rest, it stands firmly wherever placed and will beat eggs with greater rapidity than any other; while the price places it within the reach of all. It is cleaned by a moment's rapid turning in hot water."

Marked with the July 7, 1863 patent date, the EARL'S is a heavy-duty cast-iron beater. Although it bears little resemblance to the actual patent drawing (*fig. 1-5*), it is a very desirable piece.

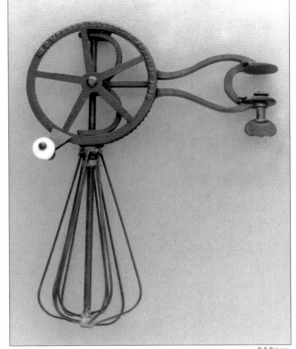

FIG. 1-3

EP MONROE
PATENTED APRIL 19 1859
Shelf-mount
10-1/2" high   8-1/2" across
—$1,200—

D G Simons

FIG. 1-4

EARL'S
PAT JULY 7 1863

Note: "e" dropped from "Earle's" in beater embossing.
10"   —$1,500—

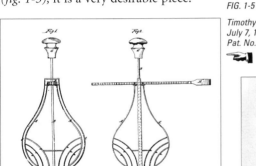

FIG. 1-5

Timothy Earle patent
July 7, 1863
Pat. No. 39,134

FIG. 1-6

1870 Dover eggbeaters (left to right):

DOVER EGG BEATER
PAT MAY 31st 1870
10"   beveled wheel   —$70—

DOVER EGG BEATER
PAT MAY 31ST 1870
16-1/2"   hotel model   —$325—

DOVER EGG BEATER
PAT MAY 31 1870
12-1/2"   —$250—
Note: A rarer version of this model comes with a table-mount.

DOVER EGG BEATER
PAT MAY 31ST 1870
10"   flat wheel   —$75—

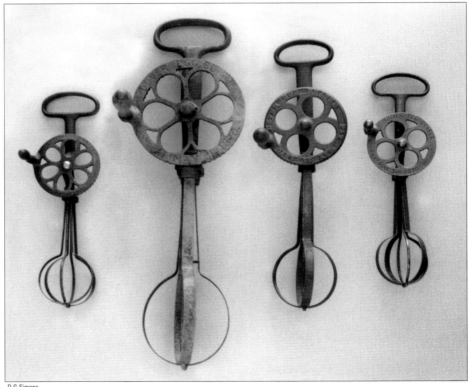

D G Simons

The real mixing revolution came when the Dover rotary went into mass production with its 1870 beaters *(fig. 1-6)*, including a rare tumbler model *(fig. 1-7)*.

And the person behind that revolution was Horace Whitney, described as a man quick to seize on and offer useful inventions patented by others, including Monroe, Earle and Turner Williams of Providence, Rhode Island.

It was Williams who patented what became the original DOVER beater *(fig. 1-8)*. First called WILLIAMS' EGG BEATER, its May 31, 1870 patent application said in part:

"The nature of my invention consists in arranging in an egg beater two revolving beater-frames, said frames occupying the same working space and arranged to revolve in opposite directions, so that they may cut against each other with a very peculiar shearing action … The advantage of having two wheels operating in the same space and revolving in different directions is that the fluid being acted upon is cut and thoroughly beaten almost instantaneously…"

An 1877 Dover Stamping Company catalog *(fig. 1-9)* attributed three dates to the DOVER — July 7, 1863, June 5, 1866 and May 31, 1870. The 1863 patent is by Timothy Earle *(fig. 1-4)* and the 1870 by Turner Williams *(fig. 1-8)*. So far the 1866 patent has proven elusive.

The 1870 DOVER is the centerpiece of many beater collections, including one model marked only BOSTON EGG BEATER *(fig. 1-10)* There also is a very rare and unusual 11" 1870 model with a coil-type bottom *(fig. 1-11)*.

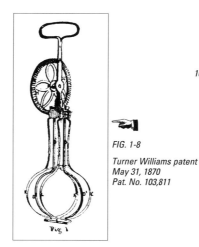

FIG. 1-8

Turner Williams patent
May 31, 1870
Pat. No. 103,811

FIG. 1-7

**DOVER EGG BEATER
PAT MAY 31ST 1870**
10" flat wheel, tumbler
model
—$150—

D Thornton

COOPER COLLECTION

FIG. 1-9

1877 Dover Stamping Company
catalog sheet

DOVER STAMPING COMPANY. 93

KITCHEN WARE AND HARD WARE.

THE

DOVER EGG BEATER.

Patented July 7, 1863,
" June 5, 1866.
" May 31, 1870.

MAMMOTH. FAMILY SIZE. FOR TUMBLERS.

ABSOLUTE PERFECTION!

Beats the WHITES of Two Eggs IN TEN SECONDS.
The WHITES of Six Eggs in TWENTY SECONDS.

And both so completely that the dish containing them may be inverted without a particle of the beaten mass falling.

Six eggs may be so thoroughly beaten as to **FILL A QUART MEASURE.**

Notice the revolving Flat Beaters are on **TWO CENTERS**; in turning, they *interlace each other* and draw the Egg to the center of the bowl, when by a

THOUSAND CROSS CURRENTS

THE EGGS ARE CUT AND AERATED IN A FEW SECONDS.

FIG. 1-10

BOSTON EGG BEATER 10"
—$85—

D G Simons

FIG. 1-11

**DOVER EGG BEATER
MAY 31ST 1870** 11"
—$550—

D G Simons

BADGER COLLECTION

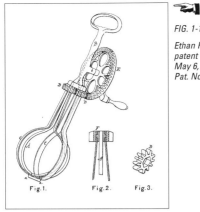

FIG. 1-12

Ethan Hadley
patent
May 6, 1873
Pat. No. 138,647

FIG. 1-13

**DOVER EGG
BEATER
PAT MAY 6TH
1873**
10"
—$95—

D Thornton

FIG. 1-14

L. Bacon Foss
patent
Sept. 7, 1880
Pat. No. 232,018

FIG. 1-15

Thomas W.
Brown patent
July 14, 1885
Pat. No. 322,250

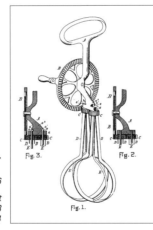

FIG. 1-16

Ethan Hadley patent
April 3, 1888
Pat. No. 380,564

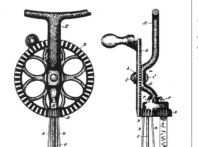

FIG. 1-17

John L. Kirby patent
July 9, 1889
Pat. No. 406,653

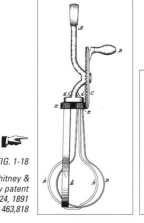

FIG. 1-18

Edward H. Whitney &
John L. Kirby patent
Nov. 24, 1891
Pat. No. 463,818

FIG. 1-19

Thomas W. Brown design patent
Dec. 27, 1898
Pat. No. 29,873

Another highly collectible beater is the May 6, 1873 10-incher, patented by Ethan Hadley of Chicopee Falls, Massachusetts (figs. 1-12 & 1-13), who described it as "an improvement on the Dover egg beater" with a "hard metal annular pinion."

On Sept. 7, 1880, L. Bacon Foss of Boston, an assignor to Dover, was granted a patent (fig. 1-14) with a bowl and a mounting device for the Dover beater. Unfortunately, apparently it was never manufactured.

Dovers are often identified by their patent dates, which were embossed on the main gear wheel. In addition to 1870 and 1873, other important Dover patent dates include:

▶ JULY 14, 1885 (fig. 1-15), appearing on a 10-1/2" Dover, a patent listing improvements by the prolific Thomas W. Brown of Belmont, Massachusetts. This patent date obviously is for the very similar STANDARD mixer and another rare beater, a cast-iron model with heavy wire and wood D-shaped handle (See Chapter 5, Standard, page 43).

▶ APRIL 3, 1888 (fig. 1-16), with more gear improvements, again by Hadley, who this time listed himself as assignor to the Dover Stamping Company. A third Hadley patent was granted June 16, 1891 and again related to Dover improvements. By this time, however, Hadley listed himself as assignor to the Lamb Knitting Machine Manufacturing Company of Chicopee Falls, Massachusetts.

▶ JULY 9, 1889 (fig. 1-17), featuring improvements in the gear "beating-floats" by John L. Kirby of Cambridge, who described himself as an assignor to Dover.

▶ NOV. 24, 1891 (fig. 1-18) by Edward H. Whitney, son of Dover founder Horace, and Kirby, for even more improvements.

▶ DEC. 27, 1898 (fig. 1-19), a design patent by Brown, this time for a steel (rather than cast-iron) handle. However, the date appears on a regular 12-1/2" cast-iron Dover with its usual handle. The steel handle itself was utilized by the Standard Manufacturing Company (See Chapter 5, Standard, page 46).

The Dover egg beater is the best in the market. It will do in five minutes the work that in former years required half an hour.

—*MISS PARLOA'S NEW COOK BOOK*, 1880

☞

FIG. 1-20

DOVER PAT JULY 14 '85 USA
(main wheel)

MADE IN BOSTON USA
(from one spoke around center)

10 *(main shaft near handle)*
10-1/2"
—$55—

D G Simons

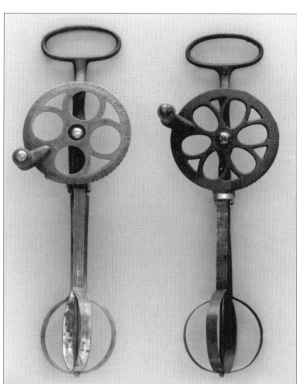

D G Simons

☞

FIG. 1-21

Dover 98s (left to right):

DOVER BEATER PAT. DEC. 27–98
Four-hole wheel
12-1/2"
—$50—

DOVER BEATER PAT. DEC. 27–98
BOSTON USA *(around center pin)*
Six-hole wheel
12-1/2"
—$45—

D G Simons

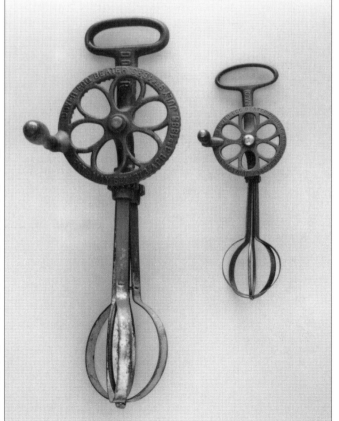

☞

FIG. 1-22

Triple-date Dovers (left to right):

DOVER EGG BEATER
PATD MAY 6TH 1873.
APR. 3RD 1888. JULY 9TH 1889.
(main wheel)

DOVER *(main shaft near handle)*

DOVER STAMPING CO.
(back of main shaft)
16-1/2"   —$295—

Note: This beater also comes in a 12-1/2" model, with the exact same markings. It is usually in the $85 range.

DOVER EGG BEATER
PATD MAY 6TH 1873.
APR. 3RD 1888. JULY 9TH 1889.
(main wheel)

DOVER *(main shaft near handle)*

BOSTON USA *(center pin)*
10"   —$45—

Many Dovers are embossed with single-year patent dates *(figs. 1-20 & 1-21)*, while others feature three dates.

The first three-date combination is 1873-1888-1889 *(fig. 1-22)*, which includes the popular 16-1/4" Dover, with optional table-mount. This beater is very similar to the 1870 model, but 1/4" shorter. And it should be noted that there is another 16-1/4" Dover model without a patent date but marked MAMMOTH DOVER EGG BEATER NO. 300 and made by the Taplin Manufacturing Company *(See Chapter 4, Taplin, page 35).*

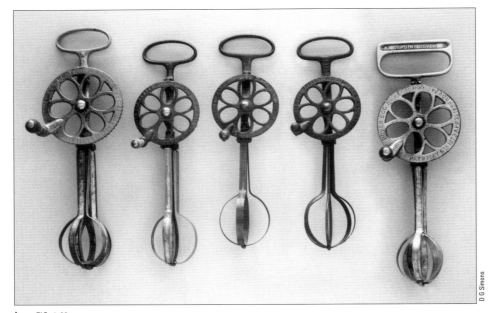

The second three-date combination is 1873-1888-1891 *(fig. 1-23)* which covers a wide range of beaters. One of the more collectible of these is the 11-1/4" nickel-plated model, with top gearing and a strong D-handle embossed GENUINE DOVER. There is an identical Dover mixer at the same height, with the same handle but no other major identification, except on a few with BOSTON U.S.A. around the center pin *(fig. 1-24)*. The 1873-1888-1891 combination also appears on 12-1/2" beaters *(fig. 1-25)*

D G Simons

FIG. 1-23

Triple-date Dovers (left to right):

DOVER EGG BEATER PATD MAY 6TH 1873 APR. 3D 1888 NOV. 24TH 1891
MADE IN BOSTON U.S.A. *(from one spoke around center)*
DOVER EGG BEATER CO. *(back of main stem)* 11-1/4" —$55—

DOVER EGG BEATER PATD MAY 6 1873 APR. 3D 1888. NOV. 24TH 1891
BOSTON U.S.A. *(center pin)*
DOVER STAMPING CO. *(back of main shaft)* 10-1/2" —$45—

DOVER EGG BEATER PATD MAY 6TH 1873 APR. 3D 1888 NOV. 24 1891
BOSTON U.S.A. *(center pin)*
DOVER STAMPING CO. *(back of main shaft)* 10" —$45—

DOVER EGG BEATER PATD MAY 6TH 1873 APR. 3D 1888 NOV. 24TH 1891
BOSTON U.S.A. *(center pin)*
D. S. CO. NEW DOVER *(front of main shaft)*
DOVER STAMPING CO. *(back of main shaft)* 10" —$50—

DOVER EGG BEATER PATD MAY 6TH 1873 APR 3D 1888. NOV. 24TH 1891
MADE IN BOSTON U.S.A. *(to and around center pin)*
DOVER STAMPING CO. *(backside top D-handle)*
GENUINE DOVER *(top of D-handle)* 11-1/4" —$75—
Note: This model also comes with an oval-handle that has an embossing typo — 1881 instead of 1891.

D G Simons

FIG. 1-24

No-date Dovers (left to right):

GENUINE DOVER *(one side)*
DOVER STAMPING CO *(other side D-handle top)*
Nickel-plated
11-1/4" —$60—

GENUINE DOVER *(one side)*
DOVER STAMPING CO *(other side D-handle top)*
BOSTON U.S.A. *(center pin)*
11-1/4" —$60—

DOVER EGG BEATER CO. *(back side main shaft)*
BOSTON U.S.A. *(center pin)*
Oval handle 11-1/4" —$55—

R S Arnold

FIG. 1-25

Triple-date Dovers (left to right):

DOVER EGG BEATER PATD MAY 6TH 1873 APR 3D 1888 NOV. 24TH 1891
D.S. CO. NEW DOVER *(front of main shaft)*
DOVER STAMPING CO. *(back of main shaft)*
12-12" —$80—

DOVER EGG BEATER PATD MAY 6TH 1873 APR 3D 1888 NOV. 24TH 1891
1 *(front of main shaft)*
DOVER STAMPING CO. *(back of main shaft)*
12-12" —$80—

THE EGGBEATER CHRONICLES

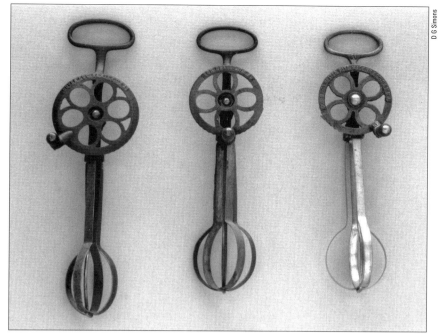

FIG. 1-26

No-date Dovers (left to right):

DOVER EGG BEATER U.S.A.
10-3/4" —$45—

EGG BEATER U.S.A. *9-1/2"* —$40—

DOVER EGG BEATER PATD MADE IN BOSTON U.S.A.
9-1/2" —$45—

A woman and her Dover Egg Beater are never separated except by death. She will not sell, exchange or lend it. To a practical housewife, it is of more importance than precious gems.

—**DOVER CATALOG**

FIG. 1-27

EGG BEATER U.S.A.
Slotted dashers
9-1/2"
—$125—

MOFFET COLLECTION

Other Dovers without embossed dates *(fig. 1-26)* feature U.S.A. in their names: DOVER EGG BEATER U.S.A., EGG BEATER U.S.A. — some with slotted dashers *(fig. 1-27)* — and DOVER EGG BEATER PATD MADE IN BOSTON U.S.A.

Dover also produced "tumbler" models, beaters with small dashers for mixing in tumblers (glasses). They came in at least three sizes *(fig. 1-28).*

FIG. 1-28

Tumbler Dovers (left to right):

DOVER EGG BEATER PATD MAY 6TH 1873 APR. 3D 1888 NOV. 24TH 1891 BOSTON U.S.A. *(center pin)*
DOVER STAMPING CO. *(back shaft)*
10" —$85—

DOVER EGG BEATER PATD MAY 6TH 1873 APR. 3D 1888 NOV 24TH 1891 BOSTON U.S.A. *(center pin)*
DOVER STAMPING CO. *(back shaft)*
9-1/4" —$80—

DOVER EGG BEATER PATD MADE IN BOSTON U.S.A.
9" —$80—

The firm also manufactured the jar-attached WHIPPO SUPER WHIPPER *(fig. 1-29)*. Its paper label says in part, "It beats anything that anything can beat … Manufactured only by Dover Stamping and Mfg Co."

The patent for the WHIPPO went to Wells G. Ruggles of Quincy, Massachusetts on Nov. 25, 1924 *(fig. 1-30)*. Quincy, an assignor to Dover, said in his patent that the different directions of the blade agitators "will form [liquid] streams at an acute angle to each other and after leaving said passages will violently intermingle."

Another Dover collectible is a stand-up model with the three-combo 1873-1888-1891 date and a heavy tin bottom stand *(fig. 1-31)*. Said a Dover brochure *(fig. 1-32)*: "How often when beating eggs, one cannot leave the beater in the bowl or beating dish; yet, it cannot well be taken out of the bowl without dripping egg. This beater will stand alone and can be left at any time standing upright in the bowl."

The stand was patented Feb. 12, 1918 by Warren H. Dunning of Cambridge, an assignor to Dover *(fig. 1-33)*. This beater is still out there.

Another Dunning item, however, is waiting to be discovered. Similar to the tin bottom stand, this patent, also granted Feb. 12, 1918, is for a spring stand bottom *(fig. 1-34)*.

D G Simons

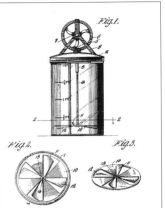

FIG. 1-29

WHIPPO SUPER WHIPPER
(on paper label)
10-1/2"
without paper label (pictured) —$225—
with paper label —$400—

FIG. 1-30

*Wells G. Ruggles patent
Nov. 25, 1924
Pat. No. 1,516,792*

FIG. 1-33

*Warren H. Dunning patent
Feb. 12, 1918
Pat. No. 1,255,993*

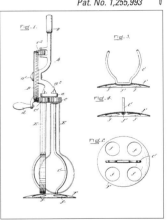

FIG. 1-34

*Warren H. Dunning patent
Feb. 12, 1918
Pat. No. 1,255,994*

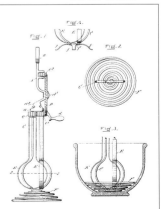

FIG. 1-31

DOVER EGG BEATER
PATD MAY 6TH 1873 APR. 3D 1888
NOV. 24TH 1891
with tin stand
10-3/4" —$275—

D G Simons

FIG. 1-32

*Dover
Stamping &
Mfg. Co.
brochure*

The STANDS ALONE
DOVER EGG BEATER
SELLS ON SIGHT
The Genuine Dover Egg Beater has always stood in a class alone. It will now stand in a bowl alone.

Family Size
No. 20

Notice the third pinion.

Prevents the wheel from slipping.

Patent Applied For.

Cut No. 123

No. 20. Family Size, Length over all 10¼ inches

This is the one feature that all Egg Beaters have lacked. A heavy perforated retinned steel disc is firmly attached to bottom of Beater (easy to clean), which not only prevents the Beater from moving around in a bowl but allows it to positively stand alone. How often when beating Eggs, one wants to add sugar, vanilla, etc., yet with the ordinary Beater, cannot leave the Beater in the bowl or beating dish; yet, it cannot well be taken out of the bowl without dripping Egg. This Beater will stand alone and can be left at any time standing upright in the bowl.

Shipping weights see page 11

On the Back of the handle of every Genuine Dover Egg Beater are the words in a panel.

DOVER STAMPING CO.

Also look for the third pinion or gear which steadies the wheel.
NONE OTHERS ARE GENUINE
PRICES ON APPLICATION
4

> Dover was the common usage, the general term, for a hand-operated eggbeater. We used the name; everybody used it.
>
> — RICHARD LIENHARD, TAPLIN CO.

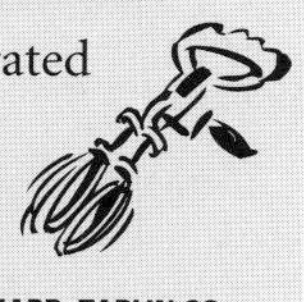

In an 1983 interview, Richard Lienhard, an authority on the history of the manufacturing of American eggbeaters, was asked about the Dover, which for years was the main competitor to his family's Taplin beater.

"I believe Dover was the first to manufacture it in the United States. It was the first mechanical eggbeater as such," said Lienhard, then 80 and a former president of the Taplin Manufacturing Company of New Britain, Connecticut, a major eggbeater maker for more than 50 years *(See Chapter 4, Taplin, page 29)*.

"Dover was the common usage, the general term for a hand-operated eggbeater. We used the name, everybody used it."

In fact, the *Good Housekeeping Magazine Institute Bulletin* of Nov. 1, 1914 paid tribute to the generic Dover, saying: "An egg beater built on the 'Dover' principal, if well constructed is always a good purchase ..."

Lienhard said it was his understanding that around 1900, Dover, noting the widespread use of its name, "kind of got sore about it and said we couldn't use it anymore. We had cast-iron eggbeaters then so we just filled it in where it said Dover."

In addition to Taplin, other firms that used the "Dover" name included Holt-Lyon of Tarrytown and later Saugerties, New York *(See Chapter 2, Holt-Lyon, page 17)*, Turner & Seymour Manufacturing Company of Torrington, Connecticut *(See Chapter 3, Turner & Seymour, page 22)*, Standard Manufacturing Company of Boston *(See Chapter 5, Standard and Other Cast-Iron Beauties, page 46)*, and National Manufacturing Company of Worcester, Massachusetts *(See Chapter 7, National Manufacturing Co., page 68)*.

In its 1877 catalog, Dover boasted that "we supply the world with egg beaters" *(fig. 1-35)* and in the same breath warned other manufacturers that they were in trouble if they infringed on Dover patents *(fig. 1-36)*. In its warning, Dover ironically listed the "Earle," a beater it had offered in its 1866 and 1869 catalogs, as an offender.

Dover was very protective of what it called its "cutting edge." In an article in the July 20, 1879 *The Metal Worker*, Dover told of several lawsuits it had filed to protect its beaters *(fig. 1-37)*. In addition to revealing a litigious side to the sale of beaters, the article also discloses the existence of several little-known beater manufacturers.

FIG. 1-35

1877 Dover Stamping Company catalog

94 DOVER STAMPING COMPANY.

A WORD ABOUT EGG BEATERS.

Beating an Egg is simply aerating its separate particles.

PROPERLY AERATED,

a single Egg will perform the office of THREE or FOUR *partially done.*

When ONE EGG is made to do the work of THREE the ECONOMY of using a

THOROUGH EGG BEATER

is apparent, and the *price* no object.

The Dover Egg Beater is the only Article that will throughly Aerate or Beat an Egg.

TEN SECONDS WILL PROVE THIS.

The Double Beating Floats Revolving and Interlacing each other,

cut the Egg instantly, and by COUNTER AND CROSS CURRENTS, FILL IT WITH INNUMERABLE AIR GLOBULES. *This is beating an Egg.*

The DOVER EGG BEATER has achieved a truly wonderful popularity. In the four years it has been on the market, it has found its way all over the world. From England, Germany, France, and other countries in Europe, Mexico, South America, Japan, China and Australia, come to us orders for this Beater, in quantities varying from *one to fifty gross.* The demand has continued until we may say *WE SUPPLY THE WORLD WITH EGG BEATERS.* A SINGLE INSTANCE OF ITS REJECTION WAS NEVER KNOWN.

IT IS WARRANTED TO PLEASE and FULLY SATISFY ALL.

If the purchaser is not DELIGHTED with it, the price given will always be returned.

DOVER STAMPING CO.,

BOSTON, MASS., U. S. A.

Sole Owners and the Only Manufacturers.

FIG. 1-36

1877 Dover Stamping Company catalog

DOVER STAMPING COMPANY. 95

NOT THE DOVER BEATER.

This and similar Beaters are sold to customers who enquire for the Dover, because the seller makes one or two cents more on them. Many do not notice the difference.

The "Dover" turns on TWO CENTERS — one inch apart ; the floats in turning interlace each other, and produce the WONDERFUL CROSS CURRENTS which are so effective. The "EARLE," "FAMILY," "WASHINGTON," "PEERLESS," "STAR," *and all such,* turn on one center, and merely set the egg whirling. They do not beat the egg like the Dover. They are not worth a tenth as much. They are all covered by our patents, and infringe them in all ways. We are constantly sueing the makers and sellers of them. Judgments are always in our favor. We suppress one to-day by an injunction of the Court, but to-morrow another starts up, when we summon the infringers into Court to answer. Suits are now going on against the "Family" and "Washington," and will be commenced against others as soon as they show themselves.

We say to the trade, sell none of these infringing Beaters. To the public, buy none of them. In this way you will avoid all liability of suits, and place in the hands of your customers the best article of the kind ever made, the

DOVER EGG BEATER.

FIG. 1-37

The Metal Worker article, July 20, 1879 issue

Egg Beater Litigation.

The Dover Stamping Co. send us the following:

BOSTON, July 14, 1879.

We are in possession of the decree of the United States Circuit Court, District of Connecticut, giving judgment to us in our suit against the Turner & Seymour Manufacturing Co., and ordering defendants to account for infringing our egg beater patents by making and selling egg beaters have cutting edges. And more particularly the so called "Family" and "Washington" egg beaters. The account of sales and assessment of damages is but a question of a few days. This decree confirms to us our rights, which has taken many years and a large amount of money to gain.

The damage to us by the sale of the "Family" beater has been very great. All who have sold them are liable to us for the damages their sales have caused. We expect to be remunerated for the same to the full legal extent, and shall promptly call upon all to account to us for what each has done. All cutting edges, in whatever egg beater they may be found, infringe our patents. The "Family," "Washington," "Vortex," "Peerless," "Propeller," "Centripetal," "Star," ("Twin," made by Joseph Scheider & Co.) "Pearl," "Novelty," and some others have cutting edges. Each will receive our special attention.

Our first suit on egg beaters was with Monroe Brothers. It was in court three years and was a complete victory for ourselves. The next suit was with Turner & Seymour Manufacturing Co., in which, before the final arguments, they found it for their interest to allow perpetual injunction, without further defense, and pay damages, which injunction issued accordingly. Then came the suit against Messrs. George H. Mason & Co., of Boston, which resulted in perpetual injunction; the suit against Johonnot & Saunders, resulting in perpetual injunction; the suit against Edwin P. Monroe, resulting in perpetual injunction. Then came the suit, now just decided, against Turner & Seymour Manufacturing Co., with perpetual injunction. We have still another suit in the courts, against Seavey & Co. of Boston. The lesson, to those who have or may be disposed to infringe our patents, which may be drawn from the above six suits, and the perpetual injunctions granted, should not be lost upon the public. We have fairly warned all, in our previous issues, to avoid dealing in infringing egg beaters. Those who have heeded our warning may congratulate themselves, while those who have not, will now have an opportunity to pay for the chances they had the hardihood to take.

It must be distinctly understood that selling any infringing egg beater, or keeping such articles for sale, lays the party so doing liable to special damages and cost.

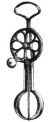

FIG. 1-38

Dover counter card advertisement, pre-1900

Over the years, Dover became known for its various catalogs and printed ads, which are as collectible as the beaters. In 1883, Edward H. Whitney, son of the founder of Dover, took over the presidency of the firm and is credited with launching its first promotional campaigns (*figs. 1-38 through 1-40*). Whitney held various executive positions until his death in 1906.

According to a newspaper obituary at the time, Whitney "died very suddenly yesterday afternoon of a heart failure, caused probably by the excitement of a collision between an automobile and a carriage in which he was riding, at the junction of Harvard and Norfolk streets, Cambridge."

The obituary said he was born March 7, 1844 in Dover, New Hampshire, and began work with the Dover Stamping Company as a boy. It listed his survivors as a son, Horace E., and two daughters, Mrs. Joseph H. Bowen of Fall River, and Miss Lillian B. Whitney.

Horace E. took over as president. Described as very much like his inventive grandfather, he moved the company into products related to the new age of the automobile. The 1930 *History of Massachusetts Industries*

described Dover as "the leader in the manufacture of gasoline and oil measurers used in the automobile trade." It also said the corporation "has capital of $300,000 and employs upwards of 150 operatives."

But during this transition period, Dover still made eggbeaters, as evidenced by a Feb. 26, 1924 trademark (*fig. 1-41*) for mixers and other items.

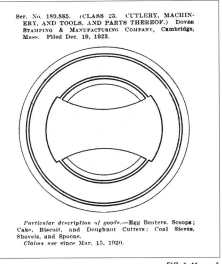

Ser. No. 189,885. (CLASS 23. CUTLERY, MACHINERY, AND TOOLS, AND PARTS THEREOF.) DOVER STAMPING & MANUFACTURING COMPANY, Cambridge, Mass. Filed Dec. 19, 1923.

Particular description of goods.—Egg Beaters. Scoops; Cake, Biscuit, and Doughnut Cutters; Coal Sieves, Shovels, and Spoons.
Claims use since Mar. 15, 1920.

FIG. 1-41

U.S. Patent & Trademark Office Official Gazette, Feb. 26, 1926, Dover beater trademark

FIG. 1-39

Early Dover Stamping Company advertisement

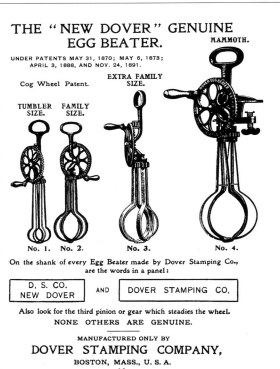

FIG. 1-40

Iron Age magazine advertisement Feb. 5, 1891

In 1934, another Whitney took over, Carlton S., followed 10 years later by Whitney Bowen, son of Mrs. Joseph H. Bowen. One year later the firm moved to Fall River, Massachusetts into the empty plant of the General Cotton Supply Company, owned by Whitney Bowen.

In 1950, Jacob Ziskand of Fall River and Sidney Goldstein of Boston acquired the company only to sell it four years later to Ohio industrialist Louis Berkman. The firm today is called Dover Parkersburg Bay State, a division of Parkersburg Steel Company.

According to a 1985 *Fall River Herald News* article on the firm, it processes more than 12 million pounds of steel annually into hundreds of items, including pails, barrels, washtubs, paint pots and trash cans, at its five-story building on Plymouth Avenue.

Although trash cans are its present and probable future, eggbeaters will always be Dover's soul and legacy, at least for kitchenware collectors. Who else but Dover, the king of early American mixers, would manufacture the massive LEVIATHAN *(fig. 1-42),* and market its beaters with what at the time must have been considered extravagant displays *(fig. 1-43).*

The Dover Egg Beater is generally regarded as the best in the market, and we know of no rival that has all its excellencies. It is not costly, and is very durable.

By an ingenious contrivance the inner circle revolves in a contrary direction to the outer circle. With this the egg beating is a very simple matter.

—PRACTICAL HOUSEKEEPING, A CAREFUL COMPILATION OF TRIED AND APPROVED RECIPES, BUCKEYE PUBLISHING COMPANY, MINNEAPOLIS, MINN., 1883

FIG. 1-42

Leviathan Dover, 4' high, 287 lbs., 20" base diameter, 20" pulley with 4" face. Value undetermined.

FIG. 1-43

Dover eggbeater exhibit at the Philadelphia Exposition, 1876. Note dasher crown and motorized mechanism at bottom to turn the exhibit.

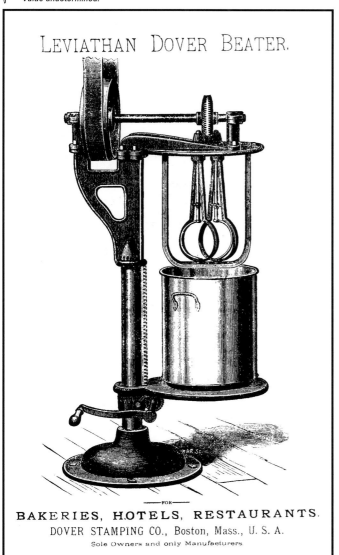

Dover is still loved today — confirmed in a July, 1992 James D. Julia of Fairfield, Maine, auction of antique advertising. Item 274 (fig. 1-44) was described as "Dover egg beater paper sign. Wistful maid using Dover brand beater whisking eggs in a bowl with product pictured in border. 'For Sale Here.' An early 1870s litho. Size: Approx. 9" x 12". Condition: Excellent. Edges Trimmed, minor soiling." The selling price: $1,400.

Dover's humble beginnings as Horace Whitney & Co. on Main Street in Dover, New Hampshire 1833

FIG. 1-44

Early Dover full-color advertising poster sold at auction in 1992 at $1,400.

"Dover Egg Beater, Patented 1870" is stamped upon the circumference of the iron wheel. I know nothing more of its antecedents. But if I could not get another I would not sell mine for $50 — nor $100.

Egg whipping ceased to be a bugbear to me from the day of which I speak. Light, portable, rapid, easy and comparatively noiseless, my pet implement works like a benevolent brownie. With it I turn out a meringue in five minutes without staying my song or talk; make the formidable 'snow-custard' in less than half an hour, with no after tremulousness of nerve or tendon.

In its operation it is impartial, yolks thickening smoothly under it as easily as whites heighten into a compact snow-drift, that can be cut into blocks with a knife. Winter and summer, it has served me with invariable fidelity, and it is to all appearance, stanch as when it first passed into my reluctant hands.

—MARION HARLAND, BREAKFAST, LUNCHEON AND TEA (PART OF THE COMMON SENSE IN HOUSEHOLD SERIES), 1875

In the 1930s, Dover moved into the automotive accessories field:

(left): Funnel 5-1/2" **DOVER**

(right): 6" high oil can **DOVER 1 PT LIQUID U.S. STANDARD MASS. APPRD D.S. NO. 1**

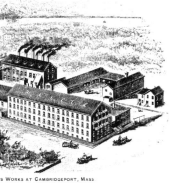

DOVER STAMPING COMPANY'S WORKS AT CAMBRIDGEPORT, MASS

Dover's Cambridge, Massachusetts plant opened in 1866.

D Thornton

THE EGGBEATER CHRONICLES

Chapter 2

Holt-Lyon

Propellers and Flares

*N*elson and George Lyon and inventor Edward J. Scopes introduced the propeller eggbeater to the American public in Albany, New York, at the end of the 19th century.

Lyon Brothers & Sadd (with E.A. Sadd) was first listed in the *Albany City Directory* in 1890 as a manufacturer of heel stiffeners, brushes, ice creepers and flexible harrows at 55 N. Pearl.

Scopes made his first appearance in the 1893 directory as a machinist/fore-man. By 1896, Nelson Lyon and Scopes had teamed up and were producing "egg beaters and heel stiffeners" at 52 Green Street.

In 1899 Nelson Lyon was still listed as manufacturing eggbeaters at 52 Green Street but his brother, George, had started a new operation at 22-24 Dewitt. The new concern was the Perfection Novelty Works and Scopes was listed as manager.

Nelson Lyon was still making egg-beaters at 52 Green in 1900 and 1901, but was missing from the city directory in 1902. In the meantime, Scopes con-

tinued for several years as manager of Perfection Novelty Works.

Scopes, who died May 19, 1914, was awarded three patents for propeller egg-beaters. The first was granted Sept. 7, 1897 *(fig. 2-1)* and resulted in the LYON EGG BEATER *(fig. 2-2)*. In that patent, Scopes listed himself as assignor to Nelson Lyon.

Ad appearing on business envelope, Nelson Lyon firm , 1898

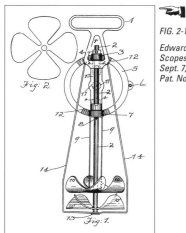

☞ FIG. 2-1

Edward John Scopes patent Sept. 7, 1897 Pat. No. 589,795

☞ FIG. 2-2

Lyon beaters (left to right):

LYON EGG BEATER ALBANY N.Y. PAT APPLD FOR
10" —$185—

LYON EGG BEATER ALBANY N.Y. PAT. SEP. 7 '97
10" —$175—

**LYON EGG BEATER & CREAM WHIP ALBANY, N.Y.
PAT. SEPT. 7 '97 NO. 2**
10" —$175—

D G Simons

Scopes called the dashers of his beater "flukes," rather than propellers. He described his 1897 invention as "an egg beater having a plurality of flukes in two oppositely-rotating series, one above the other, the said flukes having rear up-turned edges and forward cutting edges, and the lower flukes also concaved from their center of rotation upwardly, thereby adapting to fit close to the surface of the concaved bottom of a cup, dish or other similar receptacle in which the beater is to be used…"

Scopes' second beater patent was granted Feb. 22, 1898 *(fig. 2-3)* and was for the PERFECTION *(fig. 2-4).* The PERFECTION came in two sizes, the larger with two bottom propeller dashers that turned in opposite directions, and the smaller with a propeller-type bottom that turned in the opposite direction of a vertical dasher. The timing of this beater fits the first appearance in the *Albany City Directory* of the Perfection Novelty Works.

The third propeller patent was awarded Dec. 3, 1901 *(fig. 2-5)* for the BALL BEARING beater *(fig. 2-6).* Scopes assigned this patent to George Lyon. There are two models of the BALL BEARING, one with the PERFECTION patent date of Feb. 22, 1898, and a later model with the same date, plus Dec. 3, 1901.

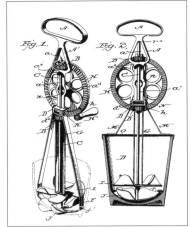

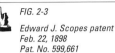

FIG. 2-3

Edward J. Scopes patent
Feb. 22, 1898
Pat. No. 599,661

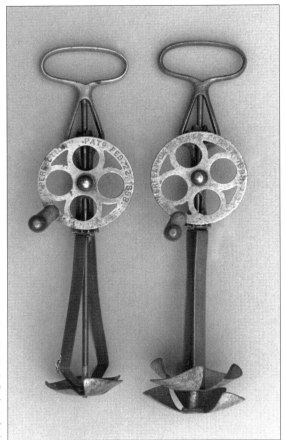

FIG. 2-4

Perfections (left to right):

"PERFECTION"
PATD FEB. 22, 1898 ALBANY, N.Y. *(very faint)*
9-1/2"   —$350—

"PERFECTION"
PATD FEB. 22, 1898
10"   —$350—

D G Simons

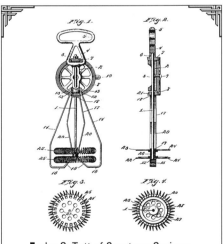

John C. Tutt of Saratoga Springs, New York, borrowed liberally from Edward J. Scopes' designs to patent his own beater on April 10, 1900, No. 647,341. The basic design comes from Scopes Feb. 22, 1898 beater, but instead of propellers, it has two disks with spiral springs. "These springs inclose or encompass the edges of the disks and their convolutions constitute radial stirring arms or blades," Tutt said. There is no evidence this beater was ever manufactured.

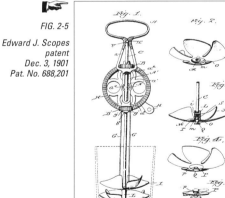

FIG. 2-5

Edward J. Scopes patent
Dec. 3, 1901
Pat. No. 688,201

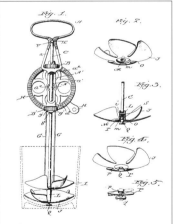

C Badger

FIG. 2-6

"BALL BEARING" PATD FEB. 22, 1898. B.B.B
9-1/4"   —$425—

Note: A later model is marked: **"BALL BEARING"**
PATD FEB 22, 1898 DEC. 3, 1901, *some of which come in at 10"*

BADGER COLLECTION

THE EGGBEATER CHRONICLES

The Lyon Cream Whip and Egg Beater

Is the best and quickest Cream Whip made. Will whip Cream and Milk, half and half, without Spattering.

IT IS ALSO A VERY EXCELLENT EGG BEATER

Sells For a Large Profit Has No Competitor

HOLT'S IMPROVED EGG BEATER

Made in 10, 15, 20 and 25 Cent Sizes, with our New Processes for Riveting.

ALL SOLD BY JOBBERS

Also shipped direct. Freight allowed on 10 gross orders and upward.

Ask for Mch. 12-page Catalogue.

HOLT-LYON CO., Tarrytown, N. Y.

FIG. 2-7

June, 1908, House Furnishing Review

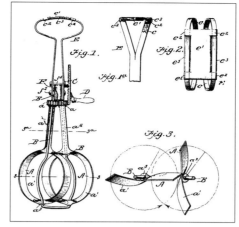

FIG. 2-8

Thomas Holt patent
Aug. 22, 1899
Pat. No. 631,715

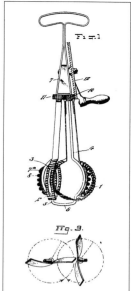

FIG. 2-9

Thomas Holt patent
April 3, 1900
Pat. No. 646,736

FIG. 2-10

September, 1909, House Furnishing Review

Holt-Lyon Company

TARRYTOWN-ON-THE-HUDSON, N. Y.

Holt's New Cup Beater

BEATS one egg in a cup in 20 seconds, or 4 eggs in a bowl in

One Half One Dover's Time.

The Flared Dashers Do It.

Holt Egg Beaters are made in 10, 15, 20 and 25 cent sizes.

Cleaner, Rug and Carpet Beaters

ARE acknowledged to be the Best in the World.

Have Large Head Elastic Shank.

Made From the Very Best Spring Steel Wire.

Over 300,000 sold from July, 1908, to July, 1909.

Holt's Egg Beater and Mayonaise Mixers Combined

Are the Best in the World

Can be Retailed for 30 to 50 cents each

The Oil Dripper gives perfect control of the oil. To make good Mayonaise, the oil must be applied very slowly at first.

Can be detached in 5 seconds.

Beats Eggs elegantly in 20 seconds. Makes them much lighter.

Holt's New One- and-Two Quart Cream Whips, Egg Beaters and Butter Churns.

Retail Price : 50 and 75 Cents.

Holt's Double Rotary Flared Dashers

Are rapid in operation, and make Eggs and Cream very light.

Most Durable Beaters on the Market.

SEND FOR NEW CATALOG.

Sold by Jobbers and Shipped Direct to Retailers with Freight Allowance.

Meanwhile, Nelson Lyon took his LYON EGG BEATER to Tarrytown, New York, where in 1904 he joined forces with Thomas Holt. That was the year their Holt-Lyon Company first appeared in the *Tarrytown City Directory,* a listing that continued through 1919. Lyon was secretary/treasurer and Holt was president.

Sales of the LYON EGG BEATER continued for years. For example, a *House Furnishing Review* ad *(fig. 2-7)* in June of 1908 said of the LYON: "It is the best and quickest cream whip made. Will whip cream and milk, half and half, without spattering. It is also a very excellent egg beater. Sells for a large profit. Has no competitor." And the 1912-13 *Tarrytown City Directory* said the firm specialized in making "egg and carpet beaters, cream whips and flue stops."

Nelson Lyon later returned to Albany, where he died Dec. 23, 1921 at the age of 77.

Holt joined the beater market with his own invention — a mixer patented Aug. 22, 1899 *(fig. 2-8)* and added his trademark dashers with flares in another patent, April 3, 1900 *(fig. 2-9).* He described the flared dashers as "guard-plates attached to the frame and having their inner surfaces curved axially…"

An ad in a September, 1909, *House Furnishing Review (fig. 2-10)* made note of them: "Beats one egg in a cup in 20 seconds, or four eggs in a bowl in one half one Dover's time. The flared dashers do it."

Holt also patented on Nov. 4, 1913 (fig. 2-11) an Archimedes, or up-and-down, beater (fig. 2-12) that is very rare.

The Holt-Lyon factory, located at the foot of Josephine Street in Tarrytown, was leveled in a 1960s urban renewal project. In a 1962 article, "More Factories of Our Earlier Days," the *Daily News* of Tarrytown said: "At the turn of the century U. Grant Teetsell, local shoe merchant, bought the Holt-Lyon egg beater firm. The factory was located on Josephine Street … Many a good egg beater was manufactured in this plant. Mr. Teetsell hired mostly girls."

In correspondence in 1991, Ruth Teetsell, daughter-in-law of Ulysses Grant Teetsell, said he owned the firm two or three years before moving it to Saugerties, where it continued in business until 1941.

And it was Holt-Lyon — not Tupperware — that should be credited with what is today a revered in-home marketing standard.

"U. Grant Teetsell (figs. 2-13 & 2-14) would have individual ladies invite several friends for an afternoon party then he would beat his eggs and make mayonnaise in the quart jar with large beater attached. These proved very popular as the ladies received door prizes of these items," said Ruth Teetsell.

The firm also made several different carpet beaters and "flower holders were good. These were wound wires branching off into three prongs. They were great for holding branches of delphiniums and the giant snapdragons. Harold [her husband, U. Grant's son] developed these."

Ruth Teetsell described her father-in-law as "a most jovial, warm person [who] enjoyed being with people."

One story she recalls: "In my teens, I remember seeing him at a Sunday school picnic. People rode on hay wagons pulled by teams to a spot eight miles away. He was very popular at the picnic. Then on the way home a shower came up. No protection for anyone. He got people arranged in groups to sing 'How Dry I Am' to see which group could win. Soon everyone forgot their misery and were laughing and carrying on."

In 1925, the eldest Teetsell son, Lewis, died at the age of 31 and "right here everything changed for U. Grant. He quit church, didn't want to see anyone. Kept the factory going is about all. This happened in 1925 — and January 1927 U. Grant died of a massive angina attack.

Poor Sarah [his wife] had all this to handle. She was a strong lady."

Mrs. Teetsell said the Saugerties eggbeater plant "was about 45 feet long. Both sides the complete length had four-foot by eight-foot windows. Hardwood benches ran the length under these windows. On the right hand side the eggbeater section, the left carpet beaters.

It was powered by overhead shafts with various sizes of pulleys and belts — from three inches wide to nearly five inches. The slap, slap of these belts were audible when running … One real large electric motor supplied the power."

In Tarrytown, Mrs. Teetsell said, "they hired women, but in Saugerties it was boys solely over 17 years. One time or another I imagine every [local] boy worked a stint. There were two or three older men, mechanics who kept everything repaired and running. The work force ranged from 24 to 30."

And that work force and earlier ones made some very distinctive eggbeaters, ranging in size from 9" to 12-1/2" (figs. 2-15 through 2-17).

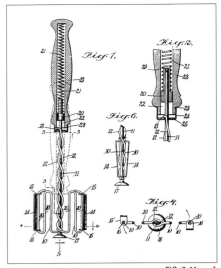

FIG. 2-11

Thomas Holt patent
Nov. 4, 1913
Pat. No. 1,077,832

FIG. 2-12

No I.D.,
but Holt's patent
14-1/4"
—$325—

Note: There is a smaller model at 12-1/2".

FIG. 2-13

Ulysses Grant Teetsell at his Saugerties area farm

HOY COLLECTION

D G Simons

Photos courtesy Ruth Teetsel

FIG. 2-14

Teetsell, his wife, Sarah, and son, Harold

THE EGGBEATER CHRONICLES

FIG. 2-15
H-L CO. NO. 0 TARRYTOWN, N.Y.
9" —$50—

D G Simons

D G Simons

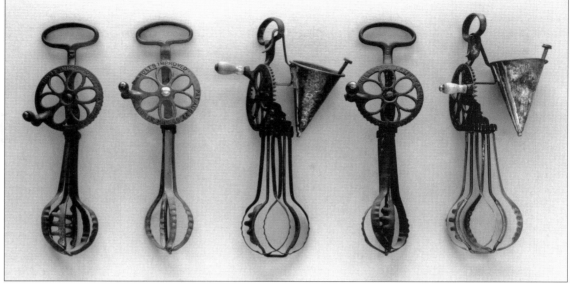

FIG. 2-16

Holt's eggbeaters (left to right)

HOLT'S IMPROVED DOVER AUG. 22, 99 10-1/2" —$55—

HOLT'S IMPROVED [space where Dover had been] **AUG. 22, 99 APRIL 3, 1900**
10-1/2" —$45—

HOLT'S PATENTED FLARED DASHER EGG BEATER U.S.A.
No date, but flanged handle for funnel.
10-1/2" —$55—; *value of funnel:* —$50—

HOLT'S EGG BEATER PAT AUG. 22, 1899 APR 3, 1900 10-1/2" —$50—

HOLT'S EGG BEATER & CREAM WHIP PAT. AUG. 22-99, APR 3-00
Flanged handle for funnel. 10-1/2" —$55—; *value of funnel:* —$50—
Note: Probably the rarest of this model is marked:
HOLT'S DOVER EGG BEATER & CREAM WHIP PAT. AUG. 22D 99 IN U.S.A. & ENG.
This model noting the English patent raises the price to $75.

D G Simons

FIG. 2-17

Holt's eggbeaters (left to right)

HOLT'S EGG BEATER PAT AUG. 22 1899 APR 3, 1900
12" —$55—

**HOLT'S IMPROVED DOVER PATENTED
MADE BY HOLT-LYON CO. TARRYTOWN, N.Y. U.S.A.**
12-1/2" —$50—

Thomas Holt's improvement in egg beaters and cream whips … followed an entirely different plan from those manufacturers who had sought to improve on the Dover egg beater by accelerating its speed. His egg beater is slower in action, but at the same time it is quicker in results, for Mr. Holt claims that the flaring of one edge of the beating wires and the contracting of the other creates a greater vacuum as they revolve, and introduces four times as much air, thereby beating the eggs or whipping the cream in one-fourth the time.

—MARCH 1904 *HOUSE FURNISHING REVIEW*

The most fragile of the Holt-Lyon beaters, and thus the most valuable, were jar models that came in three sizes: pint, quart and two-quart (*fig. 2-18*).

Turn-of-the-century ads in *The House Furnishing Review* also show that Holt-Lyon made even larger metal container beaters (*fig. 2-19*) for hotels and bakers, boasting, "9 and 16 quart beaters, 24 and 48 eggs in four minutes."

Utilizing a much smaller container is a Holt-Lyon with a different handle and an apron that fits over a small jar (*fig. 2-20*).

FIG. 2-19

Holt-Lyon cross-section House Furnishing Review

FIG. 2-20

H-L CO No 0 TARRYTOWN NY
9-1/2" with apron —$175—

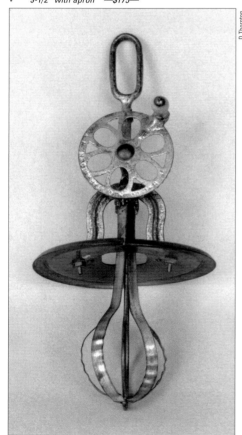

HOWE COLLECTION

D G Simons

FIG 2-18

Holt-Lyon jar mixers (left to right):

HOLT'S EGG BEATER & CREAM WHIP. PAT. AUG. 22-99. APR 3-00 USA (on main gear)
THE HOLT-LYON JAR CREAM WHIP AND MAYONNAISE MIXER,
THE HOLT-LYON CO. TARRYTOWN, N.Y. (embossing on pint jar)
11-1/2" —$500—; value of funnel: —$75—

HOLT'S IMPROVED PATENTED. MADE BY HOLT-LYON CO. TARRYTOWN, N.Y. (on main gear)
THE HOLT-LYON JAR CREAM WHIP AND MAYONNAISE MIXER,
   THE HOLT-LYON CO. TARRYTOWN, N.Y. (embossing on quart jar)
14-1/2" —$650—

HOLT'S IMPROVED PATENTED. MADE BY HOLT-LYON CO. TARRYTOWN, N.Y. (on main gear)
HOLT'S BUTTER MERGER. HOLT-LYON CO. SAUGERTIES, N.Y. (paper label on quart jar)
14-1/2" —$350—

HOLT'S EGG BEATER PAT AUG 22 1899 APR 3, 1900 (on main gear)
HOLT'S JAR CREAM WHIPS, HOLT-LYON CO., TARRYTOWN, N.Y.
   SANETY, WIDE MOUTH, MASON, SALEM GLASS WORKS, SALEM, N.J. (embossing on two-quart jar)
Tested and approved by Good Housekeeping Institute. Conducted by Good Housekeeping Magazine.
   October 1st, 1911, Certificate No. 421 (paper label in part)
16-1/2" —$1,500—

The first side-handle mixer can be attributed to Abraham Caufman of Winfield, Kansas. A patent for his "pot stirrer" was awarded Nov. 28, 1882, No. 268,185. Caufman said his device could be used with a cooking vessel "of a size such as are used for making fruit-butter." It's doubtful this invention was ever manufactured.

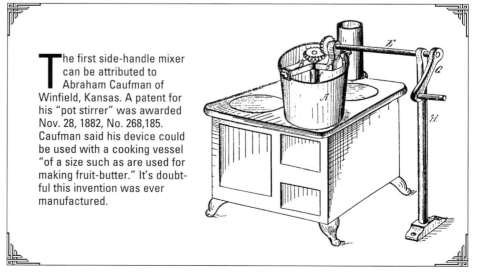

THE EGGBEATER CHRONICLES

FIG. 2-21

Holt's side-handles (left to right)

HOLT'S EGG BEATER & CREAM WHIP PAT. AUG. 22-'98 APR. 3-00
8-1/2"   —$350—

No. I.D., with center wheel drive, similar to the wheel on Taplin's Light Running, but some with confirming I.D. of **H-L CO.** *on the handle. Note the "guard rail" from handle to just above dashers along gear wheel.*
8-1/2"   —$400—

D G Simons

R S Arnold

FIG. 2-22

Holt's side-handles (left to right)

HOLT'S PATENTED FLARED DASHER EGGBEATER N.Y. U.S.A.,
with elongated dashers and a "guard rail" (on backside, hidden in photo) from handle along gear wheel to top of gear wheel.
8-1/2"   —$310—

HOLT'S IMPROVED PATENTED MADE BY HOLT-LYON CO. TARRYTOWN, N.Y. U.S.A.
10-1/2"   —$800—

HOY COLLECTION

FIG. 2-23

Ulysses Grant Teetsell patent Feb. 14, 1922 Pat. No. 1,406,778

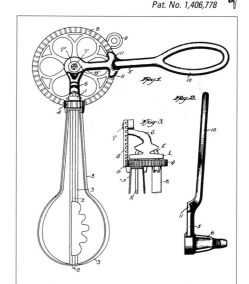

One of the most collectible Holt-Lyon mixers is the famous side-handle (*figs. 2-21 & 2-22*) with at least four different models. Although the side-handle has 1898 and 1900 Holt patent dates, it should be noted that Ulysses Grant Teetsell obtained a patent Feb. 14, 1922 (*fig. 2-23*), for just such a model.

In his patent papers, Teetsell said: "This invention relates to improvements in egg beaters, the primary object of the invention being to provide a novel form of handle for the beater.

"It is customary in all devices of this character in which one or more dashers are mounted in a vertical frame to have a handle member located in substantially vertical alignment with the dasher frame. The inconvenience and disadvantages are the tendency of the beater to slide around in the bowl where it is being used, due to a lack of proper leverage to hold it steady, and the fact that while the operator holding the beater often scratches his knuckles on the gear wheel which is commonly used to actuate the dashers."

Hardware Dealers' Magazine December, 1922 issue said: "The patented side handle feature gives the operator an easy method of holding this beater firmly without hand-cramping fatigue caused by a small upright handle. In addition to the side handle this beater has Holt's patented flared dashers and finger tin attachments for rapid beating.

"The makers say: 'By actual trial, it whipped the white of one egg to a stiff standing froth in twenty seconds and brought four whites to the same pitch of excellence in less than sixty seconds.'"

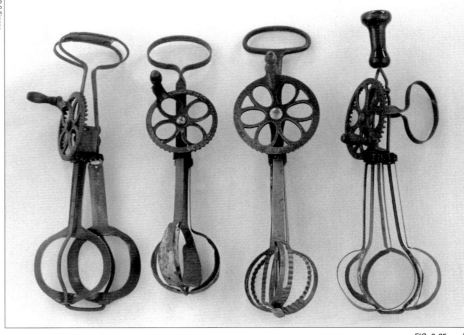

FIG. 2-24

No I.D. but probable Holt-Lyon manufacture with center wheel drive, "guard rail" and waffled dashers 11-1/8" —$450—

MAIR COLLECTION

FIG. 2-25

Holt-Lyon experimental models, values undetermined (left to right):

STEEL HANDLE DOVER EGG BEATER 10"
Note: This beater fits Holt's 1899 patent, fig. 2-8

STEEL HANDLE DOVER EGG BEATER 9-3/4"

TAPLIN'S DOVER IMPROVED JAN. 21 '90 10"

JAN. 21 '90 11"

FIG. 2-26

USE MINARD'S LINIMENT "KING OF PAIN" *12" Experimental model, value undetermined*

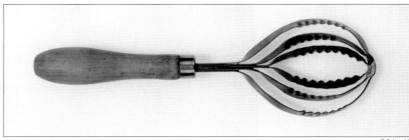

 FIG. 2-27

No markings, but with Holt-Lyons' patented flared dashers. 10" —$50—

The so-called "guard rail" on the center wheel drive sidehandle is also the distinctive feature on a very rare upright Holt-Lyon *(fig. 2-24)*. This beater has no I.D. but is obviously part of the Holt-Lyon family, more than likely the experimental branch. It has a wooden handle (not a standard feature on Holt-Lyon beaters) and a "guard rail" that extends from just above the dasher to the top of the main gear just below the handle.

In her correspondence, Mrs. Teetsell recalled a box of old beaters in her attic. They turned out to be experimental mixers *(fig. 2-25)* and it is interesting to note the Teetsells did not experiment with their own beaters.

All of the dasher experiments were made on competitor's beaters, including a 12-1/4" beauty *(fig. 2-26)* with its main gear wheel marked USE MINARD'S LINIMENT "KING OF PAIN" *(See Chapter 5, Standard, page 44).*

Another beater, probably experimental, was found by collector/dealer Carole Meeker at a Teetsell tag sale in 1994 — a hand-held with wavy dashers *(fig. 2-27)*.

Ruth Teetsell noted that her husband Harold "was only 22 when his father demised. His mother told him it was his job to run the factory. By the late '30s he was in trouble. Electric beaters made the items mainly unsaleable except in the Middle West a little longer."

Harold Teetsell continued the eggbeater business until 1941, when he sold the plant to a plastic goods manufacturer. He died in 1976.

Turner & Seymour

The Admiral Byrd connection.

FIG. 3-1

Frederick J. Seymour patent
Feb. 22, 1876
Pat. No. 174,015

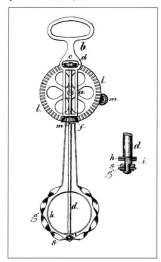

FIG. 3-2

Frederick J. Seymour patent
May 16, 1876
Pat. No. 177,574

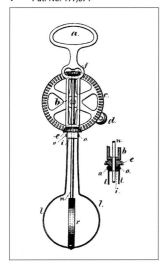

From hooks and eyes to suspender buckles and World War I canteens, to thumb tacks and a wild variety of chains — with a few eggbeaters in between — the Turner & Seymour Manufacturing Company is a historic mainstay of manufacturing in New England.

It got its start in 1848 when Elisha Turner and Philander Hine pooled $6,000 to form a partnership making hooks and eyes in Waterbury, Connecticut. The firm prospered and in 1852, with new stockholders and $16,000 in capital, the Waterbury Hook & Eye Company was launched.

One of those stockholders was Turner's good friend, Lyman W. Coe, who through marriage played a role in the future of the firm.

In 1864, Waterbury Hook & Eye was incorporated as Turner & Clark Manufacturing Company and moved to Wolcottville (later Torrington), after purchasing a local suspender buckle firm.

Meanwhile, only a year earlier, Coe's brother-in-law, Frederick Seymour, launched the Seymour Manufacturing Company in Torrington, producing brass window trimmings and curtain hooks. He started the firm with $20,000 in

S Scharnhorst

FIG. 3-3

WASHINGTON. EGG. BEATER. PAT' FEB' 22, 1876

11-1/4"   —$1,500+—

SCARBOROUGH COLLECTION

capital, with two major investors being Turner and Coe, according to the 1878 *History of Torrington*.

In 1866 Turner & Clark consolidated with Seymour Manufacturing and also purchased E. M. Judd & Company of New Haven. The firm then became Turner, Seymour & Judd, finally settling on the name Turner & Seymour in 1874.

Who were the two men behind Turner & Seymour? An 1897 article in the *Torrington Register* provided the following description of Turner:

"While wholly free from ostentation, few in the community have done so much for the material and moral welfare of its people. He is in touch with every movement that will tend to the development of the town or forward betterment of the community, of which he, for a third of a century, has been a part …"

Turner, a native of New London, was "a veteran manufacturer and has long been identified with the industrial life of the town," including firms other than T&S, according to the article.

For example, he was a vice president of the Eagle Bicycle Manufacturing Company and of the Coe Brass Manufacturing Company. "He also is president of the Torrington Savings Bank and in early life occupied a seat in the State Legislature."

As for the other half of T&S, Seymour was born and raised in Wolcottville. He worked for the Waterbury Brass Co. from 1847 to 1862 when in response to President Lincoln's call, he organized a company for the 14th Regiment. But shortly after rising to the rank of captain, he contracted typhus and was honorably discharged.

Seymour was an inventor — two of his creations being cast-iron rotary crank eggbeaters, patented Feb. 22 and May 16, 1876 *(figs. 3-1 & 3-2)*. The Feb. 22 date graces the WASHINGTON EGG BEATER *(fig. 3-3)*. This very rare beater probably got its name because of the birthday of George Washington, Feb. 22, 1732.

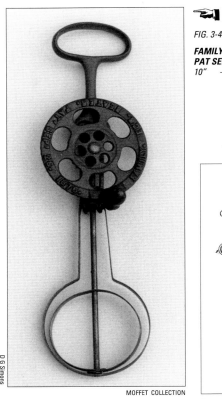

D G Simons

MOFFET COLLECTION

FIG. 3-4

FAMILY EGG BEATER
PAT SEP' 26 1876
10"   —$1,000+—

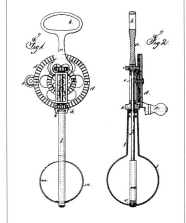

FIG. 3-5

John G. Brothwell patent
Sept. 26, 1876.
Pat. No. 182,639.

PAUL SMITH COLLECTION

 *FIG. 3-6*

TRIUMPH SEPT 26, 1876
9-1/2"   —$500—

FIG. 3-7

T&S cast-iron beaters (left to right):

T&S NO. 40 MADE IN USA   12-1/4"   —$55—

DOVER EGG BEATER MADE IN U.S.A.   *12-1/4"*   —$50—

DOVER EGG BEATER MADE IN U.S.A. PAT APPLIED FOR   T&S   *10-1/2"*   —$45—

T&S NO. 20 MADE IN U.S.A.   *10-1/2"*   —$48—

T&S DOVER BEATER   *10-1/4"*   —$45—

T&S NO. 10 MADE IN U.S.A.   *9-3/4"*   —$45—

DOVER EGG BEATER MADE IN USA. PAT APPLIED FOR   T&S   *9"*   —$48—

D G Simons

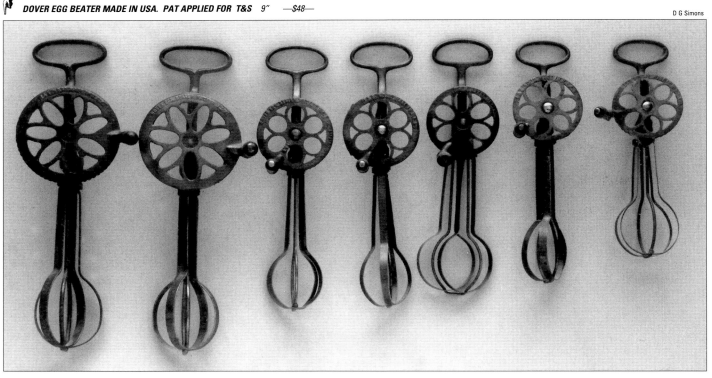

THE EGGBEATER CHRONICLES

The WASHINGTON was followed in the late 1870s by the FAMILY EGG BEATER (*fig. 3-4*). The FAMILY was patented Sept. 26, 1876 by John G. Brothwell of Wolcottville (*fig 3-5*). In his patent, Brothwell described himself as assignor to Turner & Seymour, and said "the beaters [dashers] are revolved in opposite directions, but the outer bow or beater revolves faster than the inner beater." The same patent was used on another T&S beater, the TRIUMPH (*fig. 3-6*).

Over the years Turner & Seymour produced an astounding variety of items, including scissors, curtain bands, furniture ornaments, coat and hat hooks, brackets, sash lifts, fasteners, cornice hooks and eyes, upholstery hardware, picture hooks and some 200 different styles of nails with ornamental heads.

It wasn't until the 1880s that Turner & Seymour began to really mix it up, introducing several different size cast-iron beaters (*fig. 3-7*). None of these have patent dates and although some are marked with the generic "DOVER" they were actually made by Turner & Seymour and usually have a "T&S" marking, including one with an unusual spoke wheel (*fig. 3-8*).

It was about this time T&S also offered what is commonly called the "footprint" cast-iron beater. The "footprint" (*fig. 3-9*) was always thought of as part of the Dover Stamping Company family — until one was found distinctly marked "T&S." The discovery was made in Springfield, Ohio in September, 1998 by collector/dealer Paul Smith. Nicknamed the "footprint" because of the circle and footprint holes in the main gear, all of these beaters are marked with the generic "DOVER."

Turner & Seymour, which in 1915 obtained two trademarks (*figs. 3-10 & 3-11*) to protect its T&S designation,

FIG. 3-8   PAUL SMITH COLLECTION

EGG BEATER MADE IN U.S.A. PAT. APPLIED FOR T&S
8-3/4"   —$60—

FIG. 3-9

Dover "footprints" (left to right):

DOVER EGG BEATER   PAT. APLD FOR   MADE IN U.S.A. T&S
9"   —$100—

DOVER EGG BEATER   MADE IN U.S.A.
9-3/4"   —$85—

 DOVER EGG BEATER   MADE IN U.S.A.
10"   —$90—

PAUL SMITH COLLECTION

FIG. 3-10

U.S. Patent & Trademark Office Official Gazette, Nov. 9, 1915 Turner & Seymour trademark

Ser. No. 89,851. (CLASS 23. CUTLERY, MACHINERY, AND TOOLS, AND PARTS THEREOF.) THE TURNER & SEYMOUR MANUFACTURING CO., Torrington, Conn. Filed Oct. 14, 1915.

T. & S.

Particular description of goods.—Egg-Beaters. *Claims* use since prior to 1879.

FIG. 3-11

U.S. Patent & Trademark Office Official Gazette, Nov. 16, 1915 Turner and Seymour trademark

Ser. No. 89,854. (CLASS 23. CUTLERY, MACHINERY, AND TOOLS, AND PARTS THEREOF.) THE TURNER & SEYMOUR MANUFACTURING CO., Torrington, Conn. Filed Oct. 14, 1915.

T&S PRODUCTS OF EXPERIENCE

Particular description of goods.—Egg-Beaters. *Claims* use since Oct. 1, 1914.

CHAPTER 3: TURNER & SEYMOUR

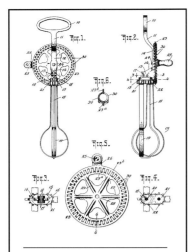

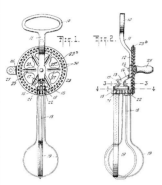

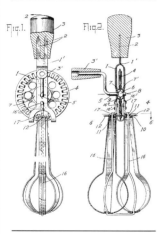

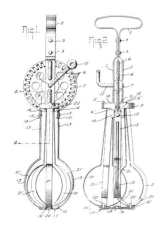

☞ FIG. 3-12

Sidney C. Hills patents (top to bottom):

Nov. 28, 1916   Pat. No. 1,206,327

July 23, 1918   Pat. No. 1,273,486
(Although it doesn't appear on any beaters, this patent for gear refinements is noteworthy if only because it weighs in at seven pages, a record for long-winded patent applications.)

Aug. 2, 1921   Pat. No. 1,386,405

Oct. 24, 1922   Pat. No. 1,433,508

came into its own in the beater business with Sidney C. Hills' series of patents beginning Nov. 28, 1916 *(fig. 3-12)*.

The 1916 and 1921 dates appear on an all metal model with an unusual eight-hole center drive wheel *(fig. 3-13)* — which resulted in a T&S trademark for the use of the color blue *(fig. 3-14)*. Other metal-pressed beaters were produced over the years by T&S *(fig. 3-15)*, including one with an abbreviated Turner & Seymour: TURNSEY CO.

☞ FIG. 3-13

T&S NO. 1 *(top of handle)*

PAT. NOV. 28, 1916 AUG. 2, 1921 PAT. PENDING MADE IN U.S.A. *(center wheel)*

11"   —$30—

D G Simons

FIG. 3-14

U.S. Patent & Trademark Office Official Gazette, January 12, 1926 Turner & Seymour trademark ☞

Ser. No. 218,585.   (CLASS 23.   CUTLERY, MACHINERY AND TOOLS, AND PARTS THEREOF.)   THE TURNER & SEYMOUR MANUFACTURING CO., Torrington, Conn. Filed Aug. 8. 1925.

The trade-mark as shown in the accompanying drawing consists in coloring the grip portions of the handles of the utensil kitchen blue.   No claim is made to the representation of the utensil apart from the trade-mark as shown.

Particular description of goods.—Egg Beaters and Can Openers.

Claims use since Mar. 27, 1923.

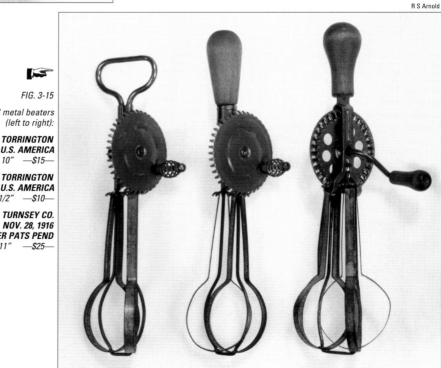

R S Arnold

☞ FIG. 3-15

T&S metal beaters (left to right):

T&S TORRINGTON MADE IN U.S. AMERICA
10"   —$15—

T&S TORRINGTON MADE IN U.S. AMERICA
10-1/2"   —$10—

TURNSEY CO. PAT. NOV. 28, 1916 OTHER PATS PEND
11"   —$25—

HOY COLLECTION

The WHIRL beaters can provide the beginning collector a very rewarding challenge — most of these are still available at flea markets and antique shows at reasonable prices.

The WHIRL series, according to a 1920s catalog, include:

▶ BLUE WHIRL: "It instantly appeals to the housewife because of its apparent value. It is fast, easy turning, easy to clean, and sturdily made" (fig. 3-16). This beater came in two sizes, medium and large (fig. 3-17), and is embossed with the patent dates NOV. 28, 1916, and AUG. 2, 1921. T&S also obtained a trademark for its BLUE WHIRL design (fig. 3-18).

▶ DAINTY WHIRL: "In no other beater designed to retail at the same price will you find the apparent value, or the unusual profit margin, of the Dainty Whirl Beater." It came in a D-handle and vertical wood handle (fig. 3-19).

The BLUE WHIRL and DAINTY WHIRL also had tumbler models for use in mixing in tumblers (glasses) (fig. 3-20).

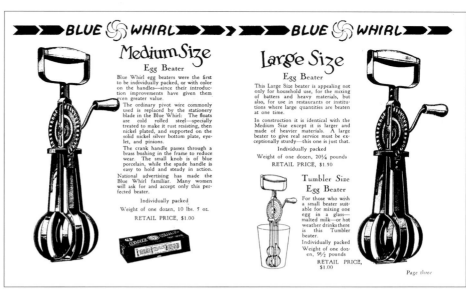

FIG. 3-16
Early T&S Blue Whirl catalog

FIG. 3-18
U.S. Patent & Trademark Office Official Gazette, July 10, 1923 Turner & Seymour trademark

Ser. No. 178,580. (CLASS 23. CUTLERY, MACHINERY, AND TOOLS, AND PARTS THEREOF.) THE TURNER & SEYMOUR MANUFACTURING CO., Torrington, Conn. Filed Apr. 4, 1923.

BLUE WHIRL

Particular description of goods.—Egg Beaters. *Claims use* since Mar. 27, 1923.

DAINTY WHIRL

Egg Beater

The Dainty Whirl with its handle and knob of attractive blue is made to sell on appeal to the eye.

Built to give years of steady service it will make satisfied customers for you. In its construction the same easy running gear is used as that on the Blue Whirl—retailing at one dollar.

The Dainty Whirl is popularly priced, which means for you quick turnover. Better still it offers you a better margin of profit than any beater, in its price range, that we know of.

It has been proved that placed on the counter with other beaters the Dainty Whirl has greater appeal because of the blue handle and knob—they attract attention.

Your egg beater sales will become more profitable with the addition of this leader.

Packed one-half dozen to carton.

Weight 3¼ pounds.

Retail Price, 50c.

FIG. 3-19
Early T&S Blue Whirl catalog featuring Dainty Whirl

FIG. 3-17

BLUE WHIRL
PAT. NOV. 28, 1916
AUG. 2, 1921
PAT PENDING.
MADE IN U.S.A.
12-1/2″ —$15—

D G Simons

FIG. 3-20

T&S tumblers
(left to right):

DAINTY
(top of handle)
PAT. AUG. 2, 1921
NO. 1386405
PAT PENDING
MADE IN U.S.A.
12″ —$80—

BLUE WHIRL
PAT. NOV. 28, 1916
AUG. 2, 1921
PAT. PENDING.
MADE IN U.S.A.
10-3/4″ —$75—

BLUE WHIRL
PAT. NOV. 28, 1916
AUG. 2, 1921
PAT. PENDING.
MADE IN U.S.A.
10-1/2″ —$75—

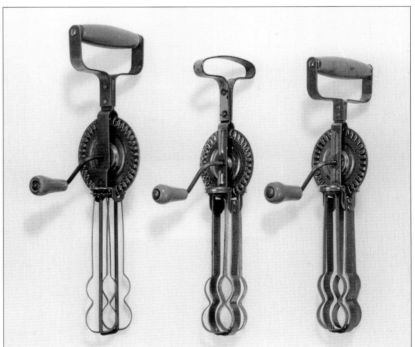

R S Arnold

KITCHEN WHIRL: "A companion number to the Dainty Whirl and like it, except for the metal handle used" *(figs. 3-21 & 3-22)*. This beater features the Nov. 28, 1916 patent date.

MERRY WHIRL: Probably the most popular of the WHIRL series, it features a vertical wood handle *(fig. 3-22)*. One early model with cast-iron frame is marked on the gear wheel, PAT. 11-28-16-OTHER PAT PEND.

One odd MERRY WHIRL was designed for the kitchen sink. Featuring the rotary top of the MERRY WHIRL, it's a snake-style drain cleaner — six feet long — mounted on the main shaft where dashers would normally be found *(fig. 3-23)*.

Many MERRY WHIRLS came with aprons and were utilized atop 4-cup measuring pitchers, embossed on the bottom T&S TORRINGTON HANDIMAID MADE IN USA. Standing about 12" tall, with beater, these pitchers came in transparent green and clear glass. There also was a smaller 2-cup measuring pitcher *(fig. 3-24)*.

One of the most coveted of T&S beater measuring cups is the transparent green pint model. "You will find it an unusual value for such an inexpensive combination. It is of green glass, graduated — has lip, handle and base, as well as a small ledge inside the rim of the pitcher on which the cover rests," said one catalog *(fig. 3-25)*. And what a great rim! Taplin and A&J aprons also fit perfectly *(fig. 3-26 & 3-27)*.

FIG. 3-21

Early T&S Blue Whirl catalog featuring Kitchen Whirl

D G Simons

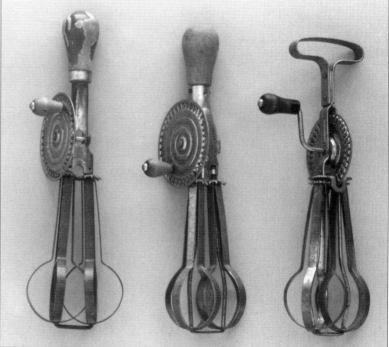

FIG. 3-22

T&S Whirls (left to right):

MERRY WHIRL PAT. 11-28-16 OTHER PAT. PEND., with cast-iron frame 11-1/2" —$20—

MERRY WHIRL PAT. 11-28-16 OTHER PAT. PEND., with metal frame 11-1/2" — $15—

KITCHEN WHIRL (top of handle), **PAT. NOV. 28, 1916 MADE IN U.S.A.** (center wheel) 11" —$15—

FIG. 3-23

MERRY WHIRL PAT. 11-26-16 OTHER PAT. PENDING MADE IN UNITED STATES OF AMERICA, with six-foot drain snake —$40—

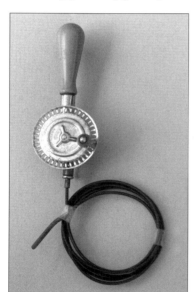

D G Simons

FIG. 3-24

T&S pitcher mixers (left to right):

T&S TORRINGTON MADE IN U.S. AMERICA 2-cup measuring pitcher clear glass 10" —$40—

MERRY WHIRL PAT. 11-28-16 OTHER PAT. PENDING MADE IN UNITED STATES OF AMERICA 4-cup transparent green measuring pitcher marked: **T&S TORRINGTON HANDIMAID MADE IN U.S.A.** 12" —$65—

MERRY WHIRL PAT. 11-28-16 OTHER PAT. PEND. 4-cup clear glass measuring pitcher marked: **T&S TORRINGTON HANDIMAID MADE IN U.S.A.** 12" —$55—

D G Simons

THE EGGBEATER CHRONICLES

FIG. 3-25

T&S catalog featuring
Non-Splatter Beater and
Handimaid Pitcher

D G Simons

The T&S beater that goes with the pint pitcher has a vertical wood handle with the main wheel gear marked "T&S NO. 39 MADE IN USA." The beater also comes without apron and is collectible in itself *(fig. 3-28).*

T&S also offered heavy 4-cup pitchers that came in "skookie green or seville yellow," *(fig. 3-29)* and were perfect fits for Taplin apron beaters *(See Chapter 4, Taplin, page 34).*

FIG. 3-27

MERRY WHIRL PAT. 11-28-16
MADE IN UNITED STATES OF AMERICA
T&S HANDIMAID MADE IN U.S.A. (embossed on jar)
12" —$75—

FIG. 3-28

T&S NO. 39 MADE IN USA
11-1/2" —$10—

FIG. 3-29

T&S catalog
4-cup pitcher

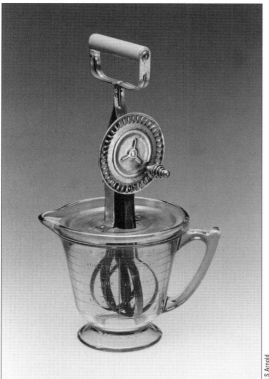

R S Arnold

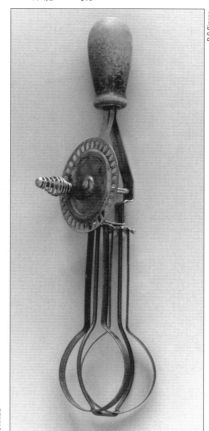

D G Simons

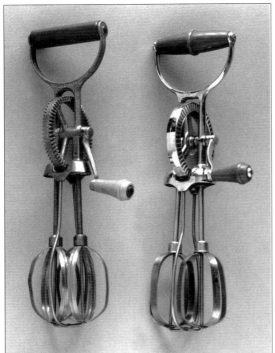

D G Simons

👉

FIG. 3-30

T&S Super Whirls (left to right):

SUPER WHIRL THE TURNER AND SEYMOUR CO. TORRINGTON, CONN. MADE IN U.S.A.
Bakelite handle   11-1/2"   —$25—

SUPER WHIRL THE TURNER AND SEYMOUR MFG. CO. TORRINGTON, CONN.   MADE IN U.S. AMERICA
Plastic handle   11-1/2"   —$15—

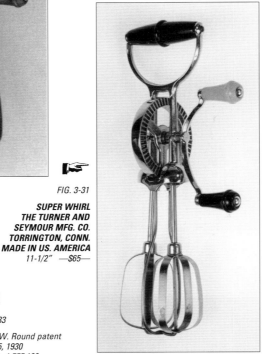

👉

FIG. 3-31

SUPER WHIRL THE TURNER AND SEYMOUR MFG. CO. TORRINGTON, CONN. MADE IN US. AMERICA
11-1/2"   —$65—

R S Arnold

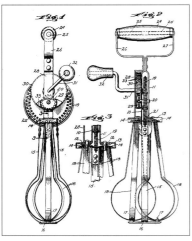

Lester T. Pullen patent
April 3, 1934
Pat. No. 1,953,722

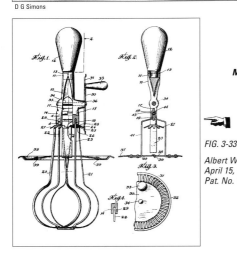

FIG. 3-34

FIG. 3-33

Albert W. Round patent
April 15, 1930
Pat. No. 1,755,132

R S Arnold

👉 *FIG. 3-32*

**PAT. AUG. 2, 1921 No. 1386405
PAT. PENDING MADE IN U.S.A.**
12-1/2" with jar —$75—

▶ A final whirl — the heavy-duty SUPER WHIRL, a very durable model sought today more for use in the kitchen than for display in a collection (*fig. 3-30*). The SUPER WHIRL also came with two handles, for tight and long strokes (*fig. 3-31*).

In addition to the WHIRLS, there is a T&S screw-on jar model (*fig. 3-32*). It is not known if it is an experimental model, or a homemade improvement, but it is a super beater that fits most wide mouth quart jars.

A memorable highlight in T&S beater history came in 1923 when the firm spent a then unheard of sum (for mixers anyway) of $20,000 for an advertising campaign for the BLUE WHIRL. In 1926 another advertising bonanza occurred: Admiral Byrd took T&S eggbeaters and can openers on his Antarctic expedition, according to company literature.

A later T&S patent date worth noting is April 15, 1930, by Albert W. Round of Torrington. This vertical wood handle model came with an apron for to mount on a jar (*fig. 3-33*).

There also is a super gear model, by Lester T. Pullen of Bridgeport, Connecticut, an assignor to T&S, that if ever manufactured, would be a very popular collectible. However, it appears the gadget (*fig. 3-34*) was never made, leaving only a tantalizing patent drawing.

Meanwhile, T&S survived. The company expanded over the years, acquiring various firms, including a sash chain maker, a novelty chain company, and a barbecue tool maker. In 1960, it purchased the Taplin Manufacturing Company of New Britain and its line of mixers.

As for T&S eggbeaters, it ended in 1973 when the housewares business was sold. F. G. Roscoe, T&S vice president, said in correspondence in 1980 that the beater line was discontinued "due to the heavy influx of similar products from abroad." But T&S is still going strong with its chain and other metal products, including thumb tacks.

THE EGGBEATER CHRONICLES

Chapter 4

Taplin

"Beats to the bottom of the bowl."

FIG. 4-1

Richard B. Lienhard, 1983

S Rice

FIG. 4-2

Clarence A. Taplin patent
April 14, 1903
Pat. No. 725,507

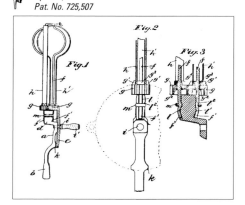

☞

FIG. 4-3

1903 models (left to right):

APRIL 14, 1903   *9-3/4"*   —$35—

APRIL 14, 1903   *8-3/4"*   —$35—

DOVER PATTERN IMPROVED APRIL 14, 1903
8-3/4"   —$35—

The advertising slogan for Taplin Manufacturing Company eggbeaters for most of the New Britain, Connecticut, firm's nearly 65 years in the mixing business: *Beats to the bottom of the bowl.*

The slogan refers the fact that the dashers on all but a very few Taplins are bent flat on the bottom — a feature that provides a quick means of identification.

"Since 1897 we have devoted ourselves to the manufacturing of egg beaters and have studied the practical and sales requirements from every angle," said a 1950s sales sheet.

"We take pride in having pioneered many of the most widely copied features of modern egg beaters. New developments are incorporated with time-tested mechanical principles to produce beaters that always represent the best of the time. They have been sold the world over in great numbers and have given universal satisfaction."

Although the sales pitch said 1897, it really started a year earlier, in 1896,

according to Richard B. Lienhard, who spent most of his life making Taplin beaters.

"… The name of the company came from a Mr. Clarence Taplin … who was tool maker for Corbin Screw Corp. of New Britain," Lienhard *(fig. 4-1)* wrote in a 1980 historical piece for the New Britain Public Library. "The Dover eggbeater had been invented and developed some years before by others, but he had patented several ingenious improvements."

In addition to an eggbeater, Taplin also patented a window stop adjuster and a lamp burner, which he manufactured at his small factory in Forestville (a section of Bristol, Connecticut). Although the eggbeater apparently was already in production, Taplin didn't file for it until Aug. 5, 1897 and the patent wasn't granted until April 14, 1903 *(fig. 4-2)*.

The April 14, 1903 patent date is the only identification on several cast-iron Taplin beaters, with DOVER PATTERN IMPROVED added later *(fig. 4-3)*.

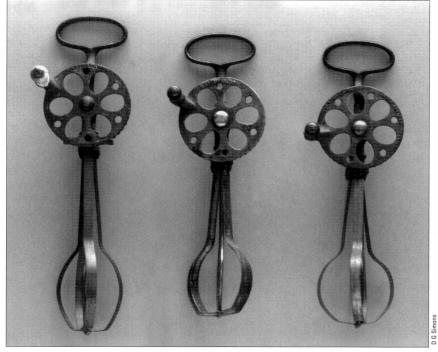

D G Simons

The DOVER PATTERN IMPROVED identification also graced two Taplins with scarce round bottom dashers (*fig. 4-4*).

Taplin is believed to be the manufacturer of a mystery beater (*fig. 4-5*) very similar to its April 14, 1903 8-3/4-incher, except for three things: its marking, its round dashers and its loop-handle. The beater is inscribed on the main wheel DOBER NO. 50 (yes "DOBER" and not "DOVER"). On the inside of the main wheel, it is embossed, just like the Taplin, MADE IN USA.

Several Taplin tumbler beaters feature the 1903 date. Taplin tumblers come with figure-8 dashers (*fig. 4-6*) and regular round dasher bottoms (*fig. 4-7*).

FIG. 4-4

Taplin Dovers (left to right):

TAPLIN'S DOVER PATTERN IMPROVED
PAT APRIL 14, 1903
12-1/4"   —$45—

DOVER PATTERN IMPROVED.
PAT. APR 14 '03
12-1/4"   —$45—

D G Simons

FIG. 4-5

DOBER No. 50
8-3/4"   —$155—

FIG. 4-6

Taplin figure-8 tumblers (left to right):

PAT'D APRIL 14, 1903   10-3/4"   —$75—

DOVER PATTERN IMPROVED EGG BEATER
PAT'D APRIL 14, 1903
10-3/4"   —$75—

LIGHT RUNNING PAT. NOV. 24 08
THE TAPLIN MFG. CO., NEW BRITAIN, CONN. U.S.A.
11"   —$150—

FIG. 4-7

Taplin round bottom tumblers (left to right):

DOVER PATTERN IMPROVED
11-1/4"   —$85—

DOVER PATTERN IMPROVED EGG BEATER
PAT'D APRIL 14, 1903
10-3/4"   —$80—

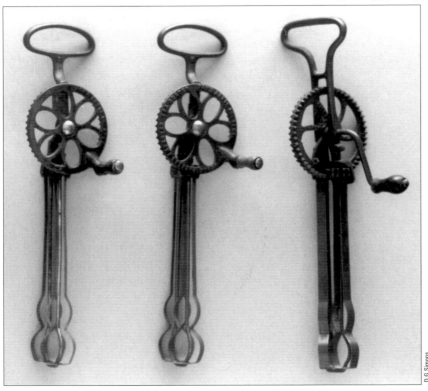

D G Simons

R S Arnold

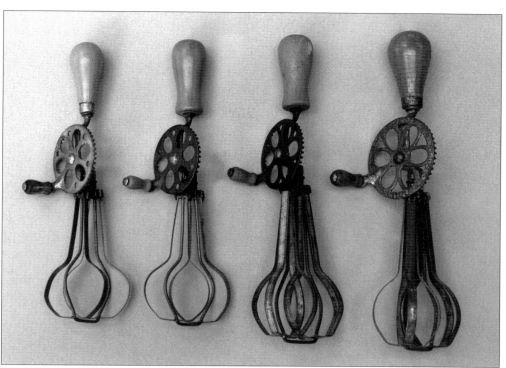

☞

FIG. 4-8

Taplin wood handles (left to right):

PAT. APRIL 14, 1903   10-1/2″   —$25—

No I.D.   10-1/2″   —$25—

No I.D.   11-1/2″   —$30—

PATTERN IMPROVED   APRIL 14, 1903
11-3/4″   —$30—

There also are 1903 cast-iron models with vertical wood handles (*fig. 4-8*).

Although the first Taplin carries the 1903 date, Lienhard said the manufacturing of beaters began before the turn of the century. "We always used 1896 as the date of the beginning of the company and the manufacture of egg-beaters," Lienhard said. "I also do not know when Clarence Taplin left the company but … it may have been 1900 when … the company was reorganized and moved to New Britain."

Fred Goodrich, who earlier had worked for the National Wire Mattress Company and Landers, Frary & Clark, took over the business at that time. The firm built a small factory on Arch Street in New Britain, but moved to Woodland Street in 1919 where it remained until its demise in 1960.

"Fred Goodrich was an enterprising man and a good salesman, but as far as I ever heard, the only manufacturing actually done by the company was that of eggbeaters, everything else having been made by other small companies," Lienhard said.

Those other items, according to *New Britain City Directory* ads in the early 1900s (*figs. 4-9 & 4-10*), included nickel-plated bathroom fixtures, sanitary soap vases, excelsior bottle stoppers, safety ladder hooks, Victor trouser hangers and Champion egg openers.

Although historic details are few, it's obvious Goodrich left his mark. At a special meeting of stockholders following his death in 1906, it was resolved "that the Taplin Manufacturing Company continue the aggressive business policy, the open honesty and forthrightness, the complete loyalty to the highest ideals, which always characterized his management of the affairs of the company."

At the time of Goodrich's death, Lienhard described the business as "well organized and successful, employing perhaps 20 to 30 persons, mostly women who did the assembling and boxing, the major part of the work."

Goodrich's son, Arthur, who helped his father run the company during the months of his final illness, was elected to succeed him as president and treasurer.

It meant an offbeat chapter in the Taplin story. Arthur was a playwright, a very successful playwright. His front page obituary in the *Hartford Courant* in 1941 cited two of his Broadway plays, "So This Is London," and "The Balance of Power." It called him "an internationally known playwright and author." It said nothing about eggbeaters.

Lienhard described Arthur's business career: "As time went on he spent less and less time at the factory, devoting himself more and more to his writing …"

In 1914, Arthur Goodrich sold Taplin to Albert Pope and Henry A. Lienhard, Richard's father. Pope, Richard Lienhard wrote, "had been president of the Pope Manufacturing Company in Hartford, makers of the famous Columbia Bicycles and Pope-Hartford automobiles which failed in 1918.

"He was a wealthy man and his interest in buying a small business was more likely to give him a base for other operations. He was only moderately active in the company."

His father, Lienhard recalled, had been the manager of the export department at Pope Manufacturing. He was "friendly with Albert Pope and his interest was to provide for his family of five children. He was the active operator of the business."

FIG. 4-9

1905 New Britain City Directory ad

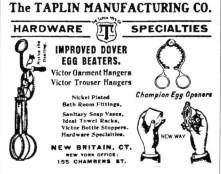

FIG. 4-10

1908 New Britain City Directory ad

Richard Lienhard joined Taplin in 1920. "I worked at whatever needed doing and became familiar with everything in the business."

As for the firm's beaters, Lienhard, who holds several beater patents himself, said, "From the beginning of the company, all of the eggbeaters were of the 'Dover' pattern, with frame, large gear and two small pinion gears made of cast iron, either lacquered or tinned finish. The large gear was on the side and engaged only one of the pinion gears."

Lienhard also noted the price of a turn-of-the-century Taplin beater. "The entire manufacturing operation consisted almost completely of three models of [cast-iron] eggbeaters: small, medium and large, selling at retail for 5¢, 10¢ and 15¢ respectively, the manufacturer's price for which were 2-1/2¢, 5¢ and 7-1/2¢."

Those were all "Dover" style beaters. The Dover name "itself I don't believe was ever protected by any patent," Lienhard said in a 1983 interview. "The Dover referred to this rotary type. Later on we used the word Dover in our printed matter and we actually had it on the gears. We used the term for the beaters that had the large gear on the side."

The firm in 1906 even obtained a trademark *(fig. 4-11)* featuring the Dover name.

However, the Dover Stamping Company of Boston, which produced the first Dover in 1870, "said we couldn't use it any more. We had cast-iron eggbeaters then so we just filled in where it said Dover."

George J. Angerbower of Forestville, Connecticut was responsible for the next major patent in the Taplin beater family. Angerbower, an assignor to Taplin, was granted his patent Feb. 9, 1904 *(fig. 4-12)*. The date appears on another DOVER PATTERN IMPROVED and the very collectible model *(fig. 4-13)* with D-O-V-E-R in the wheel *(See Chapter 8, Circular ID and Other Rarities, page 69)*.

One of the shows at Brimfield, Massachusetts, in 1997 produced a unique D-O-V-E-R beater that was discovered by collector/dealer Bob Grossman. The dealer selling the beater said his father worked for a time for Taplin and that it was the firm's practice to make experimental models and send them home with the employees to test. This experimental model, the dealer said, went home with his dad. It has one of the dashers removed and a turbine placed on the bottom *(fig. 4-14)*.

FIG. 4-11

U.S. Patent & Trademark Office Official Gazette, Oct. 2, 1906 Taplin trademark

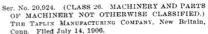

Ser. No. 20,924. (CLASS 26. MACHINERY AND PARTS OF MACHINERY NOT OTHERWISE CLASSIFIED.) THE TAPLIN MANUFACTURING COMPANY, New Britain, Conn. Filed July 14, 1906.

Particular description of goods.—Rotary Egg-Beaters.

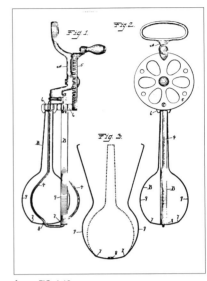

FIG. 4-12
George J. Angerbower patent Feb. 9, 1904 Pat. No. 751,601

D G Simons

FIG. 4-13

Taplin 1904 models (left to right):

D-O-V-E-R
PATENTED FEB. 9, 1904
NEW STYLE
10" —$250—

DOVER PATTERN IMPROVED
PAT'D FEB. 9, 1904
10-1/2" —$45—

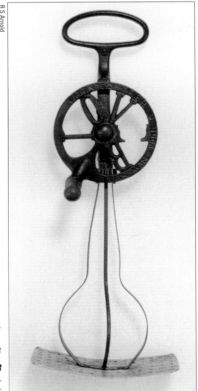

R S Arnold

FIG. 4-14
*Experimental **D-O-V-E-R** with turbine bottom.*
10" —$200—

The mainstay of Taplin's cast-iron beaters, the LIGHT RUNNING, appeared on the market next. "During the war [World War I] the patent rights *(fig. 4-15)* for a new model were acquired and preparations made to introduce it. This new model also had a cast-iron large gear, frame and pinion gears but the large gear had teeth on both sides and ran between the two pinion gears. It cost more to make, but was much more durable and performed better," Lienhard said.

The regular 1908 LIGHT RUNNINGS, with their distinctive off-center handles, came in two sizes *(fig. 4-16)*. A third all

cast-iron model, considered rare, has a heavy-duty D-handle *(fig. 4-17)*.

A possible Taplin experiment *(fig. 4-18)* involved the LIGHT RUNNING with a table-mount frame. The frame is 16-1/2" high with a 6" wooden platform. The shaft/crank extends to both sides of the frame and allows the 12-1/2" LIGHT RUNNING to swing up to allow insertion of a bowl.

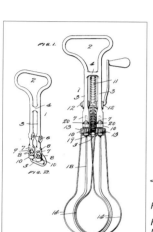

FIG. 4-15

Harlan P. Wells patent
Nov. 24, 1908
Pat. No. 905,036

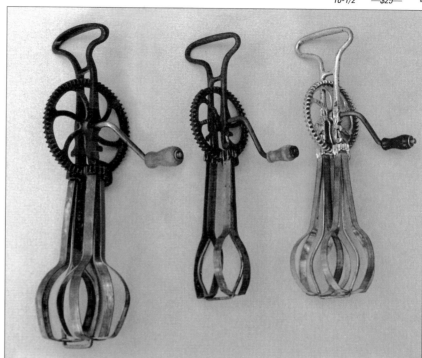

D G Simons

Fig. 4-17

**LIGHT RUNNING
PAT. NOV. 24 '08
THE TAPLIN MFG. CO.
NEW BRITAIN CONN. U.S.A.**
D-handle   11"   —$75—

D G Simons

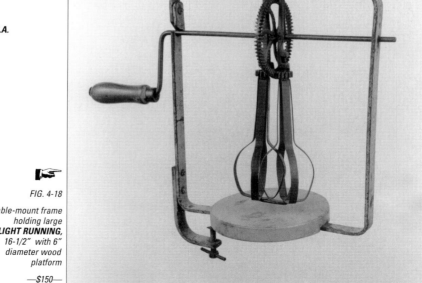

R S Arnold

FIG. 4-18

Table-mount frame
holding large
LIGHT RUNNING,
16-1/2" with 6"
diameter wood
platform

—$150—

OLIVARES COLLECTION

Dover Egg Beaters

No. 450 Family Size
No. 550 Hotel Size

Reduced cuts

No. 500
Hotel Size

Frame and Handle Malleable Iron, Chestnut Bronzed
Beating Blades Flat Tinned Wire

Nos.	450 Family	500 Hotel	550 Hotel
Length over all, inches,	10½	12½	12½
List. per gross,	$65.00	90.00	135.00

No. 450, one-twelfth gross in a box
No. 500, one twenty-fourth gross in a box
No. 550, one twenty-fourth gross in a box

Other styles Dover Beaters shown on page 163,
Catalogue No. 7

 FIG. 4-19

1915 The Wire Goods Company catalog

FIG. 4-20

Light Runnings with wooden handles

(left to right):

LIGHT RUNNING PAT. NOV. 24 '08 THE TAPLIN MFG CO.
NEW BRITAIN CONN. U.S.A. 11-1/2" —$25—

LIGHT RUNNING PAT. NOV. 24 '08 THE TAPLIN MFG CO.
NEW BRITAIN CONN. U.S.A. 15" —$60—

A 1915 catalog by The Wire Goods Company of Worcester, Massachusetts, listed the large LIGHT RUNNING at $135 per gross and the smaller model at $65 per gross *(fig. 4-19)*. In addition, there were 1908 models with vertical wood handles, coming in at least two sizes *(fig. 4-20)*.

The 11-1/2" LIGHT RUNNING also came with an apron, many of which ended up on Turner & Seymour jars *(fig. 4-21)*, particularly the heavy 4-cup pitchers, which have become very collectible items on their own *(See Chapter 3, Turner & Seymour, pages 26-27)*.

It should be noted that there is also a 16-3/4" center wheel drive, all-cast-iron giant, but without any identification. Some were outfitted with a welded-on shelf-mount *(fig. 4-22)*. It is not known if it was made by Taplin. However, Taplin did in fact make another giant beater, the MAMMOTH, with scarce round dashers *(fig. 4-23)*.

FIG. 4-22

No I.D. but very similar to
LIGHT RUNNING
16-3/4"
—$300 without shelf-mount—
—$375 with shelf-mount—

FIG. 4-21

LIGHT RUNNING's with wooden handles atop T&S 4-cup pitchers *(no identifying marks) in "skookie green" and "seville yellow"* 11-1/2" —$75 each—

D G Simons

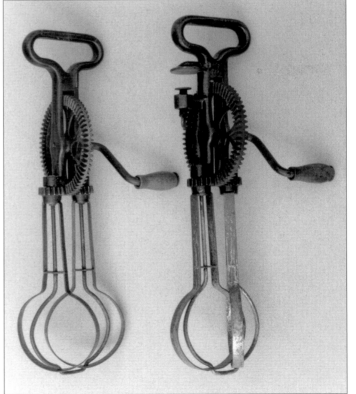

D G Simons

The smaller LIGHT RUNNING had its imitators. Nearly identical to the LIGHT RUNNING except for the handles, are models at about 10-1/4" and 11-1/2" high.

When shown one of the imitators, Lienhard was amazed at what a good copy it was but he was not able to pinpoint its origin. The mystery was solved when a scarce all-cast-iron model, with a loop handle, turned up. It is marked DRGM on the frame — the German patent mark (fig. 4-24).

FIG. 4-23

Taplin Mammoths (left to right):

MAMMOTH DOVER EGG BEATER NO. 300
TAPLIN MFG CO. (back of main shaft)
16-1/2" —$325—

MAMMOTH DOVER EGG BEATER NO. 300
with shelf-mount
16-1/2" —$395—

FIG. 4-24

German, Light Running look-alikes
10-1/4 to 11-1/2" —$25—

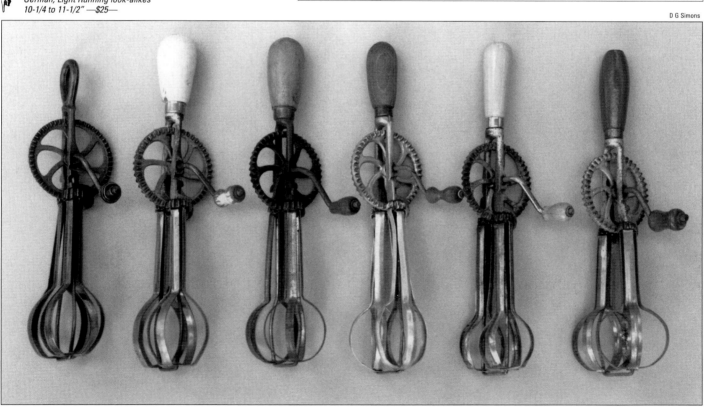

FIG. 4-25

Betty Taplins (left to right):

BETTY TAPLIN EGG BEATER
red plastic cup marked to 6 oz.
6" —$50—

BETTY TAPLIN EGG BEATER,
clear glass cup marked to 4 oz.,
embossed on bottom:
BETTY TAPLIN MADE IN U.S.A.
6" —$70—

BETTY TAPLIN EGG BEATER
in promotional yellow plastic
in chefs hands 6" —$45—

BETTY TAPLIN EGG BEATER
loop handle 5-1/2" —$15—

BETTY TAPLIN EGG BEATER
vertical wood handle
5-1/2" —$15—

FIG. 4-26

 BETTY TAPLIN EGG BEATER
very scarce model with D-wood handle
5-3/4" —$75—

Two years after Richard Lienhard joined the firm, his father came up with a marketing idea that proved to be a fantastic success.

"In 1922 we began production of a half-scale child's size toy eggbeater *(figs. 4-25 & 4-26)*. It proved an instant success and sold widely for 10¢ at retail under the trademark BETTY TAPLIN. This was not made with cast-iron parts, but was all sheet steel and was our introduction to new skills involving metal stamping."

The BETTY TAPLIN was named after Richard's younger sister, who at the time was eight years old.

"He [father] had had the thought that we could sell a toy eggbeater. We took a gamble on it and tooled up for it. We probably paid $3,000 to $4,000 for the complete set of tooling for the thing.

"I remember Mr. Pope, father's associate, took one of the samples on to Woolworth in New York.

"And he told us the [Woolworth] fellow took it and just sat playing with it and talking, dickering. He asked the price, which was probably in the vicinity of $10 a gross. They [Woolworth] would sell them for 10¢ and that didn't give them what they wanted, the markup. The guy played with it and said, 'Well, I'd like to talk to our other marketing managers. Could you leave the sample here?' Mr. Pope agreed that he could leave it with them for a couple of days. He was going to be in New York for a couple of days.

"He went back there two days after that and the guy said, 'Everybody thinks this is going to be a good seller and we would like to order some but the price is too high.'

"Pope said, 'We know it's high but we're prepared to make deliveries

promptly and we can't make it for less money.'

"The guy kind of squirmed and Mr. Pope said, 'Well, what do you want to do?' And the fellow said, 'I can buy this for $9 [a gross],' and he opened the desk drawer and handed over an eggbeater sample made by A&J. They [A&J] made it [a prototype] up in a day and a half" after obviously being shown the Taplin model. Pope, aware of what was going on, could only warn that if Woolworth went with A&J, 'You can't get delivery for quite a while.' *(See Chapter 10, A&J, page 105.)*

"Business was that way. After that we just never went to Woolworth, which of course was like cutting off your nose because they were as big as all the others put together in those days ... We got one order, something like a gross to all stores and after that A&J was in production."

Despite the Woolworth ploy, the BETTY TAPLIN *(fig. 4-27)* was, and is, a success. Asked how many Taplin sold, Lienhard replied, "Roughly 25 million. But that was over a number of years. And it was sold all over the world."

FIG. 4-27

Taplin catalog ad

THE EGGBEATER CHRONICLES

Taplin phased out its cast-iron beaters in the early 1930s and "began production of a complete new line of eggbeaters with sheet steel frame, gear and pinion gears, also wooden handles, but retaining the double dashers and center drive of the cast iron models. These new models were equally as good as the cast-iron and very much better looking," Lienhard said.

"We had a patent on a … press-metal gear. We bought it about 1930 (fig. 4-28). I think we paid probably $2,500," Lienhard said.

The beater was an immediate success. "You know, after a while it was very well accepted by the trade and it wasn't long before — to our shock, surprise — a firm, a leader in the housewares business, came out with one using a gear just like this. It was the A&J HIGH SPEED (See Chapter 10, A&J, page 100).

"We had a couple of patent attorneys take a look at it. They said that without a doubt this was an infringement. Father was running the business then. I think he wrote them and told them they were infringing, and so forth. And my recollection is he got a letter [back] referring to another patent [held by A&J] which had long since expired. They said our patent was invalid.

"We thought about it and we investigated that original [A&J] patent and it was completely inoperable … It wouldn't have worked. Our attorneys both said if you want to sue we believe we can get your infringement. Father thought about it and finally said, 'At my age I'm not going to risk everything we've got to bring suit.' And so we just abandoned it."

The 1924 center-wheel-drive patent by Wessell graced a wide variety of models with different handles — most at 11" (fig. 4-29). And like-new ones can still be found — or at least a few still with their original labels (fig. 4-30).

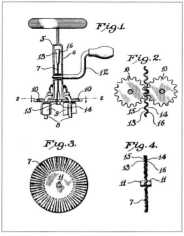

FIG. 4-28

George Wessell patent
Dec. 9, 1924
Pat. No. 1,518,285

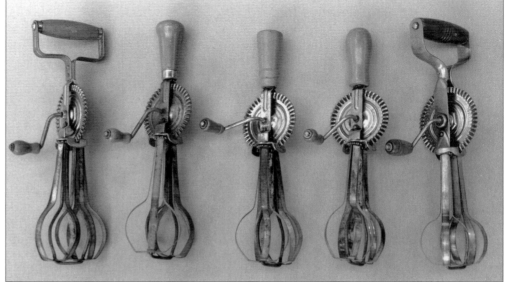

D G Simons

FIG. 4-29

1924 Taplin models (left to right):

**THE TAPLIN MFG CO. NEW BRITAIN, CONN.
PAT. 12-9-24 MADE IN USA**
11"   —$15—

**THE TAPLIN MFG CO. NEW BRITAIN, CONN.
PAT. 12-9-24 MADE IN USA**
11"   —$10—

**THE TAPLIN MFG CO. NEW BRITAIN, CONN.
PAT. 12-9-24 MADE IN USA**
11"   —$10—

**THE TAPLIN MFG CO. NEW BRITAIN, CONN.
PAT. 12-9-24 MADE IN USA**
11"   —$10—

**THE TAPLIN MFG CO. NEW BRITAIN, CONN.
MADE IN U.S.A. PAT. NO. 1518285
TAPLIN BALL BEARINGS
PAT. NO. 2193461**
11-1/2"   —$15—

D G Simons

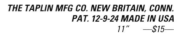

FIG. 4-30

Never-used Taplins with original sales labels

—$35 each—

GRIFFITHS COLLECTION

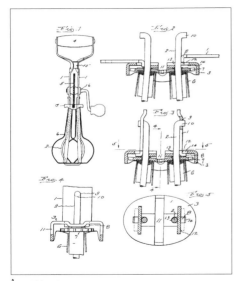

FIG. 4-31

Richard B. Lienhard patent
March 12, 1940
Pat. No. 2,193,461

handles

Handsomely finished in new synthetic enamels or of plastic. Comfortable to grasp.

drive gear

Center Drive Gear, a famous Taplin patent, easiest running of all. Wide hubs, reinforced with heavy hexagon shaped insert to insure positive drive.

dashers

Are the widely copied original Taplin design, wide spread, flexible, shaped to beat bottom of bowl. Best for small quantities as well as large.

frame

Another Taplin patent, has been re-designed to make it the strongest pressed-metal frame ever produced. Five-piece, interlocking construction with dasher guide - rod riveted securely in place provides rigidity and durability.

ball bearings

An original application of balls providing a combination radial and thrust bearing. The crank floats on special ball cups and does not come in contact with the balls at any point. Widely spaced on outside of frame, giving steadiness and balance.

pinions

Hardened Pinions are enclosed by frame.

No. 52

THE TAPLIN MANUFACTURING CO.
NEW BRITAIN, CONNECTICUT, U.S.A.

FIG. 4-32

Taplin 1950s catalog

Patent No. 2,193,461 was granted to Richard B. Lienhard on March 12, 1940 (*fig. 4-31*) for an improvement on the frame of the center wheel drive, a fact that was touted in a later Taplin catalog (*fig. 4-32*).

Lienhard also was granted two earlier patents, the dates of which do not appear on any of the Taplin beaters. The April 5, 1927, patent was related to gearing on the LIGHT RUNNING and the Aug. 31, 1937 was for a reinforced handle (*figs. 4-33 & 4-34*).

FIG. 4-33

Richard B. Lienhard patent
April 5, 1927
Pat. No. 1,623,256

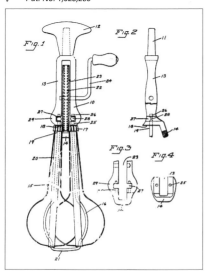

FIG. 4-34

Richard B. Lienhard patent
Aug. 31, 1937
Pat. No. 2,091,786

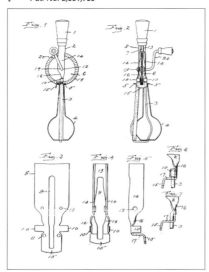

Several eggbeater holders were invented over the years, and Taplin had a patent in its possession — but never manufactured it. The "holding bracket for egg beaters" was patented Feb. 26, 1907, No. 845,326, by George F. Bailey of New Britain, assignor to Taplin. Bailey said the main object of his invention was "to provide a bracket that may be fastened to a rigid vertical support or side wall and to which bracket the ordinary handle of an egg-beater can be secured for holding the machine instead of having to hold it by one hand."

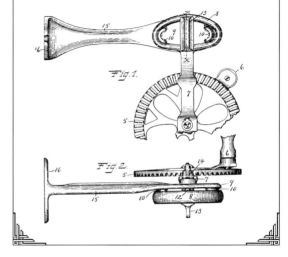

Taplin closed during World War II but reopened at the end of the war with Richard Lienhard becoming president in 1949.

In the years following the war, business was good and Taplin even made beaters for other companies, including the Automatic Wire Goods Manufacturing Company *(fig. 4-35)*, which in 1947 obtained a trademark for its WHIRL-A-WHIP beater *(fig. 4-36)*.

However, business peaked in 1950 and it then went downhill. "It seemed as though competition was hitting us from all sides: increasing use of electric beaters, imports from West Germany and Japan, and most particularly, the trend on the part of customers to buy from manufacturers who could supply complete lines of kitchen tools, including eggbeaters, which we were not in a position to do," Lienhard wrote.

FIG. 4-35

Automatic Wire Goods beaters (left to right):

AUTOMATIC WIRE GOODS MFG CO.
11" —$20—

AUTOMATIC WIRE GOODS MFG CO.
10-3/4" —$20—

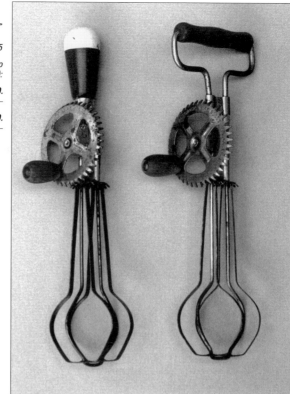

D G Simons

FIG. 4-36

U.S. Patent & Trademark Office Official Gazette, Automatic Wire Goods' 1947 trademark for Whirl-a-Whip

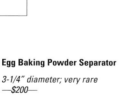

344,417. (Class 23. Cutlery, Machinery, and Tools, and Parts Thereof.) Automatic Wire Goods Mfg. Co., Inc., New York, N. Y. Original filed, act of 1946, Principal Register, Oct. 31, 1947; amended to application, Supplemental Register, Mar. 26, 1949, Serial No. 539,625.

Whirl-a-Whip

For Egg Beaters.
Claims use since Sept. 1, 1947.

Egg Baking Powder Separator

3-1/4" diameter; very rare
—$200—

COOPER COLLECTION

A cardboard, counter top advertisment standing 11-3/4" high for Buffalo Brand Vanilla Substitute featured a winsome cook and a Taplin beater. The cast-iron mixer is easily identifed by its flat bottom dashers (see page 29).

One of the last beaters made by Taplin was die-cast, ironically harking back to the firm's cast-iron origins. This "beautifully styled" PRESTIGE beater had plastic handles in the then-modern colors of black, red, yellow and turquoise. "Over sixty years of egg-beater manufacturing experience are behind this product," said a catalog sheet *(fig. 4-37)*.

The Pope family, which held a controlling interest in the firm, discharged Richard Lienhard in 1959. In 1960, Taplin folded, selling its machinery to Turner & Seymour Manufacturing Company *(See Chapter 3, Turner & Seymour, page 21)*.

Taplin was typical of early American manufacturing. The firm filled a need — but its particular niche in the kitchen market finally disappeared. Was Taplin a success? Judging from a personal note concluding Richard Lienhard's history of the firm — Taplin was, and more.

"Even though we did not survive the rigors of the competitive business world, I can take pride in many things: We always made good, honest, contemporary merchandise and we always paid our bills on time and nobody lost any money in our dissolution; we ran a clean shop with great employee cooperation, never had a strike or a union, lived in peace with our neighbors, did our share of community projects and local manufacturer affairs, among whom we had many friends.

"To me, these add up to at least a measure of success."

Richard's younger brother, Robert, asked about Taplin in correspondence in 1993, said: "I loved the factory with its elaborate overhead belts and pulleys supplying power to the individual machines — the incredible four-slide machine that formed the dashers, the smell of oil and even the organic and articulate quality of the 1920 heavy timber mill construction of the building itself. The budding architect found this fascinating and his delight must have prompted the factory family to explain in great detail the intricacies of fabrication."

Robert Lienhard was also asked to describe his brother. "These words of Dick's so perfectly expressed his philosophy and values — decency, humanity and absolute honesty," Robert said.

Richard Booth Lienhard died April 10, 1985 at the age of 83.

FIG. 4-37

Prestige beater ad

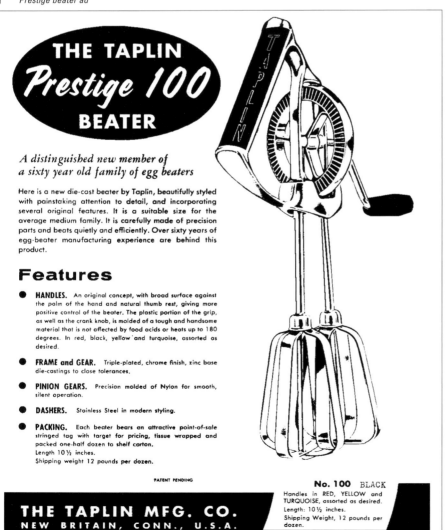

THE TAPLIN Prestige 100 BEATER

A distinguished new member of a sixty year old family of egg beaters

Here is a new die-cast beater by Taplin, beautifully styled with painstaking attention to detail, and incorporating several original features. It is a suitable size for the average medium family. It is carefully made of precision parts and beats quietly and efficiently. Over sixty years of egg-beater manufacturing experience are behind this product.

Features

● **HANDLES.** An original concept, with broad surface against the palm of the hand and natural thumb rest, giving more positive control of the beater. The plastic portion of the grip, as well as the crank knob, is molded of a tough and handsome material that is not affected by food acids or heats up to 180 degrees. In red, black, yellow and turquoise, assorted as desired.

● **FRAME and GEAR.** Triple-plated, chrome finish, zinc base die-castings to close tolerances.

● **PINION GEARS.** Precision molded of Nylon for smooth, silent operation.

● **DASHERS.** Stainless Steel in modern styling.

● **PACKING.** Each beater bears an attractive point-of-sale stringed tag with target for pricing, tissue wrapped and packed one-half dozen to shelf carton.
Length 10½ inches.
Shipping weight 12 pounds per dozen.

PATENT PENDING

No. 100 BLACK
Handles in RED, YELLOW and TURQUOISE, assorted as desired.
Length: 10½ inches.
Shipping Weight, 12 pounds per dozen.

THE TAPLIN MFG. CO.
NEW BRITAIN, CONN., U.S.A.

We take pride in having pioneered many of the most widely copied features of modern egg beaters … They have been sold the world over in great numbers and have given universal satisfaction.

— **TAPLIN EGG BEATER CATALOG**

THE TAPLIN MANUFACTURING CO.
SINCE 1897
NEW BRITAIN, CONN.

Standard and Other Cast-Iron Beauties

Standard of Excellence.

The STANDARD EGG BEATER set the standard of excellence for turn-of-the-century mixers. It was one of several cast-iron marvels manufactured by various firms that competed with, but never reached the mixer output of the early big four, Dover, Holt-Lyon, Turner & Seymour and Taplin.

But the Standard Manufacturing Company came close. In addition to the STANDARD beater, the Boston firm produced the ACME, DUPLEX, KINGSTON AND RIVAL, according to a listing in the December 12, 1888 issue of the New York weekly trade magazine, *Iron Age*. Standard also had a Dover-type beater with wood D-handle with various names and its own DOVER-marked beaters.

The flagship of the firm, the STANDARD, still merits top billing because of its rarity, its unique dashers and its patentee, the famous inventor Thomas W. Brown.

The Standard Manufacturing Company first appeared in the 1880 *Boston City Directory* on Sudbury Street. In 1881 the company moved to Portland Street where it remained through 1894.

It was during this period that "kitchen furnishings," followed by the words "egg beater" in parentheses, were added to its directory listing.

In 1888, the firm became known simply as the Standard Company, moving in 1895 to Beverly Street. In 1897, it made another move, to Haverhill Street, where it was located at different numbers, including 107. It remained on Haverhill until 1906, the last date the firm appeared in the directory.

The first Standard beater was patented June 29, 1880 *(fig. 5-1)* by Brown, a resident of nearby Belmont, Massachusetts, who said: "The nature of my invention consists in constructing in an egg beater a central stationary piece of thin metal, shaped by incurving the two sides of a circle, and in combining with this a revolving device, also made of thin metal, and having one portion of each side incurved to correspond to the incurvation of the fixed piece."

It's the "incurvation" of the dashers that gives the Standard beater *(fig. 5-2)* its distinct look. But Standards can mix

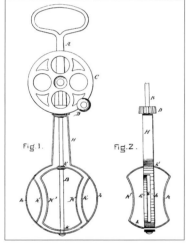

FIG. 5-1

Thomas W. Brown patent
June 29, 1880
Pat. No. 229,372

FIG. 5-2

Standards (left to right):

STANDARD EGG BEATER PAT. JUNE 29 SEPT 21 '80, MARCH 8 '81	10-1/4″	—$400—
JUNE 29 '80	9-3/4″	—$350—
No I.D.	9-1/2″	—$325—
JUNE 29 '80	9-3/4″	—$325—

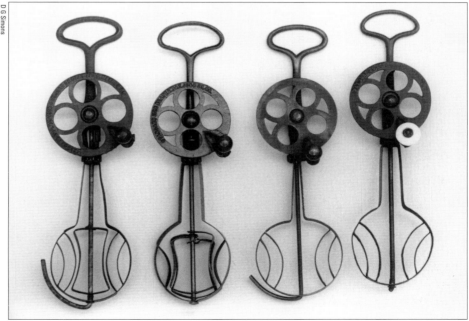

MOFFET COLLECTION

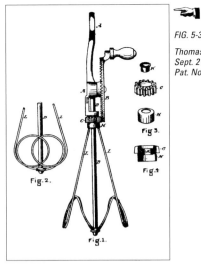

FIG. 5-3

Thomas W. Brown patent
Sept. 21, 1880
Pat. No. 232,328

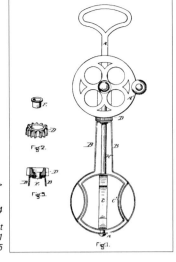

FIG. 5-4

Thomas W. Brown patent
March 8, 1881
Pat. No. 238,565

you up. There are different dates, markings and dashers. Some are marked STANDARD EGG BEATER and others just have dates. Others have completely different names or no identification whatsoever. However, all STANDARDS have an identifiable straight back shaft.

Brown was listed in the 1890 *Belmont City Directory* as "manufacturer egg beaters etc. (Standard Manufacturing Company), 129 Portland, B. Pleasant, next Town Hall." According to the reference book *A Brief History of the Trapola Browns,* Thomas W. was born March 6, 1832; married Frances Harley of Philadelphia April 16, 1869, and died May 12, 1902.

Such a small bit of information for such a great inventor.

Brown's beater patents cover the period from 1880 to 1890 and there are at least two cross-overs on patents being used by the Dover Stamping Company *(See Chapter 1, Dover, page 4)* and the National Manufacturing Company *(See Chapter 7, National Manufacturing Co., page 67).* In addition, Brown was granted patents for a teapot cover and bottle cap *(figs. 5-3 through 5-10).*

FIG. 5-5

Thomas W. Brown patent
July 14, 1885
Pat. No. 322,250
(used by both Standard and Dover)

FIG. 5-6

Thomas W. Brown patent
Aug. 30, 1887
Pat. No. 369,273

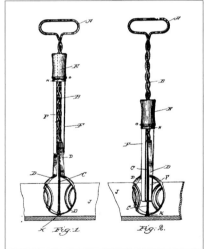

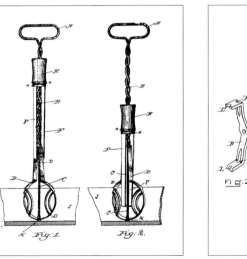

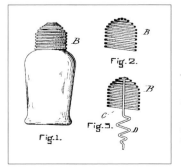

FIG. 5-7
Thomas W. Brown patent
Jan. 21, 1890
Pat. No. 419,631

FIG. 5-8

Thomas W. Brown patent
Dec. 27, 1898
Pat. No. 29,873
(design patent for a Dover beater handle)

FIG. 5-9

Thomas W. Brown patent
Jan. 25, 1881
Pat. No. 236,931

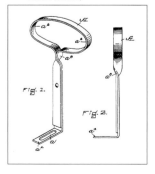

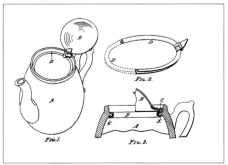

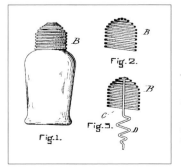

FIG. 5-10

Thomas W. Brown patent
July 26, 1881
Pat. No. 244,740

THE EGGBEATER CHRONICLES

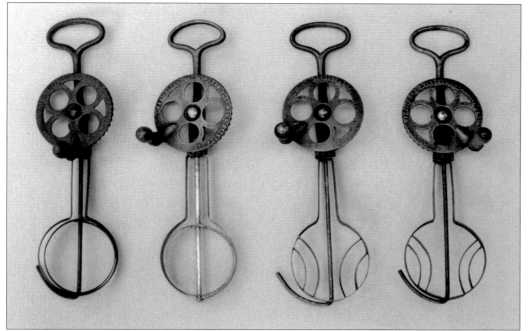

FIG. 5-11

Benjamins and Standards (left to right):

MANHATTAN G. P. BENJAMIN N.Y. PAT SEPT 21 80 MARCH 8 81
9-1/2" —$425—

"MANHATTAN" PAT JUNE 29 80 GEO P BENJAMIN NEW YORK
9-1/2" —$350—
Note: This model is also marked EGG BEATER PAT. JUNE 29, 1880

PAT JUNE 29 80
9-3/4" —$425—

PAT JUNE 29 80 SEP 21 80 MAR 8 81 JULY 14 85
9-3/4" —$325—
Note: This model is also marked only: PAT. MARCH 8, 81

D G Simons

FIG. 5-12   PAUL SMITH COLLECTION

STANDARD
PAT. MARCH 8 81
JULY 14 85
9-3/4" —$400—

R S Arnold

D G Simons

FIG. 5-13

PAT MAR 8 '81
JULY 14 '85
10-1/4" —$410—

MOFFET COLLECTION

Other Brown patent cross-overs include the unexplained "George P. Benjamin" connection. The patent dates Sept. 21, 1880 and March 8, 1881 appear on a cast-iron beater marked: MANHATTAN, GEO. P. BENJAMIN, NEW YORK.

The only difference between it and the usual STANDARD is that the BENJAMIN has double-circle dashers. There also is a variation on the MANHATTAN, with another model featuring Brown's June 29, 1880 date *(fig. 5-11)*. And there is a STANDARD with a double circle *(fig. 5-12)*.

All these beaters sharing the same dates raises the question of how incestuous were the manufacturers? For example, the line between Dover and Standard fades somewhat with an 1870 DOVER look-alike that is marked with Brown patent dates. It also features slotted dashers *(fig. 5-13)*.

Timothy Earle

Rivaling Thomas W. Brown as one of the 19th century's top eggbeater inventors was Timothy Earle of Smithfield, Rhode Island. In addition to his EARL'S BEATER *(See Chapter 1, Dover, page 2)*, he was granted five beater and one beater-holder patents.

April 4, 1866

January 25, 1870

July 5, 1870

September 27, 1870

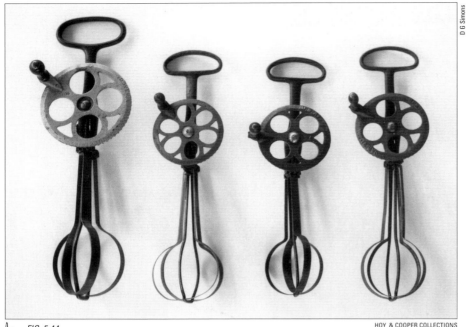

FIG. 5-14

Standard Dovers (left to right):

DOVER MAR 8 81 JULY 14 85
12" —$95—

DOVER PAT MAR 8 81 JULY 14 85 U.S.A.
10-1/2" —$95—
Note: This model is also marked: **THE "RIVAL" EGG BEATER U.S.A.**

PAT MAR. 8, 81 JULY 14, 85 U.S.A.
10" —$75—

DOVER U.S.A. PAT. MAR 8 81 JULY 14 85 JAN. 21 '90
10-1/2" —$75—

FIG. 5-15

R S Arnold

More Standards (left to right):

GENUINE DOVER EGG BEATER U.S.A.
10-1/2" —$145—

DUPLEX PAT. MAR 8, 81 JULY 14, 85
10" —$175—

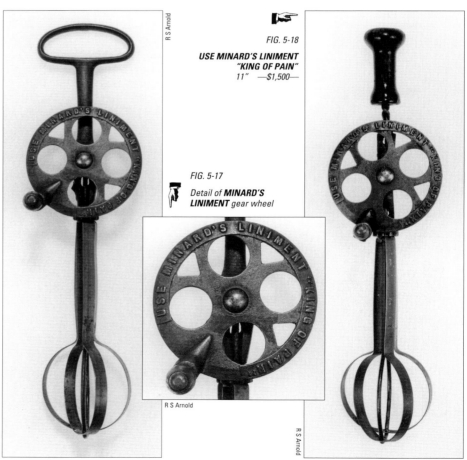

FIG. 5-16

**USE MINARD'S LINIMENT
"KING OF PAIN"**
10-3/4" —$1,500—

FIG. 5-18

**USE MINARD'S LINIMENT
"KING OF PAIN"**
11" —$1,500—

FIG. 5-17

Detail of **MINARD'S
LINIMENT** *gear wheel*

R S Arnold

The key to identifying STANDARDS, including those marked DOVER, is the previously-noted straight back shaft *(figs. 5-14 and 5-15)*.

The different markings on STANDARDS include the only known embossed advertisement: "KING OF PAIN" on two rare STANDARDS, one with a cast-iron handle and the other with a vertical wood handle *(figs. 5-16 through 5-18)*. "For rheumatism, neuralgia, sciatica, corns, colds, coughs, etc, etc," said an early brochure for the "KING OF PAIN" *(fig. 5-19)*.

FOR RHEUMATISM, NEURALGIA, SCIATICA, CORNS, COLDS, COUGHS, ETC., ETC.

Use Minard's Liniment

BRANCH FACTORY
ST. JOHN'S, NEWFOUNDLAND

For
Tired, aching, swollen feet.
Just rub on.

Manufactured by MINARD'S LINIMENT COMPANY Limited, Yarmouth, N.S.
Sales agents HAROLD F. RITCHIE & Co. Limited, Toronto

"BEVERAGE FOR BROKERS."

MINARD'S LINIMENT,
KING OF PAIN.

FIG. 5-19
Early Minard's Liniment ads

In the same class of rarity as the "KING OF PAIN" is the BELMONT EGG BEATER *(fig. 5-20)*. The BELMONT appears to be a good match for Brown's Sept. 21, 1880 patent *(fig. 5-3, page 42)* and Brown's hometown as noted previously is Belmont, Massachusetts.

An early STANDARD flyer listed the vertical wood handle DOVER PATTERN or DOVER USA eggbeater with three Brown dates *(fig. 5-21)*.

A nearly identical beater, but with a wood D-handle, is marked U.S.A. The U.S.A., although a perfect match for the patent drawing, does not carry the Jan. 21, 1890 patent date. Instead, embossed on the wheel are the two other Brown dates, MARCH 8, 1881 and JULY 14, 1885.

FIG. 5-21

DOVER USA
PAT MAR 8 '81   JULY 14 '85 *(faint)*
JAN 21 '90 *(heavy embossing)*
Note: This mixer is also marked:
THE RIVAL EGG BEATER
10"   —$275—

FIG 5-20

BELMONT EGG BEATER
9-1/2"   —$1,500—

R S Arnold

D Thornton

ALLEN COLLECTION

CONTENTS 1 FL. OZ.

EZEWAY

JIFFY-WHIP

FOR
WHIPPING
TOPS OF MILK,
SINGLE CREAM
AND
EVAPORATED MILK

A MIXTURE OF CALCIUM
SUCRATE, SUGAR AND WATER

SAVES TIME, MONEY
AND TROUBLE

EZEWAY PRODUCTS DIV.,
THE AMERICAN PRODUCTS CO.
CINCINNATI, OHIO, U.S.A.

"You just add a few drops of Jiffy-Whip to ordinary cream (20% butter fat), the 'tops' of milk, or evaporated milk and you can quickly whip up a delicious whipped cream," says the ad on the side of the box of this whipping additive.

CHAPTER 5: STANDARD AND OTHER CAST-IRON BEAUTIES

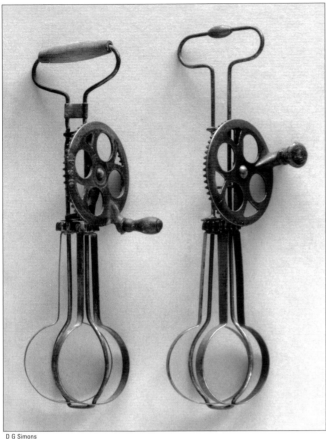

D G Simons

R S Arnold

The MARCH 8, 1881 date also appears on a very similar beater with a wire handle with a fat metal bead called the DUPLEX, which is listed in early trade papers as being manufactured by STANDARD *(fig. 5-22)*.

More incest: A U.S.A. duplicate is listed in an early Hamblin & Russell Manufacturing Company catalog as the DOUBLE *(See Chapter 8, Circular ID and Other Rarities, page 73)*.

Another wire top, obviously in the same family , features two Brown patent dates *(fig. 5-23)*. It has a heavy cast retainer for the two wire braces leading up to the top handle. In C. M. Linington's *Silent Salesman*, Chicago, wholesale catalog of August, 1890, this beater is called "THE PEOPLE'S." Said the catalog: "This is the very latest thing in the egg beater line, having many of the desirable points found in the Dover. We think this is the cheapest egg beater in the market for the money. A leader for 10 cents. Put up 1 dozen in box $.88."

D G Simons

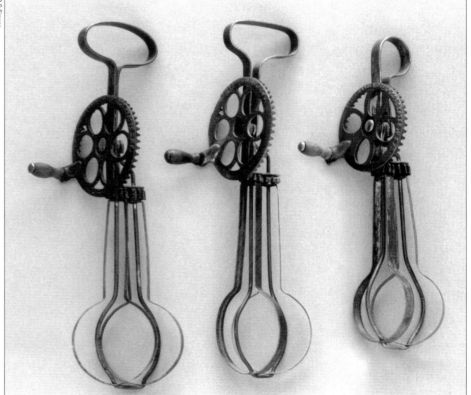

👉 FIG. 5-25
STEEL HANDLE DOVER EGG BEATER U.S.A.
with slotted dashers
10-1/2"
—$135—

D G Simons

MOFFET COLLECTION

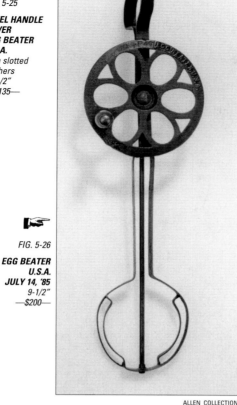

R S Arnold

👉 FIG. 5-26
EGG BEATER U.S.A. JULY 14, '85
9-1/2"
—$200—

ALLEN COLLECTION

D G Simons

👉 FIG. 5-27
THE "RIVAL" EGG BEATER U.S.A.
11"
—$600—

PAUL SMITH COLLECTION

The STEEL HANDLE DOVER *(fig. 5-24)*, long believed to be part of the Dover Stamping Company family, was in fact made by Standard, based on Brown's Dec. 27, 1898 design patent *(See Chapter 1, Dover, page 4)*. The April 7, 1898 *Iron Age* magazine featured a drawing of the beater and said: "The Standard Company, 107 Haverhill Street, Boston, Mass., are manufacturing a new patented Dover egg beater, differing from the usual style in the construction of the handle, which is made of one piece of bright steel instead of cast iron, and is shaped so that it can be grasped and held firmly with one hand. The steel handle adds to the strength and beauty of the beater and, it is claimed, is much lighter and cheaper."

The April 20, 1899 *Iron Age* featured another Standard steel handle and said: "The new loop shaped handle of the No. 5C beater is referred to as especially adapted to export trade, as they stack in less pace than the same sized beater with the regular style of handle."

The January 19, 1899 *Iron Age* featured still another steel handle with slotted dashers *(fig. 5-25)*. In describing this beater, *Iron Age* gave this plug to

Standard: "The company manufactures an extensive line of beaters of varying sizes, adapted to the requirements of private families, boarding houses, hotels, &c. Making beaters has been the company's specialty for the past 20 years." A similar steel handle with slotted dashers featured Brown's July 14, 1885 patent date *(fig. 5-26)*.

The April 20, 1899 *Iron Age also* listed Standard's RIVAL *(fig. 5-27)*. "The Rival

beater is spoken of as a new pattern, and is held in high estimation by the makers, because of its construction and operation," *Iron Age* said. The RIVAL surfaced in 1994 in an antique mall in Illinois. The unique handle and circular frame around this beater are very distinctive. The same model, with a different dasher configuration, is marked STEEL HANDLE DOVER EGG BEATER U.S.A.

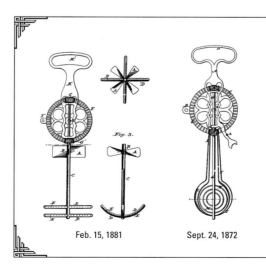

Feb. 15, 1881   Sept. 24, 1872

Thomas W. Brown wasn't the only inventor to offer different dasher designs. Two examples of beaters with unique dashers —that if manufactured have yet to turn up — include:

George W. Gill of Columbus, Ohio, Feb. 15, 1881 patent, No. 237,741, with a hollow tube and fans to force air out of the perforated dashers.

William O. Crocker of Laconia, New Hampshire, Sept. 24, 1872, patent No. 131,600, with dashers turning in opposite directions resulting in "inward" and "outward" mixing actions.

The Standard Manufacturing Company also produced the ACME EGG BEATER with Brown's June 29, 1880 patent date *(fig. 5-28)* and a similar model marked only Acme *(fig. 5-29)*. It should be noted that Hamblin & Russell offered an IMPROVED ACME BEATER *(fig. 5-30)* and there is a very rare ACME with a spring wire bottom *(figs. 5-31 & 5-32)*.

☞

FIG. 5-28

**ACME EGG BEATER
PAT. JUNE 29, 80**
9-1/2" —$500—

FIG. 5-30

☝

*Hamblin & Russell
Manufacturing Co.
19th Century catalog*

FIG. 5-29

☝

ACME *9-1/2"* —$500—

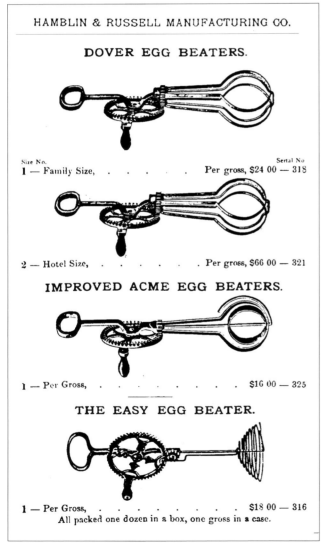

HAMBLIN & RUSSELL MANUFACTURING CO.

DOVER EGG BEATERS.

Size No.				Serial No
1 — Family Size,	. . . .	Per gross,	$24 00 — 318
2 — Hotel Size,	. . . .	Per gross,	$66 00 — 321

IMPROVED ACME EGG BEATERS.

1 — Per Gross, ... $16 00 — 325

THE EASY EGG BEATER.

1 — Per Gross, ... $18 00 — 316
All packed one dozen in a box, one gross in a case.

FIG. 5-31

☝

*Wm. Frankfurth Hardware Co.
1885 catalog with line drawing
of The Acme*

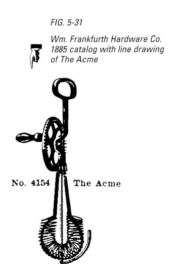

No. 4154   The Acme

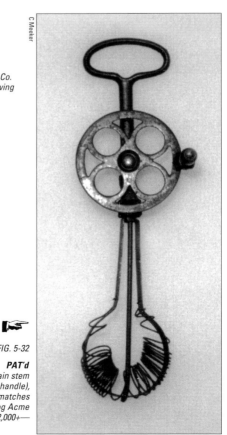

☞

FIG. 5-32

PAT'd
*(back of main stem
just below handle),
only I.D. but matches
catalog Acme*
10" —$2,000+—

THE EGGBEATER CHRONICLES

Brown's June 29, 1880 patent date also appeared on the Kingston *(fig. 5-33),* listed at 25 cents in the Simmons Hardware Company of St. Louis catalog of 1881.

Similar to the Standards, but based on a patent *(fig. 5-34)* by James R. Hughes of Saugus, Massachusetts, are several beaters with the enticing names of AMERICAN, ADVANCE, BIJOU, GRECIAN, and HUB *(figs. 5-35 & 5-36).* Hughes also was responsible for a wire Archimedes *(See Chapter 12, Archimedes, page 114).*

FIG. 5-33

**KINGSTON EGG BEATER
PAT. JUNE 29, 80.**
9-3/4" —$550—

MAIR COLLECTION

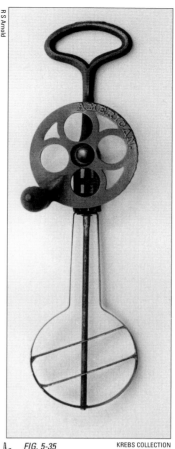

FIG. 5-35

AMERICAN
9-1/2" —$800—

KREBS COLLECTION

FIG. 5-34

James R. Hughes patent
Dec. 7, 1880
Pat. No. 235,245

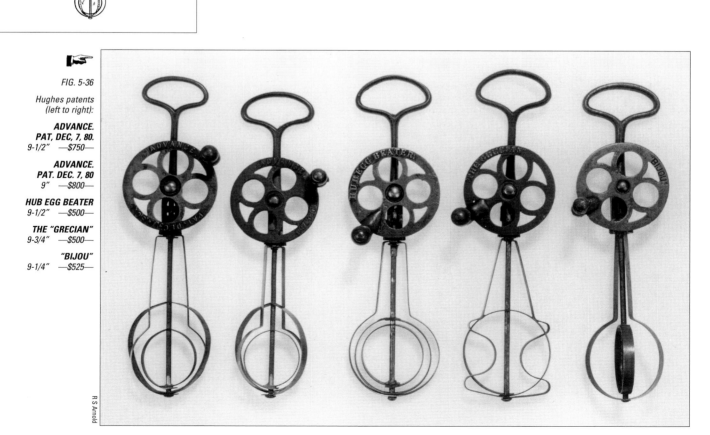

FIG. 5-36

Hughes patents
(left to right):

**ADVANCE.
PAT, DEC, 7, 80.**
9-1/2" —$750—

**ADVANCE.
PAT. DEC. 7, 80**
9" —$800—

HUB EGG BEATER
9-1/2" —$500—

THE "GRECIAN"
9-3/4" —$500—

"BIJOU"
9-1/4" —$525—

CHAPTER 5: STANDARD AND OTHER CAST-IRON BEAUTIES

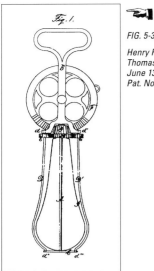

FIG. 5-37

Henry F. Jenks and
Thomas Marsh patent
June 13, 1871
Pat. No. 115,862

In addition to the Standard line, there were dozens of other cast-iron beauties made by smaller, little known firms. including:

▶ The CENTRIPETAL was patented June 13, 1871 by Henry F. Jenks and Thomas Marsh of Pawtucket, Rhode Island (*fig. 5-37*). This is a very rare beater, with only a few known to exist. One is marked CENTRIPETAL (*fig. 5-38*) and another is marked H. F. JENKS.

▶ The CHRISTY involves the story of the second son of the second son of the second son. Here's how it started: Timothy Earle of Smithfield, Rhode Island, and William T. Nicholson, of Providence, patented a table-mount, cast-iron beater Sept. 25, 1860 (*fig. 5-39*) that is known today as the CHRISTY.

The beater obviously was produced years after its patent date, and the only identifying mark is on a metal slot that holds the interchangeable dashers. It says "CHRISTY KNIFE, PATENTED, FREMONT." It comes with two dasher arrangements, one a regular type double dasher that goes in two directions, and a simple paddle one (*fig. 5-40*).

Later models had heavy-duty features, a removable gear top and a strong band to hold a bowl. One has an extra large funnel (*fig. 5-41*) and another a smaller funnel (*figs. 5-42 & 5-43*). Although it has different gearing, there also is a similar heavy duty model that could be part of the Christy family (*fig. 5-44*).

Christy Knife, now The Christy Company of Fremont, Ohio, celebrated its 100th anniversary in 1991 — owned and operated by the second son of the second son of the second son.

In correspondence in 1991, E. B. Christy, president of the firm, recalled his grandfather, Russ J. Christy, the founder.

"I, of course, knew granddad. I was 26 when he died in 1947. He started the company in 1891, the year my dad was born. He told me he had 75 different items for use in the kitchen. He had the original patent on the scalloped edge bread knife (*fig. 5-45*)."

Russ J. Christy, according to his grandson, was born the second son in Clyde, Ohio, in 1862. A machinist and tool maker, he ended up in Fremont "where he put up his patents [on the scalloped edge], and his mechanical ability and two men put up the cash and the Christy Knife Company was born."

D G Simons

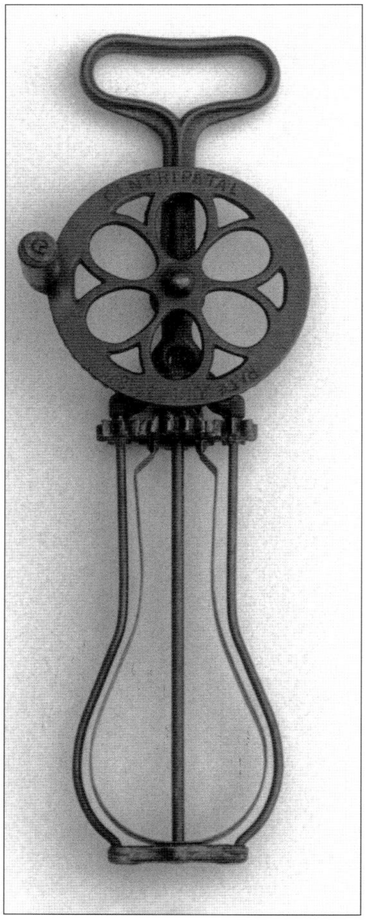

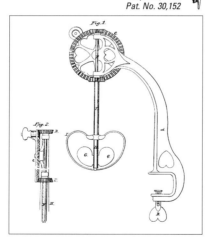

FIG. 5-39

William T. Nicholson and
Timothy Earle patent
Sept. 25, 1860
Pat. No. 30,152

MOFFET COLLECTION

FIG. 5-38

CENTRIPETAL
PAT'D JUNE 13, 87
10-1/2"   —$1,500—

FIG. 5-40

**CHRISTY KNIFE
PATENTED
FREMONT**
11-1/2"
with metal ring-mount and funnel
—$450—

without metal ring-mount and funnel
—$275—

D Thornton

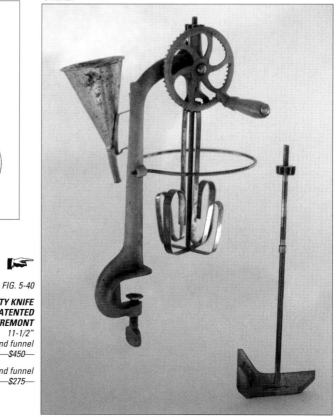

THE EGGBEATER CHRONICLES

E. B. Christy said he assumed the now famed table-mount mixer was purchased from another manufacturer and sold by Christy, but that whatever the manufacturing/selling arrangement, it all came to an end around 1914.

"World War I killed the kitchen cutlery business because materials were restricted. In 1906, granddad invented the safety razor *(fig. 5-46)* and we continued manufacturing razors and blades until 1959.

"We began manufacturing the Christy Sliding Blade Pocket Knife (which granddad invented 15 years after he retired to Florida) and that is our principle product today *(fig. 5-47)*."

When Russ J. Christy retired, his second son, D. LaMar Christy, ran the company. LaMar Christy died in 1955, at which time his second son, E. B. Christy, took over management.

After 100 years, Christy, with the slogan "products with an edge — since 1891," is still going strong.

D Thornton

☞

FIG. 5-41

No I.D. on mixer
CHRISTY MAYONNAISE MIXER *(on jar)*
12-3/4" to top of funnel
—$1,000—

GILSON COLLECTION

FIG. 5-42

Early Christy ad

R S Arnold

☞

FIG. 5-43

No I.D., but later model CHRISTY
12"
—$500 without bowl—

MAIR COLLECTION

R S Arnold

☞

FIG. 5-44

No I.D., but possibly CHRISTY
12" —$300—

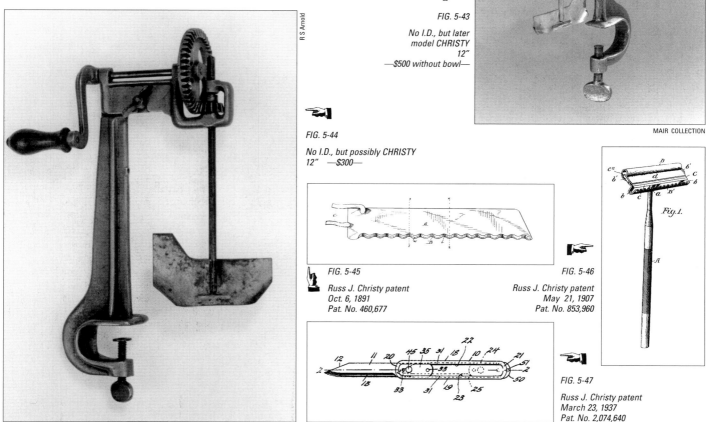

☞ **FIG. 5-45**

Russ J. Christy patent
Oct. 6, 1891
Pat. No. 460,677

☞ **FIG. 5-46**

Russ J. Christy patent
May 21, 1907
Pat. No. 853,960

Fig.1.

☞ **FIG. 5-47**

Russ J. Christy patent
March 23, 1937
Pat. No. 2,074,640

OLIVARES COLLECTION

FIG. 5-48

Cyclone models (left to right):

**CYCLONE
PAT 6-25-1901 REISSUE
8-26-1902**
13-1/2"   —$95—

CYCLONE PAT 6-25 & 7-16 1901
11-1/2"   —$80—

CYCLONE PAT 6-25-1901 8-26-1902 REISSUE
11-1/2"   —$80—

CYCLONE PAT 6-25-1901 REISSUE 8-26-1902
13-1/2"   —$95—

FIG. 5-49

*William G. Browne design patent
June 25, 1901
Pat. No. 34,690*

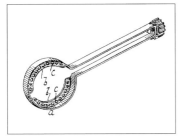

D G Simons

FIG. 5-50

*William G. Browne
patent
July 16, 1901, reissued
Aug. 26, 1902
Pat. No. 678,456*

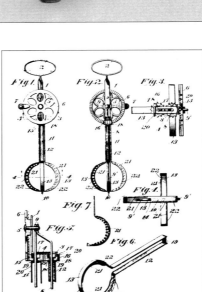

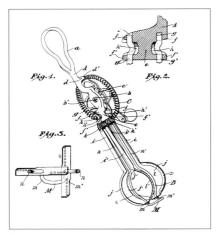

FIG. 5-51

*William G. Browne patent
July 14, 1903
Pat. No. 733,621*

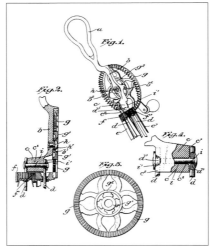

FIG. 5-52

*Graham C. Parish patent
Dec. 26, 1905
Pat. No. 808,613*

▶ The prized CYCLONE, with its drilled dashers, came in two sizes *(fig. 5-48)* and a variety of patent dates by William G. Browne of Kingston, New York *(figs. 5-49 through 5-52)*.

In his June 25, 1901 Design Patent 34,690, Browne staked claim to the perforated dasher, or "member" as he called it. "The leading feature of my design resides in an egg-beater member having bow portions with inwardly-extending perforated flanges," Browne said.

In his July 16, 1901 patent, Browne described himself as assignor to his W. G. Browne Manufacturing Company. He also had more to say about the dasher holes: "Each flange is formed with a series of apertures through which the cream or eggs are forced as the beaters revolve and divide into a plurality of streams, thus distributing the same so that it may be more effectually disrupted and quicker and more thorough beating or whipping effected."

The last Cyclone patent resulted in a bit of beater mystery: The Dec. 26, 1905 patent was granted to Graham C. Parish, also of Kingston — but added to the bottom of the patent papers is a correction from F. I. Allen, commissioner of patents, saying it "was erroneously issued to said Parish, whereas said Letters of Patent should have been issued to The W. G. Browne Manufacturing Company of Kingston, N.Y."

An early ad *(fig. 5-53)* said in part: "We only claim and guarantee to beat an egg to its lightest and stiffest possible consistency in fifteen seconds."

The Browne firm, described as manufacturers of hardware and novelties, first appeared in the *Kingston City Directory* in 1902. Over the years it offered, in addition to the CYCLONE, can openers (including "The Best," "None Such" and "The Shear Cut Clipper"), ice picks, potato mashers, and tack hammers. A large sign on the side of the two-story manufacturing plant proudly proclaimed: THE HOME OF THE CYCLONE EGG BEATER *(fig. 5-54)*.

The 1905 Kingston census listed Browne at the time as 52 years old, living with his wife, Olive, 63, and daughter, Edna, 23, on Albany Avenue.

The 1905 city directory described Browne as offering hardware specialties. By 1914 the product had shifted to "Electro plating."

"Don't throw it away — have it replated," said a directory ad. "We make a specialty of restoring antiques, repairing and replating silverware. Save labor by having the metal parts on your auto nickel plated. Prices reasonable. Work guaranteed." Browne was still listed in 1931.

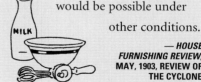

The main claim for this little machine is the perforated flanges. In them the egg and cream are caught and thrown from one to another, forcing the ingredients through the small holes and more thoroughly disrupting them in less time than would be possible under other conditions.

— *HOUSE FURNISHING REVIEW,* **MAY, 1903, REVIEW OF THE CYCLONE**

FIG. 5-53

January, 1907 House Furnishing Review ad

FIG. 5-54

The Browne manufacturing plant, Kingston Chamber of Commerce brochure, 1909

W. G. BROWNE MFG. CO., SPECIALTIES.

FIG. 5-55

CYCLONE PAT. OCT 24 76
5-1/2" —$1,000+—

CYCLONE PAT. OCT 24 76
6-1/4" —$1000+—

BOHN COLLECTION

FIG. 5-56

Inside view of how Cyclones work

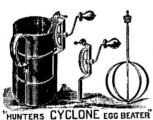

FIG. 5-57

*Ayres Manufacturing Company of Worcester,
Massachusetts early catalog*

HUNTER'S

Cyclone Egg Beater.

Mixer, Cup, Cream Whipper and

Egg Nogg Machine.

"HUNTERS CYCLONE EGG BEATER"

Six of the most useful and necessary articles known combined in, and sold for less than the price of one. Acknowledged by everybody to be far superior and much less costly than any Egg Beater heretofore offered the public. A child can beat more eggs with this Beater in less time than four grown persons with the old style. Economical house-keepers will use this beater always, as it saves money. The egg, while being beaten, is not splashed all over, but is held right in the cup, always handy and nice. Every part is adjustable and can be taken in pieces to clean.

TEN REASONS WHY

HUNTERS CYCLONE EGG BEATER

IS THE BEST !

1 It is the only Egg Beater, that can be taken into three parts to clean.

2 It combines six of the most useful articles in the household.

3 The Egg is enclosed in the cup, where it is beaten, so cannot splash all over the table.

4 It will beat one egg just as well and thoroughly, as four or five.

5 It will beat four eggs to so stiff a froth in 3 minutes that it cannot be poured out, but must be taken out with a spoon.

6 The Rings or Swedges on the Cup denote accurately ½, 1 and 1½ pints.

7 For making Egg Nogg, it is unequalled.

8 The motion is easy and rotary.—The only correct principle.

9 The crank is on the side, entirely out of the way and most convenient to use.

10 *And last,* it will beat more eggs in less time than any beater.

ON THIS GLOBE.

RETAIL PRICE.

No. 1. { Holding 1½ pints. Beats 1 to 6 Eggs. } 50 Cents. | No. 2. { Holding 3 pints. Beats 1 to 18 Eggs. } $1.00.

We Guarantee every Egg Beater Carefully Made and Superior to Others.

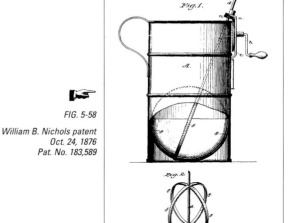

FIG. 5-58

*William B. Nichols patent
Oct. 24, 1876
Pat. No. 183,589*

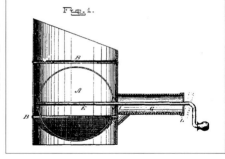

FIG. 5-59

*Jacob M. Hunter
patent
Aug. 5, 1879
Pat. No. 218,121*

▶ There is another CYCLONE — this one super rare. At first glance it appears to be a flour sifter, and in fact it was made by The Hunter Sifter Manufacturing Company of Cincinnati (*figs. 5-55 & 5-56*).

An ad in the Ayres Manufacturing Co. catalog said in part: "A child can beat more eggs with this beater in less time than four grown persons with the old style." The ad (*fig. 5-57*) priced the smaller mixer, described as holding 1-1/2 pints and beating up to six eggs, at 50 cents and the larger, described as holding 3 pints and beating up to 18 eggs, at $1.

The CYCLONE was patented by William B. Nichols of Seymour, Connecticut, who described his invention (*fig. 5-58*) as "the combination of a detachable egg-beating mechanism and a cup or measure." He also boasted that "the milk, or other fluid added to the eggs, can be measured and

mixed in the same vessel in which the eggs are beaten, and the beating contrivance being detached from the measure, it can be used for ordinary purposes."

Its manufacturer, Hunter, was first listed in the *Cincinnati City Directory* in 1879 at 30 Emery Arcade. By 1881, the directory listing had grown from just the address to: "Household and Kitchen Specialties, Hunter's Sifters, Acme Picnic Cups, Griddle Cake Floppers, Union Clothes Line Holder, Perfection Steam Washer, Favorite Coffee Pots, Novelty Ice Picks, Little Giant Carpet Stretcher." The new address was 34 and 36 E. 5th.

Hunter listings continued through 1890 at which time the directory indicates the firm was sold to J. H. Day & Co. Jacob M. Hunter, the former owner, patented his own flour sifter on Aug. 5, 1879 (*fig. 5-59*).

Samuel Short of Brooklyn, New York, patented a beautiful "staircase" beater that unfortunately has remained just a patent. The main feature of Short's patent, dated Feb. 27, 1883, No. 273,173, are the "cross-bars or arms arranged at a suitable distances apart, cast in one piece with the shaft..." Short put his patent drawing upside down, apparently to call attention to his dashers. "In most egg-beaters, heretofore in use a central vacuum is created, driving the material to be beaten away from the beater, whereas by my invention this is obviated, the fans creating a current and drawing the material to the beater," Short said.

FIG. 5-60

C. LEHMANN. NY.
PAT. SEPT. 10th 1872. FEB. 10th 1874.
BEST OF ALL.
11-1/2"   —$1,500+

KRAUS COLLECTION

R Cooper

FIG. 5-61

Charles Lehmann patent
Sept. 10, 1872
Pat. No. 131,283

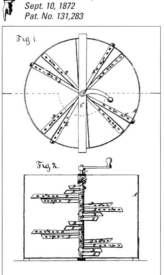

FIG. 5-62

Charles Lehmann patent
Feb. 10, 1874
Pat. No. 147,412

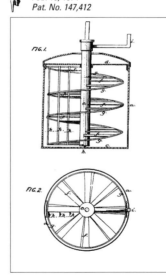

FIG. 5-63

Charles Lehmann patent
March 29, 1870
Pat. No. 101,281

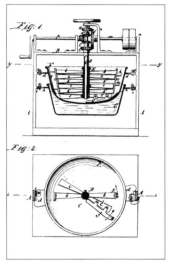

▶ One of the biggest patent stretches ever has to be for the incomparable LEHMANN'S PATENT EGG BEATER, which is believed to have been first offered around 1878 (*fig. 5-60*). Lehmann's is one of the few cast-iron beaters to emboss an advertising motto on its main gear: BEST OF ALL. In fact, Lehmann obtained a trademark Jan. 6, 1880 to protect his motto. Trademark No. 7792 is for: "The arbitrary symbol composed of a monogram of the letters 'BOA.'"

Two patent dates are listed on the 11-1/2" Lehmann: Sept. 10, 1872 and Feb. 10, 1874 (*figs. 5-61 & 5-62*). In the

first, Charles Lehmann of New York City lists his invention as "improvement in apparatus for stirring and mixing soap." The second is described as "apparatus for mixing soap, paint &c."

And neither could ever be mistaken for the LEHMANN beater.

Lehmann had another patent, this one for a device described in its patent papers of March 29, 1870 (*fig. 5-63*) as a real eggbeater. It's a dandy with a circular staircase-type dasher in a tin container with a rotary crank on top. It apparently never made it past the patent stage.

FIG. 5-64

MASTER PAT. AUG. 24 09
10-1/2" —$1,500—

MOFFET COLLECTION

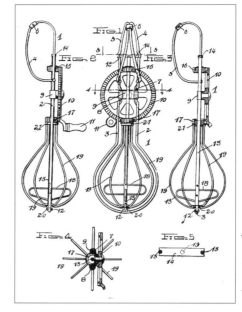

▶ The MASTER PAT AUG 24 09 (*fig. 5-64*) is in a class by itself, with its combination of heavy wire and cast-iron, and its intricate dasher within dasher arrangement.

Bartlett Kreuzberger of Meriden, Connecticut, pointed out in his patent application that the dasher arrangement shaft could be "readily removed and cleaned of any accumulated material" (*fig. 5-65*).

▶ Another mixer in the very rare category is the 3-MINUTE EGG BEATER (*fig. 5-66*), and yet another with a time element in its name is the HALF MINUTE BEATER (*fig. 5-67*).

FIG. 5-65

*Bartlett Kreuzberger patent
Aug. 24, 1909
Pat. No. 932,294*

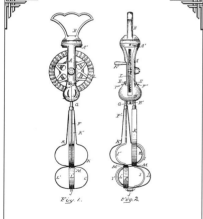

A nother patent that apparently never resulted in a manufactured beater is still worthy of note for its stacked up dashers similar to the 3-Minute Beater. Patent No. 232,125, dated Sept. 14, 1880, was granted to Frank Henry of Newport, Kentucky, who said the placing of one set of revolving beaters above the other enables "the operator to do more effectual work."

BOHN COLLECTION

FIG. 5-66

*No I.D. but early
F. A. Walker
catalog shows it
as the 3-MINUTE
EGG BEATER
11"
—$600—*

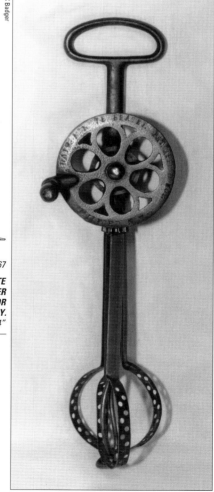

FIG. 5-67

**HALF MINUTE
BEATER
PAT APPLD FOR
MILFORD, N.Y.**
11-1/4"
—$650—

BADGER COLLECTION

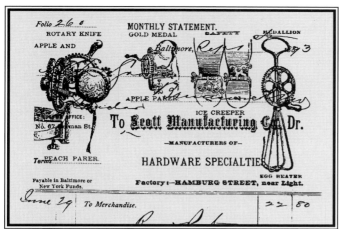

FIG. 5-68

*1889 Scott billhead featuring
the Medallion beater*

▶ The Scott Manufacturing Company of Newark, New Jersey, and Baltimore, Maryland, known for its apple parers, offered MEDALLION and VICTORIA eggbeaters. The MEDALLION was featured on a Scott billhead *(fig. 5-68)* but the beater itself is not marked with the MEDALLION name *(fig. 5-69 & 5-70)*. The VICTORIA came with two dasher arrangements *(fig. 5-71 & 5-72)*.

FIG. 5-69

**R.P. SCOTT & CO.
NEWARK, N.J. PATENTED**
10-1/2"
*Note: beater pictured is
missing a wire dasher.*
—$550—

FIG. 5-70

Detail of
R. P. SCOTT
gear embossing

FIG. 5-71

VICTORIA, *only I.D.*
10-1/2" —$685—

HOY COLLECTION

FIG. 5-72

VICTORIA, *only I.D.*
10-1/2" —$650—

BOHN COLLECTION

BOHN COLLECTION

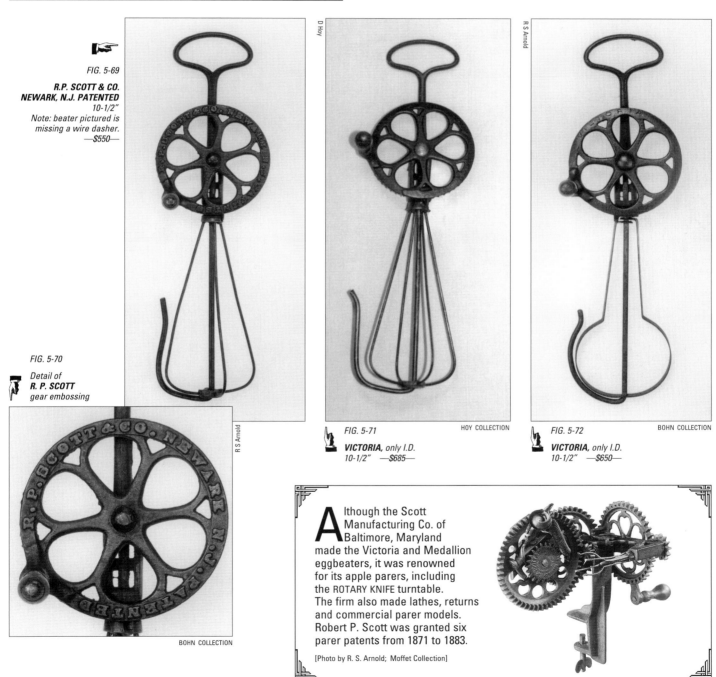

Although the Scott Manufacturing Co. of Baltimore, Maryland made the Victoria and Medallion eggbeaters, it was renowned for its apple parers, including the ROTARY KNIFE turntable. The firm also made lathes, returns and commercial parer models. Robert P. Scott was granted six parer patents from 1871 to 1883.

[Photo by R. S. Arnold; Moffet Collection]

CHAPTER 5: STANDARD AND OTHER CAST-IRON BEAUTIES

MERTZ COLLECTION

FIG. 5-73

No I.D., but featuring unique wire dashers 9-1/2"
—Value undetermined until question of origin resolved—

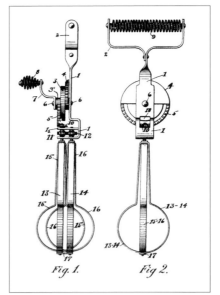

FIG. 5-74

James O. H. Cazenove patent
July 26, 1921
Pat. No. 1,385,605

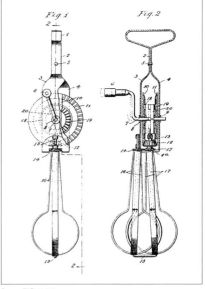

FIG. 5-75

James O. H. Cazenove patent
Oct. 30, 1923
Pat. No. 1,472,292

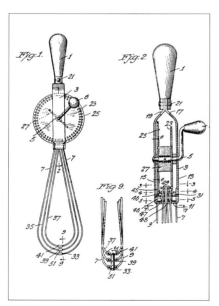

FIG. 5-76

James O. H. Cazenove patent
Dec. 11, 1928
Pat. No. 1,694,500

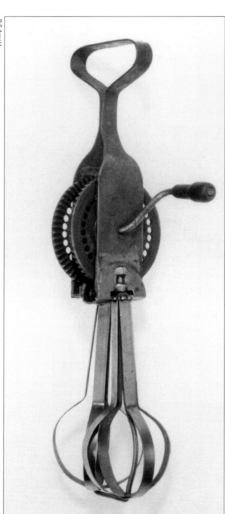

FIG. 5-77

No I.D. but Cazenove 1923 patent, prototype with dashers from a Ladd beater 12" —$800—

▶ A newly discovered 9-1/2" high cast-iron beater *(fig. 5-73)* is not marked and its origin of manufacture is in question. However, this one-of-a-kind beater does share at least two characteristics with the 3-MINUTE EGG BEATER *(See page 56)*: the back shaft designs are similar and both have unusual wire dashers. This beater was a major discovery in late 1999, turning up at a shop in Missouri.

▶ James O. H. Cazenove of New York City was granted three mixer patents from 1921 to 1928 *(figs. 5-74 through 5-76)* — two of them for very unusual "reverse direction" rotary beaters.

"It has been found by experimenting that various substances such as eggs, dressings, and other liquids which require considerable 'beating' or aerating for proper mixing may be more thoroughly mixed and in less time if the mixing means be periodically reversed," Cazenove said in his Oct. 30, 1923, patent *(fig. 5-74)*.

This is how it works on a what appears to be a prototype *(fig. 5-77)* produced by Cazenove: The crank is turned in one direction, but can engage either of the two cast-iron wheels. By pushing the crank inward, one gear is engaged. By pulling it out, the other gear is engaged, switching the direction of the dashers.

Chapter 6

Monroe Brothers

The earliest shelf-mounts and rotaries

J. F. & E. P. Monroe patent
April 19, 1859
Pat. No. 23,694

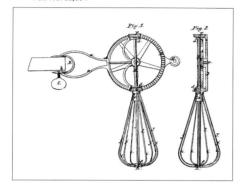

The Monroe brothers, James F. and Edwin P., of Fitchburg, Massachusetts, were responsible for the earliest eggbeaters ever manufactured in the United States.

Monroe beaters were offered in the first Dover Manufacturing Company catalogs *(See Chapter 1, Dover, page 1)*, indicating Dover produced these highly valued mixers. However, the obituary of James F. Monroe appearing in the *Fitchburg Daily Sentinel*, July 25, 1901, sets the record straight: James, in the company of his brother, Edwin, "formed the Monroe manufacturing company, and engaged in the manufacture of egg-beaters and apple-parers of their invention for several years."

Monroe Manufacturing Company first appeared in the *Fitchburg City Directory* in 1864. In 1880 the listing said: "Monroe, James F. manf. egg beaters. New place, house 97 Blossom."

Edwin Monroe's April 19, 1859 patent date *(fig. 6-1)* is embossed on the first shelf-mount MONROES *(figs. 6-2 & 6-3)*. These have an extended shelf attachment. An identical one is marked with an additional date, OCT. 16, 1860, a re-issue of the original patent.

FIG. 6-2

EP MONROE PATENTED
APRIL 19 1859
10-1/2" —$1,200—

FIG. 6-3

EP MONROE PATENTED
APRIL 19 1859
10-3/4" tumbler model
—$1,500—

D G Simons   R S Arnold

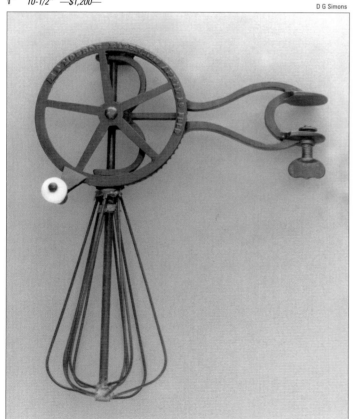

MAIR COLLECTION

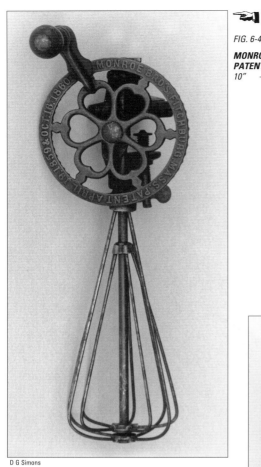

D G Simons

FIG. 6-4

MONROE BRO'S FITCHBURG, MASS.
PATENT APRIL 19, 1859 & OCT. 16 1860
10" —$950—

FIG. 6-5

MONROE BRO'S. FITCHBURG, MASS.
PATENT APR. 19, '59 OCT. 16 '60.
8-1/4" —$2,000+—

MAIR COLLECTION

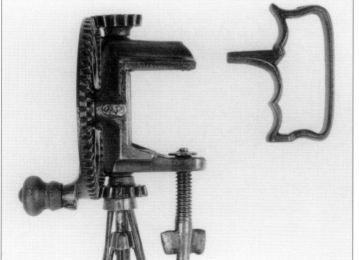

FIG. 6-6

Detail of gear embossing

FIG. 6-8

Handle in place

FIG. 6-7

Handle removed

R S Arnold

Another model, with a stubby shelf-mount, is marked on the wheel MONROE BRO'S FITCHBURG, MASS. PATENT APRIL 19, 1859 & Oct. 16 1860 (fig. 6-4).

Very similar to the stubby shelf-mount is a valuable combination shelf-mount with removable handle (figs. 6-5 & 6-6). With the handle removed, it can be easily mounted (fig. 6-7) and with the handle attached (fig. 6-8), it's a super hand rotary.

In addition to the table-mounts, there is a very unusual top crank MONROE'S PATENT APRIL 19, 1859 & Oct. 16, 1860. The first one of these turned up with a homemade handle (fig. 6-9). It was later discovered the original was a shelf-mount (fig. 6-10).

The Monroe brothers also manufactured handheld rotaries, one of which featured the 1859 and 1860 dates. This beater is marked with the name STAR, with some models having figural stars (fig. 6-11).

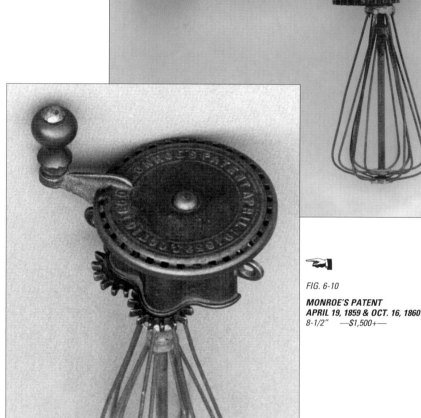

FIG. 6-9

**MONROE'S PATENT
APRIL 19, 1859 &
OCT. 16, 1860**
8-1/2"
with homemade handle
—$650—

D G Simons

FIG. 6-10

**MONROE'S PATENT
APRIL 19, 1859 & OCT. 16, 1860**
8-1/2"   —$1,500+—

D G Simons

BOHN COLLECTION

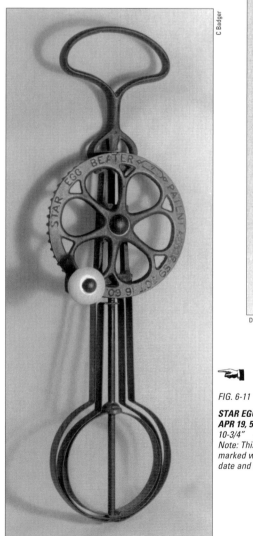

C Badger

FIG. 6-11

**STAR EGG BEATER
APR 19, 59 OCT 16, 60**
10-3/4"   —$900—
Note: This model is also marked with the patent date and figural stars

BADGER COLLECTION

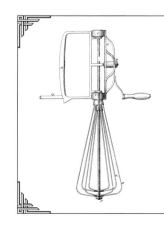

John Dane Jr. of Newark, New Jersey, borrowed liberally from the Monroe brothers in his January 23, 1872 patent, No. 122,997. In addition to having the same dasher design as Fig. 6-5, Dane said his beater "may be held in the hand or may be attached to a table by using a screw-clamp..." Dane's patent apparently did not result in a manufactured beater.

The Monroes patented two regular rotary cranks. James and Edwin together were awarded a patent Aug. 25, 1874 for a Dover-type cast-iron beater *(fig. 6-12)*. The other patent, granted May 1, 1877, went to James alone for a rotary crank with shelf-mount *(fig. 6-13)*.

The brothers' 1874 patent date is cited on two mixers, the PEERLESS and NOVELTY. The PEERLESS *(figs. 6-14 & 6-15)* is marked PATENT APPLIED FOR, and with the 1874 date. The NOVELTY is a novelty in that the dasher arrangement is quite distinctive *(fig. 6-16)*.

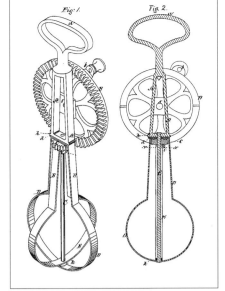

FIG. 6-12
J.F. & E.P. Monroe patent
Aug. 25, 1874
Pat. No. 154,411

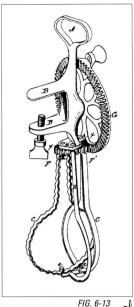

FIG. 6-13
James F. Monroe patent
May 1, 1877
Pat. No. 190,238

FIG. 6-14
**PEERLESS EGG BEATER
PATENT APPLIED FOR**
10-1/2"   —$600—

FIG. 6-15
Detail of **PEERLESS** gear featuring patent date

R Cooper

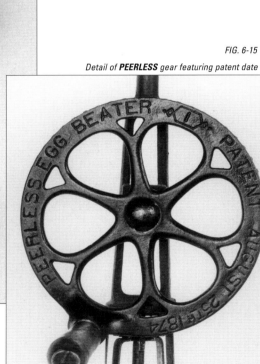

HOY COLLECTION   R S Arnold

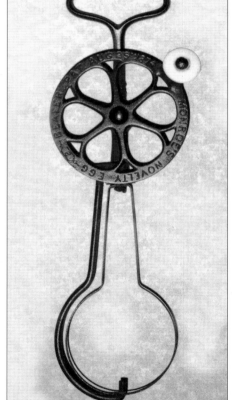

FIG. 6-16
**MONROE'S NOVELTY EGG BEATER
PAT. AUG. 25, 1874**
10-1/2"   —$900—

D G Simons

KRAUS COLLECTION

Although not identified as a MONROE, and devoid of patent dates, there is another rotary with long, vertical dashers that is believed part of the same family *(fig. 6-17)*. In addition to similar casting and length, this mixer and nearly all other MONROE'S share another characteristic — the small porcelain handle on the main gear.

FIG. 6-17

PAT. APPLIED FOR, *no other I.D., but believed to be of Monroe manufacture*
10-1/8"
—$1,500—

S Scharnhorst

SCARBOROUGH COLLECTION

Death of James E. Monroe

James F. Monroe, a widely known and esteemed citizen of Fitchburg for 52 years, died at his residence, 78 Mt. Vernon Street, Tuesday about 2:30 p.m.

He had suffered for a considerable time from a chronic disease, which at his advanced age, eventually wore him out.

He was born at Surrey, Vt., Feb. 20, 1818, and was a son of Abijah and Prudence, Monroe. He went to Boston and for a time was in company with is brother George, since deceased, in the provision business, Later, he held a responsible position at the state prison in Charlestown.

Mr. Monroe was one of the few men who was in the employ of the Fitchburg railroad more than 50 years ago.

In 1818, he was given a position with John M. Sawtell in the baggage department at the old passenger depot in Charlestown, which served the company till the one on Causeway street, Boston, was built. He continued in that place about a year, and then became baggage master on Conductor James D. Kent's train, but a little later, in 1849, he was promoted to conductor and removed to Fitchburg, his daily work being a run to Boston and return. He continued in this position till 1858, when owing to some changes he resigned his place and quit railroading.

He engaged in the provision business, and was for many years in a store the Flatiron building. He sold out to John Q. Barden, and afterward in company with his brother, Edwin P. Monroe, formed the Monroe Manufacturing company, and engaged in the manufacture of egg-beaters and apple-parers of their invention for several years.

The progress of disease and advanced age have prevented him from active employment of late.

Mr. Monroe met with more afflictions than falls to the lot of most men. His first wife, Martha M., was fatally injured in a runaway accident. Mr. and Mrs. Monroe were riding down the steep grade of Blossom street when the horse commenced to run; the harness became disarranged; Mr. Monroe was thrown out and badly injured, while Mrs. Monroe remained in the carriage till in turning into Main street she was thrown upon the pavement and never recovered consciousness. Their two sons, their only children, died in early manhood both of consumption. Edwin, Oct. 7, 1872 aged 23 years, and Herbert J., Dec. 7, 1883, at the age of 28 years.

Mr. Monroe married, July 30, 1878, Miss Lucy D. Critcherson of Boston, who survives, though in feeble health. He also leaves his brother, Edwin D Monroe of Philadelphia.

Lewis B. Monroe, the distinguished elocutionist, author of "Monroe's Readers" and "Public and Parlor Readings, Dialogues and Dramas," was a brother of J.F. Monroe.

Mr. Monroe was a member of the Masonic fraternity and Odd Fellows.

He maintained a high character and his dignified form and kindly face will be greatly missed.

—FITCHBURG DAILY SENTINEL,
TUESDAY JULY 23, 1901 PAGE 6

Akala Egg Separator

3-1/4" diameter
—$25—

COOPER COLLECTION

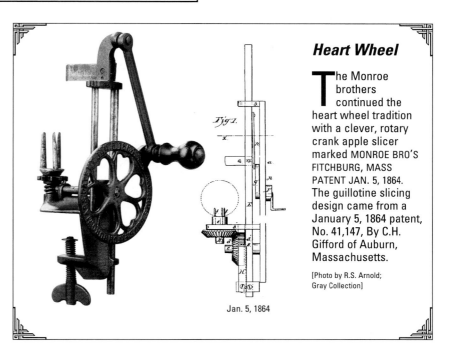

Jan. 5, 1864

Heart Wheel

The Monroe brothers continued the heart wheel tradition with a clever, rotary crank apple slicer marked MONROE BRO'S FITCHBURG, MASS PATENT JAN. 5, 1864. The guillotine slicing design came from a January 5, 1864 patent, No. 41,147, By C.H. Gifford of Auburn, Massachusetts.

[Photo by R.S. Arnold; Gray Collection]

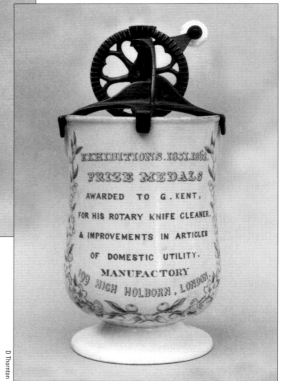

The most fabulous of all the MONROE mixers has an English connection. It is a Monroe rotary with arms that sits in a porcelain, pedestal-style jar. This item (*figs. 6-18 through 6-20*) was considered the show stopper at the 1997 KOOKS convention.

FIG. 6-18

The highest part of the front of the jar is 7-3/4", with the gearing going up to 10-1/4."

KENTS PATENT. HIGH HOLBORN. LONDON.
(on 3-1/4" in diameter main gear)

KENTS IMPROVED MONROES PATENT EGG BEATER AND BATTER MIXER.
(on jar)

Note: this model also comes without the jar and is a 9-1/4" shelf-mount. The gearing is marked the same

—*$2,500+*—

FIG. 6-19

EXHIBITIONS. 1851. 1862. PRIZE MEDALS AWARDED TO G. KENT, FOR HIS ROTARY KNIFE CLEANER, & IMPROVEMENTS IN ARTICLES OF DOMESTIC UTILITY. MANUFACTORY 199 HIGH HOLBORN, LONDON

KRUG COLLECTION

FIG. 6-20

Mixer without jar

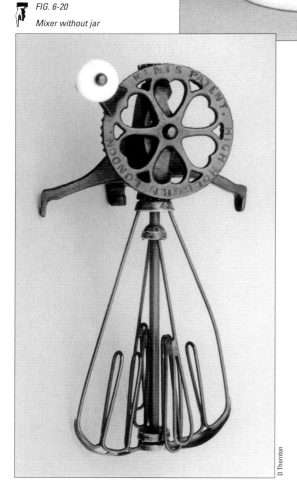

D Thornton

Another Heart Wheel

The Monroe Manufacturing Company is as well known for its apple parers as it is for its beaters. The mainstay of the Monroe parer line was a return parer marked on the heart wheel: MONROE BROTHERS FITCHBURG, MASS PATENT SEPT. 9 1856.

[Photo by R S Arnold: Arnold Collection]

Chapter 7

National Manufacturing Co.

"Beats Instead of Stirring."

*D*ating back to 1834, the National Manufacturing Company had a very small line of eggbeaters and never came close to selling as many mixers as the bigger beater makers.

The Worcester, Massachusetts, firm got its start when Jabez Bigelow began making milk, cheese and provision safes, as well as wire sieves, and grain, coal, sugar and baker's riddles.

Over the following decades he expanded into other wire goods, including bank and office railings, elevator and window guards, wire cloths and nettings, flower stands, bird cages, brass screens and household utensils.

"Managed with prudence and developed by application and industry, the business steadily increased; more capital was obtained, and in 1874 the present company formed …" according to Oliver B. Wood's 1888 book *Worcester: Its Past and Present.*

Jonah H. Bigelow, a son of Jabez Bigelow, was at that time named president of the firm, which continued to prosper over the years. It was purchased by the Morgan Spring Co. in 1916.

The household line had just two rotary crank beaters, an up-and-down Archimedes-style mixer and about a half dozen hand-held, whisk-type beaters.

But it is one of the rotary beaters and the Archimedes that put National on the collectible map.

The rotary that brought distinction to the firm is the EXPRESS, more often referred to as the "fly swatter beater" *(fig. 7-1).* This gadget has commanded higher and higher prices over the years.

The EXPRESS, on the underside of the main cross bar, is clearly marked with the patent date of OCT. 25, 1887. However, a check of date in the patent library turns up only one beater that could be remotely considered the EXPRESS, and only because it has a back-and-forth action.

The patent *(fig. 7-2)* was obtained by David T. Winter of Peabody, Massachu-

setts, who, very proud of his invention, said: "This beater has a great simplicity in construction, with unusual efficiency in action, and does the work with great dispatch and thoroughness."

Now for some mixer intrigue. A real look-alike EXPRESS was patented Dec. 4, 1906 *(fig. 7-3)* by Nicholas Stromer of Gillett, Wisconsin, and there is no apparent connection with Winter.

FIG. 7-1

PAT. OCT. 25, 1887
(on underside of cross bar), no other I.D., but described in ads as the Express 11-1/2" —$1,800—

D G Simons

FIG. 7-2

David T. Winter patent Oct. 25, 1887 Pat. No. 372,282

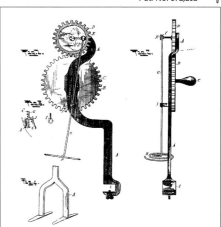

FIG. 7-3

Nicholas Stromer patent Dec. 4, 1906 Pat. No. 837,432

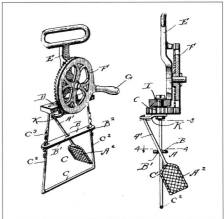

The EXPRESS was featured in the 1904 National Manufacturing Company catalog (*fig. 7-4*), two years before the 1906 patent date. The 1904 catalog says of the EXPRESS: "It literally BEATS the eggs, instead of stirring them." Its wholesale price was $24 per gross — or about 16¢ each. The firm's 1908 catalog still listed the gross price at $24, but was a bit briefer in its sales pitch: "Beats instead of stirring."

An ad in an early Rayment Novelty catalog said: "Fitted with Surprise egg whip (*fig. 7-5*), which is the best on the market. Positively beats the eggs instead of stirring them. The most successful beater ever made." The Rayment ad listed the beater at 15¢ with 7¢ postage extra.

Meanwhile, the "fly-swatter" principle was alive and well in the beater world — or at least at the U.S. Patent Office — through 1947.

Edward M. Morgan of Westmount, Quebec patented four versions. The dates for these mechanical marvels were Dec. 6, 1904; Nov. 1, 1910; May 7, 1929 and July 29, 1947. Apparently none was ever manufactured (*fig. 7-6*).

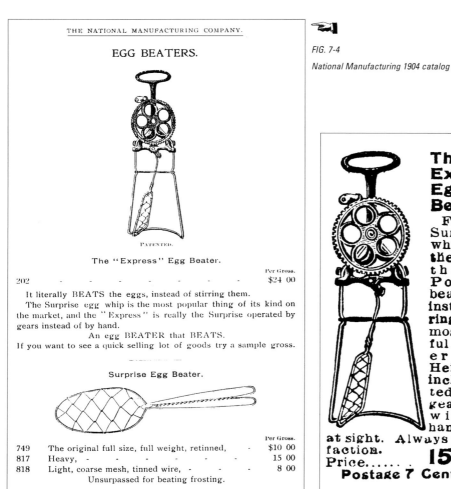

FIG. 7-4

National Manufacturing 1904 catalog

FIG. 7-5

Rayment Novelty catalog

FIG. 7-6

Edward M. Morgan patents (left to right):

Dec. 6, 1904 Pat. No. 776,791

Nov. 1, 1910 Pat. No. 974,586

May 7, 1929 Pat. No. 1,712,156

July 29,1947 Pat. No. 2,424,703

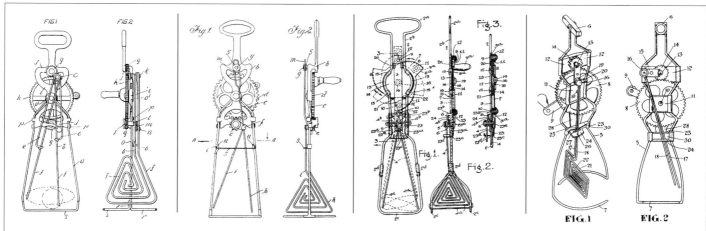

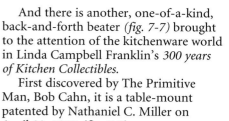

FIG. 7-7

No I.D., but believed to be
brass patent model
9-1/2"   —$1,500+—

FIG. 7-8

Nathaniel C. Miller patent
April 22, 1873
Pat. No. 138,094

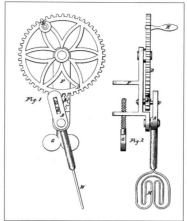

D G Simons

And there is another, one-of-a-kind, back-and-forth beater (*fig. 7-7*) brought to the attention of the kitchenware world in Linda Campbell Franklin's *300 years of Kitchen Collectibles*.

First discovered by The Primitive Man, Bob Cahn, it is a table-mount patented by Nathaniel C. Miller on April 22, 1873 (*fig. 7-8*).

Miller's patent application was brief and to the point: "The operation of my egg beater is as follows: The hand wheel, being turned by means of the handle, imparts motion to the pinion, when the wrist pin revolves within the slot of the beater-bar, imparting a vibratory motion to the same, which enables a person to perfectly beat an egg in thirty-five seconds.

"A vibratory instead of a rotary motion is obtained; and in this improvement I accomplish the end sought in a far simpler manner than that described in by patent of Feb. 1, 1870."

That earlier patent (*fig. 7-9*) was for a shelf-mount that apparently was never manufactured.

The other mixer that made National famous was the CLIPPER (*fig. 7-10*). It was patented Aug. 30, 1887 (*fig. 7-11*) by the previously noted Thomas W. Brown, who described himself as assignor to National.

FIG. 7-9

Nathaniel C. Miller patent
Feb. 1, 1870
Pat. No. 99,337

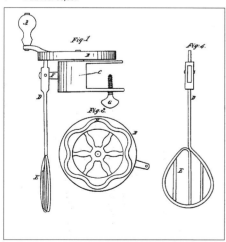

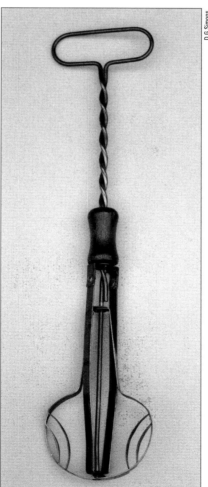

D G Simons

FIG. 7-11

Thomas W. Brown patent
Aug. 30, 1887
Pat. No. 369,273

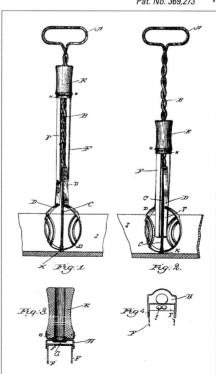

FIG. 7-10

CLIPPER
PAT. AUG. 30, 87
13"   —$375—

EGG BEATERS.

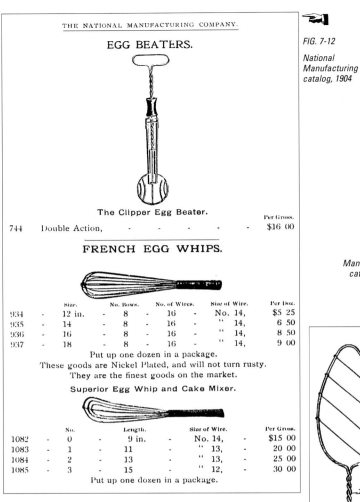

The Clipper Egg Beater.

							Per Gross.
744	Double Action,	-	-	-	-	-	$16 00

FRENCH EGG WHIPS.

Size.		No. Bows.		No. of Wires.		Size of Wire.		Per Doz.
934	-	12 in.	-	8	-	16	-	No. 14,	$5 25
935	-	14	-	8	-	16	-	" 14,	6 50
936	-	16	-	8	-	16	-	" 14,	8 50
937	-	18	-	8	-	16	-	" 14,	9 00

Put up one dozen in a package.
These goods are Nickel Plated, and will not turn rusty.
They are the finest goods on the market.

Superior Egg Whip and Cake Mixer.

No.		Length.		Size of Wire.		Per Gross.
1082	-	0	-	9 in.	-	No. 14,	-	$15 00
1083	-	1	-	11	-	" 13,	-	20 00
1084	-	2	-	13	-	" 13,	-	25 00
1085	-	3	-	15	-	" 12,	-	30 00

Put up one dozen in a package.

FIG. 7-12

National Manufacturing catalog, 1904

FIG. 7-13

National Manufacturing catalog, 1904

EGG BEATERS.

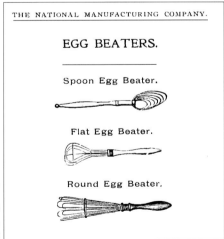

Dover Egg Beater.
Patented Aug. 10, 1897.

						Per Gross.
200	-	Size No. 1,	-	Family size, Regular Finish,	-	$24 00
204	-	" " "	-	" " Electro Tinned Finish,		30 00

The large gear has a bearing *inside* the teeth against an offset on the handle, which prevents the small gears from slipping, makes the action of the beater positive and adds greatly to its durability.

This beater is the *only one* on the market which has a bearing for the upper circumference of the large gear, *which does not bear* against the *teeth* of the gear.

We ask you to note the weight of material used in this beater, 6½ oz.

Packed one dozen in box, in one and two gross cases.

						Per Gross.
201	-	Size No. 2,	-	Hotel size, weight 14½ oz. each,		$66 00
203	-	" " "	-	" " Electro Tinned Finish,		74 00

Packed one-half dozen in box, in one-half gross cases.

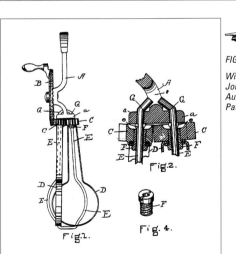

FIG. 7-14

William J. Johnson patent Aug. 10, 1897 Pat. No. 588,112

FIG. 7-15

William J. Johnson patent March 22, 1887 Pat. No. 359,976

EGG BEATERS.

Spoon Egg Beater.

Flat Egg Beater.

Round Egg Beater.

FIG. 7-16

National Manufacturing catalog, 1904

Illustrated catalogs for National Manufacturing for the years 1898, 1904 and 1908 describe the CLIPPER as "double action," selling wholesale at $16 per gross *(fig. 7-12)*.

The other rotary National offered was a Dover-style beater, of which the 1904 National catalog *(fig. 7-13)* said: "The large gear has a bearing inside the teeth against an offset on the handle, which prevents the small gears from slipping, makes the action of the beater positive and adds greatly to its durability."

It was patented Aug. 10, 1897 by William J. Johnson of Newton, Massachusetts *(fig. 7-14)*. Its price: $24 per gross.

Johnson, describing himself as an assignor to National, also on March 22, 1887 patented *(fig. 7-15)* a nifty hand-held model — "a spoon-shaped egg-beater having its handle and the outline of its head formed of a single length of wire, and provided with two or more parallel independent beaters secured to the marginal wire of the head."

National offered a variety of handheld mixers *(fig. 7-16)*, all of them available to the collector today.

Chapter 8

Circular I.D. and Other Rarities

"Beats one egg in a tea cup in 18 seconds."

FIG. 8-1

**D-O-V-E-R
PATENTED
FEB. 9, 1904
NEW STYLE**
10"
—$250—

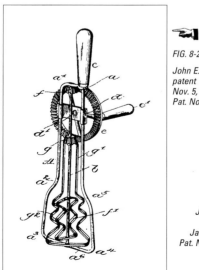

FIG. 8-2

John E. Hill
patent
Nov. 5, 1901
Pat. No. 685,986

FIG. 8-3

John E. Hill
patent
Jan. 15, 1907
Pat. No. 841,320

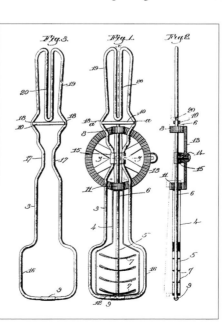

*I*n the cast-iron beater world, circular identification means an unbeatable mixer. There are four known rotary beaters with the main gear wheel spelling out the brand name. For example, where there would be spokes for the gear, there are letters.

They include Taplin's D-O-V-E-R *(See Chapter 4, Taplin, page 32),* which is the most common of the four — but please, it isn't that common *(fig. 8-1).* It's very hard to find.

The other three are T-H-E H-I-L-L, the E-A-S-Y and the P-D-&-CO. These three are very rare which makes pricing them difficult if not impossible.

Patent dates of Nov. 5, 1901 *(fig. 8-2)* and Jan. 15, 1907 *(fig. 8-3)* identify T-H-E H-I-L-L *(fig. 8-4).* They were obtained by John E. Hill of Center Harbor, New Hampshire, who cited in the first patent "a new, novel and efficient frame which may be composed mainly of one piece of metal."

In his second patent, Hill described himself as an assignor to his J. E. Hill Company of Boston. His patent provides what is sure to be surprising information

for those lucky enough to have one. Hill notes that most rotary eggbeater dashers "are fixedly secured in the frame, and cannot be removed therefrom for cleaning or other purposes."

But in designing T-H-E H-I-L-L, he said, "I have so mounted the beating members that they can be readily removed from the frame, and thus easily washed and dried."

FIG. 8-4

**T-H-E H-I-L-L
NOV. 5, 1901. JAN. 15, 1907**
11-1/2" —$1,250—

Note: Other models are marked:
NOV. 5, 1901 OTHERS PENDING

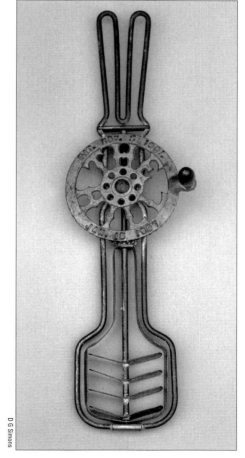

FIG. 8-5

E-A-S-Y
PAT SEPT. 28 86
(on back of main shaft)
9-3/4"
—$1,300—

D Thornton

FIG. 8-6

P-D-&-Co
DEC 1, 1885
(on back of main shaft)
10" —$1,000—

D G Simons

FIG. 8-8

No I.D. but matches E-A-S-Y
Sept. 28, 1886 patent, possibly
patent model
10" —$1,800—

D G Simons

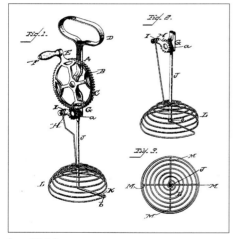

FIG. 8-7

George H. Thomas patent
Sept. 28, 1886
Pat. No. 350,023

George H. Thomas obtained patents for both the E-A-S-Y *(fig. 8-5)* and the P-D-&-CO *(fig. 8-6)*. As for the E-A-S-Y — it isn't when you are trying to find one. The E-A-S-Y comes with two dates. Those marked MARCH 6, 1886 refer to the patent application date. Those marked SEPT. 28, 1886, refer to the actual patent date *(fig. 8-7)* given to Thomas. Note the patent drawing does not have E-A-S-Y on the spokes — and there was another beater made from this exact patent *(fig. 8-8)*.

The Montgomery Ward & Co. 1894-95 catalog listed the E-A-S-Y as item No. 45087. "It consists of a spirally coiled wire, which in use opens and closes with exceeding rapidity, and instead of cutting the egg, as most beaters do, thoroughly aerates it, which is acknowledged by all experienced cooks to be the only correct way of beating an egg. For whipping cream it is just the thing. This egg beater is having the largest sale of any yet made; try it and you will like it."

Montgomery Ward priced the E-A-S-Y at 8¢ each or 87¢ per dozen. The Dec. 12, 1888 trade magazine *The Iron Age* listed Hamblin & Russell, a famous Worcester, Massachusetts, wire firm, as the manufacturer of the E-A-S-Y. An early Hamblin & Russell catalog listed the wholesale price at $18 per gross and later at $36 per gross — meaning Montgomery Ward must have had a special deal.

The tops and main gear wheels of the E-A-S-Y and P-D-&-CO are nearly identical, indicating Hamblin & Russell made the P-D-&-CO for Paine, Diehl & Company, the well-known Philadelphia wholesaler. The same distinctive top handle, straight back shaft and back gear mounting is featured on a beater marked only PATENT APPLIED FOR and with an unusual dasher arrangement *(fig. 8-9)*.

FIG. 8-9

PATENT APPLIED FOR
only I.D, but handle, shaft and
gear mounting the same as the
E-A-S-Y and P-D-&-Co.
10-1/4"
—$400— because of fragile
condition, much more if mint

D Thornton   COOPER COLLECTION

FIG. 8-10

George H. Thomas
patent
Dec. 1, 1885
Pat. No. 331,662

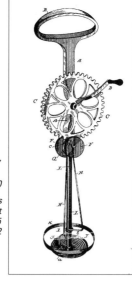

*Horizontally-coiled wire dashers
of unequal circumference, to
permit of the smaller dasher
reciprocating through the larger.*

**—GEORGE H. THOMAS
IN HIS DEC. 1, 1885
PATENT APPLICATION**

FIG. 8-12

David Hall Rice patent
Oct. 25, 1887
Pat. No. 371,976

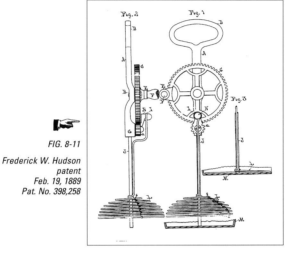

FIG. 8-11

Frederick W. Hudson
patent
Feb. 19, 1889
Pat. No. 398,258

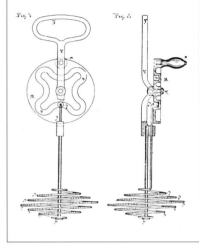

FIG. 8-13

Paine, Diehl & Company
catalog of about 1890

Thomas, of Chicopee Falls, Massachusetts, on Dec. 1, 1885, obtained the patent for the P-D-&-CO *(fig. 8-10)* — but there's a problem: the P-D-&-CO Dec. 1, 1885 patent drawing shows a different spring action bottom than the beater itself. Adding to the confusion are two other patents that are dead ringers for the P-D-&-CO: The Thomas Sept. 28, 1886 patent, previously noted, is in fact, the patent for the E-A-S-Y. And Frederick W. Hudson's Feb. 19, 1889 patent *(fig. 8-11)* is startlingly similar.

There is another ingredient in the spring dasher recipe — David Hall Rice's CAM BEATER spring dasher model patented Oct. 25, 1887 *(fig. 8-12)*. Is this an incestuous group? The fact that Rice, of Brookline, Massachusetts, was a witness to the patent obtained by Hudson of Leominster, Massachusetts, should be a clue.

An early Paine, Diehl & Company

catalog *(fig. 8-13)* said of the CAM: "This beater has the same effective dasher as the P-D-&-CO egg beater which has the only true principle in beating eggs. It adjusts itself to any shaped dish. Cheap and effective. Easy to work. It is the best egg beater made with one exception, the P-D-&-CO." The wholesale price: $15 per gross, or about 10¢ each. The price today would be in the hundreds of dollars — if one ever turns up.

The same catalog said of the P-D-&-CO: "This beater is constructed upon entirely new principles, not incorporated into any other, and which gives to it a certainty and rapidity of action and an adaptability to the form of the dish holding the egg, whether tea cup, bowl or plate, not before known or attempted … It fits into any shaped dish. TRY IT! Beats one egg in a tea cup in 18 seconds. TEST IT! Beats six eggs in a bowl in 70 seconds. Price, $24 per gross."

Paine, Diehl & Company, in addition to the P-D-&-CO and CAM beaters, offered at least two other very collectible mixers *(fig. 8-14)* — BRYANT and the DUDLEY BRYANT *(See Chapter 12, Archimedes, page 115).*

There is another eggbeater mixed up in here, or at least the patent of one, and it is the work of the George H. Paine, founder of Paine, Diehl & Company. His personal foray into the mixer world came in 1887 when he obtained a patent for a very unusual side-handle Archimedes *(fig. 8-15).* This fabulous beater apparently never was manufactured.

The first listing for Paine in the Philadelphia City Directory came in 1881 and it was for George H. Paine & Company, commercial merchant, at 105 Front Street. In 1883, the listing was for Paine, Diehl & Company at the same address, commercial merchant with partners Paine and William E. Diehl.

The firm moved to 7 Strawberry Street, 12 Bank Street and finally 1430 Penn Square. The last directory listing was in 1894. Paine apparently then joined with T. Henry Asbury to form Asbury-Paine Manufacturing Company, a maker of novelties. At the same time Asbury served as president of the well-known Enterprise Manufacturing Company of Pennsylvania, maker of coffee grinders and other kitchen items.

❖

The appeal of the circular ID beaters is obvious. But there are other rotary mixers that are even rarer, including the CARLEY, DODGE RACE COURSE, DOUBLE, TRIPLE, GILES & NIELSEN, GLASS WHIPPER, GLOBE, HEART, LOLL, LOWER and MONITOR. In somewhat alphabetical order, these rarities include:

▶ James T. Carley of Greenport, New York, was awarded two rotary crank patents. His Nov. 14, 1882 *(fig. 8-16)* features somewhat regular dashers — but with a propeller fitted onto the bottom. Unfortunately, this one apparently never made it past the patent stage. However, Carley's Dec. 21, 1886 patent *(fig. 8-17)* is alive and well — or at least one is *(fig. 8-18).*

Said Carley in his patent papers, referring to the coiled, heavy-duty wire: "The entire device is thus constructed and its parts firmly secured in operative positions without the use of solder, and the apparatus constitutes in simple, neat, compact form a revolving egg-beater of the most approved description for effective use."

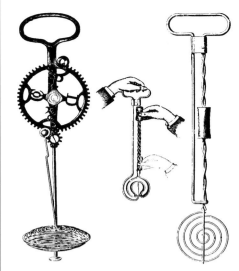

We recommend the P., D. & Co. as the most effective made.

P., D. & CO.'S EGG BEATER.
PATENTED DECEMBER 1st, 1885.

This Beater is constructed upon entirely new principles, not incorporated into any other, and which gives to it a certainty and rapidity of action and an adaptability to the form of the dish holding the egg, whether teacup, bowl or plate, not before known or attempted.

It has a double or compound dasher, having its two parts vibrating in opposition to each other upon the egg between them, and also reciprocating up and down against the egg in the bottom of the dish, these forming a series of surfaces beating against the egg simultaneously with the greatest possible efficiency.

It automatically fits itself to and gathers up the egg from any shaped dish whether spherical or flat bottomed inside, thus enabling it to gather between its double dasher and beat up a single egg, or more, perfectly and almost instantly. These features have never before been incorporated in any practical Egg Beater.

It whips one egg in a teacup in fifteen seconds, six eggs in a bowl in seventy seconds.

3200 Revolutions a Minute.

BRYANT'S PATENT EGG BEATER.

The perfection of a Beater without mechanical complications. Operated by working the nut up and down the screw, as illustrated.
Practical, unique, block tin all over, no wheels or complicated gear.

DUDLEY–BRYANT PATENT EGG BEATER.

Operated by working the nut up and down the screw.
Practical, unique, perfect, no wheels or complicated gear.
The best cheap Spiral ever devised.

FIG. 8-14

Paine, Diehl & Co. 1888 catalog

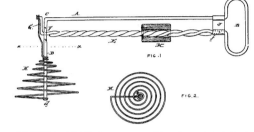

FIG. 8-15

George H. Paine patent
June 28, 1887
Pat. No. 365,624

FIG. 8-16

James T. Carley patent
Nov. 14, 1882
Pat. No. 267,491

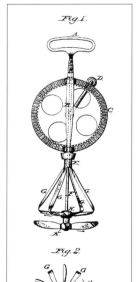

FIG. 8-17

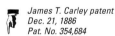

James T. Carley patent
Dec. 21, 1886
Pat. No. 354,684

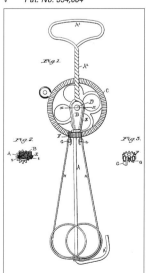

D G Simons

FIG. 8-18

No I.D., but Carley patent   11″   —$750—

▶ The DODGE RACE COURSE EGG BEATER *(fig. 8-19)* is a true museum-quality mixer. This all-cast-iron beater has no other ID and the patent search continues.

▶ The DOUBLE *(fig. 8-20)* and TRIPLE *(fig. 8-21)*, according to *Iron Age* magazine, were made by Hamblin & Russell. Embossed on the main wheel of the DOUBLE NO. 0 is: MARCH 8, 1881 — a patent obtained by Thomas W. Brown. The same patent graces an identical, or nearly identical, beater named the DUPLEX *(See Chapter 5, Standard and Other Cast-Iron Beauties, page 46)*. The TRIPLE obviously was marketed, but so far the only evidence of its existence is the early Hamblin & Russell catalog.

▶ The same catalog features a hand-held beater, the SPIRAL *(fig. 8-22)* that touches on the history of how Hamblin & Russell evolved as a manufacturer. According to the 1930 book *History of Massachusetts Industries*, in 1884 Frank H. Hamblin, a noted concert pianist and music instructor in Boston, fulfilled his dream of a manufacturing career by joining with W. T. Russell, a New York advertising agent, to purchase the firm of Samuel Ayres & Sons in Worcester.

Ayres "is said to have been the first man to press a corn-popper into shape from wire mesh cloth, and in the eighties it was his custom and that of his son to make up a quantity of wire products, and then shut up shop and peddle the articles from house to house." Ayres also was known for AYRES' SPIRAL, a hand-held mixer that was offered as the SPIRAL EGG BEATER in Hamblin & Russell's catalogs.

On April 1, 1887 the Ayres firm was incorporated as Hamblin & Russell Manufacturing Company. Over the years it offered a complete line of standard wire goods used in the kitchen, including strainers, broilers, dish drainers, rotary flour sifters, eggbeaters, corn poppers, fly traps and kitchen knives. It also offered several baseball catcher masks. In the 1930s it employed from 150 to 200 people.

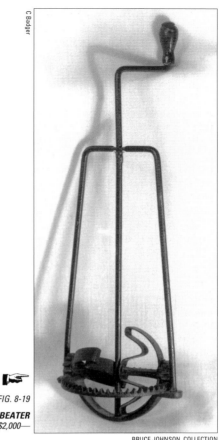

C Badger

FIG. 8-19

DODGE RACE COURSE EGG BEATER
11"   —$2,000—

BRUCE JOHNSON COLLECTION

FIG 8-20

Hamblin & Russell Manufacturing pre-1900 catalog

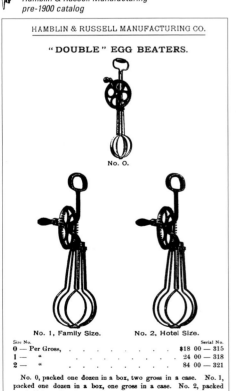

FIG. 8-21
Hamblin & Russell Manufacturing pre-1900 catalog.

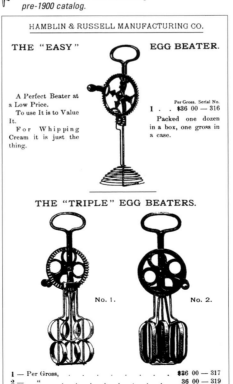

FIG. 8-22
Hamblin & Russell Manufacturing pre-1900 catalog

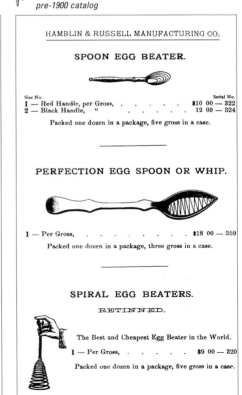

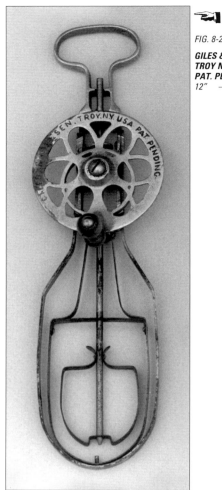

D G Simons   SEIDEL COLLECTION

FIG. 8-23

GILES & NIELSEN
TROY N.Y. USA
PAT. PENDING
12"   —$1,000+ —

FIG. 8-24

1913 Troy City Directory ad

FIG. 8-25

Rasmus Nielsen and John Imirie patent
April 19, 1910
Pat. No. 955,672

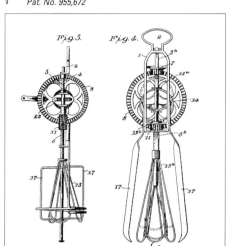

FIG. 8-26

Rasmus Nielsen patent
Feb. 7, 1905
Pat. No. 781,899

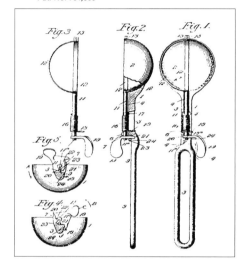

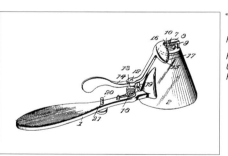

FIG. 8-27

Rasmus Nielsen patent
Oct. 16, 1906
Pat. No. 833,620

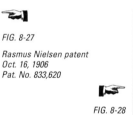

FIG. 8-28

Rasmus Nielsen patent
April 20, 1909
Pat. No. 918,893

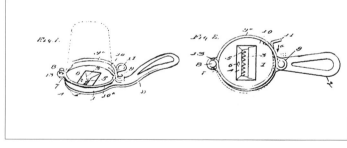

▶ Another beater that belongs in a museum is a cast-iron model marked on the wheel GILES & NIELSEN TROY N.Y. USA PAT. PENDING (*fig. 8-23*). It was manufactured by The Giles & Nielsen Nickel Works, which advertised in the 1905 *Troy City Directory:* "Nickel, copper and brass plating. Chandeliers re-burnished and lacquered. Manufacturers of Clipper Sanitary Ice-Cream Spoon. 1931 to 1937 Sixth Ave., Troy N.Y."

In an ad in the 1913 *Troy City Directory,* the beater was pictured and described as the CLIPPER EGG BEATER AND CREAM WHIPPER (*fig. 8-24*). The beater was patented by Rasmus Nielsen of Troy

and John Imirie of Washington, D.C. on April 19, 1910. One of the witnesses on the patent was L. H. Giles (*fig. 8-25*).

A newspaper obituary for Leonard H. Giles said he was born in Rome, New York, May 23, 1841 and joined his father in 1868 in H. G. Giles & Son stove works. He sold the firm in 1860 and established Giles and Nielsen Nickel Works, which was still in business when he died Feb. 24, 1930 at the age of 89. The obituary said he was "one of the best known residents of Troy and for many years prominent in its business, social and religious life."

Nielsen was better known for his ice

cream scoops than his eggbeater. His Feb. 7, 1905 patent (*fig. 8-26*) for a round bowl model was sold as the GILES AND NIELSEN, THE CLIPPER SPOON and later as THE CLIPPER DISHER. His Oct. 16, 1906 patent (*fig. 8-27*) for conical bowl model was sold as THE CONE CLIPPER. In both patents, Nielsen said he was an assignor to Giles. He also patented an "ice shaving device" (*fig. 8-28*), with Giles as one of the witnesses listed.

Nielsen died in 1944 at the age of 85. His newspaper obituary said that he was born in Denmark and came to Troy in 1883. It described him as "one of Troy's most prominent Danish residents."

C Badger

BADGER COLLECTION

FIG. 8-29

PATENT APPLIED FOR
9-1/4"   —$2,000+—

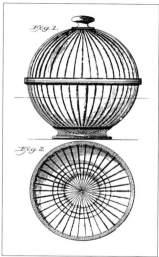

FIG. 8-30

William Helmer patent
June 7, 1904
Pat. No. D-36,957

FIG. 8-32

Detail of Loeber label

R S Arnold

MAIR COLLECTION

FIG. 8-31

**HENRY G. LOEBER
RELIABLE SODA FOUNTAINS
151 E. 126TH ST. NEW YORK**
8-12" in diameter   —$350—

Mantel's Egg Separator

3-1/4" diameter
—$30—

▶ The so-called GLASS WHIPPER (*fig. 8-29*) is an all-glass globe, with metal mechanical parts, a super rarity marked only PATENT APPLIED FOR. It stands 9-1/4" high and is about the same width. William Helmer of Boston was granted a design patent (*fig. 8-30*) for the device, which he described as "a cream-whipper bowl and cover." A turn-of-the-century publication, *The American Soda Book*, featured a drawing of the glass whipper and said: "Dainty counter furnishings please the eye, and a pleased eye tickles the palate. Cream Whipper No. 4944 makes the whipped cream look so tempting…"

▶ An all-metal globe mixer based on the same whipping principal as the GLASS WHIPPER is the Henry G. Loeber (*figs. 8-31 & 8-32*).

FIG. 8-33

THE GLOBE
FEB'Y 7, 1860
APRIL 17, 1860
with top in place
9-1/2" —$2,000+—

▶ Another round mixer is marked THE GLOBE FEB'Y 7, 1860 April 17, 1860. This cast-iron, ball-shaped wonder *(figs. 8-33 & 8-34)* is very rare. The Feb. 7 patent *(fig. 8-35)* was awarded to James M. Jay of Canton, Ohio, who described himself as assignor to John Danner, also of Canton. Jay and Danner teamed up for the April 17, 1860 patent *(fig. 8-36)* that expanded the use of the device, describing it as a "combined egg beater, ice cream freezer and churn."

FIG. 8-34

THE GLOBE
with open top

D Thornton

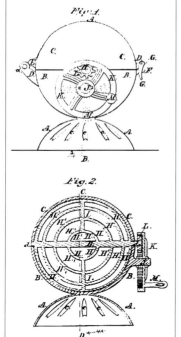

FIG. 8-35

James M. Jay patent
Feb. 7, 1860
Pat. No. 27,054

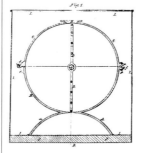
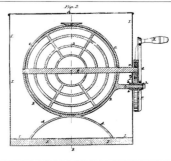

FIG. 8-36

James M. Jay and John Danner patent
April 17, 1860
Pat. No. 27,908

I n my egg beater the air which occupies the upper part of the hollow bottom, together with that which fills the cover or cap during the operation of beating the eggs, consequently it is carried down and mixed thoroughly with the eggs by the rings or dasher, which the eggs are carried up and through the air in the cap or case, so that a perfect mixture of the air and eggs is effected, which it has been found, is important in order to render the use of the eggs perfectly safe in the various forms in which they are served up after being beaten." —JAMES M. JAY IN HIS FEB 7, 1860 PATENT

THE EGGBEATER CHRONICLES

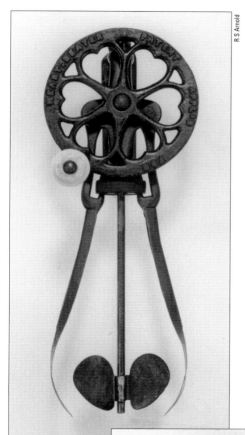

FIG. 8-37

HEART.BEATER PATENT APPL'D FOR

patent model
8-1/4"
—$2,000+—

FIG. 8-38

HEART
with view of handle

FIG. 8-39

Detail of main gear
and hearts

▶ The HEART beater is believed to be one of the first double-action mixers with two distinctive dasher movements *(figs. 8-37 & 8-38)*. The HEART features two arms "their lower extremities being in the form of a spoon bill's beak" that move in and out while inside the arms "a pair of propeller blades" rotate, according to the patent. The HEART name apparently comes from the heart shapes in the main gear *(fig. 8-39)*.

"It is obvious that when the machine is in use for agitating fluids the circling currents occasioned by the blades of the propeller will be broken at regular intervals by the action of the spoon bill arms in such a manner as to cause the agitation of very particle of the liquid within range of the machine," said the July 23, 1861 patent *(fig. 8-40)* by William T. Nicholson of Providence, Rhode Island, and Christy table-mount fame *(See Chapter 5, Standard and Other Cast-Iron Beauties, page 50)*.

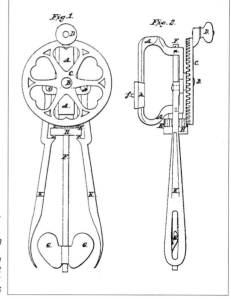

FIG. 8-40

William T. Nicholson
patent
July 23, 1861
Pat. No. 32,886

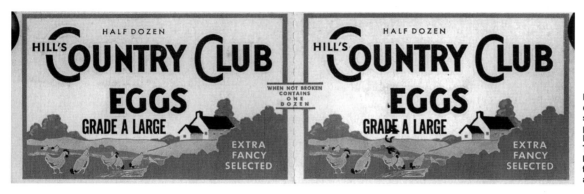

Egg carton art is very collectible. This carton, stamped 49 cents, was once packed with eggs from the H.G. Hill Company, Nashville, Tennessee. The carton also had small ads on each side for Grandma's Wonder Flour and Fit-For-A-King Coffee.

F. W. Loll Manufacturing Co.,

Manufacturers of

KITCHEN UTENSILS,

EGG BEATERS

— AND —

NOVELTIES.

45 1-2 PRATT STREET,

MERIDEN, CONN.

▶ The 1906 Meriden, Connecticut, *City Directory* listed the F. W. Loll Manufacturing Company on Pratt Street as the maker of kitchen utensils *(fig. 8-41)*. The firm apparently made only one beater *(figs. 8-42 through 8-44)*. Called the LOLL by collectors, it was patented by Frederick W. Loll of Meriden on Oct. 9, 1906 *(fig. 8-45)*.

FIG. 8-42

PAT APLD FOR
12-1/4"   —$1,500—

C Badger   BADGER COLLECTION

FIG. 8-43

PAT. 1906, only marking on dasher. This Loll features a frame to protect the dashers.
10-3/4"   —$1,500—

HOY COLLECTION

R S Arnold

FIG. 8-44

Detail of frame and dasher embossing.

FIG. 8-45

Frederick W. Loll patent Oct. 9, 1906 Pat. No. 833,069

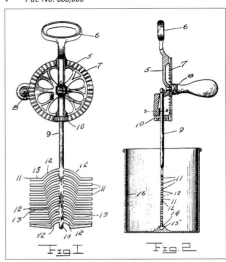

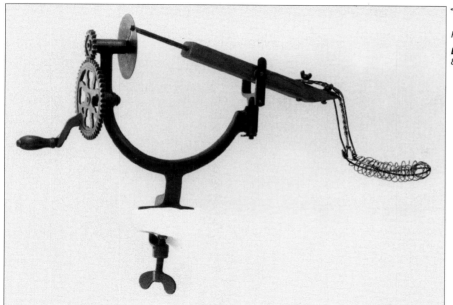

D G Simons

MOFFET COLLECTION

FIG. 8-46

LOWER EGG BEATER PAT. AUG. 8-22
8" high, 21-1/4" long, including crank —$950—

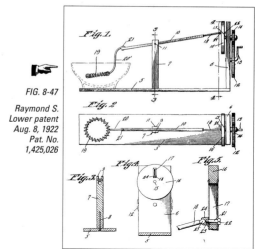

FIG. 8-47

Raymond S. Lower patent Aug. 8, 1922 Pat. No. 1,425,026

FIG. 8-48

Moses G. Crane patent June 19, 1866 Pat. No. 55,625

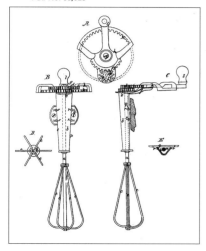

FIG. 8-49

MONITOR PAT'D JUNE 18, 1866
10-1/2"
—$2,000+—

FIG. 8-51

Side view

R S Arnold

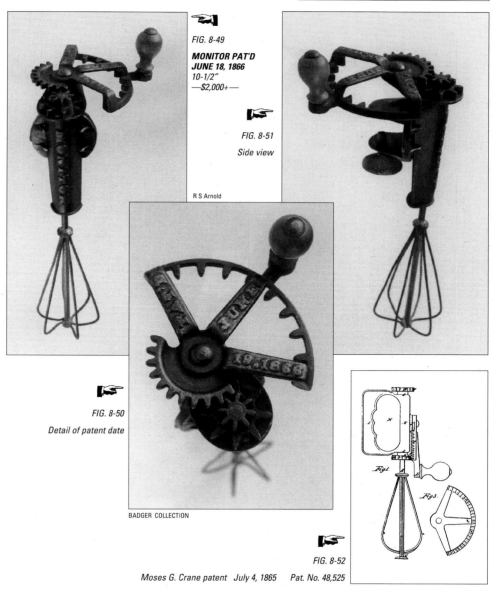

FIG. 8-50

Detail of patent date

BADGER COLLECTION

▶ Thank heaven there is patent evidence for the LOWER EGG BEATER. This contraption is so strange, most would not believe just a photo *(fig. 8-46)*.

Raymond S. Lower of Geneseo, Illinois, said in his Aug. 8, 1922 patent *(fig. 8-47)* the device "aims to provide novel means for operating the beating arm to facilitate the egg beating operation."

▶ Patented by Moses G. Crane of Boston June 19, 1866 *(fig. 8-48)*, the name of this rare beater is embossed on the main shaft cover: MONITOR *(figs. 8-49 through 8-51)*. Crane patented another beater, this one on July 4, 1865 *(fig. 8-52)* — and there's hope it, too, will surface.

FIG. 8-52

Moses G. Crane patent   July 4, 1865   Pat. No. 48,525

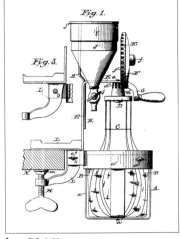

FIG. 8-53

Jennie De Witt Harvey
mayonnaise mixer patent
Oct. 10, 1893
Pat. No. 506,635

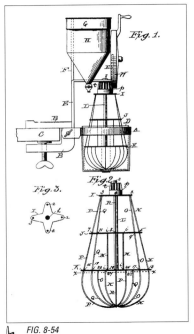

FIG. 8-54

Jennie De Witt Harvey eggbeater patent
Oct. 10, 1893
Pat. No. 506,636

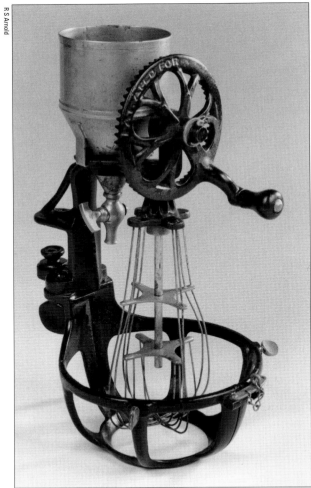

R S Arnold

FIG. 8-55

PAT. APLD FOR
12"
—$1,000—

MAIR COLLECTION

FIG. 8-57

Detail of main gear and "wire hook"

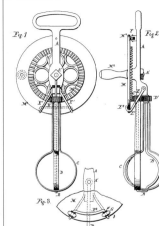

R S Arnold

FIG. 8-56

**NEVER SLIP BEATER
PAT SEPT 15 1896**
10-1/4"   —$1,000+—

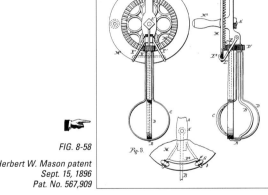

FIG. 8-58

Herbert W. Mason patent
Sept. 15, 1896
Pat. No. 567,909

▶ A very exceptional mayonnaise mixer has been nicknamed the JENNIE, after the patentee, Jennie De Witt Harvey of Wilkes-Barre, Pennsylvania. Harvey obtained two patents on Oct. 10, 1893, one described as a mayo mixer and the other as an egg beater (*figs. 8-53 & 8-54*). The JENNIE is a table-mount with a wire cage to hold a bowl (*fig. 8-55*). For such an strange mixer, there is no identification.

▶ The NEVER SLIP beater never slips (*figs. 8-56 & 8-57*). In his Sept. 15, 1896 patent (*fig. 8-58*), Herbert W. Mason of Glens Falls, New York, said the NEVER SLIP "avoids the liability of the gear-wheels to escape from engagement and slip…" This, he said, is attained "by means of a light wire hook so constructed and attached as to present a broad bearing on the front of the large gear-wheel." Mason said he applied his invention to the DOVER beater patented by Ethan Hadley May 6, 1873 (*See Chapter 1, Dover, page 4*). Although there are similarities between the two beaters, it is believed that Dover did not make the NEVER SLIP.

THE EGGBEATER CHRONICLES

▶ The PERFECTION EGG BEATER, PATENT APPLIED FOR *(fig. 8-59)* is identified in a paper label on its tip cup container. The label says in part: "The best in the world. Perfectly beat an egg in one minute. Manufactured by Alfred C. Rex & Co., Frankford, Phila."

The company was listed in Philadelphia city and business directories as early as 1884 and as late as 1913. The business was located in the Frankford section of Philadelphia, and described as a hardware manufacturer. In later years, it was described as an iron foundry.

A later PERFECTION container model was marked on the top of the gear wheel: PAT MAY 13 1884 U.S. PAT MAY 19-85 21696 CAN. The PERFECTION was the predecessor to and shared the same patent with the KING *(fig. 8-60)*, a very similar mixer that comes with a glass instead of tin container. The glass container is embossed KING EGG BEATER PAT MAY 13th 1884. Embossed on the metal gear wheel is PAT. MAY 13, 1884 *(fig. 8-61)*.

A third member of the PERFECTION/KING family is a king-size version *(fig. 8-62)*. It has a tin top with cast-iron, 4" gear wheel embossed PAT APLD FOR. The unmarked glass container is larger than the KING.

FIG. 8-59

PERFECTION EGG BEATER PATENT APPLIED FOR
tin container 3" high, 4" in diameter
—$450—

D G Simons   MOFFET COLLECTION

FIG. 8-60

KING EGG BEATER PAT MAY 13TH 1884
glass container 3" high, 4" in diameter
—$2,500+—

D G Simons   KREBS COLLECTION

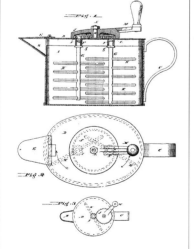

FIG. 8-61

Alfred C. Rex patent May 13, 1884 Pat. No. 298,503

Note: Patent does not mention a glass container

FIG. 8-62

PAT APLD FOR,
Only I.D. but part of the Perfection/King family. Glass container 4-3/8" high and 5-1/2" in diameter.
—$1,000+—

▶ THE PROPELLER. PAT. APP'D. FOR N.S.CO. is the genuine article (*figs. 8-63 & 8-64*). Its patent and manufacturer at this time are unknown, but its existence is noted in an article in an 1879 edition of *The Metal Worker (See Chapter 1, Dover, page 7)*.

▶ "The apparatus is held by the handle, with the lower portion resting on the bottom of the vessel containing the egg to be beaten." Those were the opening instructions given by James H. Scofield of New York City in his patent for the VICTOR BEATER PATENTED (*figs. 8-65 through 8-67*).

In his patent (*fig. 8-68*), Scofield also said: "Upon rotating the crown-wheel, an increased rotary motion will be imparted to the vertical shaft, causing the radial arms to rotate and pass between the parallel horizontal arms on the lower part of the frame, violently agitating the egg in the vessel, and bringing it speedily to the condition of froth; and, moreover, the horizontal arms being constructed with square edges, they rapidly cut the egg up."

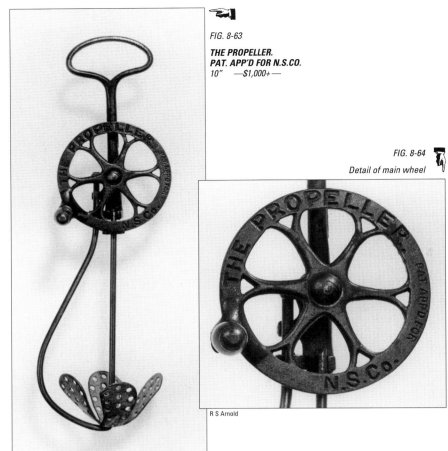

FIG. 8-63

THE PROPELLER.
PAT. APP'D FOR N.S.CO.
10" —$1,000+ —

FIG. 8-64

Detail of main wheel

R S Arnold

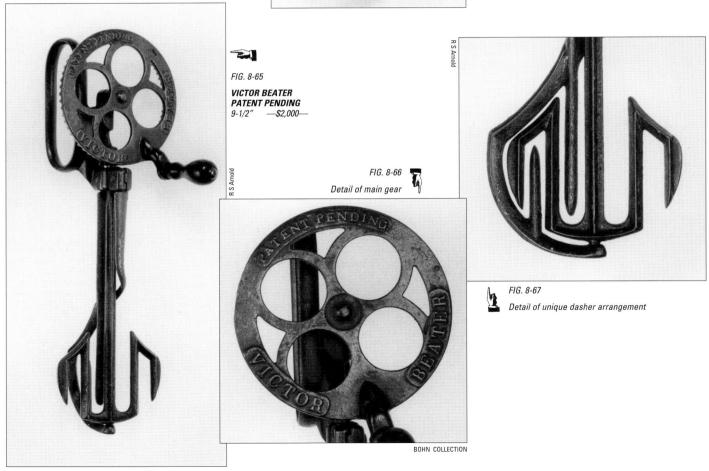

FIG. 8-65

VICTOR BEATER
PATENT PENDING
9-1/2" —$2,000—

R S Arnold

FIG. 8-66

Detail of main gear

R S Arnold

FIG. 8-67

Detail of unique dasher arrangement

BOHN COLLECTION

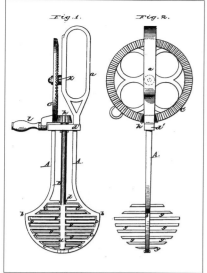

FIG. 8-68

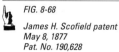
James H. Scofield patent
May 8, 1877
Pat. No. 190,628

FIG. 8-69

VORTEX
PATD JUNE 4TH,
1878
11"
—$1,000—

FIG. 8-70

No I.D. but believed VORTEX patent model
11"   —$1,000+ —

▶ The aptly named VORTEX *(fig. 8-69)* features unusual full dashers. There also is an identical model without any markings *(fig. 8-70)*.

It was patented *(fig. 8-71)* by George Mooney of Providence, Rhode Island, who cited the "peculiar arrangement of and form of the wings of the agitator."

The VICTOR and the VORTEX weren't the only American beaters with innovative dashers. Over the years there have been rotary patents with dashers ranging from big spirals to jail house bars to horizontal bars, to wire diamonds.

Although there is no evidence that any of the following patents resulted in the manufacture of beaters, all are worthy of note because of their attempts to improve on the design of the dasher -- that part of the beater that actually comes in contact with and beats the egg.

Wilson P. Dodson of Philadelphia said in his Dec. 20, 1887 patent *(fig. 8-72)* that his dashers "open spiral form" had "marked advantages, as a rotation thereof causes the egg to be lifted during the stirring or beating process, whereby it is intimately commingled with air, resulting in rapidly changing the egg to a light consistency."

FIG. 8-71

George Mooney patent
June 4, 1878
Pat. No. 204,498
Note: Mooney was granted another patent
June 3, 1879, for improvements on the original.

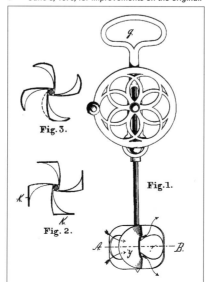

FIG. 8-72

Wilson P. Dodson patent
Dec. 20, 1887
Pat. No. 375,274

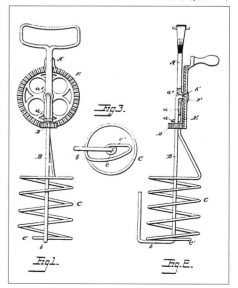

Naomi C. Burnham said in her March 21, 1905 patent *(fig. 8-73)* that her "parallel knives" and stationary vertical bars "thoroughly beat, cut, or mix the material treated without concentrating it at the center or around the periphery of the rotating parts" and thus "not splash or throw the material out of the receptacle."

Arthur Sandall of York, Nebraska, introduced one of the first "chicken wire" rotary beaters in his Oct. 2, 1906 patent *(fig. 8-74)*. Sandall said his design would provide "a simple and inexpensive" mixer with the arrangement of the wire strands guaranteeing "an effective beater action."

In addition to his unusual chicken wire dasher design, Samuel Danner of Doniphan, Missouri, added something special to his March 12, 1907 patent. The patent *(fig. 8-75)* features what is believed to be the only American rotary beater patent with a drawing of a cook at work. The beater itself has a highly unusual chicken wire paddle wheel, but it is the cook who stands out.

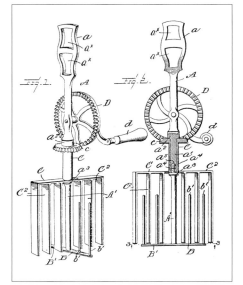

FIG. 8-73

 Naomi C. Burnham patent
March 21, 1905
Pat. No. 785,249

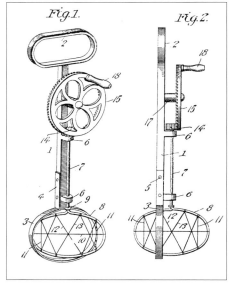

FIG. 8-74

Arthur Sandall patent
Oct. 2, 1906
Pat. No. 832,504

FIG. 8-75

Samuel Danner patent
March 12, 1907
Pat. No. 846,829

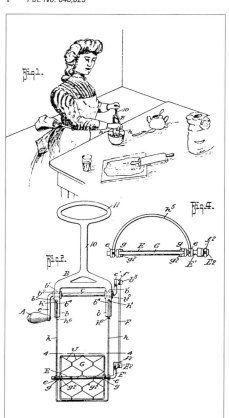

Chapter 9

Keystone and Silver

Ten Machines in One

The amazing Edwin Baltzley was the inventor behind the Keystone Manufacturing Company. Edwin concentrated on eggbeaters, and another Baltzley, Louis E., took over the tradition and expanded it to office equipment and novelties, including a ping pong paddle. More than 55 patents were awarded over the years to the Baltzleys.

Edwin Baltzley was awarded a half dozen beater patents but the one with the most impact was the first, Dec. 15, 1885 *(fig. 9-1)*. He described his device as "a culinary beater or whipper the arms of which are expanded outward and held in their expanded positions by centrifugal force, whereby the said beater or whipper is enlarged in its diametric length …" The 1885 date is embossed on one of the most popular of the Keystone products, a wall-mount that comes in two models *(figs. 9-2 & 9-3)*.

FIG. 9-1

*Edwin Baltzley patent
Dec. 15 1885
Pat. No. 332,375*

FIG. 9-2

KEYSTONE MFG CO. PAT DEC. 15 '85. PHILADELPHIA PA.
12" two-part extension arm and wall-mount —$400—

Glass jar made for the wall-mount:
KEYSTONE
embossed down one side,
1 QUART LIQUID, *across another*
7-1/4" —$150—

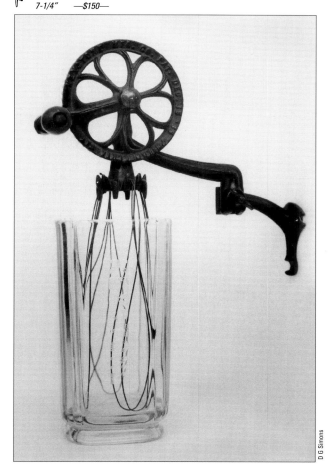

FIG. 9-3

**LICENSED TO BE SOLD ONLY ACCORDING TO ESTABLISHED PRICE LIST OF MAKER.
OIL ME
KEYSTONE PAT. DEC. 15, 85**
with wall-mount 12"
—$475—

An 1888 Keystone catalog/cook booklet, which proclaimed "Woman Emancipated!" *(fig. 9-4)*, called the wall-mount with extension KEYSTONE BEATER NO. 1. "This machine is especially designed to beat from one half gill to two quarts of light materials, and one to twelve eggs," the catalog said. The price, with wall bracket and vessel, was $1. The 1885 Baltzley date also appears on a sturdy table-mount mixer which the catalog called the KEYSTONE BEATER NO. 2, and described as "ten machines in one." Although the table-mount *(fig. 9-5)* features the 1885 date, it is based on an 1888 Baltzley patent *(fig. 9-6)*.

"This beater," said the catalog, "in from one to five minutes, mixes batters, kneads light doughs, mashes and flakes potatoes, churns butter, creams butter and sugar, mixes bread sponge, beats eggs, whips fruit into jelly sauces, creams vegetables, makes icings, salads and ice cream, mixes paint, paste, medicines,

BUY A KEYSTONE BEATER.

FIG. 9-4

Cover of Keystone Mfg. Co. Cook Book and catalog

FIG. 9-5

KEYSTONE MFG. CO.
PAT. DEC. 15 '85
PHILADELPHIA PA
19" fully extended...
main gear 5" in diameter
—$850—

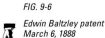

Note: A version of this model has the 5" main gear and dashers and another, interchangeable gear at 3-3/4" with dashers. One was used for heavy dough and the other for such things as creams.

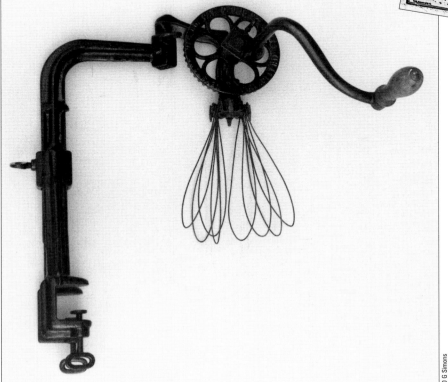

FIG. 9-6

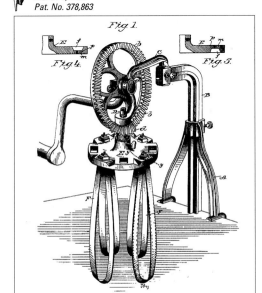

Edwin Baltzley patent
March 6, 1888
Pat. No. 378,863

D G Simons

THE EGGBEATER CHRONICLES

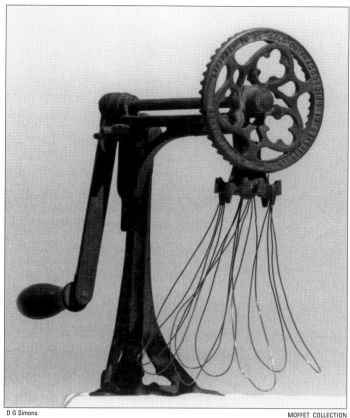

D G Simons

MOFFET COLLECTION

FIG. 9-7

KEYSTONE MFG CO. PAT. DEC. 15 '85 PHILA PA (on main bar)

LICENSED TO BE SOLD ONLY ACCORDING TO ESTABLISHED PRICE LISTING OF MAKER, (on wheel)

13-1/2" high
8" across
—$850—

FIG. 9-8

Keystone Mfg. Co. Cook Book and catalog

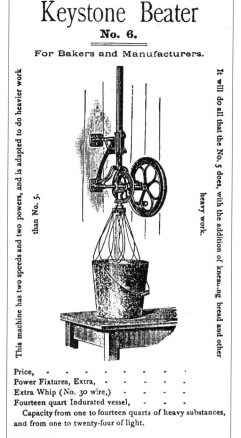

Keystone Beater
No. 6.

For Bakers and Manufacturers.

This machine has two speeds and two powers, and is adapted to do heavier work than No. 5.

It will do all that the No. 5 does, with the addition of kneading bread and other heavy work.

Price,	- - - - -	- -
Power Fixtures, Extra,	- - - -	- -
Extra Whip (No. 30 wire,)	- - -	- -
Fourteen quart Indurated vessel,	- - -	-

Capacity from one to fourteen quarts of heavy substances, and from one to twenty-four of light.

emulsions, and does many other useful things." The NO. 2 was listed at $2.75. It also came with a three-quart tin vessel to make ice cream, and four-quart, six-quart and 14-quart vessels to be used as churns. A similar, even more sturdy table-mount also carries the 1885 date (*fig. 9-7*).

Another mixer featured in the catalog, and waiting to be discovered, is the KEYSTONE BEATER NO. 6 (*fig. 9-8*), designed for bakers and candy makers.

Baltzley's first patent in 1885 listed his residence as Washington, D.C. His next patent, in 1888, showed that he had moved to Philadelphia. While in Philadelphia, he patented a lemon juice extractor, an eggbeater/tin creamer, a "motor for culinary beaters, mixers" featuring a series of gears and levers with a turntable for the beater container, and a culinary grater and chopper (*fig. 9-9*), which he assigned to his Keystone Manufacturing Company.

FIG. 9-9

Edwin Baltzley patents (left to right)

Aug. 14, 1888
Pat. No. 387,942

Sept. 18, 1888
Pat. No. 389,631

May 21, 1889
Pat. No. 403,502

Jan. 7, 1890
Pat. No. 419,103

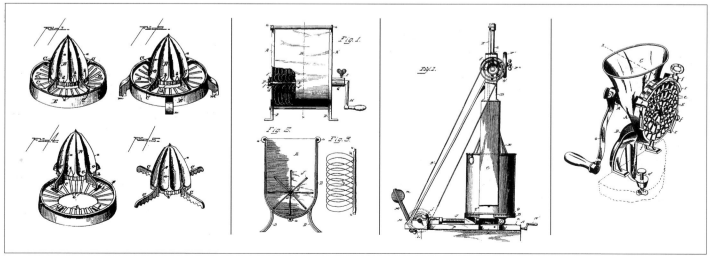

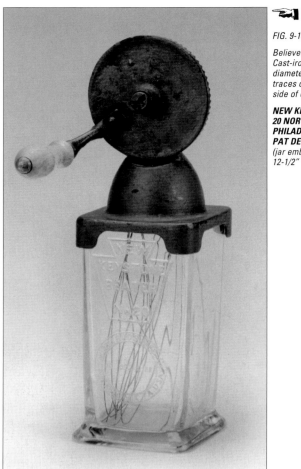

R S Arnold   SEIDEL COLLECTION

FIG. 9-10

Believed to be prototype.
Cast-iron top has 4" in
diameter solid gear, with
traces of a decal on the back
side of dome.

**NEW KEYSTONE BEATER NO.
20 NORTH BROS MFG. CO.
PHILADELPHIA, PA. U.S.A.
PAT DEC 15, 85**
(jar embossing)
12-1/2"   —$750—

D G Simons

FIG. 9-11

**NEW KEYSTONE BEATER PAT.
DEC. 15, 1885 APRIL 18, 1893,
NORTH BROS. MFG. CO.
PHILADELPHIA, PA, U.S.A.**
(on decal on back of dome)

Spoke gear is 4" in diameter.

**NEW KEYSTONE BEATER NO. 20
NORTH BROS MFG. CO.
PHILADELPHIA, PA. U.S.A.
PAT DEC 15, 85**
(on jar)

12-1/2"   —$400 —

*Note: The jar for the New
Keystone is about 7" high, while
the jar for the wall-mount is 7-1/4"*

*The wall-mount jar is marked
KEYSTONE down one side and
1 QUART LIQUID across another.*

The Keystone Manufacturing Company, with its office at 123 N. Eighth St. and its factory at 2548-2550 Callowhill St., Philadelphia, was a success, allowing Edwin Baltzley and his twin brother, Edward, to branch out into real estate. According to a February 16, 1997 article in the *Washington Post Magazine,* the brothers returned to Washington, D.C. and purchased land on the bluffs along the Maryland side of the Potomac River for what their brochure called "Glen Echo on the Potomac, the Washington Rhine." They started building mansions and selling lots, but the steep, wooded terrain proved unpopular, losing out to another new area called Chevy Chase.

During this same period, the Keystone operation, or at least part of it, apparently stayed in Philadelphia, but shifted to another firm, North Brothers Manufacturing Company.

Sheldon G. and Ralph H. North were the brothers behind the firm, makers of the New Keystone mixer. Of all the available glass jar mixers, the new KEYSTONE BEATER NO. 20 (*figs. 9-10 & 9-11*), with cast-iron top and wire whisk dashers, is undoubtedly one of the most collectible.

A great eggbeater, but do you think there's any mention of it in the official history of North Brothers? The company seemed to think a fancy screwdriver was more important.

Sheldon was first listed in the Philadelphia city directory as a machinist at 440 North 12th Street. He and Ralph teamed up in 1881, settling at Lehigh Avenue and American Street, where they produced a wide variety of tools and kitchen items, including the Gem Ice Shave and Lightning ice chipper.

Stanley Yankee Tools Incorporated, a subsidiary of Stanley Works, purchased the firm in 1946 and it remained at that address until 1958 when it was absorbed into the Stanley business family in New Britain, Connecticut.

According to the detailed *Foundation for the Future, History of The Stanley Works,* by Robert Keith Leavitt, New Britain, Connecticut, 1951, the North Brothers firm in 1946 was the nation's largest maker of spiral and ratchet screwdrivers.

Sheldon was described as "a mechanical genius," and Ralph as "a bank-trained management man."

The firm's "most famous item was a spiral screwdriver, an invention of a temperamental Maine Yankee named Zacharias Furbush. This, with other North Brothers tools under the trade name Yankee, was famous throughout the tool-using world," according to Leavitt.

Despite the screwdriver, eggbeater collectors think the most famous item made by the firm was the NEW KEYSTONE BEATER NO. 20. Although the NEW KEYSTONE is marked with Baltzley's 1885

Scrambled Eggs

Break four eggs into small saucepan; add to them two ounces of butter, four tablespoonfuls of cream, one tablespoonful of stock, half-teaspoonful of salt, a dash of black pepper; stir the whole over the fire until the eggs begin to thicken; then take it from the fire and with the small Keystone Beater beat them a half-minute, or until they are light and delicate. Return the saucepan to the fire to reheat the contents, and serve at once. These, if carefully made, are delicious.

—1888 KEYSTONE MFG. CO. COOK BOOK

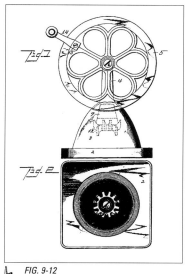

FIG. 9-12

Antonius C. Albrecht patent
April 18, 1893
Pat. No. 495,925

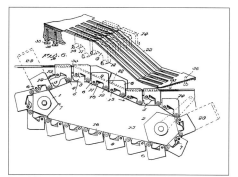

FIG. 9-13

Edwin Baltzley patent
Sept. 15, 1903
Pat. No. 739,141

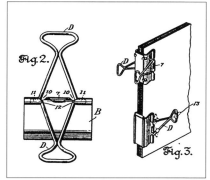

FIG. 9-15

Louis E. Baltzley patent
May 18, 1915
Pat. No. 1,139,627

patent date, the actual patent was obtained by Antonius C. Albrecht of Philadelphia, who described himself as assignor to North Brothers. In his April 13, 1893 patent *(fig. 9-12)*, Albrecht said, "A special advantage resulting from my invention is that the whips cannot rub against the bottom of the jar, which has proven a serious fault in beaters of this class."

In the meantime, Edwin Baltzley kept busy. In 1903, while living in Glen Echo, Maryland, he patented a "traveling stairway," or as he called it, a "stairvator, designed to move passengers from one elevation to another with speed, comfort, and safety" *(fig. 9-13)*.

Louis E. Baltzley, believed to be Edwin's son, obtained his first patent in

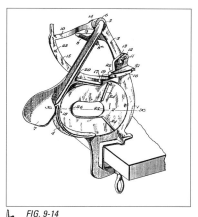

FIG. 9-14

Louis E. Baltzley patent
March 25, 1913
Pat. No. 1,056,965

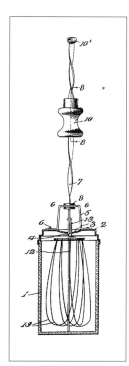

FIG. 9-16

Edwin Baltzley patent
Dec. 21, 1915
Pat. No. 1,165,307

FIG. 9-17

No I.D., but based on 1915 Edwin Baltzley patent, in Grape Ola jar. Identified in catalog as the "L.E.B. EGG WHIP"

18" —$450—

1913 *(fig. 9-14)* for a "fruit-pitting device," and followed that in 1915 with an office device that is very much in use today — a "paper binding clip" *(fig. 9-15)*. Edwin also was active in late 1915, patenting an Archimedes "culinary beater" *(fig. 9-16)*. Edwin and Louis both listed their hometown at this time as Weehawken, New Jersey.

Edwin's "culinary beater" *(fig. 9-17)* was described in the May, 1914 *Good Housekeeping* as the "L.E.B. EGG-WHIP." The beater, the magazine said, "has some novel features which increase its adaptability, and an efficiency which has not been equaled by any device similar in type … The motion necessary to operation is easy; the force obtained was sufficient to whip up a solid half-bar of soap with a cup of water into a jelly which could be used in the power washing-machine." The price was 50 cents.

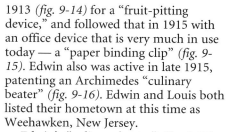

On March 27, 1917, Edwin teamed up with Louis to patent *(fig. 9-18)* a metal, instead of cast-iron, rotary top glass jar beater *(fig. 9-19)*. It is marked NEW KEYSTONE BEATER, CULINARY UTILITIES CO., NEW YORK, N.Y. BLOOMFIELD, N.J. in the metal apron and embossed on the bottom of the jar. The top sides of the heavy glass jar are marked: "Pound Flour; Liquid Weights; Even Full 1 Qt. or 4 standards measuring cups; Even Full 8 T cups or 4 coffee cups," plus various measurements listed downward. The magazine *Today's Housekeeper,* in its October 1917 edition, listed the NEW KEYSTONE, with all attachments, including a device to clamp the mixer to the edge of a table, at $1.50.

Louis, on the same date, March 27, 1917, patented the special funnel *(fig. 9-20),* or "feeding device," for the NEW KEYSTONE.

"This feeding device is particularly useful as an oil dropper to be used for olive oil and the like in preparing salad dressings. It is provided with tubular delivering means adapted to fit a hole in the top of a culinary beater and to be maintained in place by such tubular delivering means whereby the operator may have both hands free, one to operate the handle of the valve stem and the other to operate the handle of the beater," the patent said.

The jar for the NEW KEYSTONE with metal top is 6-3/4" high, compared to the North Brothers jar at just about 7". The NEW KEYSTONE is marked on the bottom of the jar on its four sides THE-NEW-KEYSTONE-BEATER. A very similar jar, found without its top, is marked on its four sides THE-NEW-MATHEWS-BEATER, meaning Keystone made at least one model with a different name, probably a special order.

Edwin Baltzley in 1919 was described in one of his patents as deceased with Louis acting as administrator. Louis continued pumping out patents over the years, including a "ping pong racket" *(fig. 9-21).* Louis and his wife, Elfie, made their home in Glen Ridge, New Jersey in 1926 and lived there until 1945 when they moved to Chicago.

FIG. 9-19

Culinary Utilities Co. New Keystones (left to right):

NEW KEYSTONE BEATER CULINARY UTILITIES CO. NEW YORK, N.Y. BLOOMFIELD, N.J. PAT'S PENDING.
11-1/2" —$175—

NEW KEYSTONE BEATER CULINARY UTILITIES CO. NEW YORK, N.Y. BLOOMFIELD, N.J. PAT'S PENDING,
with original funnel
11-1/2" —$225—

NEW KEYSTONE BEATER CULINARY UTILITIES CO. NEW YORK, N.Y. BLOOMFIELD, N.J. PAT'S PENDING,
homemade wood churn dasher, mismatch funnel
11-1/2" —$150—

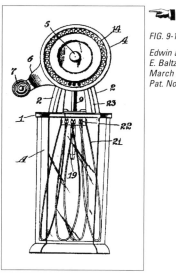

FIG. 9-18

Edwin and Louis E. Baltzley patent March 27, 1917 Pat. No. 1,220,928

FIG 9-20

Louis E. Baltzley patent March 27 1917 Pat. No. 1,220,929

D G Simons

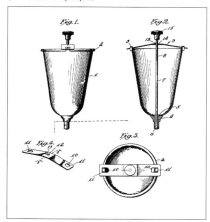

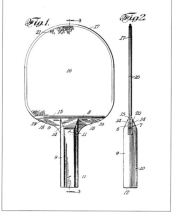

FIG 9-21

Louis E. Baltzley patent June 5, 1934 Pat. No. 1,961,473

Omelet Soufflé

First grease a quart baking dish with butter, and then see that the oven is hot. Beat the whites of 6 eggs very stiff, add 3 yolks and beat again until stiff. Then, carefully stir in 3 tablespoonful of powdered sugar and the juice of half a lemon, and quickly heap into the baking dish; dredge with powered sugar and put into the oven. Bake fifteen minutes, or until a golden brown, and serve immediately. It may also be baked in paper cases.

— **THE NEW KEYSTONE BEATER COOK BOOK**, CIRCA 1920

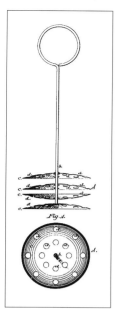

FIG. 9-22

William H. Silver
patent
June 15, 1875
Pat. No. 164,491

FIG. 9-23

William H. Silver
patent
April 30, 1878
Pat. No. 203,081

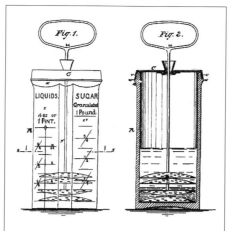

SILVER

Silver & Company got its start June 15, 1875, the date William H. Silver, then of St. Louis, patented a "churn dasher" (*fig. 9-22*), which he said would produce "the butter quickly and thoroughly."

It was followed by another patent on April 30, 1878 (*fig. 9-23*) featuring a jar plunger mixer. Silver, now listing himself as a New York City resident, called it a "dessert-maker."

The June 15, 1875 date is embossed on the jar of THE GLASS EGG BEATER AND MEASURING JAR (*fig. 9-24*). The single 1875 date appears on some models, while the 1875 and 1878 dates both appear on others. A turn-of-the-century flyer for Silver & Co., Manufacturers, 41 Broadway, N.Y., said of THE GLASS EGG BEATER, "It will whip up eggs to twice the bulk of any other beater, making a saving of at least one-third in eggs. A single egg, thoroughly beaten, will do the work better than three or four partially done." The price was 75 cents.

FIG. 9-24

**THE GLASS EGG BEATER
AND MEASURING JAR
SILVER MFG CO.
PAT JUNE 15, '75 APR 30 '78
NEW YORK**
10-1/2" to top of plunger
—$165—

D G Simons

For Good Measure

Silver produced a miniature 2-cup measuring glass — a 3-3/4" high replica of its beater container, with markings for: **2 CUPS, SUGAR 1/2 PINT,** and **TABLE SPOON-FULLS.** The bottom is embossed: **FAMILY MEASURING GLASS SILVER & CO NEW YORK.**

—$100—

D Thornton

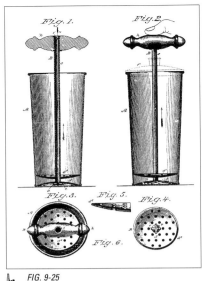

FIG. 9-25

William H. Silver patent
May 11, 1886
Pat. No. 341,697

D G Simons

FIG 9-26

Silver plungers (left to right):

SILVER EGG BEATER NO. 4 *(on aluminum top)*
SILVER'S TRADE MARK BROOKLYN *(with bridge embossed on jar bottom)*
11"   —$125—

No ID on metal top.
SILVER & CO.
PAT'D APL 30 '78 MAY 11 '86 NEW YORK *(embossed on jar bottom, without bridge drawing)*
11"   —$135—

SILVER EGG BEATER NO. 4 *(on metal top)*
SILVER'S TRADE MARK BROOKLYN *(with bridge embossed on jar bottom)*
11"   —$125—

In another patent, this one May 11, 1886 *(fig. 9-25)* for a glass jar plunger *(fig. 9-26)* Silver summed up his beating philosophy: "In beating or whipping up eggs and making egg mixtures the primary object, whatever the mode of operation, is to fill the same with air, or in other words to aerate them as thoroughly as possible. Consequently it is a desirderatum that the air forced or worked into the eggs shall be retained therein or in the mixture, and the quality retained, with the manner in which it is retained and distributed, determines the quality of the product."

The 1918 Sears catalog said of the mixer: "Round pattern. Works quickly. Dasher and tube are retinned and cover is nickel plated ... Price ... $1.10."

An early Silver & Company catalog *(fig 9-27)* said: "The No. 4 Egg Beater receptacle is made of heavy lime glass graduated dry or liquid measurements. The dashers or beaters are made of extra heavy bessemer steel, retinned bright, the air tube is made of [grade] XXXX tin which is retinned to insure its being thoroughly sanitary. The valve adjustment at the base of the tube is made of German silver ... Elegant in appearance and very durable in use. One size only, capacity one quart. ... This style egg beater introduced by us has had a world wide reputation and a largely increasing sale."

Elegant the plunger model is, but the mainstay of the Silver line is the SILVER EGG BEATER NO. 3 *(fig. 9-28)*, also called THE SILVER NEW EGG BEATER.

The 1918 Sears catalog listed the price for this rotary beauty at $1.45.

D G Simons

FIG. 9-28

SILVERS TRADE MARK BROOKLYN *(with bridge, embossed on jar bottom)*
12-1/2"   —$300—

FIG. 9-27

No. 4 Egg Beater,
Silver & Co. 1910
catalog

FIG. 9-29

Silver New Egg Beater,
Silver & Co. 1910
catalog

THE EGGBEATER CHRONICLES

Said the 1910 Silver catalog *(fig. 9-29):* "Square jar wire whip style. Combination egg beater and measuring glass receptacle. Equally good for beating eggs, whipping cream or making any kind of cakes, custards, etc."

The SILVER jar is 7-1/16" high, with the top of the sides marked: "POUND FLOUR; LIQUID WEIGHTS; 1 QUART EVEN FULL; EVEN FULL 8 T CUPS OR 4 COFFEE CUPS" — very, very similar to the NEW KEYSTONE, suggesting a connection between the two companies. The SILVERS also is marked on the bottom of each side of the jar THE-SILVER-NEW-EGG-BEATER. And the NEW KEYSTONE and SILVER tops fit both jars.

A rare version of the SILVER NO. 3 has an embossed cast-iron top *(fig. 9-30)* saying SILVER NO. 3 — MEASURING — GLASS EGG — BEATER. Silver made a similar embossed top for Horlick's Malted Milk *(See Chapter 12 Archimedes, page 114).*

Silver also made its own table and wall-mount beaters. The 1910 Silver & Co. catalog said: "The HOTEL EGG BEATER NO. 5 *(fig. 9-31)* is made in one size only, extra large. The framework of the beater is of heavy cast iron retinned with pure tin which gives it a pleasing appearance and makes it thoroughly

sanitary. The beater portion is constructed of heavy steel piano wire and will stand a great deal of hard use. It is splendid for hotels, bakers, boarding houses and other similar places where a smaller sized beater would be inadequate." The drawing is a close if not exact match for the KEYSTONE table-mount *(fig. 9-7, page 87)* — adding more to the evidence the two firms were connected.

A table-mount *(fig. 9-32)* attributed to Silver has only one piece of identification, BROOKLYN 5 on the crank handle.

Describing the WALL STYLE EGG BEATER NO. 6 *(fig. 9-33),* the catalog said: "For home use where an egg beater is desired that can be affixed to the wall, either permanently or temporarily … It is of the same structure as our No. 3 excepting that it has a suspended arm to which is cast a socket which fits into a corresponding pocket socket."

The value of the NO. 6 will have to remain undetermined until at least a few appear on the market.

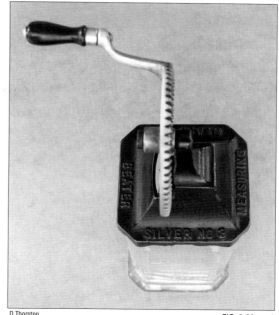

D Thornton

FIG. 9-30

SILVER NO. 3 MEASURING GLASS EGG BEATER,
(embossed in cast-iron top)
SILVERS TRADE MARK BROOKLYN
(with bridge, embossed on jar bottom)
12-1/2"
—$350—

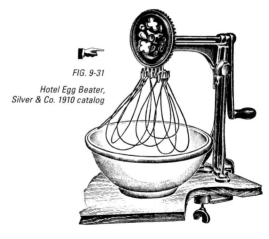

FIG. 9-31
Hotel Egg Beater,
Silver & Co. 1910 catalog

FIG. 9-32

BROOKLYN 5
(embossed on crank handle)
16" high and 9" across.
—$300—

FIG. 9-33
Wall Style Egg Beater,
Silver & Co. 1910 catalog

GASPARI COLLECTION

D Thornton

CHAPTER 9: KEYSTONE AND SILVER

No. 1 No. 2

FIG. 9-34

Brooklyn egg beaters, Silver & Co. 1910 catalog

Two scarce syllabub churns *(fig. 9-34)* were part of the Silver line, the BROOKLYN EGG BEATER NO. 1 and NO. 2 *(See Chapter 19, Syllabub Churns and Other Plungers, page 205)*.

The NO. 1 "is constructed on the same model as our celebrated Silver Measuring Glass Egg Beater," said the catalog. "It aerates the eggs or other mixtures by forcing the air through them."

As for the larger NO. 2, the catalog said it was the "same construction and finish as No. 1, and operating the same …"

Silver took out a full-page ad in the December, 1913 *House Furnishing Review* *(fig. 9-35)*, listing most of its prized mixers.

But one prize was missing — probably the rarest of the Silver mixers — the SILVER MIXING BOWL *(fig. 9-36)*. Said the catalog: "The Silver mayonnaise mixer

and mixing bowl can be used for mixing or aerating any desired ingredient. The metal parts are all solid brass, carefully nickel plated. The bowl is of imported bone china, the cover is of selected chestnut wood. The article is elegant and clean and thoroughly sanitary. Especial [sic] attention is called to the automatic drip cup arrangement … Capacity two pints."

The SILVER MIXING BOWL is believed to have been imported from England *(See Chapter 26, International Mix, page 295)*.

FIG. 9-36

Silver mayonnaise mixer and mixing bowl, Silver & Co. 1910 catalog

FIG. 9-35

December 1913 House Furnishing Review ad

You must follow instructions when using this beater. By doing this you will accomplish a WONDERFUL RESULT. Move the dasher rapidly up and down in the glass with a quick jerking motion. Always keep the round tin discs inside the mixture. It is not necessary to raise the tin discs more than an inch or two from the bottom of the glass. When the mixture comes up light you must cover the open lid of the tube at the top with a finger or hand. This will make the mixture hard and firm. Occasionally cover and uncover the open end of the tube at the top, this will keep the mixture well together and keep it from working out through the cover. Notice the valve on bottom of dasher.

—CARDBOARD TAG, WIRED TO THE HANDLE OF EARLY SILVER PLUNGER MODELS

A&J

"The original one-hand beater."

A humble beginning for a true American success story.

It started in 1908 when Edward H. Johnson *(fig. 10-1)*, a traveling salesman, purchased for $500 a patent for a unique kitchen gadget, an Archimedes, or up-and-down, eggbeater.

That purchase gave birth to the A&J Manufacturing Company of Binghamton, New York — the now dominant force in the American kitchen collectibles field.

In requesting his patent *(fig. 10-2)*, George L. Raymond of Binghamton, said, "I am aware that various egg beaters to which the necessary rotary motion is imparted by a spiral screw are already in use, but in my improved implement, I have endeavored to so simplify the parts and construction as to enable me to produce an egg beater at a minimum of cost of those already in use."

Raymond promptly sold the patent to Johnson, who teamed up with his wife's uncle, Benjamin T. Ash, who in turn invested $500 to get things rolling.

Production of the gadget began in a small building behind the Johnson home in 1909.

A Binghamton Chamber of Commerce publication just a decade later said A&J (for Ash and Johnson) was the largest factory in America dedicated to kitchenware, making 27 different kitchen tools. Just two decades after its birth, Johnson boasted that A&J had more than 200 employees producing about four million kitchen tools a year.

In a 1988 family history video, Johnson's sons, Kenneth Edward Johnson, then 82, of Binghamton, and Frederick Ash Johnson, then 77, of nearby Afton, reminisced about their father and the fabulously successful A&J Manufacturing Company.

The first eggbeater *(fig. 10-3)*, they said, was hand-made, bent into shape around wooden pegs. And the sales pitch was also that simple.

FIG. 10-1

Edward H. Johnson, 1938

Photo courtesy Frederick Johnson

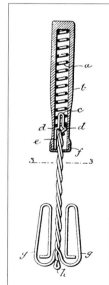

FIG. 10-2

George L. Raymond patent
Oct. 15, 1907
Pat. No. 868,124

FIG. 10-3

First A&Js (left to right):

THE A&J
PATENTED OCT. 15TH 07
13-1/2" —$35—

THE HAMILTON SILVER CO.
PAT OCT. 15-07 NEW YORK,
made by A&J
for Hamilton Silver
13" —$35—

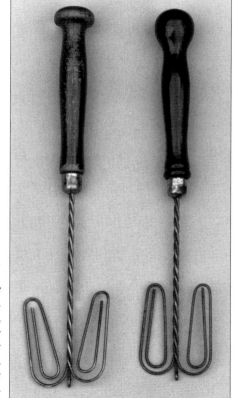

D G Simons

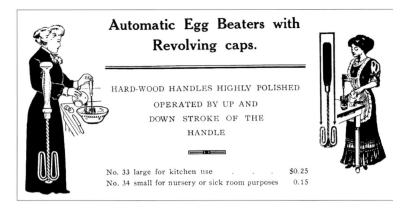

Automatic Egg Beaters with Revolving caps.

HARD-WOOD HANDLES HIGHLY POLISHED
OPERATED BY UP AND
DOWN STROKE OF THE
HANDLE

No. 33 large for kitchen use . . . $0.25
No. 34 small for nursery or sick room purposes 0.15

FIG. 10-4

Early Ritzinger &
Grasgreen of New
York household goods
catalog

FIG. 10-5

1910 Biddle Hardware
Company Catalog

"In the early days, the way father marketed his product was through what you might call street peddlers," said Kenneth Johnson. "They would stand on a corner and they had a board with a rope around it and father furnished the board and tape. They'd stand with a bowl and run these beaters up and down."

Frederick Johnson added: "Of course, you put a little soap in the bowl with it and you could make soap suds and it looked great."

Edward H. Johnson was an aggressive salesman and manufacturer and it wasn't long before his marketing included advertising (figs. 10-4 & 10-5). Other kitchen items (figs. 10-6 through 10-8) soon joined the original beater, followed by major sales to such giants as Woolworth, Kress, Sears and Montgomery Ward.

"A & J"
Egg Beater, Cream Whip and
Mayonnaise Mixer. Operated
with One Hand by a Short Up
and Down Stroke. Polished
Hardwood Handle, Enameled
Finish. Tinned Wire Wings.
Steel Ferrule, Nickel Plated.

No. 1 Family Size. Per doz. $4.00
One dozen in a Box.

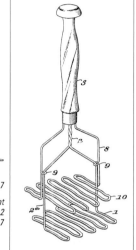

FIG. 10-7

William Allan Jackson patent
April 16, 1912
Pat. No. 1,023,317

FIG. 10-6

1911 House Furnishing Review ad

FIG 10-8

Mashers (left to right)

MADE IN U.S.A. 9-1/2" —$6—
A&J PAT'D PAT. PND 11-1/4" —$35—

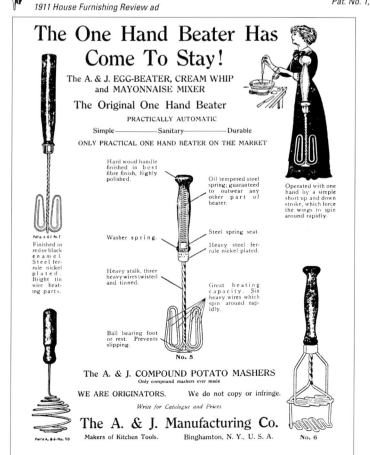

The One Hand Beater Has Come To Stay!

The A. & J. EGG-BEATER, CREAM WHIP
and MAYONNAISE MIXER

The Original One Hand Beater

PRACTICALLY AUTOMATIC

Simple————Sanitary————Durable

ONLY PRACTICAL ONE HAND BEATER ON THE MARKET

Hard wood handle
finished in best
fibre finish, highly
polished.

Oil tempered steel
spring; guaranteed
to outwear any
other part of
beater.

Operated with one
hand by a simple
short up and down
stroke, which force
the wings to spin
around rapidly.

Washer spring.

Steel spring seat.

Heavy steel fer-
rule nickel plated.

Heavy stalk, three
heavy wires twisted
and tinned.

Great beating
capacity. Six
heavy wires which
spin around rap-
idly.

Ball bearing foot
or rest. Prevents
slipping.

No. 5

Finished in
red or black
enamel.
Steel fer-
rule nickel
plated.
Bright tin
wire beat-
ing parts.

The A. & J. COMPOUND POTATO MASHERS
Only compound mashers ever made

WE ARE ORIGINATORS. We do not copy or infringe.

Write for Catalogue and Prices

The A. & J. Manufacturing Co.

Makers of Kitchen Tools. Binghamton, N. Y., U. S. A.

No. 6

D Thornton

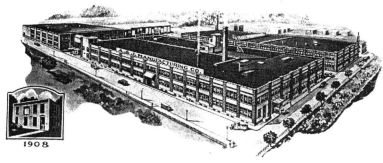

The A & J Manufacturing Company, Binghamton, N.Y.

> Here is the first egg beater to be made entirely of stainless steel. It is the most wonderful egg beater that women have ever had the opportunity of using. It is a life *investment* and if not accidentally thrown out or deliberately destroyed — it can be a family heirloom."
>
> —A&J, 1930S

Who was this man who took a simple eggbeater and turned it into a company with 200 employees?

According to the 1924 edition of *Binghamton and Broome County, New York, A History,* Johnson, a native of Missouri, before the age of 19 was a traveling salesman for the Toledo Scale Company, selling mostly to butcher shops.

He abandoned scales for real estate brokerage and settled in Binghamton, where "his energies were turned into other channels.

"There had come to his casual attention an eggbeater, upon which patents had already been obtained, but which he believed could be improved upon, with the application of new principles. Confident that the production of the improved beater was commercially practical, he rented a small building at the rear of his residence, perfected his

model, and began the manufacture of this item of a housewife's necessary equipment. From such a modest beginning has grown the concern which has come to be known as the A&J Manufacturing Co., makers of kitchen utensils and tools, a company producing the largest bulk of kitchen hardware of any concern in its class."

During its first decade, business boomed, more room was needed and A&J built its own factory on Water Street.

It was in 1922, according to his sons, that Johnson took over A&J. Said Frederick Johnson: "At that time the business had started to grow and father wanted to get out and not have any partners. Someone said he paid off Uncle Ben something like $50,000."

Kenneth Johnson agreed, saying, "For the half."

"Fifty-thousand dollars for his ($500) investment in the firm! So he did pretty good with his money," said Frederick Johnson, describing his uncle as "really in the jewelry business and real estate."

Following the buy out, "the business really started to grow, from that time until [father] sold out [in 1929]."

And grow it did. The list of products ranged from apple corers to "Zigzag" mixing spoons.

On the A&J scale of beater collectibles, the first up-and-down beaters *(fig. 10-9)* have to be considered the most desired. They are easily identified with the A&J trademark and patent date, Oct. 15, 1907, on the metal ring of the wooden handle.

A&J offered these beaters to other firms to market. For example, you can find the 1907 dated beaters marked THE HAMILTON SILVER CO. OF NEW YORK *(fig. 10-3, page 95)* and a 1910 invoice showed the firm ordered 150 gross that year.

Edward H. Johnson's own patent improvements include a bottom knob *(fig. 10-10)* and round dashers for the

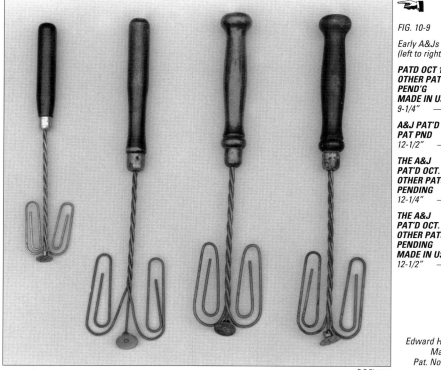

D G Simons

☞ FIG. 10-9

Early A&Js (left to right):

PATD OCT 15 07 OTHER PAT PEND'G MADE IN USA
9-1/4" —$50—

A&J PAT'D PAT PND
12-1/2" —$35—

THE A&J PAT'D OCT. 15 07 OTHER PATS PENDING
12-1/4" —$30—

THE A&J PAT'D OCT. 15 07 OTHER PATS PENDING MADE IN USA
12-1/2" —$30—

☞ FIG. 10-10

Edward H. Johnson May 14, 1912 Pat. No. 1,025,982

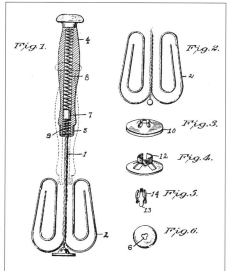

FIG. 10-11

Edward H. Johnson patent
Dec. 18, 1917
Pat. No. 1,250,889

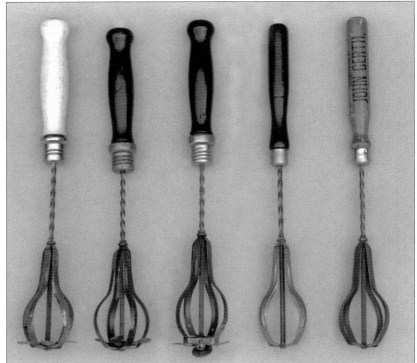

D G Simons

FIG. 10-12

A&J round dashers (left to right):

A&J PATENTED MADE IN USA   13-1/2"   —$35—

A&J MADE IN USA, *dated but unreadable*   13-1/4"   —$35—

A&J PAT'D PAT. PN'D   13-3/4"   —$40—

No I.D.   13-1/2"   —$25—

A&J MADE IN USA   10-15-07   5-14-12   12-18-17
COMPLIMENTS OF JOHN GERTH TOP PRICE FOR CREAM (advertising on handle)
13-1/2"   —$45—

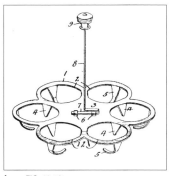

FIG. 10-13

Edward H. Johnson patent
Dec. 18, 1917
Pat. No. 1,250,888

FIG. 10-14

Edward H. Johnson patent
Dec. 18, 1917
Pat. No. 1,250,890

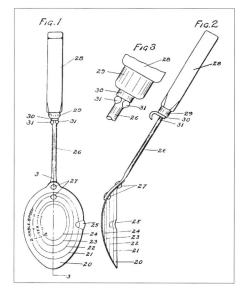

FIG. 10-15

Charles E. Kail patent
Oct. 9, 1923
Pat. No. 1,470,169

FIG. 10-16

Charles E. Kail patent
Oct. 9, 1923
Pat. No. 1,470,170

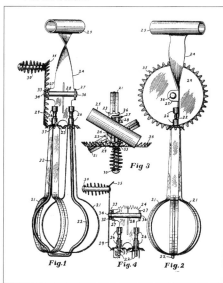
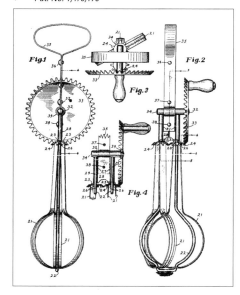

A&J Archimedes (*fig. 10-11*). The round dasher model had several different bottom attachments (*fig. 10-12*).

Johnson also patented — on the same date, Dec. 18, 1917 — an "implement for boiling eggs" (*fig. 10-13*) and a ripping kitchen spoon, with measuring marks (*fig. 10-14*).

The most common A&J patent is Oct. 9, 1923. It was on this date that Charles E. Kail of Binghamton, assignor to A&J, was granted two patents (*figs. 10-15 & 10-16*) for beaters.

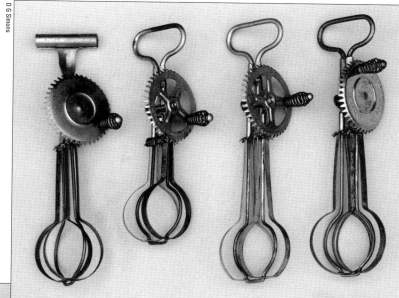

D G Simons

FIG. 10-17

Pressed metal A&Js (left to right):

No. I.D.
9-3/4″ —$15—

PAT. OCT. 9, 1923
MADE IN UNITED STATES OF AMERICA
8-1/2″ —$12—

A&J PAT. OCT. 9, 1923
MADE IN U.S. AMERICA
10″ —$12—

A&J PAT. OCT. 9, 1923
MADE IN U.S.A.
9-3/4″ —$12—

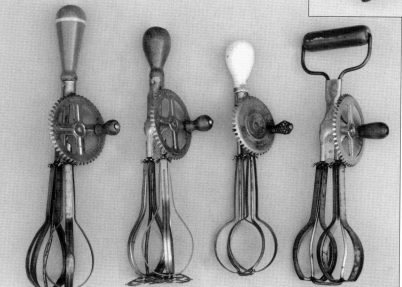

D G Simons

FIG 10-18

Wood handle A&Js (left to right):

A&J PAT OCT. 9, 1923
13-1/2″ —$15—

A&J PAT OCT. 9, 1923
with curly disk bottom
12″ —$40—

A&J PAT OCT. 9, 1923
MADE IN USA NO. 72
10-3/4″ —$10—

A&J PAT OCT. 9, 1923
MADE IN UNITED STATES OF AMERICA
11-1/2″ —$15—

The Oct. 9, 1923 patents cover a good portion of the existing beater world. For the dedicated collector, this is only a partial 1923 listing, there are many other variations out there (*figs. 10-17 & 10-18*).

Two vertical wood handle models obviously were based on the 1923 patents, but were marked PAT. APPL'D FOR. They are the BIG BINGO and the LADY BINGO, and are in addition to at least one all-metal BINGO (*fig. 10-19*).

FIG. 10-19

Bingos (left to right):

BIG BINGO PAT APL'D FOR MADE IN USA NO. 71 11-3/4″ —$15—

LADY BINGO NO. 72 A&J PAT APL'D FOR MADE IN USA 10-3/4″ —$15—

BINGO NO. 70 MADE IN USA PAT OCT. 9, 1923 11″ —$45—

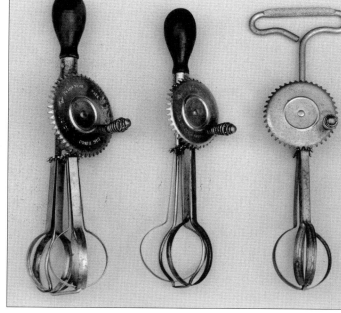

D G Simons

CHAPTER **10: A & J**

99

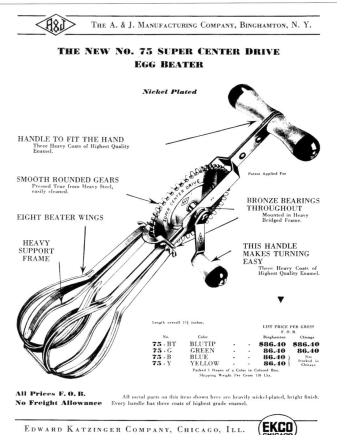

THE A. & J. MANUFACTURING COMPANY, BINGHAMTON, N. Y.

THE NEW NO. 75 SUPER CENTER DRIVE EGG BEATER

Nickel Plated

HANDLE TO FIT THE HAND
Three Heavy Coats of Highest Quality Enamel.

SMOOTH ROUNDED GEARS
Pressed True from Heavy Steel, easily cleaned.

EIGHT BEATER WINGS

HEAVY SUPPORT FRAME

Patent Applied For

BRONZE BEARINGS THROUGHOUT
Mounted in Heavy Bridged Frame.

THIS HANDLE MAKES TURNING EASY
Three Heavy Coats of Highest Quality Enamel.

▼

Length overall 11¼ inches.

No.	Color	LIST PRICE PER GROSS F. O. B. Binghamton	Chicago
75 - BT	BLUTIP	$86.40	$86.40
75 - G	GREEN	86.40	86.40
75 - B	BLUE	86.40	Not Stocked in Chicago
75 - Y	YELLOW	86.40	

Packed 1 Dozen of a Color in Colored Box.
Shipping Weight Per Gross 110 Lbs.

All Prices F. O. B.
No Freight Allowance

All metal parts on this item shown here are heavily nickel-plated, bright finish. Every handle has three coats of highest grade enamel.

EDWARD KATZINGER COMPANY, CHICAGO, ILL.   EKCO CHICAGO

FIG. 10-20

A&J/EKCO catalog sheet

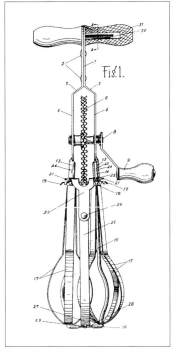

FIG. 10-21

Charles E. Kail patent
Oct. 27, 1931
Pat. No. 1,828,932

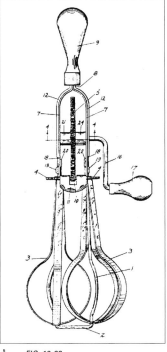

FIG. 10-22

Charles E. Kail patent
July 10, 1934
Pat. No. 1,965,650

D G Simons

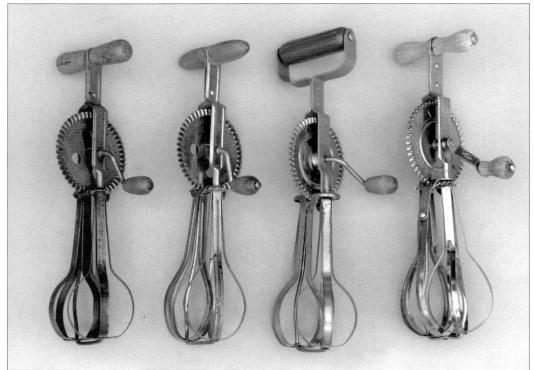

FIG. 10-23

Super Center and High Speeds (left to right):

HIGH SPEED CENTER DRIVE
MADE IN UNITED STATES OF AMERICA
11-1/2"   —$10—

HIGH SPEED SUPER CENTER DRIVE
A&J PAT APLD FOR
11-1/2"   —$10—

HIGH SPEED BEATER
A&J PAT APLD FOR
12"   —$10—

SUPER CENTER DRIVE PAT APLD FOR
STAINLESS STEEL, BRONZE BEARINGS
A&J
11-1/2"   —$25—

THE EGGBEATER CHRONICLES

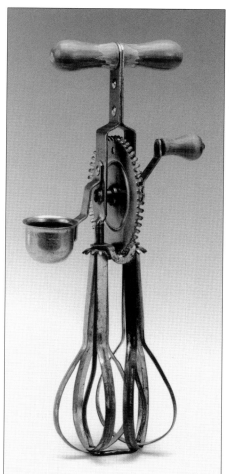

R S Arnold   ALLEN COLLECTION

☞

FIG. 10-24

**SUPER CENTER DRIVE
A&J STAINLESS STEEL,
STAINLESS STEEL BRONZE BEARINGS,**
with attached funnel or dripper
11-1/2"   —$65—

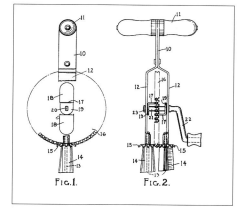

✊ FIG. 10-25

*Myron J. Zimmer patent
Aug. 4, 1936
Pat. No. 2,049,727*

☞

FIG. 10-26

**SUPER SPEED A&J
SPINNIT
CREAM AND EGG WHIP**
11-1/2"   —$40—

D G Simons

The 1923 patent line was followed by the T-handle SUPER CENTER DRIVE line *(fig. 10-20)*, based on a Kail patent for Oct. 27, 1931 *(fig. 10-21)*. Kail also patented a vertical handle center drive, this one on July 10, 1934 *(fig. 10-22)*.

The SUPER CENTER DRIVE was complemented by the HIGH SPEED CENTER DRIVE line *(fig. 10-23)*. A rare SUPER CENTER DRIVE had a small funnel or dripper attached *(fig. 10-24)*. The funnel is the same as those utilized on A&J beaters with aprons *(fig. 10-32, page 103)*.

The HIGH SPEEDS came out after A&J was sold to the Edward Katzinger Company *(See Chapter 11, EKCO, page 109)*,

but still had the A&J logo. The HIGH SPEED was patented Aug. 4, 1936 *(fig. 10-25)* by Myron J. Zimmer of Chicago, assignor to Katzinger. A Canadian version of the HIGH SPEED is marked: MASTER MIX, MADE IN CANADA, with wood D-handle and measuring 12-1/4" *(See Chapter 26, International Mix, page 292)*.

Another popular model is the somewhat scarce D-handle with turbine bottom SUPER SPEED A&J SPINNIT CREAM AND EGG WHIP *(fig. 10-26)*. This one also came with an apron to fit a beater jar. The SPINNIT was based on another patent by Zimmer *(fig. 10-27)* and the name was trademark protected by Edward Katzinger in 1940 *(fig. 10-28)*.

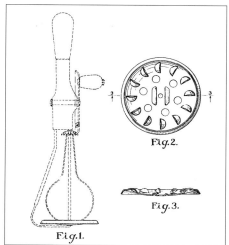

FIG. 10-27

*Myron J. Zimmer patent
May 28, 1940
Design Pat. No. 120,771*

Ser. No. 427,140. THE EDWARD KATZINGER COMPANY,
Chicago, Ill.   Filed Jan. 4, 1940.

SPINNIT

For Egg Beaters.
Claims use since Nov. 15, 1939.

FIG. 10-28

*U.S. Patent & Trademark Office Official Gazette,
Feb. 27, 1940, Edward Katzinger Company trademark*

The A. & J. Manufacturing Company, Binghamton, N. Y.

A. & J. ALL-METAL EGG BEATERS

In Combination with
Non-Spatter Cover and White Graduated
Glass Beating Bowl

No. 70	No. 70-78	No. 70-78-94
ALL METAL BEATER ONLY	ALL METAL BEATER	ALL METAL BEATER SET
	With Non-Spatter Beater Bowl Cover This represents a combination of No. 70 Beater and No. 78 Metal Cover.	Combining No. 70 Beater, No. 78 Non-Spatter Bowl Cover and No. 94 White Graduated Glass Beating Bowl.
Length overall 9¾ inches	Length overall 9¾ inches	Capacity 1 Quart

LIST PRICE PER DOZEN F.O.B.

No.	Binghamton	Chicago	No.	Binghamton	Chicago	No.	Binghamton	Chicago
70	$2.02	$2.02	70-78	$4.44	$4.44	70-78-94	$6.27	$6.27

Packed 1 Doz. in Colored Box. Shipping Weight Per Dozen 6 Lbs.

Packed 1 Doz. in Carton. Shipping Weight Per Dozen 8 Lbs.

Packed 1 Dozen Bowls in Carton and 1 Dozen Beaters with Covers in Another Carton. Shipping Weight Per Dozen Sets 2¼ Lbs.

Cost of Special Packing on Request

All Prices F. O. B. No Freight Allowance. All metal heavily nickel-plated—bright finish.

Edward Katzinger Company, Chicago, Ill. **EKCO CHICAGO**

The A. & J. Manufacturing Company, Binghamton, N. Y.

THE A. & J. JUNIOR EGG BEATER

In Combination with
Genuine Wellerware Pitchers

GREEN LUSTRE—1 QT. CAPACITY   YELLOW LUSTRE—1 QT. CAPACITY

This Combination of our No. 72 Junior Egg Beater and No. 84 Cover with our No. 90-G beautiful Green Lustre-finish, 1 quart capacity pitcher is one of the biggest selling sets of the line.

This set is exactly the same as that described at the left except for the color of the pitcher.

LIST PRICE PER DOZEN F. O. B.

No.	Color Handle	Binghamton	Chicago	No.	Color Handle	Binghamton	Chicago
G-72-84-90 - BT	BLUTIP	$14.78	$14.78	Y-72-84-90 - BT	BLUTIP	$14.78	$14.78
G-72-84-90 - G	GREEN	14.78	14.78	Y-72-84-90 - G	GREEN	14.78	14.78
G-72-84-90 - B	BLUE	14.78	Not Stocked in Chicago	Y-72-84-90 - B	BLUE	14.78	Not Stocked in Chicago
G-72-84-90 - Y	YELLOW	14.78		Y-72-84-90 - Y	YELLOW	14.78	

Packed 1 dozen Pitchers in one carton and 1 dozen Beaters and Covers in another carton.
Shipping Weight Per Doz. Sets 37½ Lbs.
Cost of special packing on request.

Packed 1 dozen Pitchers in one carton and 1 dozen Beaters and Covers in another carton.
Shipping Weight Per Dozen Sets 37½ Lbs.
Cost of special packing on request.

All Prices F. O. B. No Freight Allowance

All metal parts on every item shown here are heavily nickel-plated, bright finish. Every handle has three coats of highest grade enamel.

EKCO CHICAGO Edward Katzinger Company, Chicago, Ill.

FIG 10-29
A&J/EKCO catalog page

FIG 10-30
A&J/EKCO catalog page

A&J was one of the first to market its beaters with aprons that fit over jars, batter bowls or measuring cups, to prevent splattering (*fig. 10-29*). Some of the first apron beaters came with Weller pottery pitchers offered by A&J in the late 1920s. EKCO also offered the combination in later years (*fig. 10-30*).

&J Egg Beaters are mechanically perfect. They are built for high speed, easy operation and long life. The gears are made from specially selected hard carbon steel, cut absolutely true and uniform and cannot bend even under the heaviest whipping loads.

—A&J/EKCO CATALOG ADVERTISEMENT

FIG 10-31

1923 A&Js with glass containers, description of containers only, but value for set (left to right):

No I.D. clear glass
16 oz —$25—

No I.D. transparent green
16 oz —$30—

No I.D. white milk glass
16 oz —$35—

PATENT APPLIED FOR,
transparent green
16 oz —$30—

No. I.D. jadite
16 oz —$35—

D G Simons

D G Simons

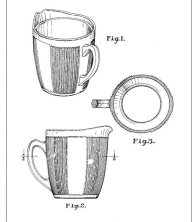

☞

FIG 10-33

Guy Nelson King design patent Aug. 16, 1938 Design Pat. No. 110,899

FIG. 10-34

Two A&J USA EKCO beaters, one with corrugated apron, with measuring pitchers

A&J MADE IN USA NO. 7218   *2-cup*   —$35 each—

D G Simons

Clear and transparent green beater jars and pitchers were made by Hazel Atlas, many marked A&J. Some were made of jadite and white milk glass *(figs. 10-31 & 10-32)*.

At least two measuring cups were designed for A&J. Guy Nelson King of London, describing himself as assignor to the Edward Katzinger Company, obtained a design patent for what he called a "jug" *(fig. 10-33)*. His design was used on 4-cup and 2-cup pitchers *(fig. 10-34)*.

The other was described as the NEW IDEA CRYSTAL BEATER PITCHER *(fig. 10-35)*.

FIG. 10-35 ☞

A&J/EKCO catalog page

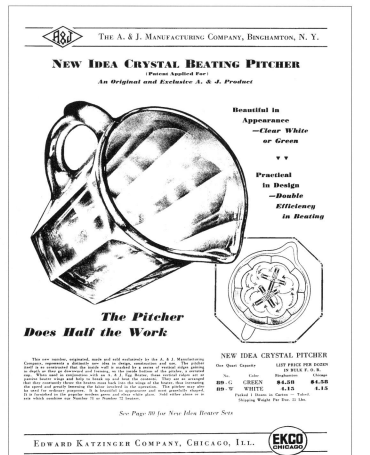

FIG. 10-36

A&J container beaters (left to right):

FULL VISION BEATER SET,
wood handle with original metal container
10″ —$30—

FULL VISION BEATER SET,
metal handle with original metal container
7-1/2″ —$30—

WHIRLPOOL WHIPPER
STIRS AS IT BEATS AS IT WHIPS
A&J WHIPS ORDINARY CREAM IN A JIFFY
8″ —$125—

FIG. 10-37

Paul Crissey patent
Feb. 21, 1939
Pat. No. 2,148,399

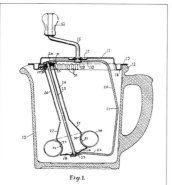

Fig.1.

FIG. 10-38

A&J MADE IN UNITED STATES OF AMERICA
(on metal top)
PATENT NO. 1890307, 504S,14
(embossed on jar bottom) jar
6-12″ —$20—

D G Simons

Other notable A&J container mixers include the FULL VISION BEATER with metal bowl and curved metal or vertical wood handle, the WHIRLPOOL WHIPPER *(fig. 10-36)*, which was patented by Paul Crissey Feb. 21, 1939 *(fig. 10-37)*, and an Archimedes *(fig. 10-38)* atop a Hazel Atlas glass container. This container is marked with PATENT NO. 1890307 *(fig. 10-39)*, and was utilized in several malted milk mixers *(See Chapter 19 Syllabub Churns and Other Plungers, page 221)*.

There is one other A&J container beater — probably the best of all — and it is right where it belongs, in the kitchen of Betty and Frederick Johnson. It utilizes the original beater, and its own jar marked "A&J MIXER" *(figs. 10-40 & 10-41)*.

FIG. 10-40

"A&J MIXER"
—$175—

FIG. 10-39

Philip B. Shailer patent
Dec. 6, 1932
Pat. No. 1,890,307

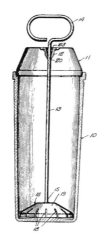

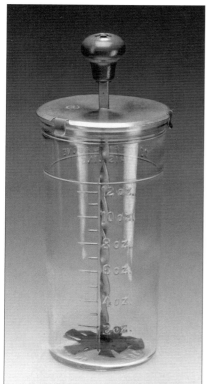

R S Arnold

FIG. 10-41

Inside detail view of
"A&J MIXER"

Photos courtesy Frederick Johnson

FREDERICK JOHNSON COLLECTION

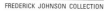

THE EGGBEATER CHRONICLES

FIG. 10-43

Packaged baby beater A&J with its own brown bowl
—$100—

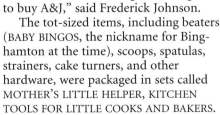

FIG. 10-44

Mother's Little Helper box advertisements

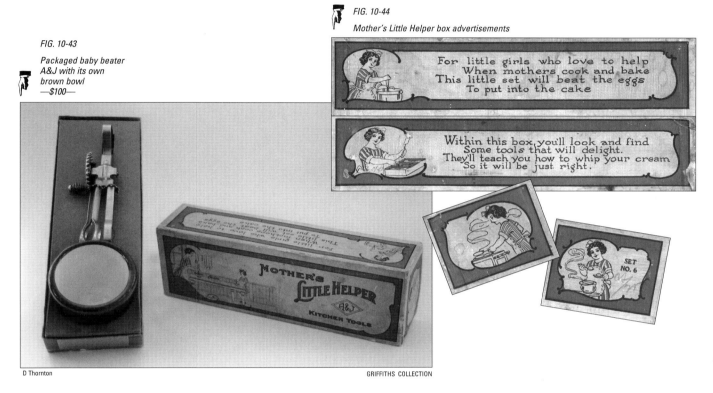

For little girls who love to help
When mothers cook and bake
This little set will beat the eggs
To put into the cake

Within this box, you'll look and find
Some tools that will delight.
They'll teach you how to whip your cream
So it will be just right.

D Thornton

GRIFFITHS COLLECTION

FIG. 10-45

A&J Blutip miniature tools, with the largest, the spatula, measuring 7-3/4" —$75—

A&J entered the toy market in 1923, producing its regular kitchen hardware in miniature. "Educating the little girls to buy A&J," said Frederick Johnson.

The tot-sized items, including beaters (BABY BINGOS, the nickname for Binghamton at the time), scoops, spatulas, strainers, cake turners, and other hardware, were packaged in sets called MOTHER'S LITTLE HELPER, KITCHEN TOOLS FOR LITTLE COOKS AND BAKERS.

A 1931 catalog listed five different sets, with from five to 21 different implements and ranging in price (retail) from 50¢ to $2 (fig. 10-42). A smaller version of the tool set included a beater and its own brown bowl (figs. 10-43 & 10-44) and A&J's famous BLUTIP line had its own miniatures (fig. 10-45) with the standard white handles with blue tips.

D Thornton

CHAPTER 10: A & J

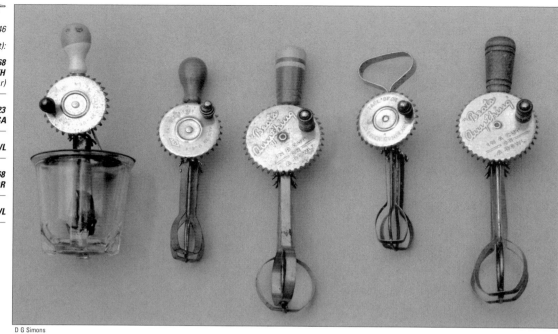

FIG. 10-46

Baby A&Js (left to right):

**PAT OCT. 9, 1923 NO. 68
PAT APLD FOR WOOLWORTH**
(embossed on jar)
5-1/2" —$100—

**A&J PAT OCT. 9, 1923
MADE IN USA**
5-1/2" —$15—

BEATS ANYTHING IN A CUP OR BOWL
7-1/2" —$25—

**BABY BINGO NO. 68
A&J PAT APLD FOR**
5-1/2" —$15—

BEATS ANYTHING IN A CUP OR BOWL
7-1/2" —$20—

D G Simons

Tens of thousands of the baby beaters were sold by Woolworths but only those with an apron and the original jar, marked: PAT APLD FOR, WOOLWORTH are super collectible. A&J also made a beater that could be considered both a toy and a real kitchen gadget, the BEATS ANYTHING IN A CUP OR BOWL *(fig. 10-46)*.

FIG. 10-47

A&J/EKCO catalog sheet

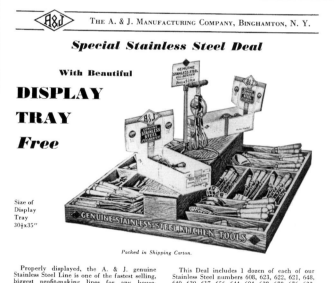

A&J THE A. & J. MANUFACTURING COMPANY, BINGHAMTON, N. Y.

Special Stainless Steel Deal

With Beautiful

DISPLAY TRAY Free

GENUINE STAINLESS STEEL KITCHEN TOOLS

Size of
Display
Tray
30½x35"

Packed in Shipping Carton.

Properly displayed, the A. & J. genuine Stainless Steel Line is one of the fastest selling, biggest profit-making lines for any house-furnishing goods department. To meet the demand for a means of so displaying this line we have provided a beautiful oak Display Tray which we will furnish without cost in connection with all orders for our Special Stainless Steel Deal.

This Deal includes 1 dozen of each of our Stainless Steel numbers 608, 623, 622, 621, 648, 640, 630, 617, 656, 644, 604, 638, 678, 676, 633, 643 and our No. 675 Stainless Steel Egg Beaters packaged individually in display cartons. Also 2 dozen of each of the following Stainless Steel knives, No. 695, 682 and 683.

No. 600 STAINLESS STEEL DEAL

Contains 23 dozen of 20 fast-selling Stainless Steel items with Display Tray free.

List Price Per Deal $99.20

Handles can be furnished in our Standard Ivory with Blue Band or Green with Ivory Band. Carried in stock in Binghamton and Chicago.

Other color combinations from Binghamton only.

EDWARD KATZINGER COMPANY, CHICAGO, ILL. **EKCO CHICAGO**

FIG. 10-48

A&J Blutip Kitchen Tools catalog

A&J
BLUTIP KITCHEN TOOLS

COLORFUL KITCHEN TOOLS of QUALITY

Tested and Approved
Good Housekeeping Institute

The A.&J. Manufacturing Co.
Binghamton, New York

A&J produced an astounding variety of mixers, but they were just a drop in the bucket compared to the firm's overall production. Consider some of the other products: Apple corers, ballers, basting spoons, batter whips, bread knives, cake and pie turners, cake whips, can openers, choppers, corkscrews, dough blenders, forks, grapefruit knives, griddle greasers, handing racks, ice picks, knife sharpeners, ladles, measuring spoons, paring knives, plate scrapers, potato mashers and ricers, potato peelers, scoops, slicers, slotted batter spoons, spatulas, strainers, strainer spoons and utility brushes. Many of these were marketed together *(fig. 10-47)*, such as the SPECIAL STAINLESS STEEL DEAL.

"Father was the first person to package kitchen utensils in a box and sell you a whole set. And he was the first person to supply a rack that you could nail or screw to the wall and hang your tools on," said Kenneth Johnson.

The packaging included the BLUTIP line *(figs. 10-48 & 10-49)*, which A&J promoted with this ad copy: "No more scrubbing and scouring of kitchen tools. A job countless women have had three times a day — 365 days a year! A job women hate! A job women need never do again! For here at last are the kitchen tools supreme! Made entirely of stainless steel … It sparkles, it glistens. It is a mirror to reflect happy satisfied faces."

In a unique offering, eggbeaters without their dashers were marketed as model airplane winders.

Said the 1931 catalog: "The tremendous interest in aviation which marks this age is evidenced by the fact that thousands and thousands of boys throughout the United States are making and flying model airplanes. These delicate models are propelled by an intricate application of long rubber bands which are wound up preparatory to flying by turning the propeller. This is a laborious process which puts unnecessary strain on the delicate mechanism of the model airplane and also requires considerable time. To meet the enormous demand for a mechanical means of winding up the rubber band power plants of model airplanes, The A&J Manufacturing Company has devised two high speed model airplane winders. There is tremendous sale for these items and no store catering to juvenile trade should be without them on prominent display *(fig. 10-50)*."

A stainless steel egg beater that has no equal — at any price — anywhere!

…The 'Blutip' egg beater means smoother, easier beating, faster than any other egg beater you can buy — bar none!

…Beats large or small quantities without splashing, and since it is stainless you will never be troubled with dark 'specks' in beating creams, eggs, etc.

—A&J BLUTIP PROMOTIONS

FIG 10-49

The Saturday Evening Post March 24, 1928, ad for A&J Blutip Kitchen Tools

FIG. 10-50

A&J/EKCO catalog page. A&J beaters were used without their dashers as toy airplane winders.

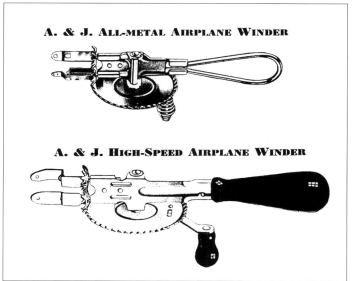

A&J also manufactured many items that didn't carry the company's diamond logo.

The firm, for example, made hubcaps for the tricycles and baby carriages produced by a Binghamton toy factory, and shoe trees, in two sizes, men's and women's, for Woolworths.

There was one unforgettable item noted by Frederick Johnson.

"One of the funny things that father made was a nose straightener. This was stamped out, a piece of steel with elastic straps across the back that would hold this contraption on your nose while you slept at night. I can't tell you who they were sold to. But their ads were in every magazine, little one-inch ads, with a line drawing of a man's head with this contraption on his nose. And I believe some showed before and after pictures. Father never marketed these things, he just stamped them out. And as we said, he'd stamp anything in the plant that anybody would want if they'd buy enough of them."

Along that same line, Kenneth Johnson said, "If you had a business and you wanted to have a little something as an advertising thing, why you could buy it from father for about six or seven cents, and they sold great. You put your slogan on the handle."

And sell they did, both premiums and direct market items. Millions and millions of A&J products went worldwide. For example, old company invoices dated 1910 show four gross of up-and-down beaters going to Havana, 11 gross to Milan, Italy, nine gross to Ontario, two gross to Honolulu and 40 gross to London.

Noting the 1910 invoices, Frederick Johnson said, "It's hard to believe that those beaters could sell at $9 for 144 and still make a profit. Times have changed."

A&J's success resulted in an overture to sell the firm to another manufacturer in 1929. Johnson accepted the offer and A&J became part of the empire of Edward Katzinger, whose Chicago-based firm later became known as EKCO (*See Chapter 11, EKCO, page 109*).

The A&J Binghamton plant remained open until 1931, when the operation was moved to Chicago. EKCO, which continues today to manufacture a fine line of beaters and other kitchen hardware, maintained the A&J trademark until the 1950s.

The year of the move to Chicago, Edward H. Johnson once again displayed his marketing genius.

"My dad did a big premium business with various schemes," said Frederick Johnson, "and I would believe the gasoline deal was one of his ideas."

And what a revolutionary idea for 1931.

It was called "The IDEAL Plan," and it offered a whole marketing deal to gas stations to increase their sales with "a genuine chromium plated kitchen tool" premium give-away (*fig. 10-52*).

Asked about their father's business philosophy and success, Kenneth Johnson said:

"He wanted to sell a good product. He never had any complaints of any consequence. He always believed in the theory that the customer is right. If you operate like that, with all of the goodness that you make due with that customer, they bring back more. He was a wonderful man. He was a wonderful father to Frederick and me. Everybody liked him. All the people of Binghamton looked up to him not only to his ability to get ahead in some proposition like he did, but they liked him as a man."

Edward H. Johnson died July 8, 1949 at the age of 70.

Said Frederick Johnson, "My father would laugh his head off to think his 10-cent store merchandise is now collectible."

Kenneth Johnson died July 19, 1997 at the age of 90. Mr. Johnson, an Army veteran of World War II, was president of Johnson's China and Glass in Binghamton for 53 years.

FIG. 10-52

A&J premium sales pitch

The Ideal Plan

Five gallons please! A common request, one that is to be heard time after time in almost every service station. Sometimes it is varied a little by recourse to another language — the customer simply holds up his hand with his fingers spread out and the attendant sees and understands 'five gallons please.'

That it is a common habit is testified to by sales statistics which show that the average gallons per fill the country over is just under five … How can it be increased.? … The answer seems perfectly obvious — premiums.

… Inasmuch as the automobile is primarily a family affair, the premium should also fall in this category. In other words, it should have a permanent place in the home. The ideal premium, or rather series of premiums … is the set of 'Chrome Plated' Kitchen Tools, which is now being used successfully by hundreds of service stations.

—1930s A&J SALES PITCH TO SERVICE STATIONS

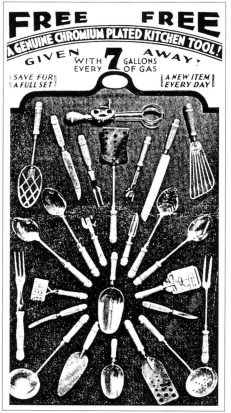

FIG 10-51

Premium advertising sheet

Chapter 11

EKCO

"With quality features usually found only on costlier beaters."

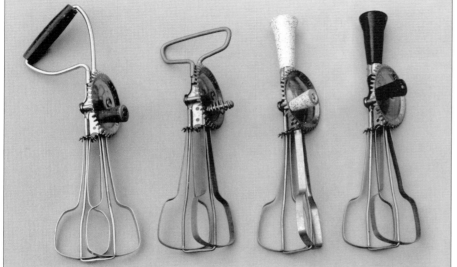

D G Simons

The year was 1881. The serious-minded, ambitious young man of 18 arrived in New York City from his native Vienna. He quickly found a job, and seven years and many promotions later he was earning $25 a week — an excellent wage in those days — as a master mechanic.

Looking for his big opportunity he headed to Chicago, where on his 25th birthday he founded the Edward Katzinger Company, manufacturer of bakery pans.

It was another humble beginning — the first headquarters was half of a store Katzinger leased at the corner of Des Plaines and Van Buren streets.

But it was the right place at the right time, and business took off. Several moves over the next three decades were made, each time to a larger plant as the firm was expanded to include equipment for confectioners and ice cream manufacturers.

Katzinger died in 1939 and his son, Arthur, who had joined the firm in 1916, took over. Arthur changed his last name to Keating, and also officially changed the name of the firm in 1945 to EKCO, which had been used extensively throughout the history of the firm.

His move to the presidency was expected. Even before he took control of the firm, it was he who spearheaded the acquisition of the very successful A&J *(See Chapter 10, A&J, page 101)* and at least a dozen other companies, making the family business the largest eggbeater and kitchenware manufacturer in the world.

And it was Keating who arranged EKCO's merger with American Home Products Corporation in 1965, two years before his death.

The result of that merger was the EKCO Housewares Company, still the world leader in kitchenware production. In addition to its eggbeaters, the 3,500-product line includes bakeware, bar accessories, barbecue tools, can openers, cookware, cutlery, mixing bowls, tableware, and every useful kitchen gadget on the market today.

EKCO, located in Franklin Park, Illinois, maintained A&J's beater line with relatively few design changes until the 1950s when a sleek new look began to evolve *(figs. 11-1 & 11-2)*.

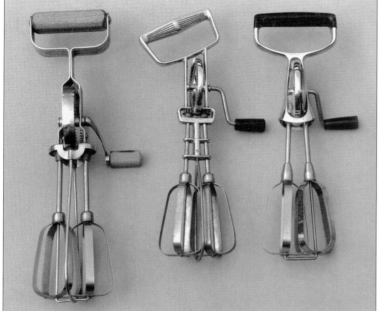

D G Simons

But EKCO still paid tribute to its A&J roots. A&J started with a hand-held Archimedes and EKCO continued that tradition with a simple but attractive mixer (fig. 11-3). This upright marvel is a readily available collectible today, and every collection should have one, just for the sake of the ad (fig. 11-4) on a shopping cart full of the mixers that said: "Works like an electric beater at a fraction of the cost."

The sleek look continued over the years, probably peaking with the Teflon ONE-HAND BEATER (figs. 11-5 & 11-6).

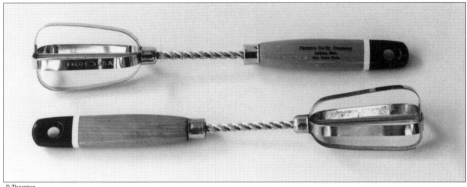

D Thornton

 FIG. 11-3

Modern Archimedes (top to bottom):

EKCO *(on stainless steel dasher)*
FARMERS CO-OP CREAMERY JACKSON, MINN.
MGR. VICTOR DICKS
(advertising on handle)
10-1/2" —$10—

EKCO *(on stainless steel dasher), no other I.D.*
10-1/2" —$3—

FIG. 11-4

EKCO 1959 catalog sheet

 FIG 11-5

*No I.D., but advertised as
One-Hand Beater
10"* —$7—

D G Simons

NEW! ACTIVATED Merchandiser for
AMERICA'S FASTEST SELLING GADGET

EKCO

A proven successful merchandising method that'll move this sales sensation faster 'n ever — an eye-catching activated header card that dramatically demonstrates the beater that mixes in a cup, glass or pitcher.

ACTIVATED HEADER CARD!

Battery Driven • Easy To Operate

Just insert 1 standard size "D" flashlight battery (not included) and push beater to start in motion. Card 27" high, 24" wide.

IT'S EASY TO BUILD A MASS DISPLAY with this beater assortment and activated header card: In A Shopping Cart (special easel back fits) • At The End Of An Aisle • On The Counter • In A Gondola • In The Ready-Mix Department

Assortment Includes:
3 Dozen—1467 RW Red handle
3 Dozen—2667 Natural handle
3 Dozen—2667YW Yellow handle
2 Dozen—2667TW Turquoise handle
1 Dozen—2667XS Pink handle
1—#339 Activated display card

EKCO'S ONE HAND BEATER IS SETTING SALES RECORDS ALL OVER THE U.S.

Shopping cart not included with assortment.

| STOCK NO. | | WT. LBS. |
Unpriced	Prepriced	EACH ASST.
C-167	C-167P	48

EKCO PRODUCTS COMPANY
EKCO—AUTO-VRE DIVISION—CHICAGO

VERTICAL HANDLE QUART BEATER SET

ENAMELED HANDLE PINT BEATER SET

DELUXE QUART BEATER SET

METAL HANDLE PINT BEATER SET

 FIG. 11-6

EKCO 1960s catalog sheet

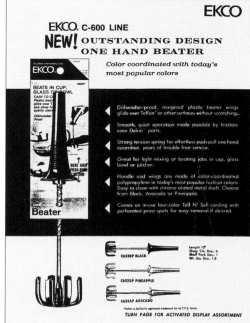

EKCO

EKCO. C-600 LINE

NEW! OUTSTANDING DESIGN ONE HAND BEATER

Color coordinated with today's most popular colors

BEATS IN CUP, GLASS OR BOWL
EASY TO
Plastic bea
glide over
and other
quality uten

Dishwasher
Proof

One Hand
Beater

► Dishwasher-proof, marproof plastic beater wings glide over Teflon' or other surfaces without scratching...

► Smooth, quiet operation made possible by friction-ease Delrin® parts.

► Strong tension spring for effortless push-pull one hand operation. years of trouble free service.

► Great for light mixing or beating jobs in cup, glass bowl or pitcher.

► Handle and wings are made of color-coordinated polypropylene in today's most popular fashion colors. Easy to clean with chrome plated metal shaft. Choose from Black, Avocado or Pineapple.

► Comes on in-use four-color Tell N' Sell carding with perforated price spots for easy removal if desired.

C652BP BLACK
Length: 10"
Shpg. Ctn. Doz.: 6
Shelf Pack Doz.: 1
Wt. Lbs. Doz.: 1.8

C652GP PINEAPPLE

C652AP AVOCADO

*Teflon is DuPont's registered trademark for its T.F.E. finish
TURN PAGE FOR ACTIVATED DISPLAY ASSORTMENT

THE EGGBEATER CHRONICLES

Mainstays offered over the years included the HI-SPEED, with pink or turquoise D-handle; a similar T-handle beater featuring turquoise, pink, yellow and gray handles, with stripes; a flared T-handle with eight wing dashers; and a "bell-shaped handle" based on the original 1921 A&J patent (*fig. 11-7*).

EKCO also made beaters under the trade names BEST, FLINT, MARY ANN and ETERNA (*fig. 11-8*).

FIG. 11-7

EKCO 1956 catalog sheet

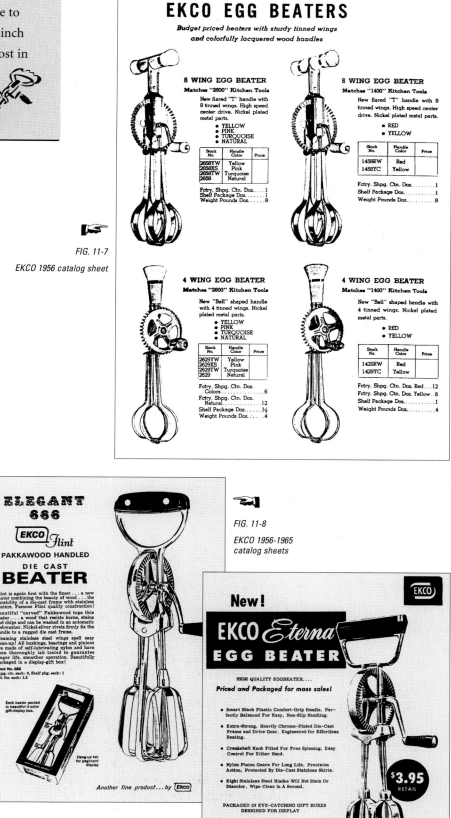

EKCO EGG BEATERS

Budget priced beaters with sturdy tinned wings and colorfully lacquered wood handles

8 WING EGG BEATER
Matches "2600" Kitchen Tools

New flared "T" handle with 8 tinned wings. High speed center drive. Nickel plated metal parts.

- YELLOW
- PINK
- TURQUOISE
- NATURAL

Stock No.	Handle Color	Price
2658YW	Yellow	
2658XS	Pink	
2658TW	Turquoise	
2658	Natural	

Fctry. Shpg. Ctn. Doz. 1
Shelf Package Doz. 1
Weight Pounds Doz. 8

8 WING EGG BEATER
Matches "1400" Kitchen Tools

New flared "T" handle with 8 tinned wings. High speed center drive. Nickel plated metal parts.

- RED
- YELLOW

Stock No.	Handle Color	Price
1458RW	Red	
1458YC	Yellow	

Fctry. Shpg. Ctn. Doz. 1
Shelf Package Doz. 1
Weight Pounds Doz. 8

4 WING EGG BEATER
Matches "2600" Kitchen Tools

New "Bell" shaped handle with 4 tinned wings. Nickel plated metal parts.

- YELLOW
- PINK
- TURQUOISE
- NATURAL

Stock No.	Handle Color	Price
2629YW	Yellow	
2629XS	Pink	
2629TW	Turquoise	
2629	Natural	

Fctry. Shpg. Ctn. Doz. Colors.......6
Fctry. Shpg. Ctn. Doz. Natural...........12
Shelf Package Doz. ......½
Weight Pounds Doz. 4

4 WING EGG BEATER
Matches "1400" Kitchen Tools

New "Bell" shaped handle with 4 tinned wings. Nickel plated metal parts.

- RED
- YELLOW

Stock No.	Handle Color	Price
1429RW	Red	
1429YC	Yellow	

Fctry. Shpg. Ctn. Doz. Red....12
Fctry. Shpg. Ctn. Doz. Yellow..6
Shelf Package Doz. 1
Weight Pounds Doz. 4

New! Low priced! STAINLESS STEEL

EGG BEATERS

in COLOR

Turquoise . . . turquoise handle with black stripe and white tip. Turquoise turning knob.

Pink . . . pink handle with black stripe and charcoal tip. Pink turning knob.

Yellow . . . yellow handle with black stripe and charcoal tip. Yellow turning knob.

Gray . . . gray handle with red tip and black stripe.

- Eight Stainless Steel Wings Mix, Whip and Beat Ingredients to the Right Consistency in Seconds
- "Sure-Grip" T-Shaped Handle and Large Turning Knob
- High Speed Center Drive Affords Easier Turning Action
- Each Beater Colorfully Labeled

Stock No. Un-Priced	Pre-Priced	Color Handles	Shipper Dozen	Shelf Pack Dozen	Wgt. lbs. Dozen
373-XS	373-XP	Pink Body, Black Stripe and Charcoal Tip	1	1	8
373-TW	373-TP	Turquoise Body, Black Stripe and White Tip	1	1	8
373-YC	373-YP	Yellow Body, Black Stripe and Charcoal Tip	1	1	8
373	373-GP	Gray Body, Black Stripe and Red Tip	1	1	8

PACKED IN CORRUGATED SHIPPER

ASSORTMENT OF 4 OF EACH COLOR ALSO AVAILABLE

Stock No. Un-Priced	Pre-Priced	Color Handles	Shipper Dozen	Shelf Pack Dozen	Wgt. lbs. Dozen
373A	373AP	4 Turquoise, 4 Pink and 4 Yellow	1	1	8

PACKED IN CORRUGATED SHIPPER

EKCO .....the Greatest Name in Housewares
EKCO PRODUCTS COMPANY, CHICAGO 39, ILLINOIS

" Beats 1 egg or 1 dozen. Fits any bowl. "

ELEGANT 666

EKCO *Flint*

PAKKAWOOD HANDLED

DIE CAST **BEATER**

Flint is again first with the finest . . . a new beater combining the beauty of wood . . . the durability of a die-cast frame with stainless beaters. Famous Flint quality construction!

Beautiful "carved" Pakkawood tops this beater . . . a wood that resists burns, stains and chips and can be washed in an automatic dishwasher. Nickel-silver rivets firmly fix the handle to a rugged die cast frame.

Gleaming stainless steel wings spell easy clean-up! All bushings, bearings and pinions are made of self-lubricating nylon and have been thoroughly lab tested to guarantee longer life, smoother operation. Beautifully packaged in a display-gift box!

Stock No. 666
Shpg. ctn. each: 6, Shelf pkg. each: 1
Wt. lbs. each: 1.5

Each beater packed in beautiful 4-color gift-display box.

Hang-up tab for pegboard display

Another fine product... by EKCO

FIG. 11-8

EKCO 1956-1965 catalog sheets

New!

EKCO *Eterna* EGG BEATER

HIGH QUALITY EGGBEATER....
Priced and Packaged for mass sales!

- Smart Black Plastic Comfort-Grip Handle, Perfectly Balanced For Easy, Non-Slip Handling.
- Extra-Strong, Heavily Chrome-Plated Die-Cast Frame and Drive Gear. Engineered for Effortless Beating.
- Crankshaft Knob Fitted For Free Spinning, Easy Control For Either Hand.
- Nylon Pinion Gears For Long Life, Precision Action, Protected By Die-Cast Stainless Skirts.
- Eight Stainless Steel Blades Will Not Stain Or Discolor, Wipe Clean In A Second.

PACKAGED IN EYE-CATCHING GIFT BOXES DESIGNED FOR DISPLAY

$3.95 RETAIL

STOCK NO.	WEIGHT EA.	SHELF PACK	SHPG. CTN.
672-B	1 lb.	1	1 doz.

EKCO .....the Greatest Name in Housewares
EKCO PRODUCTS COMPANY, CHICAGO 39, ILLINOIS

> ❝ *Works like an electric beater at a fraction of the cost.* ❞

The BEST and FLINT beaters *(fig. 11-9)* are becoming more collectible every day, especially if they are in their original boxes. EKCO also produced the MAID OF HONOR beater for Sears Roebuck & Company *(fig. 11-10)*. Other later members of the EKCO family were MAYNARD beaters *(See Chapter 21, Rotary Mix: The Later Years, page 242-243)*. EKCO acquired the Maynard Manufacturing Company of Glendale, California, in the 1950s.

EKCO should always have a warm spot in the heart of collectors — it never gave up on the rotary hand crank mixer, even when the times were tough because of the death grip popularity of the electric mixer.

FIG. 11-9

EKCO 1957 & 1965 catalog sheets ☞

R S Arnold

☞

FIG. 11-10

EKCO beaters in boxes (left to right):

MAID OF HONOR EGG BEATER SOLD BY SEARS ROEBUCK & COMPANY AND SIMPSONS — SEARS LIMITED *(on box)*, **EKCO PROD. CO. MADE IN U.S.A. PATS. PENDING** *(on main gear)* 11-1/2" —$35 with box—

DELUXE EGG BEATER FLINT EKCO-FLINT DIV. ©1959 EKCO PRODUCTS CO. CHICAGO 39, ILL. 12" —$35 with box—

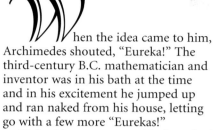

Chapter 12

Archimedes

"Look Mummie! It spins like my top."

When the idea came to him, Archimedes shouted, "Eureka!" The third-century B.C. mathematician and inventor was in his bath at the time and in his excitement he jumped up and ran naked from his house, letting go with a few more "Eurekas!"

He had just come up with the principle that bears his name, the physical law of buoyancy. His theory, obviously helped by the bath, was that any body completely or partially submerged in a fluid at rest is acted upon by an upward force with a magnitude equal to the weight of fluid displaced by the body.

Born at Syracuse in Sicily about 287 B.C., many of his other discoveries were in geometry, especially the relation between the surface and volume of a sphere and its circumscribing cylinder.

He also invented war machines, one a so-called burning mirror that terrified the Romans at the siege of Syracuse. During the battle, Archimedes was killed as he wrote mathematical formulas in the sand.

History tells this colorful story about Archimedes, but there is always one crucial fact missing: He played a major role in the development of the up-and-down eggbeater.

The connection is Archimedes' invention of the Archimedes screw, the mechanical back-bone of the family of up-and-down mixers.

The original device was designed to raise and remove water from the holds of large ships. Basically it is in two forms: as a spiral tube coiled around a shaft and as a large screw in a cylinder, both revolved by hand.

The Archimedes screw lives on as a mechanism familiar to any child who has played with a push-down spinning top, but in the kitchenware world it went by such names as the ASHLEY, CLIPPER, SPEAR'S 20TH CENTURY, and the GLOBE.

The oldest Archimedes include:

▶ The ASHLEY was patented May 1, 1860 *(fig. 12-1)* and June 26, 1866 *(fig. 12-2),* by Frederick Ashley of New York City, who said his beater "consists of a shaft having a screw thread formed upon its upper end, with a nut fitted to work thereon, and a series of 'beating' or breaking wires upon its lower end, the apparatus being operated by placing its lower end in the dish or vessel containing the eggs to be beaten, and revolving it by moving the nut up and down on the screw-threaded portion of the shaft …" It was manufactured in several sizes *(fig. 12-3).*

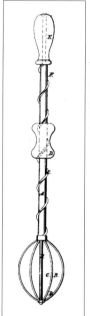

FIG. 12-1

*Frederick Ashley patent
May 1, 1860
Pat. No. 28,047*

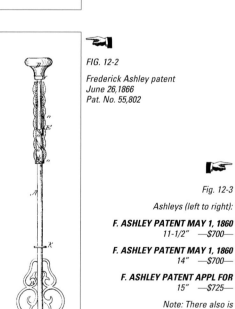

FIG. 12-2

*Frederick Ashley patent
June 26, 1866
Pat. No. 55,802*

Fig. 12-3

Ashleys (left to right):

F. ASHLEY PATENT MAY 1, 1860
11-1/2" —$700—

F. ASHLEY PATENT MAY 1, 1860
14" —$700—

F. ASHLEY PATENT APPL FOR
15" —$725—

Note: There also is an unmarked model, but definitely an Ashley, at 10-3/4"

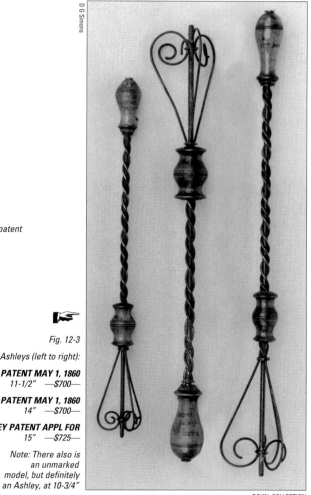

D G Simons

BOHN COLLECTION

CHAPTER 12: ARCHIMEDES

113

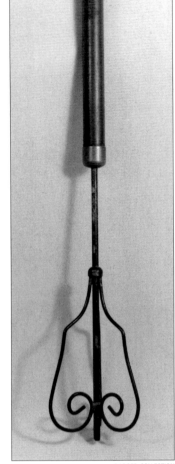

FIG 12-5

No I.D., but MacKay
11-1/4" —$325—

▶ The nicknamed MACKAY was patented Dec. 29, 1868 by D. D. MacKay of Whitestone, New York, who described his device as a "muddler" (figs. 12-4 & 12-5).

▶ A patent by James R. Hughes of Saugus, Massachusetts (fig. 12-6), was responsible for the REGENT EGG BEATER.

An 1878 Fish & Simpson catalog offered a sample by mail for 25 cents, and one dozen by express for $1.50 (fig. 12-7). The catalog ad features a wood knob, but the two known models in collections are all-wire (figs. 12-8 & 12-9).

FIG. 12-4

D. D. MacKay patent
Dec. 29, 1868
Pat. No. 85,460

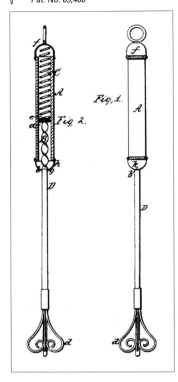

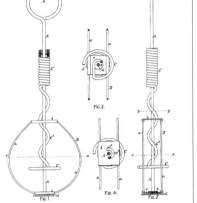

FIG. 12-6

James R. Hughes patent
April 30, 1878
Pat. No. 203,153

BADGER COLLECTION

FIG. 12-8

No I.D., but Hughes patent
10-1/2" —$550—

FIG. 12-9

No I.D. but Hughes patent
10-1/2" —$500—

FIG. 12-7

1878 Fish & Simpson catalog

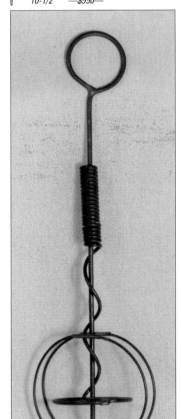

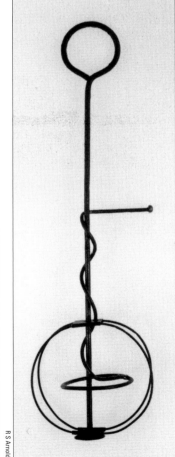

REGENT EGG BEATER.

Unequaled in its Work.   Unsurpassed for Durability.

An Indispensable Article to every Housekeeper.

Eggs are in universal use in every family in preparing Dainty Dishes, as:

Charlotte Russe, Frozen Custard, Floating Island, Sponge Cake, Omelettes, Muffins, Waffles, Meringues, Syllabubs, Nectar, Truffles, Kisses, Creams, Custards, etc., of all kinds without number.

It is of primary importance that the egg be properly aerated or beaten, thus not only will a *single* egg perform the work of *three* or *four* imperfectly done, but the article be much better. When one egg is made to do the work of three, the economy of using a *perfect* egg beater is apparent. Therefore we claim, as the Quadruple Motion "Regent" will properly beat the whites of two eggs in ten seconds, or the whites of six eggs in twenty seconds, so that the dish may be inverted without any of the egg falling out, that it will sell quickly because low in price, accomplishing a result not produced by any other egg beater in half an hour, and, as "*time is money*" in the kitchen as well as in the counting-room and factory, it commends itself to every housekeeper. Accompanying each Egg-Beater is a choice assortment of recipes for preparing the above delicacies, well worth to any housewife the price of the beater.

Sample by Mail, 25 Cents; One Dozen, by Express, $1.50; Six Dozen, $8.50; One Hundred for $10.00.

P. O. Box 4968.   FISH & SIMPSON,

182 Nassau St., New York.

BADGER COLLECTION   BOHN COLLECTION

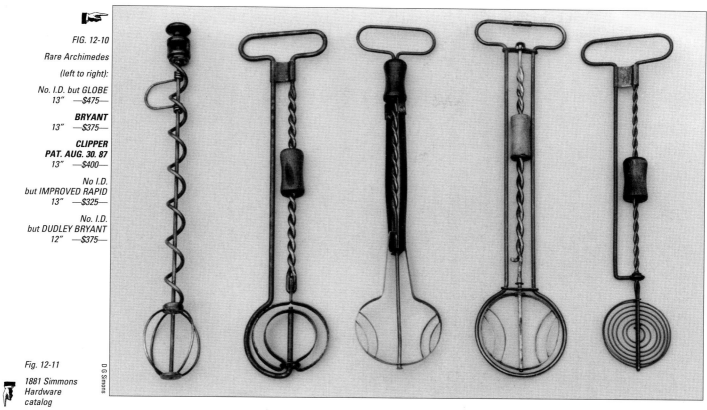

☞

FIG. 12-10

Rare Archimedes (left to right):

No. I.D. but GLOBE
13" —$475—

BRYANT
13" —$375—

CLIPPER
PAT. AUG. 30. 87
13" —$400—

No I.D. but IMPROVED RAPID
13" —$325—

No. I.D. but DUDLEY BRYANT
12" —$375—

Fig. 12-11

1881 Simmons Hardware catalog

D G Simmons

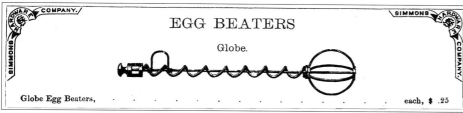

EGG BEATERS

Globe.

Globe Egg Beaters, · · · · · · · · · · · each, $ .25

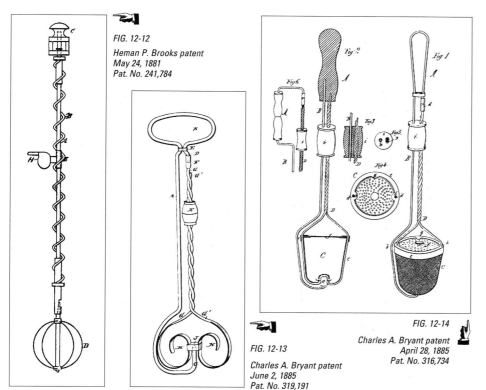

☞
FIG. 12-12

Heman P. Brooks patent
May 24, 1881
Pat. No. 241,784

☞
FIG. 12-13

Charles A. Bryant patent
June 2, 1885
Pat. No. 319,191

FIG. 12-14

Charles A. Bryant patent
April 28, 1885
Pat. No. 316,734

The next manufacturing wave of Archimedes, all with sliding mechanisms, encompass these models *(fig. 12-10):*

▶ The all-metal GLOBE was offered by the Simmons Hardware Company of St. Louis in 1881 *(fig. 12-11)*. It was patented May 24, 1881 *(fig. 12-12)* by Heman P. Brooks of Brooklyn, who said, "The object of my invention is cheapness of manufacture and ease of operation; also, to increase the leverage by increasing the weight of the instrument."

▶ The BRYANT was patented June 2, 1885 by Charles A. Bryant of Wakefield, Massachusetts. In his patent *(fig. 12-13)*, Bryant said, "As the scrolls (dashers) are revolved in opposite directions the eggs are beaten very thoroughly in a very short time, and as there is no gearing in the beater, it is not apt to get out of order." An early catalog described the Bryant as, "the perfection of a beater without mechanical complications. Operated by working the nut up and down the screw … It has no objectionable cranks and gears." The wholesale price at the turn of the century: $18 per gross.

Bryant also used the Archimedes principle in another patent *(fig. 12-14)*, this one a soap holder. He said that because of the "rapid rotation" of his device, "the soap is more quickly dissolved to the extent desired."

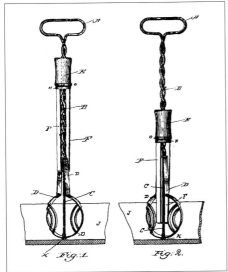

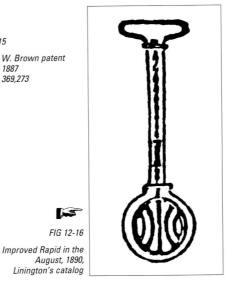

FIG. 12-15

Thomas W. Brown patent
Aug. 30, 1887
Pat. No. 369,273

FIG 12-16

Improved Rapid in the
August, 1890,
Linington's catalog

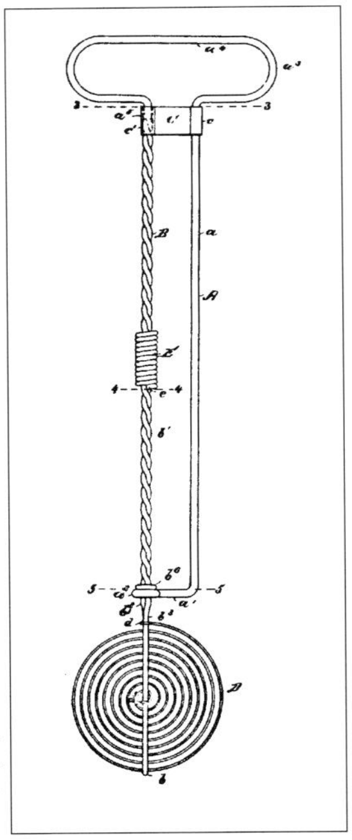

FIG. 12-17

George D. Dudley
patent
July 17, 1888
Pat. No. 386,424

▶ The CLIPPER was patented Aug. 30, 1887 (fig. 12-15) by prolific beater inventor Thomas W. Brown, assignor to the National Manufacturing Company of Worcester, Massachusetts (See Chapter 7, National Manufacturing Co., page 67).

▶ A very similar model is the IMPROVED RAPID, with a wooden knob running down the center shaft. There is no known patent for this beater, which easily could have been another Brown invention. The only identification comes from C. M. Linington's Silent Salesman Catalog, Chicago, Illinois (fig. 12-16).

▶ The DUDLEY-BRYANT PATENTED EGG BEATER was patented July 17, 1888 by George D. Dudley of Lowell, Massachusetts, assignor to Woods, Sherwood & Company of Lowell. In his patent (fig. 12-17), Dudley said his beater "is very inexpensive to construct, presents a very large agitating surface, and is easily cleaned, as the only part which enters the egg or other thing to be mixed or stirred is the agitator, the later being placed below the frame." It was described in a sales catalog as: "Practical, unique, perfect. No wheels or complicated gear. The best spiral ever devised." The price: retail 15¢ each or $12 per gross.

▶ Similar to the GLOBE, but with a circle-within-a-circle dasher, is another all-wire mixer (fig. 12-18). This model has the same wire loop mechanics, but is more than three-inches shorter than the GLOBE. A very rare all-wire, standup model uses the same loop mechanics (fig. 12-19).

R S Arnold

R S Arnold

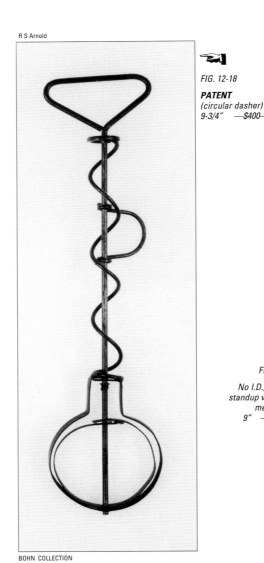

FIG. 12-18

PATENT
(circular dasher)
9-3/4"   —$400—

FIG. 12-19

No I.D., all wire
standup with loop
mechanics
9"   —$450—

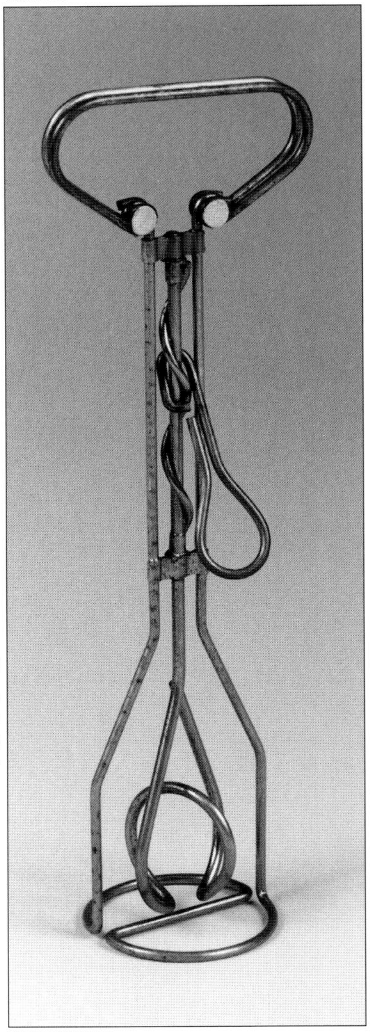

BOHN COLLECTION

MAIR COLLECTION

THE EGGBEATER CHRONICLES

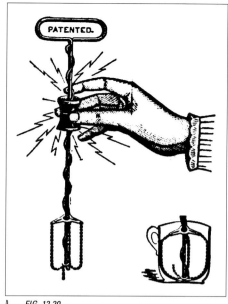

FIG. 12 20

*Lightning Chain Egg Beater in a March 1903
House Furnishing Review ad*

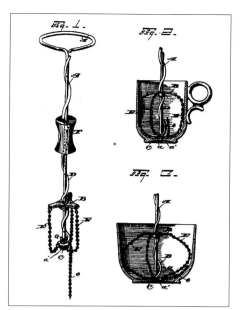

👆 FIG. 12-21

*Charles W. Stambaugh patent
May 10, 1887
Pat. No. 362,858*

👉 FIG. 12-22

*No I.D.,
center knob
mechanics
12"
—$100—*

MAIR COLLECTION

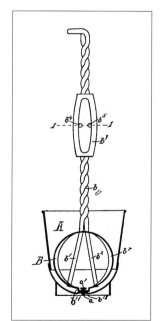

👆 FIG. 12-23

*Albert White patent
March 31, 1891
Pat. No. 449,187*

 👉

FIG. 12-24

**PECULIAR EGG BEATER
PAT'D MAR. 31.91.
ONE PINT, HALF PINT,
QUARTER PINT**
container 4-3/4" high
—$700—

KELLY COLLECTION

Photo courtesy R Kelly

R S Arnold

Detail of tin container

▶ Another model with a center
wooden knob is the LIGHTNING CHAIN
EGG BEATER. The identification is made
in a turn-of-the-century *House Furnishing Review* magazine ad for B. P. Forbes
of Cleveland, Ohio *(fig. 12-20)*. The ad
says the beater is patented, and it was
(fig. 12-21), but so far the mixer itself has
proven elusive. Center knob Archimedes
beaters also include an elegant model
standing 12" high *(fig. 12-22)*.

▶ The PECULIAR EGG BEATER is
peculiar. In his March 31, 1891 patent
(fig. 12-23), Albert White of Lowell,
Massachusetts, notes that the beater is
secured to the tin container and can
"be operated on one hand grasping the
nut" that activates the dashers. The one-
pint container is 4-3/4" high and 4" in
diameter at the top *(fig. 12-24)*.

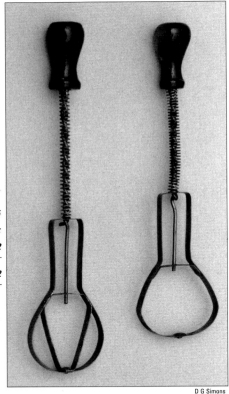

 FIG. 12-25

Roberts (left to right):

FEB. 4, 1902
10-1/2" —$125—

FEB. 4, 1902
9-1/2" —$100—

D G Simons

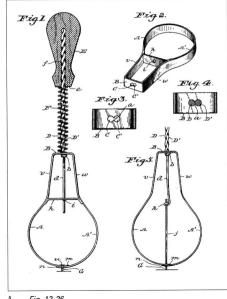

Fig. 12-26

Emmett Roberts patent
Feb. 4, 1902
Pat. No. 692,479

The 20th Century brought other Archimedes to the market, including the simple but effective ROBERTS *(fig. 12-25).* Patented Feb. 4, 1902 *(fig. 12-26),* it came in two sizes and was made by the J. B. Foote Foundry Company established in 1851 in Fredericktown, Ohio, and still in business today producing iron for pumps and some cast-iron bells.

Emmett Roberts of Indianapolis said in his patent application that his "invention relates to a hand implement to be used in a bowl or similar vessel for beating eggs or for mixing various ingredients, the object of the invention being to provide an improved beater that may be operated by one hand, so that the other hand may be employed in holding the vessel either upon or off a table …"

An early ad *(fig. 12-27)* for the mixer said: "The only automatic egg beater made that works with one hand. Every housekeeper knows the trial of using an egg beater requiring two hands. With this egg beater you simply press the handle and release." The ad also offered a "sample 18 cents prepaid by mail. Wholesale price $10.80 gross. Retail price 15 cents. Send for sample and you will be surprised at orders you take."

The ROBERTS also resulted in a spin-off. Charles G. Fitch of Indianapolis put a Roberts atop a jar in his May 7, 1912 patent *(fig. 12-28).*

A NEW IDEA IN EGG BEATERS

The only Automatic Beater made that works with one hand. Every housekeeper knows the trial of using an egg beater requiring both hands. How it slips and skates around in the bowl. With this beater you simply press on the handle and release. Easiest motion and least effort possible. Once used all other styles of beaters are thrown away. Made of steel, heavily plated, and easily cleaned.

Patented Feb. 4, 1902

Price 18c.

FIG. 12-27

Early Robert's ad

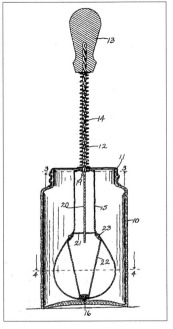

FIG 12-28

Charles G. Fitch patent
May 7, 1912
Pat. No. 1,025,798

This egg carton measures 5-1/4" by 7" and holds one dozen eggs, along with "a dozen reasons for serving eggs." The bottom is marked Pat. App'd For Sutherland Paper Co. Marvel.

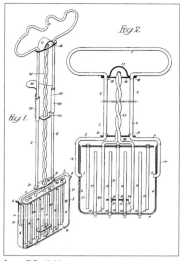

FIG. 12-29

Geroge R. Flowers patent
April 10, 1906
Pat. No. 817,635

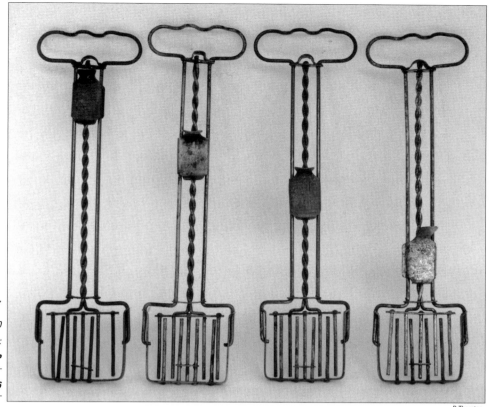

D Thornton

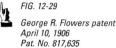

FIG. 12-30

Flowers' patent (left to right):

20TH CENTURY EGG & CREAM WHIP
11-1/4"   —$300—

THE UP TO DATE EGG CREAM WHIP APT. APR. 10, 1906
11-1/2"   —$300—

FLOWERS EGG & CREAM WHIP PAT APLD FOR
11-1/2"   —$375—

**THE HESS PAT APLD FOR.
20 SECONDS HESS MFG. CO. PHILA-PA.**
11-1/2"   —$400—

▶ An April 10, 1906 patent *(fig. 12-29)* by George R. Flowers of Philadelphia resulted in a rare mixer with four different names *(fig. 12-30)*: 20TH CENTURY EGG & CREAM WHIP, THE UP TO DATE EGG CREAM WHIP, FLOWERS EGG & CREAM WHIP PAT APLD FOR, and THE HESS PAT. APLD FOR. 20 SECONDS HESS MFG. CO. PHILA-PA. The FLOWERS and HESS are very hard to find.

▶ The STERLING EGG BEATER *(fig. 12-31)* was offered at the turn of the century by Acme Specialty Company of Piqua, Ohio, which also made the popular Sterling Can Opener. The STERLING beater dashers are extended from the woven wire shaft, somewhat diamond shaped, with a brown handle similar to early A&J models. An Acme Specialty Company catalog *(fig. 12-32)* said of the STERLING: "Simple. Durable. No Wheels. No Cranks. Operated with one hand only. Can be used in any dish or bowl. Will whip cream and eggs or mix mayonnaise or any ingredient in any quantity in one-half the time that other beaters will do it. Is practically automatic and is operated with one hand, leaving the other hand free to add ingredients … Retail price 25 cents. Postage 5 cents."

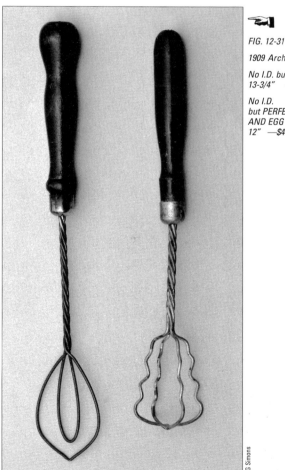

D G Simons

FIG. 12-31

1909 Archimedes (left to right):

No I.D. but STERLING
13-3/4"   —$40—

*No I.D.
but PERFECT CREAM
AND EGG BEATER*
12"   —$40—

FIG. 12-32

*Sterling Egg
Beater illustration
from the Acme
Specialty
Company catalog*

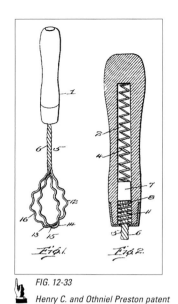

THE
PERFECT
CREAM
and
E G G
BEATER

is the only
practical
one hand
beater on
the market

Patented
Sept. 7.
1909.

FIG. 12-34

1910 House
Furnishing
Review ad

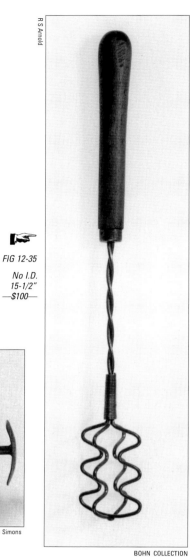

FIG. 12-33

Henry C. and Othniel Preston patent
Sept. 7, 1909
Pat. No. 933,580

FIG. 12-35

No I.D.
15-1/2"
—$100—

R S Arnold

FIG. 12-36

Spear's (left to right):

**20TH CENTURY EGG & CREAM WHIPPER
MARCH 5, 1912**
12-1/2"   —$250—

**SPEAR'S 20TH CENTURY EGG & CREAM WHIPPER
MARCH 5, 1912
IMPROVEMENTS ALLOWED
NOV. 29, 1913**
12-1/2"   —$250—

FIG. 12-37

Detail of dashers

D G Simons

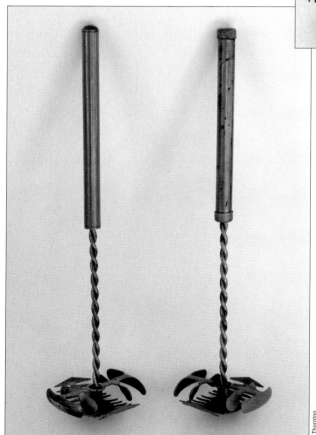

D Thornton

FIG. 12-38

Fannie G. Spear patent
March 5, 1912
Pat. No. 1,019,546

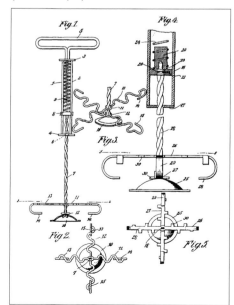

FIG. 12-39

Fannie G. Spear patent
June 23, 1914
Pat. No. 1,101,347

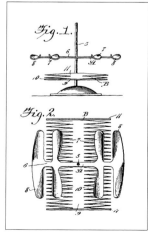

BOHN COLLECTION

▶ The PERFECT CREAM AND EGG BEATER has a black wooden handle and wavy dashers that extend from the woven-wire shaft. It was patented Sept. 7, 1909 by Henry C. and Othniel Preston of Hornell, New York *(fig. 12-33)*. Manufactured by the Hollow Cable Mfg. Company of Hornell, New York, it was described as "the only practical one hand beater on the market" *(fig. 12-34)*. The brothers Henry and Othniel launched the Hollow Cable Company, with their father, Othniel Sr., in 1872. In addition to eggbeaters, it manufactured braided barbless fence wire, hollow cable wire for clothes lines and braided wire box bands, all of their own invention.

Somewhat similar to the STERLING and PERFECT is an unmarked model with wood handle standing very tall at 15-1/2" *(fig. 12-35)*.

▶ A wild looking beater *(figs. 12-36 & 12-37)* was patented by Fannie G. Spear of New York.

This beauty, which at first glance appears to be a Ninja weapon, has two markings. There is the 20TH CENTURY EGG & CREAM WHIPPER (not whip), with a March 5, 1912 date *(fig. 12-38)*, and SPEAR'S 20TH CENTURY EGG & CREAM WHIPPER with the same patent date but also marked IMPROVEMENTS ALLOWED NOV. 29, 1913. (Note: Nov. 29, 1913 is probably a typo, the date is not a patent Tuesday.)

Said Spear, "This invention relates to egg beaters and one of the principal objects of the invention is the provision of a simple, thoroughly efficient and inexpensive beater which may be operated with one hand and which will break up the egg material in the shortest space of time."

She refined her deadly dasher arrangement in another patent, this one granted June 23, 1914 *(fig. 12-39)*, featuring "rows of spaced teeth." Spear beaters were made by Kohler Die & Specialty Company on Washington Boulevard in Chicago. The *Certified List of Illinois Corporations for 1911 and 1913* listed Henry A. and Edward C. Kohler as the top officers of the firm. Kohler also made the DREAM CREAM WHIP, a turbine beater *(See Chapter 20, Big Turbines and Blades, page 229)*.

▶ A scarce stand-up model *(fig. 12-40)*, with porcelain top knob, was patented June 16, 1914 *(fig. 12-41)* by Harry R. Sinclair of Worcester, Massachusetts, who said his heavy-duty frame allowed the "spirally-twisted stem to cause … the dasher to rotate as it is reciprocated longitudinally." A brochure described it as the NEW ENGLAND EGG BEATER AND MIXER; cost: 25¢.

"Mixes, stirs, churns, whips, lightens and aerates the material, producing a smooth, thoroughly blended mixture and rendering it free from all solid matter," the brochure said.

Two Chicago residents, Arthur W. Johnston and Alexander A. Norton, teamed up to patent an Archimedes with a curved wire and spring bottom *(fig. 12-42)*. They didn't beat around the bush in their May 18, 1915 patent *(fig. 12-43)*, saying their device was "simple, convenient, durable, efficient, and satisfactory, and that [it] may be manufactured at a comparatively small cost."

GRIFFITHS COLLECTION

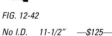

FIG. 12-40

No. I.D. but
NEW ENGLAND EGG BEATER AND MIXER
9-3/4"   —$125—

FIG. 12-41

*Harry R. Sinclair patent
June 16, 1914
Pat. No. 1,100,683*

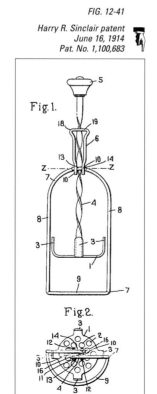

MOFFET COLLECTION

FIG. 12-42

No I.D.   11-1/2"   —$125—

FIG. 12-43

*Arthur W. Johnston and Alexander A. Norton patent
May 18, 1915
Pat. No. 1,140,341*

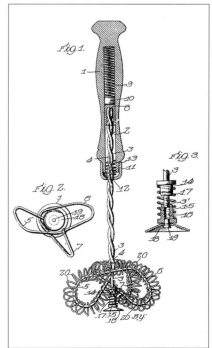

▶ A unique double-dasher Archimedes is the so-called USHER *(fig. 12-44)*. Fully extended it measures about 14". Frederick S. Usher of Indiana Harbor, Indiana, patented this marvel Feb. 6, 1917 *(fig. 12-45)*. He said the double dasher means a "two-fold action is produced upon the cream or other product without materially increasing the force necessary to operate the device."

▶ "Slight pressure on top of handle rapidly revolves beater blades," said the April, 1926 *Our Drummer* catalog of Butler Brothers in describing a no-name Archimedes with a dasher arrangement that is wire bent in a rectangle with circles inside it *(fig. 12-46)*. The catalog listed the price, for two dozen or more, at 19 cents a dozen.

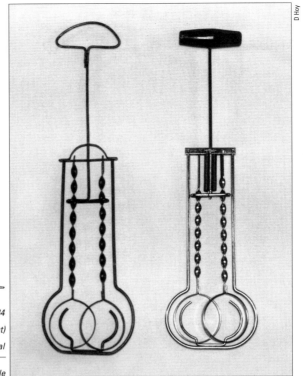

FIG 12-44

Ushers (left to right)

No I.D. but early version of Usher patent, all metal
14" —$250—

No I.D. but later version of Usher patent, with wood T-handle
14" —$200—

HOY COLLECTION

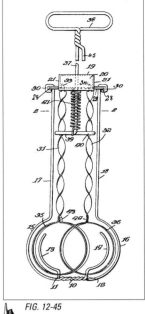

FIG. 12-45

Frederick S. Usher patent
Feb. 6, 1917
1,214,975

D G Simons

FIG. 12-46

No I.D.
14" —$150—

BOHN COLLECTION

Roberts Egg Separator

3-1/4" diameter
—$25—

FIG. 12-47

Roberts Lightning Mixers, with I.D. from metal tops
(left to right):

PAT APLD FOR 8" —$30—

PAT. SEPT. 10, 1912 DORSEY MFG CO. BOSTON, MASS USA 8" —$20—
Note: This model is also marked:
ROBERTS LIGHTNING MIXER PAT'D 1913 NATIONAL CO. BOSTON, MASS.

PAT APLD FOR 10" —$25—

PATENTED JULY 29, 1913 12" —$125—

▶ One of the first jar Archimedes was ROBERTS LIGHTNING MIXER *(fig. 12-47)*, with a snug, push-on top. All of the different models are embossed on the bottom of the jar ROBERTS LIGHTNING MIXER; other identification is on the metal apron.

The person behind the Roberts was Henry P. Roberts of Boston, who was granted several patents *(figs. 12-48 through 12-50)*.

Roberts also patented a fabulous stand-up, rotary crank mixer for drinks *(fig. 12-51)*, which apparently was only patented and not made.

The ROBERTS maker, Dorsey Manufacturing Company, was listed in the *Boston City Directory* as offering household specialties at 78 Broad Street from 1913 to 1915 and at 39 Pearl Street from 1916 to 1918.

An early sales booklet by The Boston Cooking School Magazine Company *(fig. 12-52)*, said the ROBERTS LIGHTNING MIXER, "beats whites of eggs in half a minute, whips cream and churns butter in from one to three minutes."

A Dorsey booklet *(fig. 12-53)* boasted: "High cost of living substantially reduced by the use of the Roberts Lightning Mixer. With the Roberts Lightning Mixer the butter cost of a family can be reduced by one half. Take 1/2 lb. butter, soften, as for cake, add a cupful of fresh milk, salt to taste, churn in the mixer until stiff and you have approximately double the original quantity." In addition to Dorsey, other manufacturers of the ROBERTS were the National Company and Roberts Lightning Mixer Company, both of Boston.

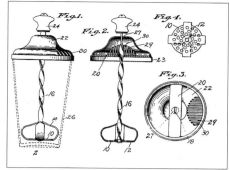

FIG 12-48

Henry P. Roberts patent
Sept. 10, 1912
Pat No. 1,038,204

FIG. 12-49

Henry P. Roberts patent
July 29, 1913
Pat. No. 1,068,450

FIG. 12-50

Henry P. Roberts patent
March 31, 1931
Pat. No. 1,798,757

FIG. 12-51

Henry P. Roberts patent
Dec. 10, 1912
Pat. No. 1,046,648

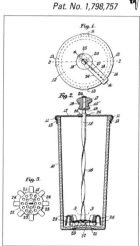
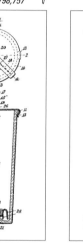

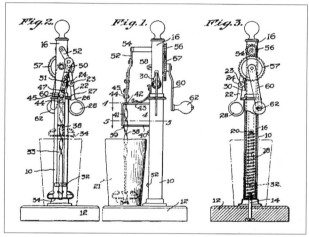

FIG. 12-52

The Boston Cooking School
Magazine Company
sales booklet

Fig. 12-53

Dorsey
Manufacturing
Company
booklet

" *The beater that beats the world.* "

—EARLY DORSEY
BOOKLET
ON THE
ROBERTS LIGHTNING
MIXER

ROBERTS LIGHTNING MIXER

TRADE MARK

The Beater that Beats the World

Dorsey Manufacturing Co.
78 Broad Street : : Boston, Mass.

MADELEINE PANS

Twelve pans or moulds on one tin 7½ x 14 inches. Sent, postpaid, for two (2) new subscriptions, or Cash Price, $1.50.

**ROBERTS'
LIGHTNING MIXER**

Beats whites of eggs in half a minute, whips cream and churns butter in from one to three minutes. In making floats, salad dressings, custards, gravies, charlotte russe, eggnog, etc., it must be used in order to achieve the best results. No spatter. Saves time and labor.

Pint size sent, postpaid, for one (1) new subscription or Cash Price, 75 cents.

Quart size sent, postpaid, for two (2) new subscriptions or Cash Price, $1.50.

SATURN CLOTHESLINE REEL

A round steel ball—dust proof, nickel plated, warranted 40 ft. line, tested to 180 lbs.—takes present clothespin. Use outdoors or indoors. Hangs anywhere. Two spreading rings. Positively the best made at any price. Nickeled. Sent prepaid, for one (1) new subscription or Cash Price, 75 cents.

BIRD'S NEST FRYER

Heavy double wire baskets, hinged together, for frying "Bird's Nests Potatoes." Sent, prepaid, for two (2) new subscriptions or Cash Price, $1.50.

GRAPEFRUIT KNIFE

Is made from the finest cutlery steel, finely tempered, curved just to the right angle and ground to a very keen edge; will remove the center, cut cleanly and quickly around the edge and divide the fruit into segments ready for eating. The feature of the blade is the round end, which prevents cutting through the outer skin, and double-edged blade. Sent, postpaid, for one (1) new subscription, or Cash Price, 75 cents.

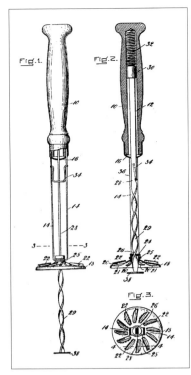

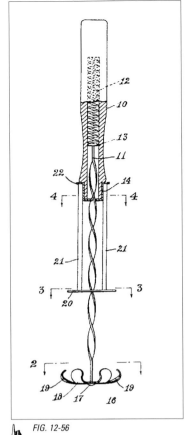

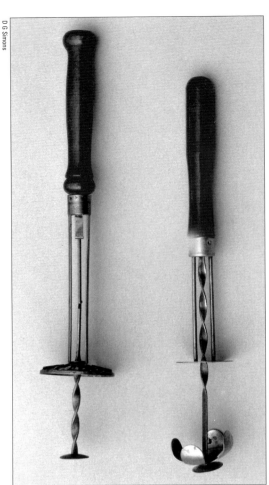

FIG. 12-54

Henry P. Roberts
patent
March 17, 1914
Pat. No. 1,090,567

FIG. 12-55

Archimedes with
dasher stoppers
(left to right):

PATENT PENDING,
only I.D., but
Henry P. Roberts
patent
13-1/2"
—$100—

No. I.D. but
Maurice H. Roberts
patent
12"
—$150—

FIG. 12-56

Maurice H. Roberts patent
April 25, 1922
Pat. No. 1,413,874

FIG 12-58

Turnet H. Stough patent
March 30, 1915
Pat. No. 1,133,413

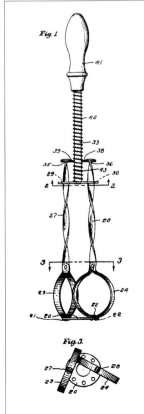

FIG. 12-57

Maurice H. Roberts patent
Dec. 31, 1918
Pat. No. 1,289,545

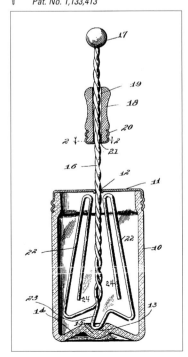

Henry P. Roberts also made his mark with a hand-held Archimedes (*fig. 12-54*). This marvel has no identification marks, other than PATENT PENDING. But it is one of the most appealing, and mechanically involved Archimedes made (*fig. 12-55, left*). The circular dasher, with slices and holes, is, at rest, 2-1/2" from the bottom, or its target. But a push takes it quickly to the bottom, and the mixing motion is unbeatable.

Now to add to the Roberts mix, another Roberts (and this is in addition to the earlier mentioned Emmett Roberts of Indianapolis) — Maurice H. Roberts, also of Boston, who produced another unique Archimedes (*fig. 12-55, right*). Patented April 25, 1922 (*fig. 12-56*), it deserves the gadget label. It has a circular, perforated guard, apparently to prevent too hard mixing, but also to aid in the beating. Maurice H. Roberts listed himself as assignor to the Harris Company of Boston. It is not known for sure, but very likely, that Henry and Maurice were related.

Maurice H. Roberts also had an earlier beater patent (*fig. 12-57*), an Archimedes with two dashers. The Dec. 31, 1918 patent described the double dashers as "a plurality of beater members ..."

The patent date March 30, 1915 (*fig. 12-58*) shows up on several jar beaters.

The patent was obtained by Turnet (yes Turnet) H. Stough of Jeannette, Pennsylvania. "The primary object of the invention is to provide an implement

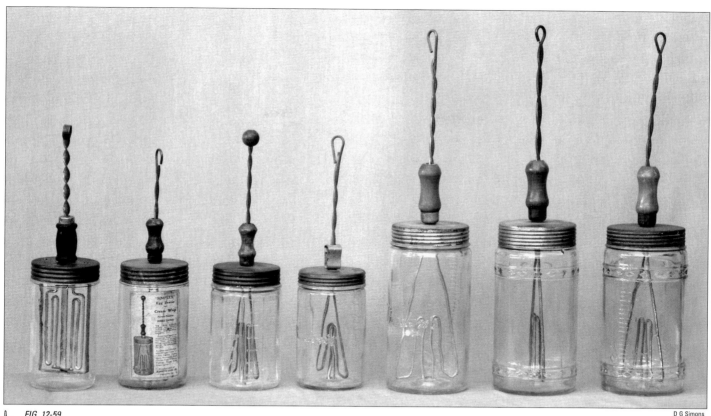

FIG. 12-59

D G Simons

Jar Archimedes (left to right):

No I.D. but Lightning Cream and Egg Whip
JEANNETTE GLASS CO. *(on jar)* 12" —$175—

SIMPLEX MANUFACTURED BY
JEANNETTE GLASS COMPANY, JEANNETTE, PA
12" —$150 with paper label—

MAR. 30TH 1915 #1,133,413-1 *12"* —$50—

BORDENS PAT MAR. 30TH 1915 #1,133,413 AD 2001-1
12" —$50—

BORDENS PAT MAR. 30TH 1915 #1,133,413 AD 2001-1
17" —$60—

No. I.D., but jar embossed with rings with diamonds in them
17" —$55—

AD PAT. MAR. 30TH 1915 2108-4 #1,133,413
17" —$55—

❝ *Do not operate too fast.* **❞**

—SIMPLEX MIXER LABEL

for use in beating, whipping and mixing ingredients for use in pastry making and cooking which shall consist of few parts which are readily taken apart and easily cleaned," Stough said.

Coming under the domain of this patent were a wide variety of mixers *(fig. 12-59)*, including the LIGHTNING CREAM AND EGG WHIP *(fig. 12-60)*, promotional items for Bordens Milk and one with a paper label marked SIMPLEX which boasts: "Apparatus especially adapted for whipped cream for coffee, egg-nog, Floating Island, Mayonnaise, Salad Charlotte-Russe, custards, puddings, sauces, fruit, cream, etc."

It also includes this quirky warning: "Do not operate too fast."

FIG. 12-60

Sheet from the 1910 Thomas Manufacturing Co., Dayton, Ohio catalog

"Lightning"
CREAM AND EGG WHIP
SANITARY~RAPID~DURABLE
WILL WHIP CREAM IN 30 SECONDS

IS SIMPLY PERFECT!

Is perfectly sanitary. Does away with all splashing or waste of material. It is easy of operation, taking little effort. It is a great time saver. In fact it is a necessity found lacking in so many kitchens. A good cream and egg whip is the delight of every housewife—the "Lightning" is the very best ever put on the market and will surely please.

It is made in two sizes. No. 81, one-half pint glass jar, just as illustrated above, with screw cap. No. 82, one pint jar with screw cap. Both sizes have the cream and egg whip invention, encased in the jars, ready for use.

PRICES:

No. 81. Suitable for small family use........35 cents
No. 82. " " general household use...50 cents

▶ Another beater that more than likely utilized the Stough patent is a no-name with wavy dashers that go from the top of the jar to the bottom *(fig. 12-61)*. In the same category is the SANITARY CREAM AND EGG WHIP *(fig. 12-62)*, with a skinny jar. The bottom of some SANITARY jars are marked: MADE IN FOUR SIZES.

▶ A well-known Archimedes jar mixer is the KEYSTONE EGG AND CREAM BEATER, which comes in two sizes *(fig. 12-63)*. The smaller stands 11" high and the name is embossed in the pedestal jar, which stands 5-1/2" alone. The bigger model would probably be about 13" overall. It has a 6-1/2" jar marked exactly like the smaller one but with additional information on the bottom: WESTMORELAND SPEC. CO., PAT APLD FOR, GRAPEVILLE, PA. Unfortunately, the jar remains topless as the search continues for the mixer that fits on top. The search for Grapeville has been more successful. The Westmoreland Glass Company had a factory there at one time. And although most maps don't show it, Grapeville is located southeast of Jeannette and west of Greensburg at the junction of State Roads 4006 and 4004.

MOFFET COLLECTION

FIG. 12-61

No I.D.
12"
—$175—

FIG. 12-62

MALONEY COLLECTION

SANITARY CREAM AND EGG WHIP
(embossed on front of jar)
PATTENT *(sic)* **PENDING**
MADE IN FOUR SIZES
(embossed on bottom of jar)
11"
—$300—

FIG 12-63

Keystones (left to right):

KEYSTONE EGG AND CREAM BEATER
11" —$80—

KEYSTONE EGG AND CREAM BEATER WESTMORELAND SPEC. CO. PAT APLD FOR GRAPEVILLE, PA.
13"
—reproduction top, thus value undetermined—

McLEAN BLACK & CO. EGG SEPARATOR

3-1/4" diameter
—$20—

FIG. 12-64

McLean Black and other jar Archimedes (left to right):

MCLEAN BLACK, BOSTON
8"   —$30—

MCLEAN BLACK BOSTON
9-1/4"   —$35—

JOHNSON COLD FUDGE JUNE 13, 1939
10"   —$250—

JIFFY MIXER
9-1/2"   —$45—

▶ Marked only MCLEAN BLACK, BOSTON *(fig. 12-64)*, this Archimedes mixer screws on the top of its embossed jar. It comes in two sizes and was patented Dec. 29, 1914 *(fig. 12-65)* by William H. Doty of West Somerville, Massachusetts. It was produced by the famous McLean, Black Company of Boston, whose massive line of products ranged from barber scissors to cheese scoops to pocket mirrors to umbrellas to vest chains. McLean Black first appeared in the *Boston City Directory* in 1906, with its last listing in 1915.

▶ Now to Hollywood, the hometown of Edward R. Hacmac, assignor to Na-Mac Products Company. Hacmac's June 13, 1939 patent *(fig. 12-66)* is for a "liquid dispenser and mixer" and was made into a pitcher marked JOHNSTON COLD FUDGE *(fig. 12-64)*. One year later Hacmac came out with his WORLBEATER two-speed rotary mixer *(See Chapter 21, Rotary Mix: The Later Years, page 252)*.

▶ The JIFFY MIXER *(fig. 12-64)* operates like a child's push top. Its beautiful Bakelite top handle came in different colors. Patented Nov. 28, 1939 *(fig. 12-67)* by Cesare Palmieri of New York, its secret, according to its specifications, is a fly-wheel: "With each downward thrust exerted upon the drive shaft, the flywheel will be given a rotative impetus, always in the same direction, and that the upward pull upon the shaft will not disturb the continuity of travel of the fly-wheel, but merely acts to position the actuator shaft for another downward thrust which imparts to the fly-wheel a fresh rotational impetus …"

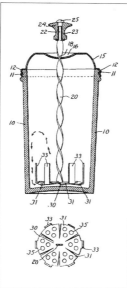

FIG. 12-65

William H. Doty patent Dec. 29, 1914 1,122,876

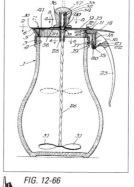

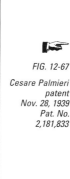

FIG. 12-66

Edward R. Hacmac patent June 13, 1939 Pat. No. 2,162,348

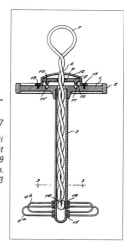

FIG. 12-67

Cesare Palmieri patent Nov. 28, 1939 Pat. No. 2,181,833

The JIFFY MIXER was manufactured by Milano Manufacturing Company of New York. "You just push the little knob up and down — a job that really takes only two (2) fingers. Fly wheel action keeps the metal whip whirling like mad for seconds after you've stopped pushing," said an early ad.

▶ An exact replica of the JIFFY MIXER is the ROUX CREME COLOR MIXER *(fig. 12-68)*, which was used for hair coloring. The label is painted on the jar and ROUX embossed in the aluminum apron, along with MADE IN U.S.A. The jar is also marked to 6 ounces.

FIG. 12-68

ROUX CREME COLOR MIXER
9-1/2"
—$45—

▶ The ECONOMY mixer *(fig. 12-69)* was sold as is, without a jar. An early ad *(fig. 12-70)* said it would fit any standard quart fruit jar, or half-gallon for that matter. This rare device extends from 10-1/2" to 17".

▶ Paul Tripke of Jersey City, New Jersey, patented four wild Archimedes, one a combination beater/reamer *(figs. 12-71 through 12-74)*. Two of Tripke's patent dates — Aug. 28, 1917 and Oct. 22, 1918 — appear on one of his creations, a beautiful, supremely rare Archimedes with reversible reamer *(fig. 12-75)* called the FOUR IN ONE.

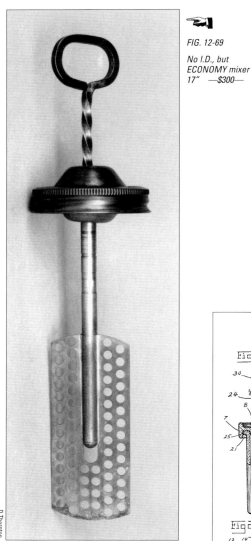

D Thornton

MOFFET COLLECTION

FIG. 12-69

No I.D., but
ECONOMY mixer
17" —$300—

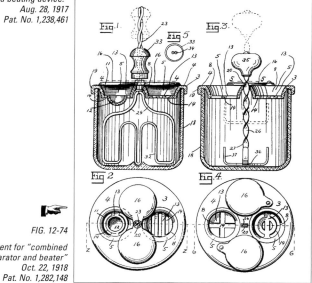

FIG. 12-70

Ad for
ECONOMY
mixer

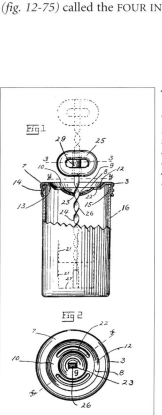

FIG. 12-71

Paul Tripke patent
for combined egg
separator and
beating device
Aug. 21, 1917
Pat No. 1,237,585

FIG. 12-72

Paul Tripke patent for "combined
egg separator and juice extractor,
and beating device."
Aug. 28, 1917
Pat. No. 1,238,461

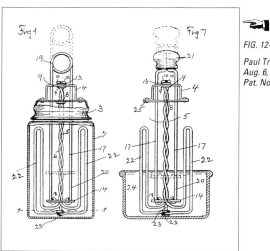

FIG. 12-73

Paul Tripke patent
Aug. 6, 1918
Pat. No. 1,274,634

FIG. 12-74

Paul Tripke patent for "combined
egg separator and beater"
Oct. 22, 1918
Pat. No. 1,282,148

THE EGGBEATER CHRONICLES

FIG. 12-75

FOUR-IN-ONE (figural four in outline of figural one)
SANITARY BESS
AUG. 28, 1917, OCT. 22, 1918
15-1/4"   —$1,500+

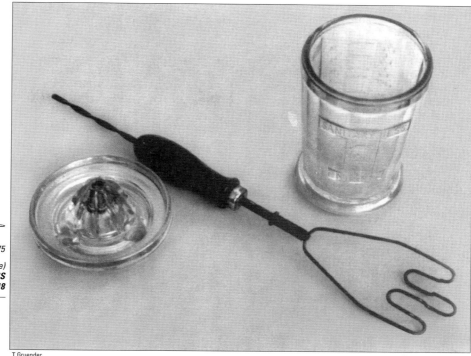

T Gruender

GRUENDER COLLECTION

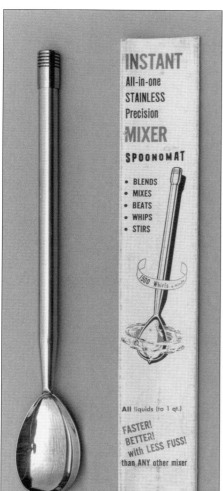

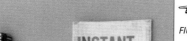

FIG. 12-76

No. I.D but SPOONOMAT
8-3/4"   —$20—

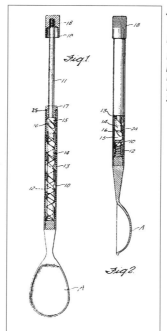

FIG. 12-77

Paul J. Rommel patent March 15, 1938 Pat. No. 2,111,407

▶ Later Archimedes include an unusual one made by the prestigious R. Wallace & Sons Manufacturing Company of Wallingford, Connecticut, silversmiths since 1835, for the Maricopa Trading Company of New York City. This mixer has a name straight out of Saturday Night Live: SPOONOMAT *(fig. 12-76)*, and an advertisement boast of "mixing speeds to 1500 or more R.P.M."

The original SPOONOMAT had no markings, but a later version was embossed on the handle: BOB HOFFMAN YORK BARRELL CO. YORK, PA.

The SPOONOMAT was patented March 15, 1938 by Paul J. Rommel of Jackson Heights, New York *(fig. 12-77)*. Rommel said the screw-on top meant the device could be used as "an ordinary long-handled spoon of attractive design" and that releasing the cap unleashed "a telescopical handle" with "a reciprocating stirring device."

The Archimedes spoon dates back to 1885 and several models have been patented over the years (*fig. 12-78 through 12-80*). The biggest spoon stands 11-1/2" and was an advertising vehicle for a liquor dealer (*fig. 12-81*).

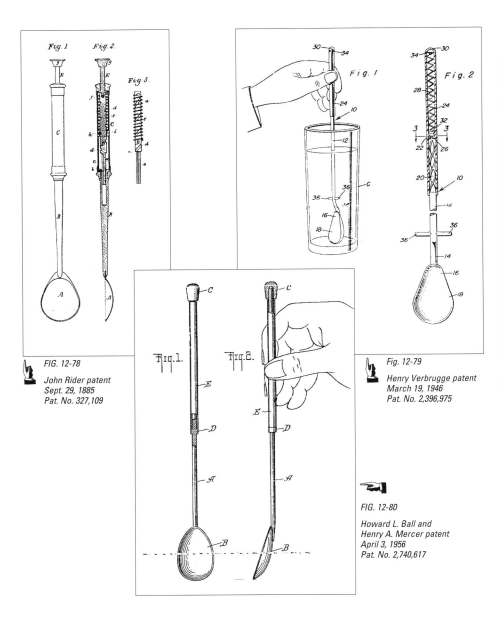

FIG. 12-78

John Rider patent
Sept. 29, 1885
Pat. No. 327,109

Fig. 12-79

Henry Verbrugge patent
March 19, 1946
Pat. No. 2,396,975

FIG. 12-80

Howard L. Ball and
Henry A. Mercer patent
April 3, 1956
Pat. No. 2,740,617

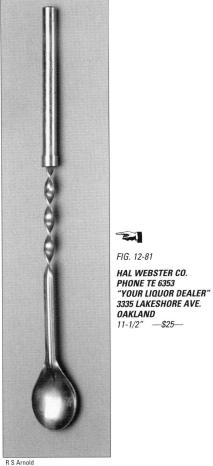

FIG. 12-81

HAL WEBSTER CO.
PHONE TE 6353
"YOUR LIQUOR DEALER"
3335 LAKESHORE AVE.
OAKLAND
11-1/2" —$25—

R S Arnold

The U.S. Post Office Department honored America's poultry industry on its 100th anniversary by issuing a commemorative 3-cent stamp in 1948.

THE EGGBEATER CHRONICLES

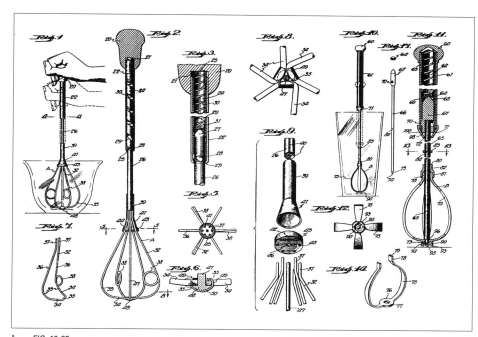

FIG. 12-82
Michael Rabb patent
May 22, 1934
Pat. No. 1,960,089

▶ On a more traditional level, Michael Rabb's May 22, 1934 patent *(fig. 12-82)* features a beater that is simple but effective and has its look-alikes *(fig. 12-83)*.

Rabb, of Newark, New Jersey, said in part: "Other features of the invention relate to certain novel and improved constructions, arrangements and combinations of parts hereinafter described … the advantages of which will be readily understood and appreciated by those skilled in the art."

The Rabb patent featured a variation on the same mixer, a skinny tumbler model. Two other beaters came under the same patent umbrella, one with changeable dashers *(fig. 12-84)* and another with permanent, round aluminum dashers *(fig. 12-85)*.

FIG. 12-83

Rabb and others (left to right):

MADE IN AMERICA, only I.D., but Rabb patent
11-3/4"   —$40—

No I.D.   12"   —$45—

TEPA DEUTSCHLAND
11"   —$35—

D G Simons

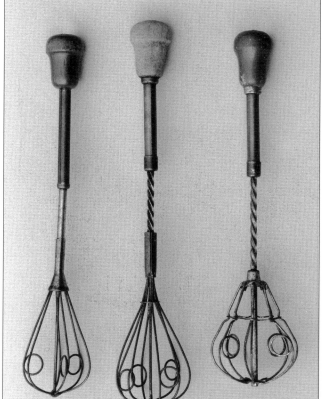

FIG. 12-84

More Rabb (left to right):

MADE IN AMERICA PAT. PEND.
matches patent tumbler drawing
9-5/8"   —$50—

MADE IN USA PAT. NO. 1960089,
with changeable dashers, —$200—

FIG. 12-85

**MADE IN AMERICA
PAT. PEND.**
11"   —$70—

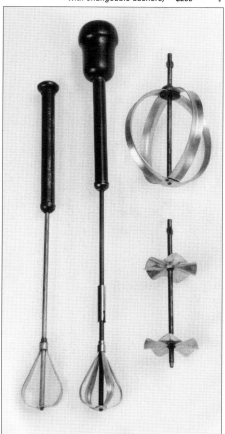

R S Arnold   MAIR COLLECTION   D Thornton

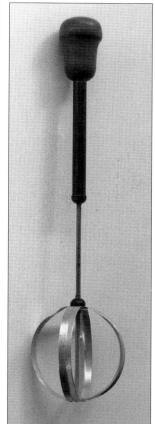

▶ The WIT WHIP was based on two patents *(figs. 12-86 & 12-87)* by Joseph H. Wittmann of Los Angeles. Offered in a plastic tube 12" long, it was "guaranteed forever."

Manufactured by Dr. JoWit Laboratories of Santa Monica, California, the advertising flier for this plastic handle model *(fig. 12-88)* is fabulous: "The most fascinating mixing and whipping instrument since 1860 … Originally created for and sold to chemical laboratories at $5 each. The present popular prices were only made possible thru the nation-wide demand from leading home economists, which required mass production, yet retaining the same high quality."

▶ Very similar to the WIT WHIP is the ARTBECK WHIP BEATER *(fig. 12-88)* made by Arthur Beck Company of Chicago in 1948. It was packaged in a cardboard tube.

▶ Other Archimedes include the novel BOUN-C-BEATER, a very early, wood-handle WIT WHIP and a raft of no names *(figs. 12-89 & 12-90)*, including one marked only MADE IN AMERICA, which is believed to be THE BEATERETTE FLIP. An ad *(fig. 12-91)* described it as "fool-proof in action, its attractive smartness has instant appeal for its many purposes." The price: 70¢.

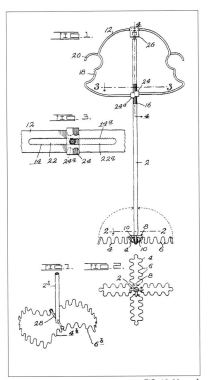

FIG. 12-86

Joseph H. Wittmann patent
Oct. 19, 1937
Pat. No. 2,096,442

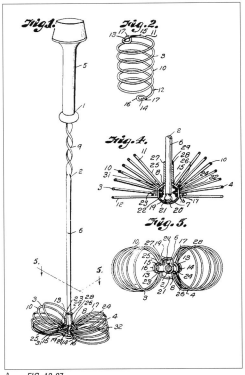

FIG. 12-87

Joseph H. Wittmann patent
March 2, 1954
Pat. No. 2,670,938

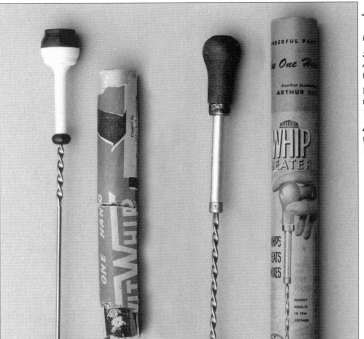

D G Simons

FIG. 12-88

Spring bottom Archimedes *(left to right):*

WIT WHIP
with container
12"   —$30—

ARTBECK WHIP BEATER
with container
12-1/4 "   —$35—

A wonderful party or bridge gift. An invaluable household aid. Use it to mix, to beat, to whip anything from a teaspoon to a bowlful.

—ARTBECK WHIP BEATER PACKAGING PITCH

FIG. 12-89

Alice Yola De Martino patent
Aug. 9, 1949
Design Pat. No. 154,752

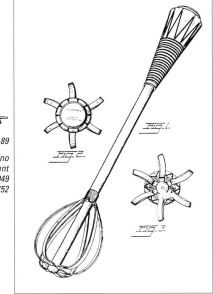

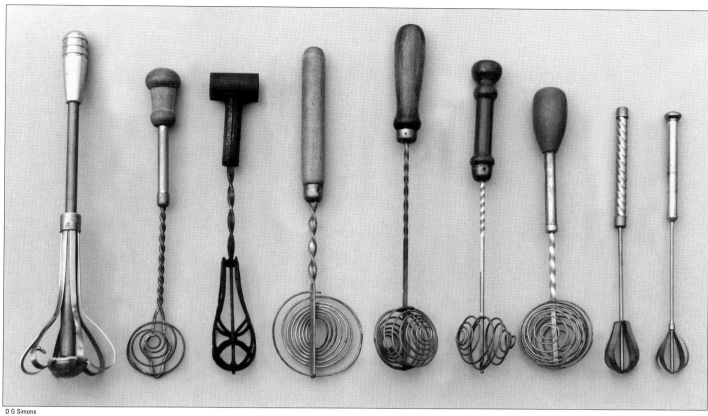

D G Simons

FIG 12-91

Ad for the Beaterette "flip"
House Furnishing Review

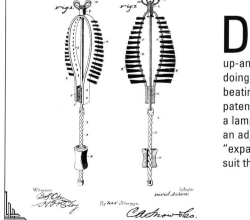

D. AIKEN.
CHIMNEY CLEANER.
No. 478,302. Patented July 5, 1892.

David Aiken of Winns-
borough, South Carolina,
put the Archimedes
up-and-down action to work
doing something other then
beating eggs. His July 5, 1892
patent No. 478,302 was for
a lamp chimney cleaner with
an adjustable brush that
"expanded and contracted to
suit the size of the chimney."

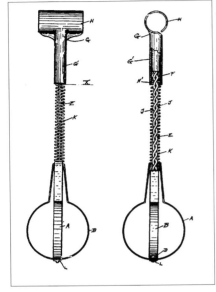

FIG 12-92

*James B. Erwin
patent
June 16, 1908
Pat. No. 890,629*

FIG. 12-93

**JESSE L. EDGREN CO.
MILWAUKEE, WIS.
PAT APPLIED FOR
JUNE 1906**
10-1/2" —$75—

BOHN COLLECTION

▶ A June 16, 1908 patent by James B. Erwin of Milwaukee *(fig. 12-92)* resulted in an all-metal beater that came in two models. One with no I.D. has the spring to return the Archimedes hidden in the handle *(fig. 12-90)*. The other has the spring outside on the main shaft and is marked JESSE L. EDGREN CO. MILWAUKEE, WIS., PAT APPLIED FOR JUNE 1906 *(fig. 12-93)* — although the actual application date was July 27, 1906. A circa 1909 Jesse L. Edgren Company, Milwaukee, Wisconsin catalog *(fig. 12-94)* described the mixer as THE MILWAUKEE WHIRLING ONE HANDED EGG-BEATER AND CREAM WHIP.

Erwin, a practicing attorney, also was credited with inventing a water meter, an air compressor and a hydraulic engine.

▶ Contrasting the simple and the elegant is an unmarked bent wire Archimedes and the chrome-plated MAHONY *(fig. 12-95)*. The MAHONY is based on two patents *(figs. 12-96 & 12-97)* by William J. Mahony, who listed his hometown as Montreal, Quebec, and later Hartford, Connecticut.

D Thornton

The Milwaukee Whirling One Handed Egg-Beater .... and Cream Whip ....

Did you ever try to beat eggs or cream or anything else with any of the egg beaters or cream whips heretofore upon the market? You turned and turned and turned, and it is a great wonder you are not turning still. With *The Milwaukee Whirling One Handed Egg Beater and Cream Whip* you can do the work in one-fourth the time formerly required. All you have to do is to press down on the handle and the *Beater* does all the work. Only *one* hand is required. The left hand

Patent applied for June, 1906.

The Milwaukee Whirling One Handed Egg-Beater and Cream Whip

is as good as the right. It is the most wonderful *Egg Beater* and *Cream Whip* ever invented. It is made of spring steel, nickel plated and highly polished and guaranteed. Do not think this Beater is made of cheap material like other Beaters, or put up cheaply because the price is low. The same skill, material and workmanship used in the construction of all Edgren's Specialties are followed to the letter. The material of which this Beater is constructed is stronger than iron bands.

Remember no more turning and turning and turning. No more holding the Beater with one hand and turning and turning with the other. No! No! The world moves forward. The march of civilization must be along the road of progress. The old, tiresome method must give away to the new, delightful way. *One hand* now only needed with this new up-to-date Beater doing the work in one-fourth the time and doing it "so easy." Again we state, no turning and turning and turning, but just press down on the handle and the Beater does all the work.

Let the Beater do the Work

FIG. 12-94

*Circa 1909
Jesse L. Edgren Company
catalog*

FIG. 12-95

*No I.D. simple wire design
10-34"* —$25—

**U.S. PAT. 1,826,356, 1,966,352
BRIT 359,332, 397,448
CAN 312,964
CZECH 45,767**
*MAHONY prototype
13"* —$1500—

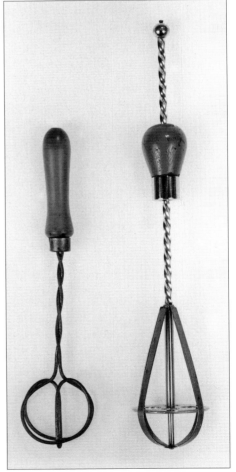

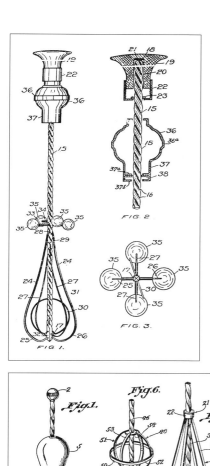

FIG. 12-96

William J. Mahony
Patent Oct. 6, 1931
Pat. No. 1826,356

FIG. 12-97

William J. Mahony patent
July 10, 1934
Pat. No. 1,966,352

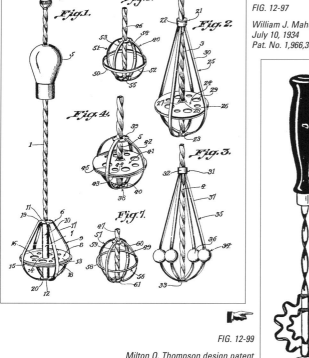

FIG. 12-99

Milton O. Thompson design patent
May 25, 1920
Pat. No. D-55340

N Kosiewski

FIG. 12-100

VICTORY
11-3/4"   —$150—

FIG. 12-98

1933
advertisement
for the Mahony
beater

COOPER COLLECTION

Mahony also obtained Canadian, English and Czech patents for his mixer — but it apparently never made it to market although three prototypes survive.

The MAHONY prototypes, along with a beautiful advertising piece *(fig. 12-98)*, were discovered by collector Reid Cooper.

▶ Milton O. Thompson of Boston was granted a design patent *(fig. 12-99)* in 1920 for his double sunburst mixer, which is marked VICTORY *(fig. 12-100)*.

Detail of Victory

KOSIEWSKI COLLECTION

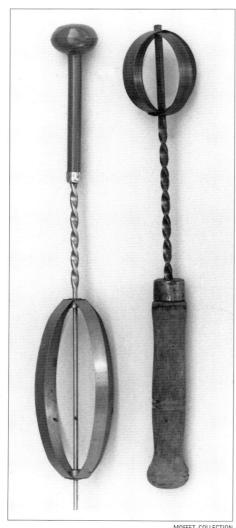

▶ The MODEL may have a name, but many other Archimedes will always remain nameless (*figs. 12-101 through 12-103*), while a few will be known by the name of the patentee, such as the PIPERI by Anthony J. Piperi of Galveston, Texas (*figs. 12-104 & 12-105*).

FIG. 12-101

(left to right):

No I.D., green plastic handle
15-3/4" —$35—

MODEL
PAT APLD FOR
15" —$75—

FIG. 12-102

Wood shank and dasher/reamers (left to right):

No I.D., center knob
12-3/4" —$245—

No I.D.
12" —$200—

FIG. 12-103

Plastic and Bakelite
(left to right):

No I.D., black Bakelite handle
9-3/4" —$35—

No I.D., of recent manufacture
11" —$4—

MADE IN GERMANY, *only I.D.*
10-1/2" —$3—

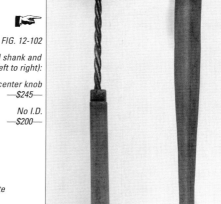

COOPER COLLECTION   BOHN COLLECTION

MOFFET COLLECTION

FIG. 12-104

No I.D., but Piperi patent with easily identifiable bird cage dashers
8-1/4" —$75—

FIG. 12-105

Anthony J. Piperi patent
May 16, 1939
Pat. No. 2,158,912

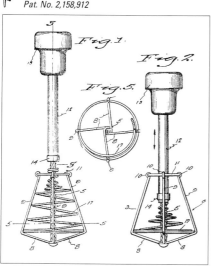

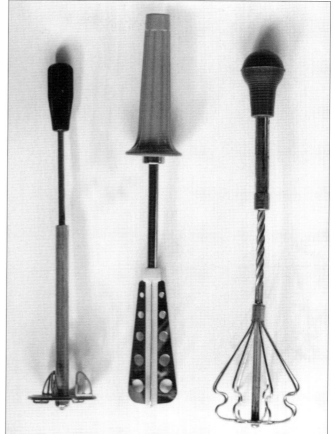

BOHN COLLECTION   D Thornton

THE EGGBEATER CHRONICLES

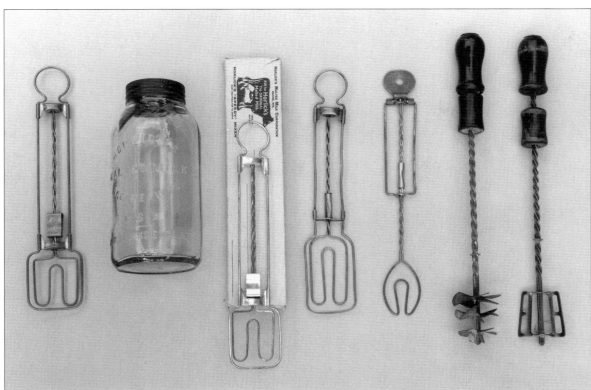

D G Simons

> I nduces sound sleep
> if taken before
> retiring. An ideal
> food beverage for
> invalids, convalescents,
> nursing mothers, the
> aged and infirm.
>
> —**HORLICK'S MALTED MILK** AD
> **AUGUST 1928**

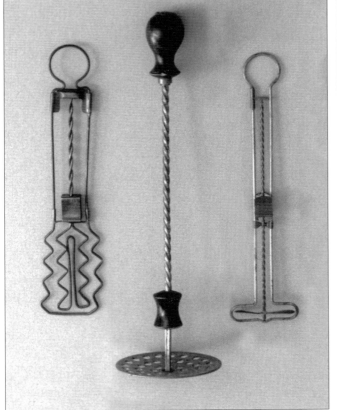

D G Simons   BREON COLLECTION

The simple Archimedes beater also made its mark as a promotional item. Leading the pack was Horlick's Malted Milk Corporation of Racine, Wisconsin.

The most common Archimedes item offered by Horlick's was the SPEEDY MIXER, with the center rectangle marked HORLICK'S in script.

Many came in cardboard mailing boxes featuring a happy black cow and "Horlick's Malted Milk, Reg. U.S. Pat Off. Horlick's Speedy Mixer, sent postpaid for 10 cents."

There is a slightly bigger model with an unmarked center cylinder mechanism, and still others with clam-like dashers, propellers and wood knobs and tops *(figs. 12-106 through 12-108).*

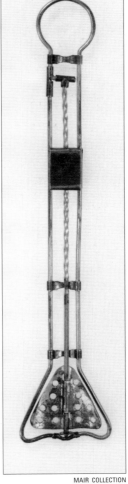

R S Arnold

MAIR COLLECTION

CHAPTER 12: ARCHIMEDES

Horlick's also utilized the ROBERTS LIGHTNING MIXER (fig. 12-109 & fig. 12-47, page 122), the SILVER EGG BEATER NO. 3 (fig. 12-110 & Chapter 9, Keystone and Silver, page 93), and the MALTED MILK MIXER (See Chapter 19, Syllabub Churns, Shakers & Plungers, page 221).

There were other glass mixers, with tin tops and metal plungers, sporting drawings of the country characters Lum and Abner, which Horlicks sponsored on the radio during the 1930s. Horlick collectibles also include the embossed jars the product came in (fig. 12-106) and the English-made plunger models with cups (fig. 12-111).

Horlick's merits some ink on its own — its very existence was based on a mix.

"The nature of our invention consists in a concentrated extract to be used as food for infants, dyspeptics, and invalids…

"It will keep good for any time in any climate, and is easily prepared for infants in the following manner: Dissolve from a half to a whole table-spoonful, according to age, in half a pint of warm cow's milk and water, equal parts, and give it to the infant by means of an ordinary nursing bottle."

So said the May 18, 1875 patent obtained by James and William Horlick. The two Scottish brothers started their firm in Chicago, but moved to Racine, Wisconsin, shortly thereafter, incorporating as Horlick's Food Company, and starting an advertising campaign featuring wholesome girls and cows (fig. 12-112).

The next big change came July 27, 1905, when the name of the firm was changed to Horlick's Malted Milk Corporation. And the mixing premiums began.

In 1908 the firm acquired a site in Slough, Bucks, England and James moved there to launch a new plant. The success of that venture led to the knighting in 1920 of James, who, unfortunately, died a year later. During the 1920s, 1930s, and early 1940s, premiums were going strong (fig. 12-113).

In 1946 the name of the firm was changed to Horlicks Corporation and the apostrophe was deleted. In 1969 Beecham Group Limited of London purchased the corporation and moved its headquarters to England.

D G Simons

FIG. 12-109
HORLICK'S MALTED MILK (on metal lid) **ROBERTS LIGHTNING MIXER** (on jar) 8"
—$65—

FIG. 12-110
HORLICK'S (embossed three sides of square Silver Egg Beater) **DRINK HORLICK'S MALTED MILK** (fourth side) 12-1/2"
—$500—

R Cooper   COOPER COLLECTION

D Thornton

FIG. 12-111
Ceramic Horlick's pitcher 7-3/4", **HORLICK'S** cup 4"
—$100—

FIG. 12-112
Early Horlick's cardboard advertising stand

Fig. 12-113
Woman's Home Companion August 1928 ad

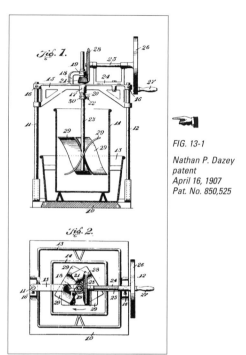

FIG. 13-1

Nathan P. Dazey
patent
April 16, 1907
Pat. No. 850,525

FIG. 13-2

Nathan P. Dazey patent
Dec. 18, 1917
Pat. No. 1,250,810

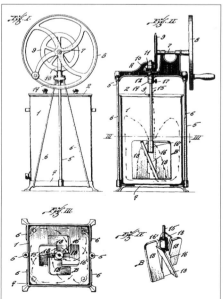

Dazey and Other Churns

"I used to dread churning — now I enjoy it."

Nathan P. Dazey was the patriarch of the Texas Dazey clan. And it was in Texas where Nathan experienced a few shortcomings before he got on track with churns.

Ventures into buggy and piano sales and later furnaces, according to his granddaughter, Suzanne Dazey, proved unsuccessful, one spectacularly so.

"Nathan purchased in 1890 or so a number of buggies. He sold them to the Indians who liked these things. It didn't last long as a trade because the Indian ponies kicked those buggies to pieces in no time at all," Suzanne said in correspondence beginning in 1991.

He then tried selling pianos, but there wasn't much of a market for them in late nineteenth century Texas.

"His next venture was building a furnace for central heating and he sold one to a small town west of Dallas. It was installed in the town hall with much fanfare. Well, it got so hot that the entire structure burned to the ground. Nathan hurriedly left for home leaving angry town folks gunning for him.

"Then," she said, "into less dangerous ventures such as the churn business."

And into history — with the Dazey firm at one time bragging: "The name Dazey on the kitchen mixer is equivalent to the word Sterling on silver."

Nathan P. Dazey was listed in the *Dallas City Directory* in 1905 as manager of the E-Z Butter Maker Manufacturing Company and it was about this time that he became acquainted with a Mr. E. B. Jones, who had a small, unique glass butter churn. The churn interested Dazey, but his first attempt to persuade Jones to let him market it was unsuccessful. But Jones later became ill, lost all his money and sent for Nathan.

Nathan lent Jones the money needed to pay his debts and gave him a salary and one-third interest in the new concern manufacturing glass-bottom churns. Jones later got bored with the deal and sold his interest back to Dazey for $1,500.

In 1906, Nathan and his first son, Jack Philip Dazey, moved the family business from Dallas to St. Louis to get closer to suppliers and to utilize cheaper freight.

Jack and his siblings — Harry, Margaret, James and Tom — were all involved in the new company with their father.

On April 16, 1907, Nathan patented a stand-up, metal container churn *(fig. 13-1)* featuring "a receptacle in which the body or milk receptacle is disposed, the receptacle being considerably larger than the body and providing means for hot or cold water with which to temper the milk in the body. When using the churn in cold weather, the churning action is materially improved by slightly heating the milk or cream in the body, and in warm weather it is frequently desirable to cool the milk or cream and this can be readily accomplished by supplying hot water or cold water to the receptacle as circumstances may require."

The next two patents in the Dazey line also were by Nathan, a Dec. 18, 1917 *(fig. 13-2)* stand up with improvements, and a Feb. 14, 1922 *(fig. 13-3)* glass-bottom model featuring a small screen strainer.

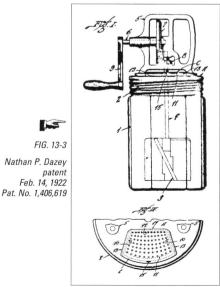

FIG. 13-3

Nathan P. Dazey
patent
Feb. 14, 1922
Pat. No. 1,406,619

He said in the 1922 patent: "This invention relates to improvements in churns, the object being to provide a churn particularly of the small capacity type for household use in which the highest quality of butter can be made and very easily and quickly washed without removing the dasher from the churn." Mainly the invention consisted of a screen covered drain, on the top of the jar lid, that allowed the removal of buttermilk without having to pour everything through a strainer cloth.

The Dazey family kept the patent office busy for things other than churns. Nathan patented a large advertising sign March 23, 1909 *(fig. 13-4)* and a nifty dispenser for straws Nov. 28, 1911 *(fig. 13-5)*. Nathan's second son, Harry L., patented a pneumatic tire May 3, 1910 *(fig. 13-6)* and he later formed the Dazor Lighting Company, apparently utilizing his father's patent. Harry L. also was partly responsible for the popular Dazey can opener *(fig. 13-7)*.

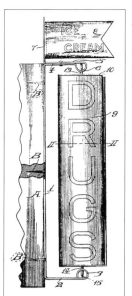

FIG. 13-4

Nathan P. Dazey patent
March 23, 1909
Pat. No. 916,116

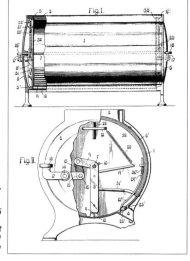

FIG. 13-5

Nathan P. Dazey patent
Nov. 28, 1911
Pat. No. 1,010,121

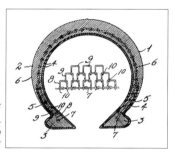

FIG. 13-6

Harry L. Dazey patent
May 3, 1910
Pat. No. 956,948

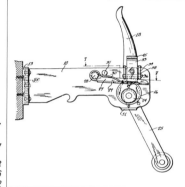

FIG. 13-7

Harry L. Dazey patent
Feb. 4, 1936
Pat. No. 2,029,812

Dazey: The Prince of Churns

By Butch and Dea Allen

Would you believe that the day would come that a Dazey churn would bring $2,000+ at an auction? A collector recently attended an auction in Sedalia, Missouri where a one-quart Dazey sold for $2,710. At an auction in Columbia, Missouri., a beveled edge one-quart Dazey ran up to $2,500 and a round label one-quart Dazey sold at $2,100.

We have been collecting Dazey and other churns for 11 years. When we started, we thought that the prices at that time were outlandish, but as you can see from the prices paid recently, we had real bargains years ago.

Our first one-quart Dazey was purchased in two parts. Butch found the top in a junk store for $12.50 and through an ad in the Antique Trader, the jar was purchased for $280. I growled that I had to pay that much for a jar. In years past, you could purchase a common Dazey No. 40 for around $45 at any auction. I was spoiled.

As time goes on, we are finding more and more collectors of Dazey churns. The new collector is quite aggressive and the prices continue to escalate to a point where they are getting out of reach of the older collector. When the new breed discovers that Dazey not only produced different sizes, but also different styles, the race is on to complete a collection containing all the various sizes and styles.

We have also encountered the real die-hard Dazey collector who has found most of the Dazey churns and has turned to other searches for such things as eggbeaters, mayo mixers and the like. Butch and I are among the guilty.

Butch and Dea Allen, the pride of St. Joe, Missouri, are advanced collectors and dedicated churn historians. Their churn and related ephemeral collections are among the best in the country (check out their website at www.ponyexpress.net/~butchnd). Without their help, this chapter would not have been possible.

Another major contributor to this chapter was Gale Scarborough of Wichita, Kansas.

FIG. 13-8

Comparison of one-quart Dazeys (left to right):

Slope shouldered:
DAZEY CHURN NO. 10 DAZEY CHURN & MFG. CO. ST. LOUIS, MO. MADE IN U.S.A.
Back side marked: **DAZEY CHURN NO 10**
Embossed on the bottom of the jar is the daily flower and the name **DAZEY** *twice, horizontally & vertically, with the* **Z** *shared in the center.*
6-3/4" jar   —$3,000+—
This is the rarest of the one-quarts.

Round label:
DAZEY CHURN & MFG. COMPANY ST. LOUIS, MO 1QT
Original paper label on back side: **SAVES LABOR   DAZEY CHURN & MFG. CO. ST. LOUIS USA BETTER BUTTER**
7-1/2" jar   —$2,300—
A hard-to-find version of this one-quart has **MADE IN AMERICA** *embossed in a line under the round label. Note the top of the threads on this churn and the one to the right of it. The one to the right has an indentation at the top of the threads. These will interchange but the one on the right will not screw all the way down on the round label jar in the center.*

Beveled edge, horseshoe label:
DAZEY CHURN & MFG. COMPANY ST. LOUIS, MO
Jar bottom is embossed with the number **10**
7-1/2" jar   —$2,200—

It was in St. Louis that the glass-bottom DAZEY churn came into its own. The Dazey Churn and Manufacturing Company had a series of glass churns, with variations within each set. There were three main sets of DAZEYS, with the smallest, the one-quarts, always bringing top dollar *(fig. 13-8).*

And the Cat Came Back.

Just like Dazey Churn sales, Mr. Dealer. One Dazey sale in a neighborhood and five sales or more are sure to follow.

It's what users tell their friends about the Dazey making more butter, better butter and so easily, that has made it the largest selling Churn in the world.

Open your door to increased churn sales by placing a few churns throughout your district and watch them multiply.

Dazey Churns are sold only through dealers and jobbers

We have prepared elaborate folders, booklets, counter and window displays, finely illustrated and beautifully colored, which help you sell Dazey Churns to old and new customers. Free for the asking. A post card will do. No matter how busy you are, write for and make use of them now.

DAZEY CHURN & MFG. CO.
Carter & Warne Aves.   -   -   -   St. Louis, Mo.

Dazey promotional flyer for dealers

DAZEY CHURNS

ALLEN COLLECTION

FIG. 13-9

Beveled edge Dazey churns with unmarked tops (left to right):

One-quart: **DAZEY CHURN & MFG. COMPANY ST. LOUIS, MO**
7-1/2" jar   —$2,200—

Two-quart: **DAZEY CHURN & MFG. COMPANY ST. LOUIS, MO**
8" jar   —$900—

Three-quart: **DAZEY CHURN & MFG. COMPANY ST. LOUIS, MO**
9" jar   —$1,000—

Four-quart: **DAZEY CHURN & MFG. COMPANY ST. LOUIS, MO**
9-1/2" jar   —$1,000—

▶ The oldest of the three sets of Dazeys came with beveled corners. a horseshoe label, and a number on the bottom. This churn was manufactured around 1907 in four sizes — one, two, three and four-quart *(fig. 13-9)*. The beveled edge churn top was not marked, which has caused some confusion among collectors. The bottom of jar number indicates the size, 10 for one-quart, 20 for two-quart, 30 for three-quart, and 40 for four-quart. The beveled edges evolved into round edges *(fig. 13-10)*, with an early Dazey catalog *(fig. 13-11)* saying: "New style jar of the improved Dazey has no sharp upper corners to collect cream that would remain unchurned. This improved jar is far easier to clean, more attractive, and more durable."

FIG. 13-10

Round-edge compared to beveled edge Dazeys (left to right):

Four-quart:
DAZEY CHURN & MFG. COMPANY ST. LOUIS, MO
9-1/2" jar with rounded edges but horseshoe embossing, instead of round label. Believed to be rare transitional piece.
—$1,000—

Four-quart:
DAZEY CHURN & MFG. COMPANY ST. LOUIS, MO
9-1/2" jar
—$600—

ALLEN COLLECTION

THE EGGBEATER CHRONICLES

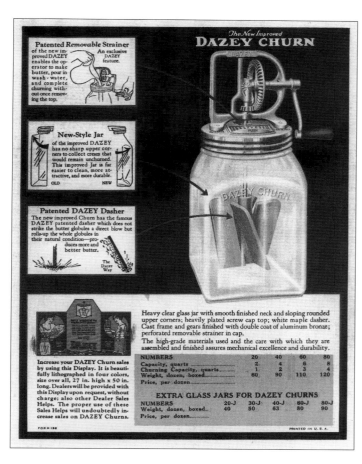

FIG. 13-11

Early Dazey catalog sheet

▶ The second series of Dazey churns had round labels, unmarked tops, and high shouldered jars (*fig. 13-12*). Dazey varied the writing on these churns, some with fine embossing, others with bold. The circle embossing said: DAZEY CHURN & MFG. CO., ST. LOUIS U.S.A. In a line across the bottom of the jar, some are marked MADE IN USA, and others MADE IN AMERICA. The MADE IN AMERICA versions are harder to find and command a higher price. These churns were produced until 1922.

A hard-to-find high shoulder, believed to be another transitional piece (*fig. 13-13*), has a circle embossed in the jar to outline a paper label. Embossed around the circle is DAZEY CHURN & MFG CO, with ST. LOUIS, MO USA MADE IN AMERICA underneath. Embossed above the circle is NO 40 DAZEY CHURN.

FIG. 13-12

Round label Dazey churns (left to right):

One-quart: **DAZEY CHURN & MFG. COMPANY ST. LOUIS, MO 1QT**
7-1/2" jar   —$2,300—
Note: The back of the original paper label can be seen on the other side of the jar.

Two-quart: **DAZEY CHURN & MFG. COMPANY ST. LOUIS, MO 20 MADE IN AMERICA**
8" jar   —$300—

Four-quart: **DAZEY CHURN & MFG. COMPANY ST. LOUIS, MO 40 MADE IN AMERICA**
9-1/2" jar   —$175—
Note: The three-quart round label, not pictured, has a 9" jar and is valued at $275 with the **Made in America** line.

FIG. 13-13

DAZEY CHURN & MFG CO ST. LOUIS, MO USA MADE IN AMERICA
NO. 40 DAZEY CHURN, believed to be transitional piece, shown here with reproduction paper label
9-3/4" jar   —$225—
With original label, probably double

R S Arnold   ALLEN COLLECTION

R S Arnold   ALLEN COLLECTION

ALLEN COLLECTION

FIG. 13-14

Raised screen Dazey churns (left to right):

**2 QT DAZEY CHURN & MFG. CO
NO. 20
MADE IN ST. LOUIS USA,**
with original paper label: *IT'S A DAZEY CHURN*
8" jar   —$300—

**3 QT DAZEY CHURN & MFG. CO
NO. 30
MADE IN ST. LOUIS USA**
8-3/4" jar   —$300—

**4 QT DAZEY CHURN & MFG. COMPANY
NO. 40
MADE IN ST. LOUIS USA**
9-1/2" jar   —$300—

FIG. 13-15

*Detail of two-quart
raised screen*

The "raised screen" Dazey was believed introduced prior to 1922. The tops in some cases were marked DAZEY and others were not. The raised screen tops were used on the round label jars with very fine embossing (*figs. 13-14 & 13-15*).

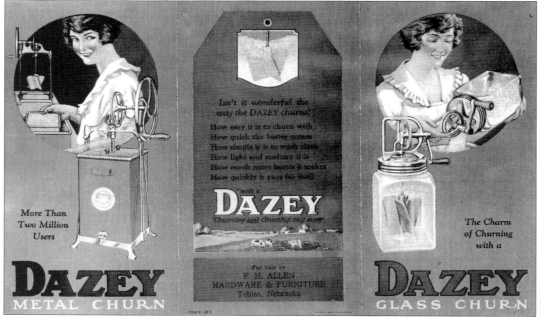

Isn't it wonderful the way the DAZEY churns?

How easy it is to churn with
How quick the butter comes
How simple it is to wash clean
How light and sanitary it is
How much more butter it makes
How quickly it pays for itself

DAZEY
Churning isn't Churning any more

For Sale by
F. H. ALLEN
HARDWARE & FURNITURE
Tobias, Nebraska

More Than
Two Million
Users

DAZEY
METAL CHURN

The Charm
of Churning
with a

DAZEY
GLASS CHURN

**Dazey
promotional
brochure**

R S Arnold   ALLEN COLLECTION

FIG. 13-16

One-quart and dated Dazeys (left to right):

One-quart:
DAZEY CHURN NO. 10
DAZEY CHURN & MFG. CO. ST. LOUIS, MO.
MADE IN U.S.A.
Back side marked: **DAZEY CHURN NO 10**;
Embossed on the bottom of the jar is the daily
flower and the name **DAZEY** twice, horizontally
& vertically, with the **Z** shared in the center.
6-3/4" jar   —$3,000+—

Two-quart:
DAZEY CHURN NO. 20 PATENTED FEB 14, 22
DAZEY CHURN & MFG. CO. ST. LOUIS, MO.
MADE IN U.S.A.
8" jar
—$325 without jar flower, $550 with jar flower—

Three-quart:
DAZEY CHURN NO. 30 PATENTED FEB 14, 22
DAZEY CHURN & MFG. CO. ST. LOUIS, MO.
MADE IN U.S.A.
8-3/4" jar
—$350 without jar flower, $600 with jar flower—

▶ The third set of Dazeys has Nathan's Feb. 14, 1922 patent date on the jar *(figs. 13-16 & 13-17)* — with one exception, the one-quart. The top was marked DAZEY with a daisy flower, with the exception again being the one-quart, and it had a screen for pouring off the whey. There were six sizes, one-quart to eight-quart, Nos. 10, 20, 30, 40, 60 and 80. There are variations on the patent-dated Dazeys: Some have a daisy flower embossed on the bottom of the glass jar, and some are marked on both sides of the jar.

FIG. 13-17

Dated Dazeys (left to right):

Four-quart:
DAZEY CHURN NO. 40   PATENTED FEB. 14, 22
DAZEY CHURN & MFG. CO.   ST. LOUIS, MO.   MADE IN U.S.A.
9-1/2" jar
—$125 without jar flower;
$150 with jar flower—

Six-quart:
DAZEY CHURN NO. 60   PATENTED FEB. 14, 22
DAZEY CHURN & MFG. CO.   ST. LOUIS, MO.   MADE IN U.S.A.
10-1/4" jar
—$285 without jar flower, $600 with jar flower—

Eight quart:
DAZEY CHURN NO. 80   PATENTED FEB. 14, 22
DAZEY CHURN & MFG. CO.   ST. LOUIS, MO.   MADE IN U.S.A.
11-1/4" jar
—$285 without flower—
Note: The search for an eight-quart with jar flower continues, and thus its value remains undetermined.

R S Arnold

ALLEN COLLECTION

Around 1936 Dazey is believed to have offered a lower priced churn to meet the competition of what it called "inferior" imitations. An ad with an illustration similar to a Dazey churn said: "The success of Dazey Churns has, of course, inspired many imitations necessarily inferior to genuine Dazey Churns because they cannot use patented Dazey features and because quality is deliberately 'skimped' to make a price. For dealers who feel they must have a lower priced churn to meet such competition, the new 'PRICE' Churn is now available. But — if you put it beside a Dazey on your counter, and compared features, you will sell the Dazey every time. In comparison with cheap imitations of the Dazey, the 'PRICE' Churn offers a much better value." The ad said the PRICE came only in a four-quart size.

During this same time period, an English Dazey was being produced. English Dazeys (fig. 13-18) have been found in two-, three-, four- and six-quart sizes. Other sizes may exist. Some will have tops marked DAZEY with the daisy flower, some will have straight handles and others curved, and some will have a screen punched in the top.

R S Arnold

ALLEN COLLECTION

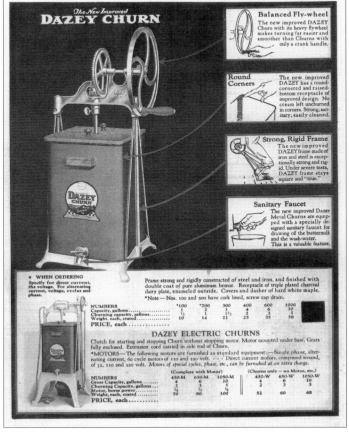

FIG. 13-18

British Dazeys (left to right):

DAZEY CHURN NO. 20
2 QUART ALL BRITISH
W.A.M. LTD LON
8" jar —$600—

DAZEY CHURN NO. 30
3 QUART ALL BRITISH
W.A.M. LTD LON
8-3/4" jar —$600—

DAZEY CHURN NO. 40
4 QUART ALL BRITISH
W.A.M. LTD LON
9-1/2" jar —$600—

DAZEY CHURN NO. 60
6 QUART ALL BRITISH
W.A.M. LTD LON
10-1/4" jar —$600—

No. 100—1 Gallon   No. 200—2 Gallons   No. 400—4 Gallons   No. 600—6 Gallons   No. 1000—10 Gallons   No. 1600—16 Gallons

Some Reasons Why the Dazey Saves Time and Labor

1—The powerful dasher, aided by the square corners of receptacle, produces a scientific agitation, making it possible to churn in from two to eight minutes.
2—The dasher is adjustable, therefore when drawn to top of cream (point of least resistance), the DAZEY runs as light as on a small churning.
3—More butter is produced with a DAZEY dasher by rolling all butter-making properties up with the butterfat into grains.
4—Working of butter is eliminated by the DAZEY. To wash off outside of grains is all that is necessary.
5—Temperature correct for churning is quickly obtained by placing the receptacle or the whole churn in warm or cool water.

6—Better butter is made by building up the butter globules in their natural condition.
7—Removing butter is easy and convenient as the entire top of receptacle is open.
8—Cleaning is as easily accomplished as cleaning an ordinary tin pail, because there are no cracks or complicated gearings inside. Not a single bearing inside of receptacle.
9—Sanitary, because nothing to absorb the cream and become rancid as with wooden churns. Can be sunned without warping and without handling entire churn. Just lift the receptacle out.
10—Durable, because made of best steel and iron, by skilled mechanics. With ordinary care will last for years.

SEND FOR FREE COLORED CATALOG OF HAND AND POWER CHURNS

FIG. 13-19

Some Reasons Why the Dazey Saves Time and Labor - catalog sheet

FIG. 13-20

Early Dazey catalog sheet

Metal Dazey churns date back to at least 1910 when they were first listed in an E.C. Simmons catalog. The original churns were produced in one-, two-, three-, four-, six-, 10- and 16-gallon sizes *(fig. 13-19)*. In the 1911 catalog, a 28-gallon size was added. The first metal churns had straight edges, which were later rounded for easier cleaning *(fig. 13-20)*. The size of the churn is easy to identify by checking the numbers embossed in the cast-iron top. For example, if it states 130B, the first number tells you that it is a one-gallon. If it's 230B, it is a two-gallon, and so on. The larger size Dazeys could be operated manually or with an electric motor. The one-gallon churn *(fig. 13-21)* is the most desirable. The metal containers were usually painted blue and marked: DAZEY CHURN, ST. LOUIS MO. Later versions had a colorful round decal.

Over the years Dazey thrived, adding new kitchen products to its line of glass and metal churns, starting with now rare ice cream freezers *(fig. 13-22)*. In a trademark for the Dazey name granted Nov. 4, 1941 *(fig. 13-23)*, it listed its products as churns, cutlery sharpeners, can openers, jar and bottle openers, fruit juicers, nut crackers and ice crushers. These were followed by a rotary hand eggbeater and a gadget called the MIX-ER-ATOR.

The Dazey hand eggbeater *(fig. 13-24)* was described as the BLEND-R-MIX featuring an adjustable handle that "permits right and left-hand use." A later model had a set handle.

FIG. 13-22

DAZEY ICE CREAM FREEZER
WHIP / EGG BEATER / BUTTER CHURN / MOLD
DAZEY CHURN MFG. CO. ST. LOUIS, MO.
11" —$800—

MOFFET COLLECTION

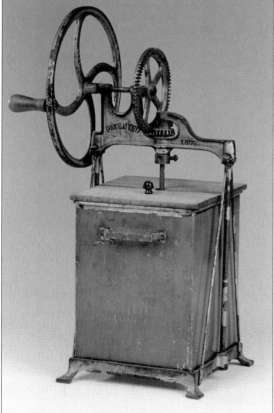

 FIG. 13-21

PATENTED 130B
DAZEY CHURN & MFG. CO. ST. LOUIS MO *(on cast-iron top)*
DAZEY CHURN NO 100 ONE GALLON
(stenciled on metal container)
7-1/2" high
—$550—
Other, more common, sizes can go for as much as $165.

R S Arnold   ALLEN COLLECTION

FIG. 13-23

U.S. Patent & Trademark Office Official Gazette, Nov. 4, 1941 Dazey Churn and Manufacturing Company trademark.

391,437. (CLASS 23. CUTLERY, MACHINERY, AND TOOLS, AND PARTS THEREOF.) DAZEY CHURN AND MANUFACTURING COMPANY, St. Louis, Mo. Filed Aug. 23, 1941. Serial No. 446,488.

DAZEY

FOR CHURNS, CUTLERY SHARPENERS, CAN OPENERS, JAR AND BOTTLE OPENERS, FRUIT JUICERS, NUT CRACKERS, AND ICE CRUSHERS.
Claims use since 1906.

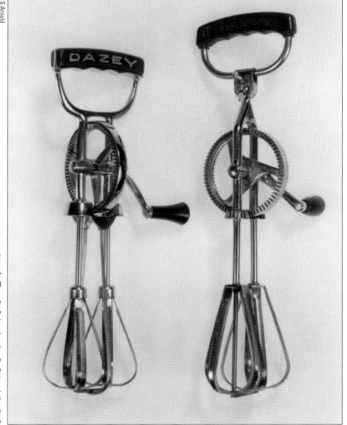

 FIG. 13-24

Dazey rotaries (left to right)

DAZEY in white on red plastic handle
11-1/2"
—$20—

DAZEY in red plastic, adjustable handle
12-3/4"
—$25—
Note: This model also comes with an all metal handle

HOY COLLECTION

FIG. 13-25

DAZEY MIX-ER-ATOR
10″ —$125—

FIG. 13-26

Dazey red tops (left to right):

DAZEY CHURN PAT APPLIED FOR NO. 4
ST. LOUIS, MO. U.S.A. DAZEY CORPORATION
Four-quart jar 9-1/4″ —$100—

DAZEY CHURN PAT APPLIED FOR NO. 8
ST. LOUIS, MO. U.S.A. DAZEY CORPORATION
Eight-quart jar 11-1/2″ —$125—

FIG. 13-27

Dazey catalog sheet

A catalog sheet said of the MIX-ER-ATOR plunger *(fig. 13-25):* "Time saver, blends, whips, purees, mixes, aerates. Full quart capacity. Stainless steel perforated disc whips cream, egg whites, churns milk drinks, baby formulas and butters. Convenient pouring lip." The MIX-ER-ATOR, with bright red plastic top and a large black ball on the top of the plunger, lists the number of strokes needed for such things as whip cream (60), frozen orange juice (12), scrambled eggs (20), and egg whites (60). The MIX-ER-ATOR had an exact twin, the WHIXIT, made by Taylor Brothers Churn and Manufacturing Co.

During World War II, the Dazey factory was all but closed. "The government would not allow Dazey the metals used in producing their products. Manufacturing of their entire line had to be shut down, but they did make 50 mm ammunition for the armed forces," Suzanne Dazey said. It was during the war, in 1944, that Dazey changed its name from the Dazey Churn and Manufacturing Company to Dazey Corporation.

Following the war, Dazey resumed production and introduced a churn with an "amazing new jar design." Nicknamed the RED TOP or FOOTBALL TOP *(fig. 13-26)* by collectors, this is how one catalog sheet *(fig. 13-27)* described it: "New four leaf clover design jar makes easier churning and eliminates loss of unchurned cream in square corners." Catalogs listed two, four and eight-quart red tops, along with a six-quart replacement jar. Only the four and eight-quart red tops have turned up in collections.

The war didn't stop all of the Dazey churn forces. Suzanne Dazey's brother, Jack Jr., purchased the Taylor firm in St. Louis in 1945 and produced many a churn *(fig. 13-28)* through 1948, when he moved to Columbus,

CONSUMER ACCEPTED *it's a* **DAZEY** KITCHEN HELPS

DAZEY CHURNS

For over a half century the Dazey Churn has maintained its leadership in the field, with both hand and electric churns incorporating each new improvement. For this reason Dazey Churns are quicker and eliminate the loss of unchurned cream due to inefficiency. Their special scientific design makes them more sanitary and easier to clean.

DAZEY HAND CHURNS – Model 4 and 8

MODEL 4
Gross capacity 4 quarts—
churning capacity 2 quarts.

MODEL 8
Gross capacity 8 quarts—
churning capacity 4 quarts.

New four leaf clover design jar makes easier churning and eliminates loss of unchurned cream in square corners. High speed fully enclosed gears, streamlined dashers. Patented removable strainer eliminates need of removing gearing to test temperatures, remove buttermilk or add wash water.

DAZEY five year guarantee: All DAZEY products are guaranteed to be free of defects in material and workmanship. If kept clean and instructions followed these items will give excellent service under ordinary household conditions.

DAZEY CORPORATION • • • ST. LOUIS 7, MISSOURI

FIG. 13-28

Dandys and Taylors (left to right):

Paper label on two-quart:
DANDY DELUXE CHURN QUICK EASY   FULLY GUARANTEED
DESIGNED BY J. P. DAZEY JR. MADE BY TAYLOR BROS. CHURN & MFG. CO. ST. LOUIS, MO. U.S.A.
6-1/4" jar   —$75—

Paper label on four-quart:
DANDY DELUXE CHURN QUICK EASY   FULLY GUARANTEED
DESIGNED BY J. P. DAZEY JR. MADE BY TAYLOR BROS. CHURN & MFG. CO. ST. LOUIS, MO. U.S.A.
8-1/4" jar   —$75—

Paper label on four-quart:
DANDY NEW ICE CREAM FREEZER
THE FIRST AND ONLY "KITCHEN SHELF FREEZER" WITH BIG FREEZER ADVANTAGES.
1-1/2 QT CAPACITY. SAVE 1/3 TO 1/2 THE COST OF DAIRY MADE ICE CREAM BY MAKING YOUR OWN.
NO MESS NO FUSS NO DRIP EASY TO USE EASY TO CLEAN FULLY GUARANTEED.
TAYLOR BROS CHURN & MFG CO. 4460 FINNY AVE ST. LOUIS MO MADE IN USA
10-1/2" jar   —$75—

Paper label on four-quart:
TAYLOR BROS. CHURN AND MFG. CO. ST. LOUIS, MO. NO. 4 DANDY CHURN
9-34" jar   —$75—

Mississippi. In Mississippi he "continued to manufacture churns for Sears and Wards through mail order. He also made churns named Dandy," Suzanne Dazey said.

A catalog sheet at the time said of the DANDY: "These high speed churns have fully enclosed gearing. Streamlined dasher and jar shape assures complete churning action, and maximum agitation. Popularly priced, it surpasses competition in features and value."

Production of the DANDY, which came in two-, four- and eight-quart models, ended about four years later. But before the DANDY demise, there was a GEM DANDY (*fig. 13-29*), an electric model with two different dashers.

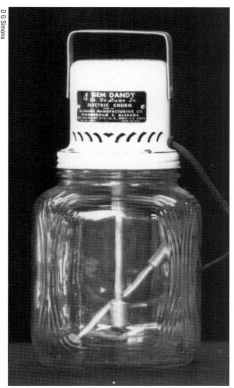

FIG. 13-29
GEM DANDY 4 QT. DE LUX JR.
ELECTRIC CHURN
9-3/4" jar   —$60—

This Dazey brochure illustration was accompanied by the following ad copy: "I used to dread Churning,—now I enjoy it."

Jack P. Dazey, the force behind the move to St. Louis, died in 1964 in Grand Rapids, Michigan, at the age of 79.

When asked about her father and the firm, Suzanne Dazey provided these nuggets: "My father was a fine man — he had a great sense of humor which he needed with five children around. He whole-heartedly believed in being punctual. If I was one minute late to be at the car, he would be gone and I had two miles to walk to school. A lesson I adhere to daily.

"He was a slight man who played a low handicap game of golf, loved to play gin rummy and bridge, usually coming out well ahead. He was an excellent businessman and ran the corporation with an iron hand, making Dazey a big success."

In the late 1940s, the Dazey family sold the firm to a small group of investors doing business as Central States Manufacturing Company of St. Louis. In 1954, the firm ended up in the Landers, Frary & Clark corporate family *(See Chapter 14, Landers Frary & Clark, page 165)*, but things didn't work out. In the late 1950s and early 1960s LF&C faced its biggest marketing declines, with a group of New York financiers moving in to gain control of the company and things quickly doing downhill.

In 1964, LF&C sold the wholly owned Dazey subsidiary to the Talge family of Kansas City, which previously had been associated with the Rival Manufacturing Company.

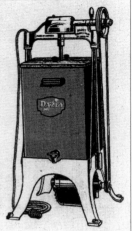

Dazey Electric

Adding electric power to a churn which already holds leadership as a butter maker, establishes the Dazey Electric as the most perfect churn obtainable.

Dazey Electric Churns are made in 4, 6, 10, 16 and 28 gallon sizes with the following motors as standard equipment: Alternating current, Single Phase, 60 Cycle, 110 or 220 Volts. Direct Current, 32, 110 or 220 Volts. When ordering, state kind of Current used and also Voltage and cycle.

Sold by Stores throughout the world.

U. S. and Foreign Patents

Dazey brochure advertisement

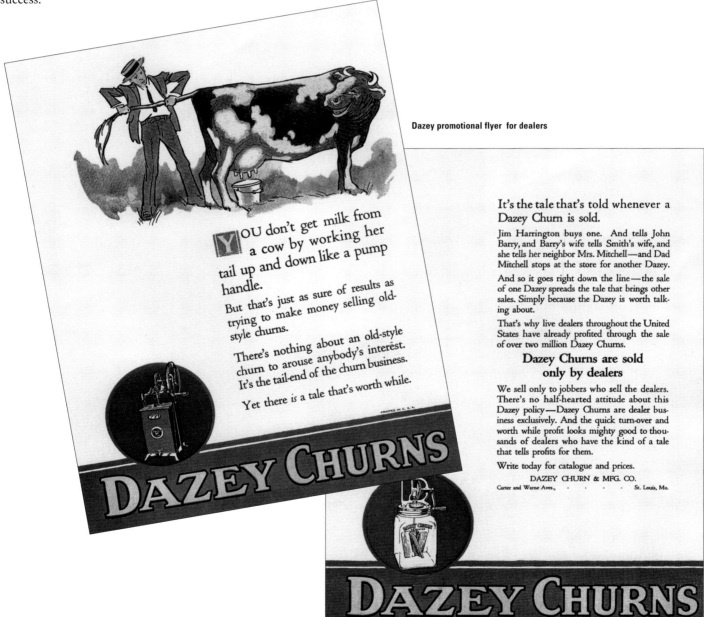

Dazey promotional flyer for dealers

YOU don't get milk from a cow by working her tail up and down like a pump handle.

But that's just as sure of results as trying to make money selling old-style churns.

There's nothing about an old-style churn to arouse anybody's interest. It's the tail-end of the churn business.

Yet there *is* a tale that's worth while.

PRINTED IN U. S. A.

DAZEY CHURNS

It's the tale that's told whenever a Dazey Churn is sold.

Jim Harrington buys one. And tells John Barry, and Barry's wife tells Smith's wife, and she tells her neighbor Mrs. Mitchell—and Dad Mitchell stops at the store for another Dazey.

And so it goes right down the line—the sale of one Dazey spreads the tale that brings other sales. Simply because the Dazey is worth talking about.

That's why live dealers throughout the United States have already profited through the sale of over two million Dazey Churns.

Dazey Churns are sold only by dealers

We sell only to jobbers who sell the dealers. There's no half-hearted attitude about this Dazey policy—Dazey Churns are dealer business exclusively. And the quick turn-over and worth while profit looks mighty good to thousands of dealers who have the kind of a tale that tells profits for them.

Write today for catalogue and prices.

DAZEY CHURN & MFG. CO.

Carter and Warne Aves., ... St. Louis, Mo.

DAZEY CHURNS

Dazey represents the nobility of churns, but there are dozens of other very collectible churns, including standup models and a wide assortment of glass-bottom mixers.

▶ The Taylor Brothers Churn Company of St. Louis (later purchased by Jack P. Dazey Jr.) produced the very desirable RELIABLE CHURN beginning in 1910 *(fig. 13-30)*. Brothers John E. and Thomas G. Taylor said in their Jan. 4, 1910 patent *(fig. 13-31)* that their device related "particularly to improvements in the gear-driven vertical dasher type whereby simplicity, strength and cheapness of construction, as well as smooth easy action, are secured."

▶ Another prized vertical standup *(fig. 13-32)* was patented May 29, 1894 by John M. Hughes of Knoxville, Tennessee, who described his device as a "vibratory churn" *(fig. 13-33)*.

G Scarborough

SCARBOROUGH COLLECTION

FIG. 13-30

**THE RELIABLE CHURN
MADE BY TAYLOR BROS. CHURN CO.
ST. LOUIS MO.
PAT. JAN 4, 1910**
36"   —$650—

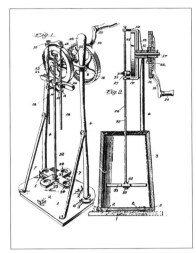

FIG. 13-31

*J. E. and T. G. Taylor patent
Jan. 4, 1910
Pat. No. 945,639*

S Scharnhorst

SCARBOROUGH COLLECTION

FIG. 13-32

PAT MAY 29.94, *only I.D.*
34-1/2"   —$475—
Below: detail of brackets

G Scarborough

FIG. 13-33

*John M. Hughes patent
May 29, 1894
Pat. No. 520,566*

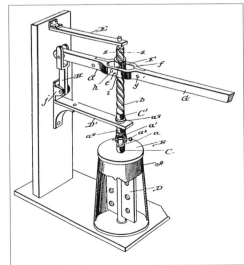

CHAPTER 13: DAZEY AND OTHER CHURNS

FIG. 13-34   D Thornton

☞ Bigger churns in the same family (left to right):

No I.D., six-gallon heavy-duty standup churn with spring release dasher
28-1/2" overall   —$400—

No I.D., one-gallon standup churn with spring release dasher
20" overall   —$175—

FIG. 13-35 ☜

Other churns (left to right):

PHOENIX EMULSIFIER WHITALL, TATUM & CO.,
all cast-iron, heavy duty, 12" porcelain container   —$350—

No I.D. tin container churn, but others with
green paint identifed by paper label as ELGIN
19-3/4"   —$95—

FIG. 13-36

Culinary churns (left to right)

1 QT, no other I.D.
6-3/4" jar   —$450—

**THE EZ HOUSEHOLD CHURN
FOR ALL BEATING
EASILY OPERATED SANITARY
ECONOMICAL DELICIOUS BUTTER ...
CULINARY MFG ...
NEWARK NEW JERSEY**
(on paper label)
CULINARY MFG. CO. ORANGE, N.J.
(embossed on glass jar)
7-3/4" jar   —$175—

CULINARY MFG. CO. ORANGE, N.J.
(embossed on glass jar)
9" jar   —$125—

ALLEN COLLECTION

FIG. 13-37

Culinary churns (left to right):

No I.D. but identified by old label as
THE "PREMIER" TWO-MINUTE HOUSEHOLD BUTTER CHURN, CULINARY MFG. CO.
6" jar —$450—

No I.D. but identified by ads as the CREST
6" jar —$450—

ALLEN COLLECTION

R S Arnold

The Monarch

Isenberg Brothers & Company of Charleston, Mississippi, offered The Monarch, an electric-powered, cabinet churn circa 1930 that it described as the "greatest of all electric home labor saving machines." And if the current went out, there was a detachable hand crank "a small child can operate with very little effort."

FIG. 13-38

Gimbel Bros. New York, New House Furnishing Department, 5th Floor, brochure cover

▶ Other large, early churns were used to make butter, of course, and emulsify drugs *(fig. 13-34 & 13-35)*.

▶ The Culinary Manufacturing Company of Orange, New Jersey, is believed to have produced several models of churns, including the SUPERIOR, the EZ, the TWO-MINUTE, and the CREST *(figs. 13-36 &13-37)*. The SUPERIOR, the EZ and TWO-MINUTE are the same model. The SUPERIOR name comes from a Gimbel Brothers brochure *(fig. 13-38)*, the churn itself is not marked as such. This same churn came with a paper label identifying it as the EZ. All except the one-quart have jars embossed CULINARY MFG. CO. ORANGE N.J.

The TWO-MINUTE and the CREST are exactly alike, except for one detail: The crank handles are on opposite sides of the main gear. An early ad for the TWO-MINUTE said it came in one-, two-, three-, and four-quart sizes. The June 1914 Charles Broadway Rouss of New York City catalog listed the one-quart TWO-MINUTE at $7.25 a dozen, or 65-cents each. A paper label on one said: THE "PREMIER" TWO MINUTE BUTTER MACHINE, CULINARY MFG. CO.

The CREST was described in the J. Hofmann Co. 17 Battery Place, New York, catalog as "the fastest churn made." Two pieces of additional evidence all these churns were related:

— A "Jobbers prices on Crest brand Household Specialties" found with an old CREST ad listed the factory in Orange, New Jersey.

— The EZ and the CREST used the same advertising words: "Easily Operated," "Sanitary" and "Economical."

FIG. 13-39

THE GUNN SANITARY BUTTER CHURN AND MIXER DOUBLE QUICK NO 2 CAPACITY 2 QTS (on paper label)
GUNN MFG. CO. PHILA. PAT APPLD (handle embossed)
2QT (embossed on jar)
8" jar —$200—

THE THOMAS MFG CO DAYTON, OHIO
9-3/4" jar —$300—

THE LIGHTNING BUTTER MACHINE
STEWART-SKINNER CO. MANUFACTURERS WORCESTER, MASS. U.S.A.
FOR PURE BUTTER AND PERFECT MIXING
(on paper label)
3QT (embossed on jar)
8-3/4" jar —$150—

1 QT. (embossed on jar and handle), no other I.D. but one-quart LIGHTNING
6-1/4" jar —$450—

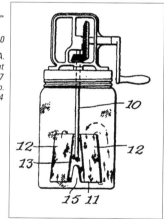

FIG. 13-40

Charles A.
Stewart patent
Feb. 6, 1917
Pat. No.
1,215,214

▶ The GUNN, the THOMAS and the LIGHTNING *(fig. 13-39)* are all collectible.

The GUNN has a distinctive horizontal 0-top and a paper label which boasts: "double quick." It was made by the Gunn Manufacturing Company of Philadelphia.

The THOMAS churn is very similar to the Dazey beveled-edge churn. It was made by the Thomas Manufacturing Company, 38 and 40 West 5th, Dayton, Ohio. The company was listed in the *Dayton City Directory* from 1908 to 1926 as a manufacturer of metal specialties, phonograph motors and parts and general merchandise.

Thomas Manufacturing also made the "LIGHTNING" CREAM AND EGG WHIP *(See Chapter 12, Archimedes, page 125)*. This LIGHTNING was a screw-on Archimedes that came in two sizes, one-half pint and one pint.

▶ There is another LIGHTNING, this one THE LIGHTNING BUTTER MACHINE, which came in four sizes, one-, two-, three- and four-quart. This LIGHTNING was manufactured by Stewart-Skinner Company of Worcester, Massachusetts.

A 1918 brochure said: "The Lightning Butter Machine is sanitary in every respect and rapid in its action. It is made entirely of metal and glass which can be thoroughly and easily cleansed. There is no wooden dasher to absorb different substances and carry the stain from one mixture to another, when the machine is used for the various purposes for which it is designed."

The LIGHTNING Feb. 6, 1917 patent *(fig. 13-40)* was obtained by Charles A. Stewart of Worcester, who said his invention "relates to a dasher particularly adapted for small churns, but

capable also of use for large churns and for use as an egg or batter beater, cream whip and for other similar purposes."

The three-wing dasher, Stewart said, "is particularly advantageous on account of its simplicity, cheapness in manufacture, and the ease with which it can be cleaned. Although it has the necessary angles for causing the desired circulation of liquid, it has no reentrant angles that cannot be readily cleaned, and no spaces where dirt can lodge."

Stewart also invented a sewing awl and launched Stewart-Skinner in Worcester in 1911 to produce it, along with household gadgets. In 1923, the Reynolds-Brown Company of Beverly, Massachusetts, purchased from Stewart-Skinner the LIGHTNING portion of its business and began manufacturing the churn in Beverly.

FIG. 13-41

Advertising drawing of Speedo Churn.
Until one or more show up on the
market, a value cannot be determined.
However, it will certainly set new
records.

▶ In addition to the THOMAS churn, there is another DAZEY look-alike, the SPEEDO CHURN. Currently only an advertising drawing of the SPEEDO exits *(fig. 13-41)*, showing SPEEDO CHURN embossed on the front of the glass jar. An advertising sheet for the glass-bottom SPEEDO identified the maker as the Thompson Manufacturing Company, 1127-29 Pine Street, St. Louis, Missouri. The sheet contained customer testimonials from across the country, indicating nationwide distribution. The same sheet listed sizes and prices:

- NO. 10, price $1.90, holds 3 pints, churns 2 pints
- NO. 20, price $2.50, holds 5 pints, churns 3 pints
- NO. 30, price $3.25, holds 7-1/2 pints, churns 4 pints
- NO. 40, price $3.85, holds 9 pints, churns 5 pints

Another ad said Thompson also made a large, stand-up metal container SPEEDO that held six gallons and churned four gallons. It was listed at $7.

Adding to the confusion surrounding the SPEEDO and the DAZEY is the fact that on April 24, 1951, the company which at that time owned Dazey, the Central States Manufacturing Company of St. Louis, was granted a trademark for a stylized name SPEEDO with an arrow running through it *(fig. 13-42)*. However, it is not believed to be related to the churn — the trademark identifies only can openers and knife sharpeners.

▶ The HOME BUTTER MAKER *(fig. 13-43)* was made at various times by Kohler Die & Specialty and A.D. Foyer & Company, both of Chicago and both manufacturers of the DREAM CREAM WHIP *(See Chapter 20, Big Turbines and Blades, page 229)*. It was sold by, among others, Sears, Roebuck and Company. A Sears brochure on the HOME BUTTER MAKER called it "an economical luxury," saying: "If creamery butter is 34 cents a pound and milk 4 cents a pint, your milk-charged table-butter made with this churn will cost 19 cents a pound. (The proportion is one pound of butter to one pound of milk, about 7/8 of a pint.)"

FIG. 13-42

U.S. Patent & Trademark Office Official Gazette,
April 24, 1951 Dazey Corporation, doing business as
Central States Mfg. Co., St. Louis, Mo., trademark

Ser. No. 604,625. Dazey Corporation, doing business as Central States Mfg. Co., St. Louis, Mo. Filed Oct. 9, 1950.

For Hand Operated Kitchen Appliances—Namely, Can Openers and Knife Sharpeners.
Claims use since 1928.

FIG. 13-43

Home Butter Makers (left to right):

THE HOME BUTTER MAKER, MANUFACTURED BY KOHLER D&S CO., CHICAGO, U.S.A.
Top rests on 8-1/2" jar   —$150—
Note: This model is also marked: **MANUFACTURED BY A.D. FOYER & CO., CHICAGO, U.S.A.**

THE HOME BUTTER MAKER, KOHLER DIE & SPECIALTY CO. DEKALB, ILL USA
Top screws on 8-1/4" jar   —$150—

THE HOME BUTTER MAKER USA (on metal top)
2QT (embossed in glass)
7-3/4" jar   —$225—
Note: This model is also marked: **KOHLER DIE & SPECIALTY CO. DEKALB, ILL.** (on top)

R S Arnold

CHAPTER 13: DAZEY AND OTHER CHURNS

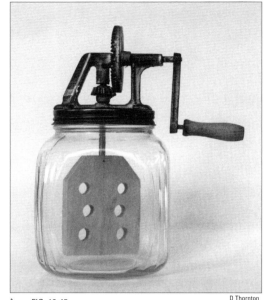

 FIG. 13-44

Elgin churns (left to right):

2QT (embossed in jar), only I.D., but according to ads the ELGIN
8-1/4" jar —$150—

No I.D., but ELGIN
9-1/2" jar —$100—

ALLEN COLLECTION

FIG. 13-45

D Thornton

 FIG. 13-45

No I.D., only marking on jar bottom
H over **A** (Hazel Atlas) **5275**
6-1/2" jar, 10" overall
—$75—

FIG. 13-46

**THE QUICKEST BUTTER
CHURNER ON THE MARKET
MANUFACTURED BY** (a star
symbol inside a double circle)
NEW YORK CITY
8" jar —$1,000+—

FIG. 13-47

No I.D.
8-1/2" jar
—$1,000+—

▶ Elgin glass-bottom churns, with a
distinctive slant handle, were offered by
Sears, Roebuck and Company in two-,
four-, six- and eight-quart sizes *(fig.
13-44).* "Handy for mixing malted milk,
salad dressing and whipping cream,"
said the 1932 Sears catalog. The catalog
listed the two-quart at $1.25 and the
1941 catalog listed it as 97 cents.
The 1941 catalog also offered Elgin
churns with metal containers in two-,
three-, four- and six-gallon sizes. In
addition, the Elgin name was featured
on a dairy scale and cow hobbles.

▶ A two-quart without identification,
and no advertising to track its identity,
is a squat model on a Hazel Atlas jar
(fig. 13-45). This churn has no handle
on the top to hold it down, meaning the
operator probably had to push down on
the tin, screw-on lid.

▶ Two very rare churns *(figs. 13-46 &
13-47)* reside in the collection of Gale
Scarborough, one of which advertises
itself as the "quickest butter churner
on the market." The QUICKEST stands
14-1/2" overall and has an involved
gearing system. The other churn is
15-1/4" overall and has four metal wings
that extend to the bottom of the jar.

SCARBOROUGH COLLECTION

SCARBOROUGH COLLECTION

S Scharnhorst

SCARBOROUGH COLLECTION

FIG. 13-48

No I.D., but MAK-MOR
**BROWN SUGAR, GRAN.
SUGAR, FLOUR, POUNDS,
QUARTS, PINTS OZ**
(embossed on jar)
12-1/2" overall
—$500—

FIG. 13-49

1911 Saturday
Evening Post
ad

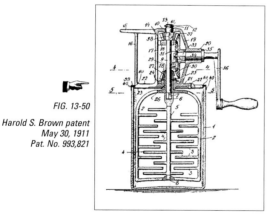

FIG. 13-50

Harold S. Brown patent
May 30, 1911
Pat. No. 993,821

D G Simons

FIG. 13-51

No. I.D.
13-1/2" overall
—$600—

MOFFET COLLECTION

▶ The MAK-MOR BUTTER MACHINE
(fig. 13-48) was advertised for $5 in
a 1911 magazine ad (fig. 13-49) that
promised "the fresh flavor is seldom
excelled in the best quality butter sold
at a fancy price." Harold S. Brown of
Stratford, Connecticut, obtained the
patent for the MAK-MOR on May 30,
1911 (fig. 13-50). The MAK-MOR was
offered by the Mak-Mor Sales Company,
4 South Street, New York City. Very
similar to the MAK-MOR, and possibly
a member of the same manufacturing
family, is a 13-1/2" mixer (fig. 13-51)
with a heavy jar with a handle like a cup.

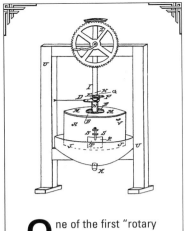

One of the first "rotary churn" patents was awarded April 2, 1850 to Osbert B. Loomis of Windsor, Connecticut. The dashers rotated one way and the container rotated the other.

FIG. 13-52

No I.D.
21" overall
—$1,500+—

D G Simons   MOFFET COLLECTION

FIG. 13-53

Tin container churns (left to right):

No I.D.
12" overall, container 9" high,
6-3/4" in diameter
—$80—

BERNHARDT NOVELTY CO. 1216 W. BROADWAY SPOKANE-WASH. (on brass label)
13" overall, container 9" high, 6-3/4" in diameter
—$95—

▶ Probably the most mechanically attractive of all churns is a brass and glass model that stands 21" high (*fig. 13-52*). It is double geared so the center dasher rotates in one direction while the outside dasher rotates the opposite way.

▶ Several collectible churns come with round metal containers, including stand alones and a table-mount. Two have identical containers but different tops (*fig. 13-53*).

▶ A heavy duty table-mount (*fig. 13-54*) has no identification but can be easily recognized by its main gear — 6-3/4" in diameter — which is just about the same size as its metal container. This churn is double geared on the top and has two sets of vertical wood churns that turn within each other in opposite directions.

D Thornton   FIG. 13-54

No I.D., table-mount
8" container
—$200—

D Thornton

D Thornton   COOPER COLLECTION

FIG. 13-55

**HOME BUTTER MERGER
PATD. SEPT. 14, 1909**
7-1/2" outside container
7-1/8" inside container
—$200—

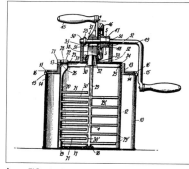

FIG. 13-56

Benjamin N. Hawes patent
Sept. 14, 1909
Pat. No. 934,169

▶ The HOME BUTTER MERGER (*fig. 13-55*) utilizes a container within a container — the outside container for hot water to speed up the process, the inner container the mixing vessel. The HOME BUTTER MERGER was patented Sept. 14, 1909 (*fig. 13-56*) by Benjamin N. Hawes of Washington, D.C., who said his invention was "designed particularly for use in the practice of merging milk with butter and producing an emulsion." The HOME BUTTER MERGER was manufactured by the Family Butter Merger Company, Ogen and Court Streets, Indianapolis, Indiana. Early fliers (*fig. 13-57*) said in part: "NOTICE: Never buy a machine of any kind unless it is protected by patents. They are always frauds and may get you in trouble. Our Butter Mergers are the only ones in the world that are protected by honest patents."

FIG. 13-57

Fliers for the Home Butter Merger

Where Our Butter Mergers are Manufactured

THE above cut shows the location of our factory in Indianapolis, Indiana, the greatest shipping center in the United States. Our factory is within Two Hundred feet of the Court House which is in the center of the city.

NOTICE: We ship you goods the next day after we receive your order. This is our positive rule.

Every Merger is inspected before it leaves the factory.

We carry a surplus stock of over 1,000 Mergers always on hand.

We employ only intelligent Union Labor. We pay our employees good wages and treat them with kindness and respect. Don't you think this is a good plan? The result is our Mergers are perfectly made and we have no trouble.

CAUTION

We are the originators, patentees and exclusive owners of four distinct and separate patents protecting this process and the machines for merging butter and milk together.

Look out for anyone trying to sell you something else. Any machine that uses heat in any way for merging butter and milk together infringes on our patents and the law makes the purchaser just as liable as the manufacturer. We have got an honest machine that does all we claim for it. We make the retail price within the reach of every family, so our agents can make a fair profit and our price to our agents gives us a fair profit. We think this is a fair deal all around.

NOTICE: Never buy a machine of any kind unless it is protected by patents. They are always frauds and may get you in trouble. Our Butter Mergers are the only ones in the world that are protected by honest patents.

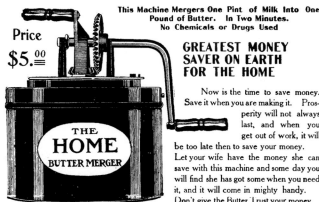

ONE PINT OF MILK
MERGED INTO ONE POUND OF

BUTTER. 4c. POUND

This Machine Mergers One Pint of Milk Into One Pound of Butter. In Two Minutes.
No Chemicals or Drugs Used

Price $5.00

GREATEST MONEY SAVER ON EARTH FOR THE HOME

Now is the time to save money. Save it when you are making it. Prosperity will not always last, and when you get out of work, it will be too late then to save your money. Let your wife have the money she can save with this machine and some day you will find she has got some when you need it, and it will come in mighty handy. Don't give the Butter Trust your money.

THE HOME BUTTER MERGER

(Capacity **2** Pounds in Two Minutes)

BUTTER is one of the most necessary articles of food, and the price is going higher every year. One can hardly eat a meal of victuals without butter. Now, while we admit all of this, and also that butter is the most expensive food used on our table, costing from 30 to 50 cents a pound, the great question comes into our mind, how can we help ourselves? It was the solution of this question that has brought to light this wonderful machine.

ONE PINT OF MILK WEIGHS A POUND
This is what the machine does—

IT TAKES ONE PINT of MILK, PRICE 04c
IT TAKES ONE POUND of BUTTER, PRICE . .36c
TOTAL 40c

It merges the two together making two pounds, that is sweeter than any Creamery Butter, giving you TWO POUNDS for FORTY CENTS, that looks the same, gets just as hard, and is used for the same purpose as any creamery butter, which would cost you SEVENTY-TWO CENTS for the same amount, SAVING you THIRTY-TWO CENTS on two pounds. *Don't You Think This is Worth Saving?*

MECHANICAL AND PROCESS PATENTS DATED; May 4, 1909, August 10, 1909, September 7, 1909 and September 14, 1909

Several churns utilize a full 360-degree turn of the container, many of them English and featuring a loose dasher in the glass jar to help mix things up (figs. 13-58 & 13-59).

English models include another full-turn, an unmarked model, an odd paper label over BLOW embossing, and the famous BLOW churns themselves (figs. 13-60 through 13-62). A "directions for use" sheet for the BLOW said in part: "The 'Blow' Churn is a perfect mixer.

For whipping cream or beating eggs turn the handle rapidly for about one minute. For making a superb salad cream the Blow churn has no equal." The BLOW churns were made by J. J. Blow Ltd., Oldfield works, Chatsworth Road, Chesterfield, Derbyshire. They were made with covered and uncovered gears similar to the DAZEYS.

In addition, English churns have such names as the ROLWAY and MIRACLE, ranging in jar size from 6-3/4" to 12" (fig. 13-63). An instruction sheet for the MIRACLE said in part: "Before the war

one person in a hundred thousand bought a butter churn and they were, naturally, quite costly. With the coming of butter rationing there arose the opportunity to supply very many homes with a churn if one could be designed simply and sold cheaply. We set out to do this under the none too easy wartime conditions affecting prices and supplies of materials. The 'Miracle' Home churn was the outcome. We believe that we can truthfully claim our churns to be the only purposely designed articles of their type and price available in England today."

FIG. 13-58

No I.D.
14" overall —$150—

Note: There is a near replica at 10"
THE COTWAYS UNIVERSAL CHURN
(embossed on aluminum bracing)
EASIWORK PAT. NO. 271182
(embossed on jar bottom)

D G Simons

FIG. 13-59

RYLANDS ATLAS TRADE MARKS
7-3/4" overall
—$200—

BRUCE JOHNSON COLLECTION

R S Arnold

FIG. 13-60

Various English (left to right):

IMPERIAL KILNER LTD
(on jar lid)
THE KILNER JAR IMPROVED REG 2.
(embossed on jar)
12" overall —$250—

No I.D. but believed English,
on mismatched 10" jar —$75—

SANITARY E *(in diamond)* **CHURN**
(on paper label)
BLOW BUTTER CHURN, MADE IN ENGLAND, 4 IMPERIAL QUARTS
(embossed on jar under paper label)
10" —$100—

ALLEN COLLECTION

THE EGGBEATER CHRONICLES

ALLEN COLLECTION

FIG. 13-61

Blow churns (left to right):

BLOW (on metal top)
B 713 (on jar bottom)
7-1/2" jar —$450—

BLOW (on metal top)
BLOW BUTTER CHURN NO 20
MADE IN ENGLAND (embossed on 8" jar)
—$150—

BLOW (on metal top)
BLOW BUTTER CHURN J.J. BLOW LTD
CHATSWORTH ROAD
CHESTERFIELD, ENGLAND
(on paper label)
LR 458 BLOW MADE IN ENGLAND NO 4
(on jar bottom)
10-1/2" jar —$150—

FIG. 13-62

Big Blows (right to left):

BLOW BRITISH REGD. 856612 (on metal top)
BLOW BUTTER CHURN 3/30
MADE IN ENGLAND 3 IMPERIAL QUARTS
(embossed on 9-1/2" jar)
—$150—

BLOW (on top)
9 QUARTS BLOW BUTTER CHURN 90
MADE IN ENGLAND (embossed on 12" jar)
—$200—

D Thornton

FIG. 13-63

Rolways and Miracles (left to right):

ROLWAY NO 10 (on cast-iron top)
BRITISH MADE (on jar bottom)
6-3/4" jar —$250—

ROLWAY (on cast-iron top)
MADE IN ENGLAND NO 5179
(on jar bottom)
12" jar —$250—

MADE IN ENGLAND only I.D. but
identified by ad as MIRACLE
9" —$175—

JL&CO LOC 145L4 only I.D. but
identified by ad as MIRACLE
7-1/2" jar —$250—

ALLEN COLLECTION

CHAPTER 13: DAZEY AND OTHER CHURNS

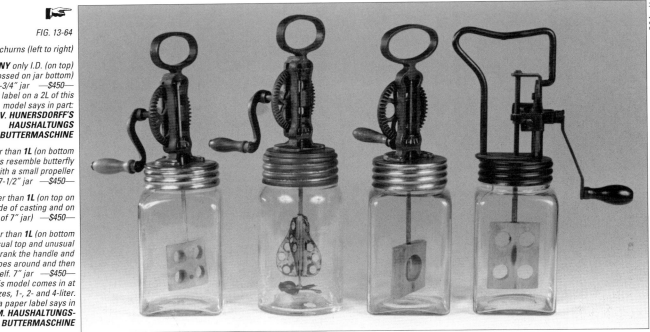

R S Arnold

☞

FIG. 13-64

German churns (left to right)

GERMANY *only I.D. (on top)*
1L *(embossed on jar bottom)*
6-3/4" jar —$450—
Note: A paper label on a 2L of this model says in part:
R.V. HUNERSDORFF'S HAUSHALTUNGS BUTTERMASCHINE

No I.D. other than **1L** *(on bottom of jar), dashers resemble butterfly wings with a small propeller underneath. 7-1/2" jar* —$450—

No I.D. other than **1L** *(on top on back side of casting and on bottom of 7" jar)* —$450—

No I.D. other than **1L** *(on bottom of jar), unusual top and unusual motion — crank the handle and the paddle goes around and then reverses itself. 7" jar* —$450—
Note: This model comes in at least three sizes, 1-, 2- and 4-liter. One with a paper label says in part: **D.R.G.M. HAUSHALTUNGS-BUTTERMASCHINE**

ALLEN COLLECTION

FIG. 13-65

☞ **SCHUTZMARKE MIT DEM BAREN**
1 liter with two-way dasher
7-1/4" jar, 13-1/2" overall —$450—

S Scharnhorst

SCARBOROUGH COLLECTION

FIG. 13-67

☞ **CHABLAISIENNE MODELE DEPOSE**
(on paper label)
7-1/4" container, 14-1/4" overall
—$650—

S Scharnhorst

SCARBOROUGH COLLECTION

☞

FIG. 13-66

No I.D. but rare German "doll house" churn.
2-3/4" jar, 5" overall —$1000—

R S Arnold   ALLEN COLLECTION

A good many German churns *(figs. 13-64 through 13-66)* have made their way to America over the years, including those with reversible and butterfly dashers, models called the BUTTER-MASCHINE, and a very rare "doll" churn.

Among the wide variety of French churns that have surfaced in the United States are one with a wooden container and another with heart-shaped holes in the main gear *(figs. 13-67 & 13-68)*.

A wooden top, the nicknamed STOMPER, and the U-turn dasher are three unusual churns that come without any identification — other than their different characteristics *(fig. 13-69)*.

A very rare churn with a graniteware container and an unusual outside pouch features the patent date Sept. 14, 1897 *(figs. 13-70 & 13-71)*. Lima, Ohio inventor John S. Mumaugh described the pouch as "a hot-water jacket which is

FIG. 13-68

French churns (left to right):

MENAGES AVANTAGES RESULTAT RAPID QUANTITE MAXIMUM
(on paper label)
1L *(on bottom of 7" jar)*
—$350—

1L *on bottom of jar only I.D., believed French with unique ratchet power, 7" jar* —$500—

MODELE DEPOSE
(on gear with heart-shaped holes)
MLE DEPOSE *(embossed on 8" jar)*
—$150—

MODELE DEPOSE
(on gear with heart-shaped holes)
MLE DEPOSE *(embossed on 7" jar)*
—$150—

R S Arnold

ALLEN COLLECTION

R S Arnold

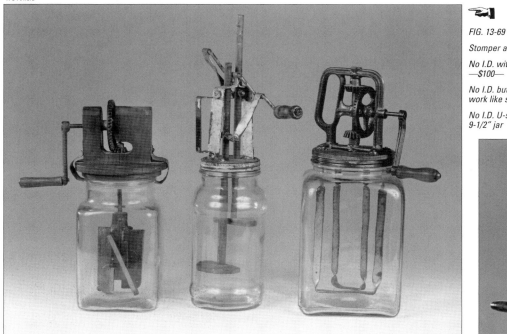

ALLEN COLLECTION

FIG. 13-69

Stomper and friends (left to right):

No I.D. with unusual wooden top, mismatched 7-3/4" jar —$100—

No I.D. but nicknamed the Stomper because the dashers work like stomping feet. 9" jar —$300—

No I.D. U-shaped dashers that turn in different directions 9-1/2" jar —$150—

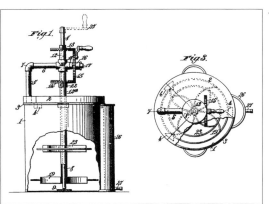

FIG. 13-70

John S. Mumaugh patent
Sept. 14, 1897
Pat. No. 590,160

FIG. 13-71

PAT SEPT 14, 97, *only I.D.*
18-1/4" container,
9-3/4" container diameter,
31-1/2" overall
—$1,500—

R S Arnold

ALLEN COLLECTION

secured to the body of the churn in a suitable manner ... At its lower end this hot-water jacket is provided with an outlet through which the water may be withdrawn. Hot or cold water, as the circumstances may require, may be introduced into this hot-water jacket for lowering or increasing the temperature of the contents of the churn." This churn comes in at least two sizes, with the pictured container measuring 18-1/4" high. Another container, without beater, measures 23" high.

The paper history of the MONKEY, a Maytag washer attachment and the BUTTERKWIK bring this chapter to a close:

▶ Benjamin F. Emery of Des Moines, Iowa patented the MONKEY Feb. 21, 1899 *(fig. 13-72)*, saying: "My object is to facilitate the labor of churning butter by means of the simultaneous actions of centrifugal and centripetal forces as a means of agitating and aerating milk to separate the cream therefrom and to produce butter." An early ad *(fig. 13-70)* said in part: "The Monkey Butter Separator and Churn combine with an Ice Cream Freezer, the only machine of its kind ever invented. ... Don't forget the name, the Monkey."

▶ "Necessity is the Mother of Invention," said a 1927 flier *(fig. 13-74)* for an offbeat butter churn. "The great demand of Maytag Washing Machine users has made necessary the invention and manufacture of the Better Butter Churning Attachment." The BETTER BUTTER CHURN was designed to be used with the Maytag electric washer and "successfully churns from three to four gallons of properly tested cream in the minimum length of time. The cream can be brought to the proper temperature by partially filling washing machine tub with cold or warm water, as desired."

▶ The BUTTERKWIK is a wood dasher device that came in two sizes and could be used with all wide mouth one-half and one-gallon Mason jars. A simple, effective churn device that is distinguished only by its label *(fig. 13-75)*.

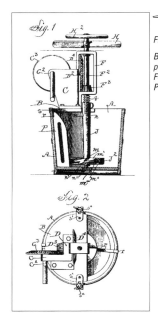

FIG. 13-72

Benjamin F. Emery patent Feb. 21, 1899 Pat. No. 619,739

FIG. 13-73

Ad for the "Air Monkey" or "the monkey that controls the air"

FIG. 13-74

1927 flier for Overgaard Sales Company's Better Butter Churn

FIG. 13-75

Frank R. Shinn Sr. churn label

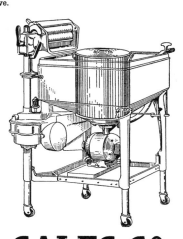

Chapter 14

Landers, Frary & Clark

Universal appeal.

*L*anders, Frary & Clark of New Britain, Connecticut: Another humble beginning.

George M. Landers in 1842 launched the business in New Britain, offering furniture casters, cupboard catches, coat and hat hooks and other hardware items. The firm evolved into Landers, Frary & Clark (LF&C) in 1856, and the famous trade name "Universal" came into existence in 1890 with the marketing of a food chopper.

It was followed by a bread maker, raisin seeder, potato masher and dozens of other items.

LF&C's foray into eggbeaters began in 1888 with a patent *(fig. 14-1)* by John Gerard of New Britain. At least one beater was produced, probably the patent model *(figs. 14-2 through 14-4)*. Gerard described himself as assignor to LF&C and said his rotary beater had a perforated "chamber" on the bottom inside of which a blade turned. The blade, he said, "acts as a pump to draw the egg or material to be operated upon into the chamber in advance of it, and them, as the blade continues its revolution … the material is forced from the chamber through the perforations, which produces a thorough disintegration of the material."

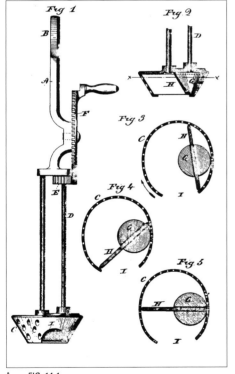

FIG. 14-1

John Gerard patent
March 27, 1888
Pat. No. 380,200

FIG. 14-2

LF&C EGG BEATER   PATD MAR 17 1888 USA
10-1/2" —$2,000—

R S Arnold

FIG. 14-3

Detail of
"chamber"

FIG. 14-4

Detail of back

MOFFET COLLECTION

FIG. 14-5

LANDERS, FRARY & CLARK, NEW BRITAIN, CONN. USA

10-1/4"   —$95—

D G Simons

"CROWN" RAISIN SEEDER

Heavily Tinned and easy to clean
Will seed one pound of raisins in five minutes
No. 4   Per dozen $12.00
Packed three dozen in a case. Weight per case, 117 pounds.

"DOVER" EGG BEATER

All Beating Parts Heavily Tinned
No. 2 Family Size   Per dozen $2.50
No. 12 Family Size, tinned all over   Per dozen 2.75
Packed one dozen in a box, 6 dozen in a case. Weight
per case, 39 pounds.

"UNIVERSAL" KNIFE CLEANER

For keeping steel blades bright
A machine for any kitchen. It does away with the old
fashioned knife and polishing brick. Does the work better
in one quarter the time and with infinitely less labor.
Each $2.50
Packed one in a box, six in a case. Weight per case, 55 pounds.

POTATO MASHER

Seamless Steel Bowl, Heavily Tinned.   Steel Handles
No. 1   Per dozen $4.80
Packed one dozen in a case. Weight per case, 22 pounds.

Cuts are all ⅛ size, showing actual relative proportion between sizes of objects.

FIG. 14-6

1914
LF&C
catalog sheet

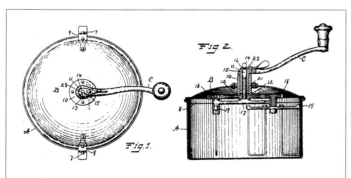

FIG. 14-7

Alonzo A. Warner patent
July 18, 1905
Pat. No. 795,082

D G Simons

In later years, LF&C offered another cast-iron rotary beater *(fig. 14-5)*. A 1914 LF&C catalog *(fig. 14-6)* described it as a "Dover" style and listed its price as $2.50 per dozen for the family size and $2.75 per dozen for the same size but tinned.

An important inventor for Landers, Frary & Clark was Alonzo A. Warner of New Britain. Warner patented a mixer on July 18, 1905 *(fig. 14-7)* that LF&C offered as a "cake maker" *(fig. 14-8)* saying in a catalog that "it beats eggs, whips cream and mixes thoroughly all kinds of batters."

FIG. 14-8

UNIVERSAL CAKE MIXER PATENTED JAN. 14 96 APRIL 18 05 JULY 18 05 NOV. 7 05 LANDERS, FRARY & CLARK NEW BRITAIN, CONN. U.S.A.

with additional blade dasher

9" diameter   —$50—

Warner's patent was an improvement on an earlier one, Jan. 14, 1896, by Elizabeth J. Eynon of Philadelphia *(fig. 14-9)*. Eynon apparently had her own mixer manufactured before her patent ended up in the LF&C family. Hers is a very rare, heavy-duty cast-iron model embossed on the top THE EYNON MIXER & BEATER PAT. JAN. 14, 1896. The same date is also featured on an early LF&C mixer named the UNIVERSAL CAKE MAKER *(fig. 14-10)*. To help date the early cake maker, it should be noted that LF&C was granted trademark No. 36,463 on May 21, 1901 for the UNIVERSAL name for "egg-beaters and cream-whips."

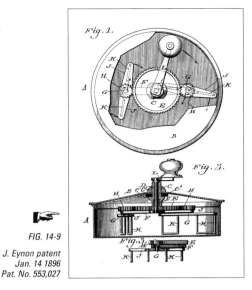

☞ FIG. 14-9

Elizabeth J. Eynon patent Jan. 14 1896 Pat. No. 553,027

Trouble in Churning is frequently complained of in winter. Much of the trouble is due to a neglect of the temperature which can not be told with any approach to accuracy except by using a thermometer. If the cream is brought into a warm room until the thermometer shows it to stand at 60 degrees, we rarely find any difficulty. In old times the cream was thought to be bewitched, and as the power of a horse-shoe to keep witches away is well known, it was used to drive the witches from the churn. The horse-shoe was heated red hot and dropped into the cream in the churn. It drove the witches away when it brought the cream to the right temperature.

—*AMERICAN AGRICULTURIST*, MARCH 1880

R S Arnold

☛ FIG. 14-10

Eynon and Universal (left to right):

THE EYNON MIXER & BEATER PAT. JAN. 14, 1896 8-3/4" in diameter —$400—

UNIVERSAL CAKE MAKER PAT. JAN. 14, '96 OTHER PATENTS PENDING LANDERS FRARY & CLARK NEW BRI(TAIN, CONN. U.S.A. 8-3/4" in diameter —$200—

MAIR COLLECTION

Landers, Frary and Clark produced a war effort brochure proclaiming: "Save the fats for the fighters by making 1 pound of butter do the work of two."

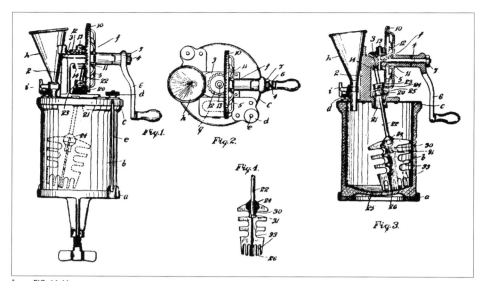

FIG. 14-11

Alonzo A. Warner patent
April 27, 1915
Pat. No. 1,137,037

FIG. 14-12

1914 LF&C catalog sheet

"UNIVERSAL" MAYONNAISE MIXER

WITH GLASS JAR AND TABLE CLAMP

FIG. 14-13

1919 LF&C catalog sheet

UNIVERSAL Home Needs   (UNIVERSAL)

"UNIVERSAL" HOME NEEDS

"UNIVERSAL" BREAD MAKERS

There is no guesswork, no waste of materials, time or labor. There is nothing to do but put in the ingredients, turn the crank for three minutes and the dough is thoroughly mixed.

The only sanitary way to make bread, as the dough is not touched by the hands. Also better bread is made by the UNIVERSAL Bread Maker, as sufficient moisture is always used to expand all cells of the flour.

By using the UNIVERSAL Bread Maker you do away with the bread raiser and the bread board, as the raising of the dough takes place in the Bread Maker.

FOR VERY SMALL FAMILIES

No. 2   Per dozen $33.00

Capacity 2 loaves
Depth of Pail 7½ in.
Packed 6 in case
Weight 4½ lbs.; 6 in case 40 lbs.

REGULAR FAMILY SIZE

No. 4   Per dozen $45.00

Capacity 2 to 6 loaves
Depth of Pail 9 in.
Packed 6 in case
Weight 7¼ lbs.; 6 in case 65 lbs.

LARGE FAMILY SIZE

No. 8   Per dozen $54.00

Capacity 4 to 10 loaves
Depth of Pail 11¾ in.
Packed 6 in case
Weight 10½ lbs.; 6 in case 85 lbs.

"CLIMAX" BREAD MAKER

REGULAR FAMILY SIZE

No. 44   Per dozen $39.00

Capacity 2 to 6 loaves
Depth of Pail 9 in.
Packed 6 in case
Weight 7¼ lbs.; 6 in case 65 lbs.

CAKE MAKERS

The UNIVERSAL Cake Maker mixes batter for all kinds of cake, easier, more uniformly and a great deal quicker than by hand. It beats eggs, whips cream and mixes thoroughly all kinds of batters.

Each cake maker supplied with a kneading rod for mixing bread or biscuits in small quantities.

No. 1   Per dozen $50.00

Showing Kneading Rod
Capacity 4 qts.
Depth of Bowl 4¼ in.
Packed 1 in box, 6 in case
Weight 4¾ lbs.; 6 in case 50 lbs.
Both attachments furnished

No. 2   Per dozen $67.50

Showing Mixing Fliers
Capacity 7 qts.
Depth of Bowl 5 in.
Packed 1 in box; 6 in case
Weight 4¾ lbs.; 6 in case 50 lbs.
Both attachments furnished

MAYONNAISE MIXER

The UNIVERSAL Mayonnaise Mixer makes perfect mayonnaise in from three to four minutes. No especial skill is required and any recipe can be used. The valve adjustment on the funnel regulates the flow of oil from a few drops to a small steady stream.

The metal parts can be removed intact from the jar, allowing the latter to be easily cleaned. All inside metal parts are heavily tinned or plated and are perfectly sanitary. The table clamp eliminates the necessity of holding the mixer.

No. 150   Per dozen $42.00
Mixing capacity 1 pint
Weight packed 6 in wooden case, 43 lbs.

POTATO RICER

No. 11   Per dozen $11.25

Seamless Steel Bowl, Heavily Tinned. Steel Handles.
Packed 1 dozen carton
Weight per case 22 lbs.

The dual beater action of the cake makers was revolutionary for its time and set the stage for Warner's and LF&C's most famous mixer, an engineering marvel patented April 27, 1915 (*fig. 14-11*).

In his patent application, Warner called it a "mixing machine." LF&C formally called its table-mount churn the UNIVERSAL MAYONNAISE MIXER AND CREAM WHIPPER.

If you are fortunate enough to have a Universal Mayonnaise Mixer, try the following recipe from the "Universal Cook Book," date unknown.

Mayonnaise Dressing

Yolks of 2 eggs	1/4 cup vinegar
1 even teaspoon salt	1/4 salt spoon red pepper
2 cups olive oil	1/2 teaspoon mustard
Juice of 1 lemon	

Beat the yolks and salt until stiff. Fill the oil cup with olive oil and beat it in, drop by drop at first, increasing the flow until it becomes a small steam. When it stiffens turn off the oil and put in a little vinegar. Alternate the oil and vinegar in this way until the two cups of oil and the vinegar are all mixed in. Toward the end add the mustard and red pepper. The lemon juice is optional, but if beat in thoroughly as a last operation the mayonnaise will keep perfectly good for weeks.

The 1914 LF&C catalog (*fig. 14-12*) listed the price of this mixer at $2 and boasted:

"The Universal Mayonnaise Mixer makes perfect mayonnaise in from three to four minutes. No special skill is required and any recipe can be used. The valve adjustment on the funnel regulates the flow of oil from a few drops to a small steady stream … The metal parts can be removed intact from the jar, allowing the latter to be easily cleaned. All inside metal parts are heavily tinned or plated and are perfectly sanitary."

The mixer proved successful and the price went up. In the 1919 catalog, with the same sales pitch (*fig. 14-13*), the price was $42 per dozen.

The first version of the one pint mixer had an unmarked cast-iron apron top, with the wheel embossed: LANDERS, FRARY & CLARK NEW BRITAIN, CONN.

U.S.A. PAT'S APLD FOR. Later versions have an unmarked wheel but are embossed on the apron top: LANDERS, FRARY & CLARK, NEW BRITAIN, CONN. U.S.A. PAT. APR. 27, 1915 GR. BT. JULY 14, 1914 NO. 16,753/14. The one-pint mixer was followed by other churns with glass and tin containers (*figs. 14-14 & 14-15*).

A history of the firm by the New Britain Public Library tells how it survived during World War I by converting "to military products such as gas masks, mess knives and kits, and canteens. Even cavalry sabers were produced, though never used."

After the war the firm went into the large home appliance business, with such items as vacuum cleaners, electric ranges and clothes washers. Smaller items included waffle irons, mixers, sandwich toasters and heating pads.

FIG. 14-14

Universals (left to right):

UNIVERSAL MAYONNAISE MIXER AND CREAM WHIPPER MADE BY LANDERS, FRARY & CLARK NEW BRITAIN, CONN. USA
(embossed on jar which is 5-1/4")   —$550; with funnel: $650—

UNIVERSAL CHURN NO. 25 LANDERS, FRARY & CLARK NEW BRITAIN, CONN. USA PAT APPLIED FOR
7-1/2" jar   —$500—

UNIVERSAL MADE BY LANDERS, FRARY & CLARK NEW BRITAIN, CONN. USA PAT'S APPLIED FOR
10-1/2" container   —$350—

UNIVERSAL BUTTER MERGER AND FAMILY CHURN NO. 135 (on front) **UNIVERSAL CHURN PAT'S APPLIED FOR G.R. PAT. 636,801 OCT. 1, 1915** (on top)
8" container   —$400—

FIG. 14-15

UNIVERSAL CHURN NO. 45 LANDERS, FRARY & CLARK NEW BRITAIN, CONN.
(embossed on glass jar)
16" —$900—

R S Arnold

SEIDEL COLLECTION

But things turned sour in later years and on May 17, 1965 LF&C with its Universal trademark, assets, inventories and equipment, was sold to General Electric's Housewares Division. What happened?

Several factors help explain the decline, according to the library piece. "First, it was in an industry which was not growing quickly enough to offer sales growth to the substantial number of competitors. The growing popularity of pre-processed foods did not help. The acquisitions of the 1950s were in areas close to Landers' expertise, but were not in areas which promised high growth. Sound operations such as the cutlery business were discontinued. Furthermore, LF&C's 'top of the line' strategy might have come to hurt the company in that the high quality was not the prime concern of the customers."

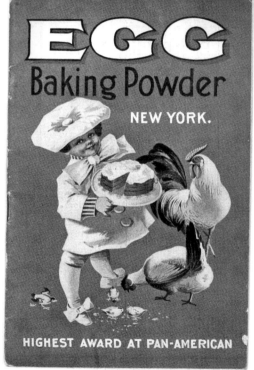

HIGHEST AWARD AT PAN-AMERICAN

COOPER COLLECTION

The Egg Baking Powder Company of New York offered several recipe booklets just before and after 1900. Measuring 4" by 6-1/2" the booklets touted the "King of baking powders."

Landers, Frary and Clark manufactured several different apple parers, including this unusual turntable. Marked RICE'S PAT. JULY 5, 1881 LANDERS, FRARY & CLARK. NEW BRITAIN, CONN U.S.A., this parer is mounted on a frame with a chute for the pared/cored apple.

[Photo by R.S. Arnold; Gray Collection]

THE EGGBEATER CHRONICLES

Chapter 15

Ladd

"3 Eggs Go as Far as 4 … It Aerates."

Earnest W. Ladd of Washington, D.C., summed it up best: "My invention relates to mixers, kneaders and beaters, but has particular reference to rotary egg-beaters of the multiple blade type, such as exemplified by that form known to the trade as the 'Dover.'

"It has for its object various improvements upon the Dover among which may be noted simplicity and economy of construction, lightness, durability and a greater general efficiency than ever before attained by beaters of the Dover or any other type."

It was that invention, patented July 7, 1908 *(fig. 15-1)*, and the Ladd name, that resulted in a great American eggbeater, with a notable variety of styles *(fig. 15-2)*.

FIG. 15-1

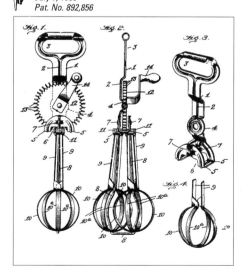

Earnest W. Ladd patent
July 7, 1908
Pat. No. 892,856

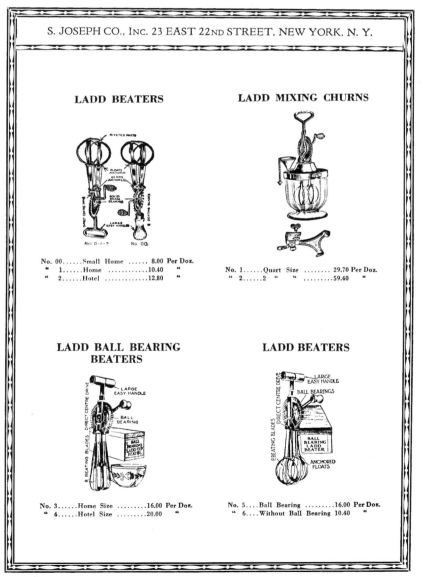

S. JOSEPH CO., INC. 23 EAST 22ND STREET, NEW YORK, N. Y.

LADD BEATERS

No. 00.....Small Home ...... 8.00 Per Doz.
"   1.....Home ....10.40   "
"   2.....Hotel ....12.80   "

LADD MIXING CHURNS

No. 1......Quart Size .... 29.70 Per Doz.
"   2....2   "   " ....59.40   "

LADD BALL BEARING BEATERS

No. 3......Home Size ....16.00 Per Doz.
"   4......Hotel Size ....20.00   "

LADD BEATERS

No. 5....Ball Bearing ....16.00 Per Doz.
"   6....Without Ball Bearing 10.40   "

FIG. 15-2

S. Joseph Co., Inc., New York, catalog sheet

Ladd's parent company, United Royalties Corporation, first appeared in R. L. Polk & Company's 1921-22 *New York City Copartnership and Corporation Directory:* "United Royalties Corporation; Lavern Bordwell, Pres.; O. F. Bishop, Sec.; Cap. $150,000; Dir., Lavern Bordwell, O.F. Bishop; Hardware specialties, 1133 Broadway, Room 401."

According to Richard Lienhard of Taplin eggbeater fame *(See Chapter 4, Taplin, page 29),* Ladds were manufactured by New Britain's Traut & Hine Company and Humphrey Manufacturing Company.

Research indicates that the New York headquarters of Ladd was just a mail drop — New Britain was where the real action was and it centered on one man, Ernest N. Humphrey, a Connecticut native born in Waterbury in 1870.

According to the *History of Hartford County, Connecticut 1633-1928,* Humphrey in 1892 "entered into the employ of Traut & Hine, manufacturers of sheet metal and wire novelties. He became associated with that enterprise as foreman and when the business was closed he was … vice president. In the previous year, he had established the Humphrey Manufacturing Company, opening a plant for the manufacture of kitchenware."

Humphrey, it continued, "has always followed this line of manufacturing since starting out in the business world and he is now president and treasurer of the company, which is controlling a steadily growing business, its trade relations constantly reaching out over a broader territory, for the output fully meets modern-day requirements and therefore finds a ready sale on the market."

It also noted that "associated with Mr. Humphrey in this undertaking is Lavern Bordwell, who is the vice president and sales manager of the company."

Both Humphrey and Bordwell obtained patents for Ladd mixers. Humphrey had three, while Bordwell had nine.

Bordwell, listing his residence as the New York address of United Royalties, was granted two patents Feb. 15, 1916 *(figs. 15-3 & 15-4)* for one of the best of the Ladd collectibles — "a receptacle within which a [Ladd] beater may be placed …"

This mixer-churn was featured in a 1919 *Hardware World,* a trade publication, that took a shot at cast-iron beaters, until then the top-of-the-line in the mixer market.

It said: "Again — why all steel? Chiefly to produce a real, satisfactory, lasting tool. Nickel-plated over all, makes a complete smooth surface … Castiron has long been used; always unsatisfactory, gathers dirt, dust and discharges same into mixture; is unsanitary, hard to clean and easily broken."

Ironically, Ladd himself patented a cast-iron beater Dec. 28, 1915 *(fig. 15-5),* although there's no evidence it was ever manufactured.

Bordwell's churn, a really ingenious device that came in two sizes, one- and two-quart, was described in an E. L. Wilson Hardware Company catalog *(fig. 15-6)* as: "Heavy Glass urn with fluted sides and nickel plated polished top; easily detachable; furnished with Ladds ball-bearing egg beaters, which can be used separately."

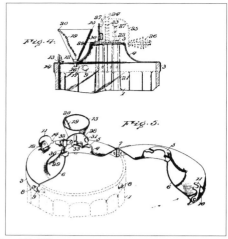

FIG. 15-3

Lavern Bordwell patent
Feb. 15, 1916
Pat. No. 1,171,922

FIG. 15-4

Lavern Bordwell patent
Feb. 15, 1916
Pat. No. 1,171,923

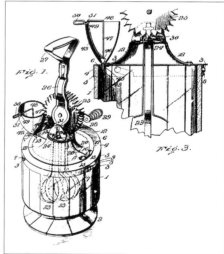

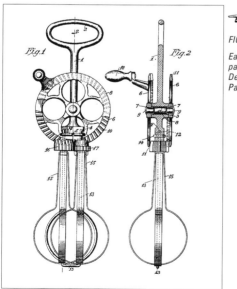

FIG. 15-5

Earnest W. Ladd patent
Dec. 28, 1915
Pat. No. 1,165,423

FIG. 15-6

E. L. Wilson Hardware Company catalog

MIXER CHURNS

LADD—BALL BEARING

Heavy glass urn with fluted sides and nickel plated polished top; easily detachable; furnished with Ladds ball-bearing egg beater, which can be used separately. This article is attractive, sanitary, easily cleaned, strong and well made.

Nos.	Capacity, Quarts	Height Overall, Inches	Weight per Dozen, Lbs.	Per Dozen
1	1	12½	46	$48.00
2	2	13¾	75	72.00

FIG. 15-7

D Thornton

Glass bottom Ladds (left to right):

LADD MIXER NO. 1
(embossed on jar)
NO. 1 LADD BEATER (on beater)
two-part fold-apart apron
13"
—$300 with funnel;
$225 without funnel—

LADD MIXER NO. 1
(embossed on jar)
No. 3 LADD BEATER (on beater)
solid piece all chrome apron
12-1/2"   —$250—

LADD MIXER No. 2
(embossed on jar)
No. 2 LADD BEATER (on beater)
13-1/2" —$300—

LADD
(embossed on green glass tumbler)
No. 6 LADD BEATER (on beater)
12" —$175—

LADD
(embossed on clear glass tumbler)
No. 5 LADD BALL BEARING BEATER
(on beater)
12" —$175—

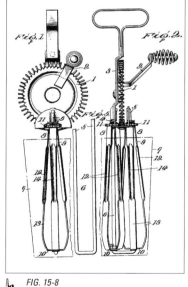

R S Arnold

FIG. 15-8
Lavern Bordwell patent
April 16, 1929
Pat. No. 1,709,769

FIG. 15-9
Unmarked original funnel with
stopper on chain. 2" high and
1-7/8" in diameter.   —$75—

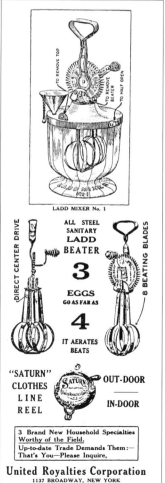

LADD MIXER No. 1

DIRECT CENTER DRIVE

ALL STEEL
SANITARY
**LADD
BEATER**

8 BEATING BLADES

3
EGGS
GO AS FAR AS
4
IT AERATES
BEATS

"SATURN"
CLOTHES
LINE
REEL

OUT-DOOR
IN-DOOR

3 Brand New Household Specialties
Worthy of the Field.
Up-to-date Trade Demands Them:—
That's You—Please Inquire,

United Royalties Corporation
1137 BROADWAY, NEW YORK

FIG. 15-10
January 1914
House
Furnishing
Review ad

Ladd jar models *(fig. 15-7)* include:
▶ In the one-quart size, there is the two-part, attachable top, with pedestal clear glass jar embossed LADD MIXER NO. 1. It utilizes a NO. 1 LADD beater. Also with the same one-quart jar is an art deco type model, one-piece apron of chrome spot-welded to a NO. 3 wood, T-handle beater.
▶ The LADD MIXER NO. 2 two-quart is the most coveted of Ladd items.

There also is a NO. 2 art deco model (not pictured). The tumbler mixer, yet another very collectible item, was patented by Bordwell *(fig. 15-8)*.

The one- and two-quarts came with a detachable funnel *(fig. 15-9)* that fits into a hole in the apron. The stopper for the funnel is attached to the end of the chain. An ad in the *House Furnishing Review (fig. 15-10)* featured the funnel.

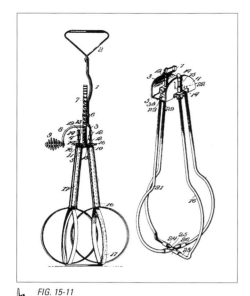

FIG. 15-11

Lavern Bordwell patent
Oct. 18, 1921
Pat. No. 1,393,941

"The primary object of this invention is the making of an eight-bladed beater specifically constructed so that the blades have their upper or collateral portion interlaced, as well as their lower portion, so that it is particularly adapted for use for beating the material in a cup or a long narrow receptacle such as a tall glass, jar and the like," Bordwell said in his 1929 tumbler beater patent.

Ladds are still very much available — a real American collectible. The Ladd list, seemingly always expanding with new discoveries, includes the aforementioned patent dates July 7, 1908 by Ladd; Feb. 15, 1916 by Bordwell; and April 16, 1929 by Bordwell.

Other engraved dates include Oct. 18, 1921 by Bordwell; Nov. 30, 1926 by Humphrey; Nov. 1, 1927 by Humphrey; July 3, 1928 by Bordwell and the same date for Humphrey; and April 16, 1929 by Bordwell for his BALL BEARING beauty. Note the tumbler beater has the same date as the BALL BEARING (figs. 15-11 through 15-16).

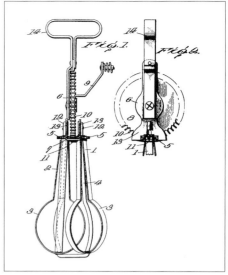

FIG. 15-12

Ernest N. Humphrey patent
Nov. 30, 1926
Pat. No. 1,609,254

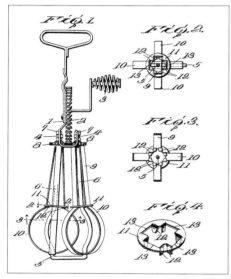

FIG. 15-13

Ernest N. Humphrey patent
Nov. 1, 1927
Pat. No. 1,647,800

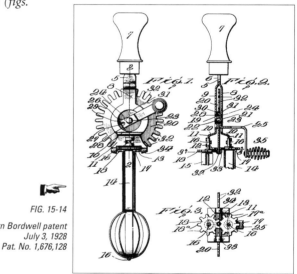

FIG. 15-14

Lavern Bordwell patent
July 3, 1928
Pat. No. 1,676,128

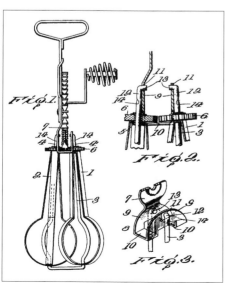

FIG. 15-15

Ernest N. Humphrey patent
July 3, 1928
Pat. No. 1,676,189

FIG. 15-16

Lavern Bordwell patent
April 16, 1929
Pat. No. 1,709,768

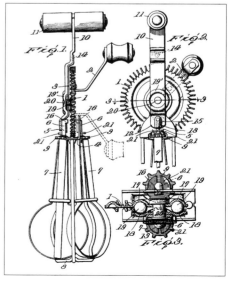

THE EGGBEATER CHRONICLES

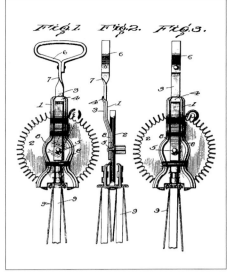

FIG. 15-17

Lavern Bordwell patent
Dec. 5, 1922
Pat. No. 1,437,957

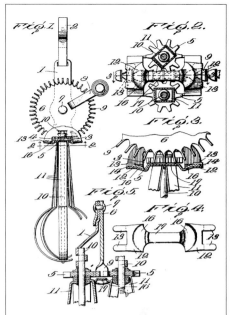

FIG. 15-18

Lee Edgar Earle patent
July 17, 1928
Pat. No. 1,677,754

There are other Ladd patents, the dates of which didn't end up on beaters: Dec. 5, 1922 by Bordwell; July 17, 1928 by Lee Edgar Earle of Albany, New York, described as an assignor to United Royalties; and a final beauty by Bordwell on Oct. 21, 1952 — 44 years after it all began — that apparently never made it to market (*figs. 15-17 through 15-19*).

The variety of handheld Ladd beaters — like the patents — is amazing. Some models came with three different handles (*fig. 15-20*).

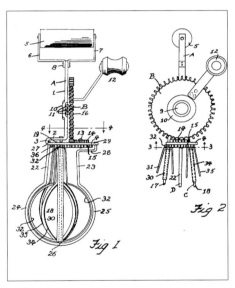

FIG. 15-19

Lavern Bordwell patent
Oct. 21, 1952
Pat. No. 2,614,818

FIG. 15-20

August 1918
House
Furnishing
Review ad

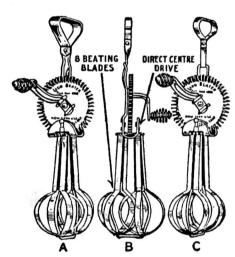

The construction provides a beater in which rapid or accelerated rotation of the beater blades is obtained even when the main operating gear is slowly rotated. This rapid and efficient beating can be obtained with the minimum of physical effort.

— LAVERN BORDWELL IN HIS FINAL PATENT, OCT. 21, 1952

Although the beaters carry patent dates ranging from 1908 to 1929, they were made for decades, as evidenced by the Dec. 28, 1948 trademark obtained by United Royalties Corporation (fig. 15-21). Most Ladds are marked with numbers, ranging from NO. 0 to NO. 9, relating to style and size (figs. 15-22 through 15-25).

Fig. 15-21

U.S. Patent & Trademark Office
Official Gazette, Dec. 29, 1948
United Royalties Corporation's Ladd trademark

CUTLERY, MACHINERY, AND TOOLS, AND PARTS THEREOF

Ser. No. 518,443. UNITED ROYALTIES CORPORATION, New York, N. Y. Filed Jan. 22, 1948. Under section 2f of the act of 1946.

FOR EGG BEATERS; MIXER CHURNS; BEVERAGE BEATERS; FRUIT JUICE EXTRACTORS; AND BREAD SLICERS; ALL OF SAID GOODS FOR HOUSEHOLD USE AND BEING MANUALLY OPERATED.
    Claims use since Jan. 1, 1909, on egg beaters; and since Jan. 1, 1926, on other goods named.

FIG. 15-22

No. 0 Ladds (left to right):

No. 0 LADD BEATER
PAT'D JULY 7, 1908 FEB. 2, 1915
UNITED ROYALTIES CORP.
9-3/4"   —$20—

No. 0 LADD BEATER
OCT. 18, 1921 OTHER PATENTS PENDING
UNITED ROYALTIES CORP
9-3/4"   —$20—

No. 0 LADD BEATER
UNITED ROYALTIES CORP.
NEW YORK
"OIL HERE" *(at center hole)*
10"   —$20—

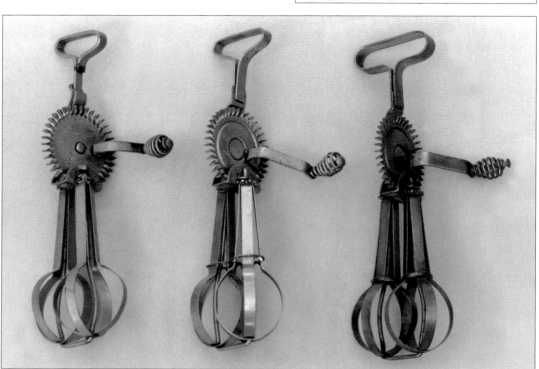

D G Simons

D G Simons

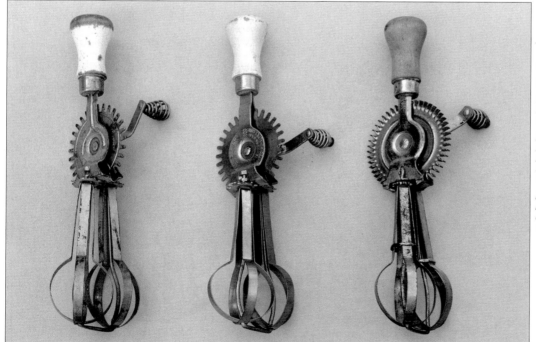

FIG. 15-23

No. 00 Ladds (left to right):

No. 00 LADD BEATER
PATD JULY 7, 1908 OCT. 18, 1921
11"   —$15—

No. 00 LADD BEATER
PATD JULY 7, 1908 OCT. 18, 1921
NEW YORK USA
UNITED ROYALTIES CORP
11"   —$25—

No. 00 LADD BEATER
PATD OCT. 18, 1921
UNITED ROYALTIES CORP
11"   —$15—

D G Simons

FIG. 15-24

No. 1 and No. 2 Ladds (left to right):

No. 1 LADD BEATER *JULY 7, 1908* *OCT. 18, 1921* *11-1/2"* —$20—

No. 1 LADD BEATER *JULY 7, 1908* *FEB. 21, 1915* *11-1/2"* —$18—

No. 1 LADD BEATER *JULY 7, 1908* *OCT. 18, 1921* *11-1/2"* —$18—

No. 1 LADD BEATER *OCT. 18, 1921* *OTHER PATS PENDING* *11"* —$15—

No. 2 LADD BEATER *JULY 7, 1908* *OCT. 18, 1921* *12-1/2"* —$20—

FIG. 15-25

No. 3 to No. 9 Ladds (left to right):

No. 3 LADD **BALL BEARING BEATER** *OCT. 18, 1921* *OTHER PATS PEND* *11"* —$15—
Note: This beater also comes with a Bakelite handle.

No. 4 LADD *NOV. 30-26* *NOV. 1-27* *JUL. 3-28* *APR. 16-29* *12"* —$15—

No. 5 LADD **BALL BEARING BEATER** *OCT. 18, 1921* *tumbler model* *11-1/2"* —$50—

No. 5 LADD **BALL BEARING BEATER** *OCT. 18, 1921* *tumbler model* *11-1/2"* —$60—

No. 9 LADD **BALL BEARING BEATER** *11-1/2"* —$20—

D G Simons

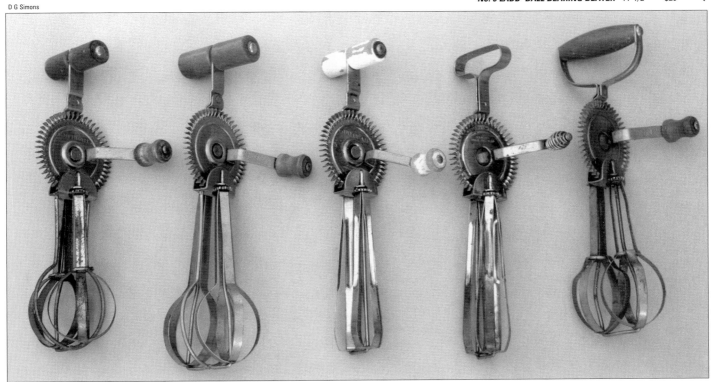

United Royalties offered two other beaters, which are a bit harder to find than Ladds. They are the SATURN A and SATURN B *(fig. 15-26)*, patented Feb. 12, 1929 by Bordwell *(fig. 15-27)*.

In addition to beaters, there are other United Royalties products that make great collectibles, including another Bordwell invention, patented July 20, 1915 *(fig. 15-28)*, the SATURN clothes line reel. There also was a can opener, a SATURN CHOPPING KNIFE, a LADD BREAD SLICER, and LADD FRUIT JUICE EXTRACTOR. But Ladd beaters are and will continue to be the legacy of United Royalties, especially "the new and improved Ladd" described in ad copy as of "thoroughbred quality" with gears and beating blades that "run permanently true — spin as smoothly as a top" *(fig. 15-29)*.

One final note on Humphrey, who died at the age of 76 in 1946. *The History of Hartford County,* noting he served as a city councilman and alderman, a member of the water board, the finance board and the board of public works, said, "Throughout his entire life Mr. Humphrey has recognized the duties and obligations of citizenship and has measured up to every requirement in that connection."

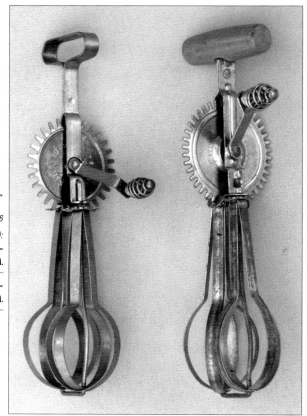

FIG. 15-26

Saturns (left to right):

SATURN BEATER "A"
U.R.C. N.Y. U.S.A.
10-1/2" —$25—

SATURN BEATER "B"
U.R.C. N.Y. U.S.A.
10-1/2" —$25—

D G Simons

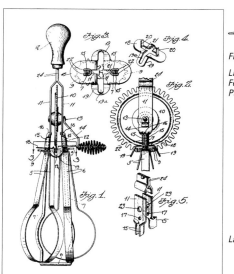

FIG. 15-27

Lavern Bordwell patent
Feb. 12, 1929
Pat. No. 1,701.605

FIG. 15-28

Lavern Bordwell patent
July 20, 1915
Pat. No.
1,147,599

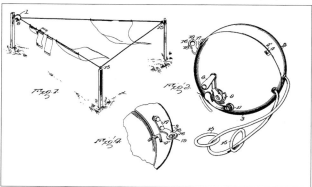

FIG. 15-29

October 1925
Good
Housekeeping

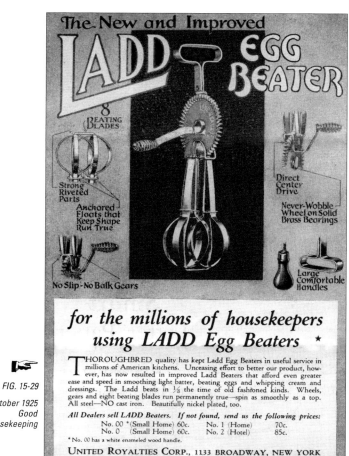

Chapter 16

Aurelius

"Made by home folks for home folks."

The mix of ingredients: A chicken shed, a millwright brother on vacation, a savvy World War II veteran, a famous fishing lure firm — and quality products.

In other words, another continuing American success story.

Bernard E. Aurelius was granted a patent Nov. 9, 1926 *(fig. 16-1)* for his unique two-direction dasher HIGHSPEED beater, launching a manufacturing concern that continues today in Braham, Minnesota.

Said Bernard: "My present invention has reference to an egg beater or cream whipper and has for its object to provide a device of this class with two beater members [dashers], one revoluble in the other, but each turnable in an opposite direction and further within the beaters are enclosed by a suitable guard which permits of the device being arranged at varying desired angles in the operation thereof."

That, the shed, and brother Eugene launched the Aurelius Brothers fabulous eggbeater manufacturing firm.

The year was 1926 when production first began on Bernard's farm on the south edge of Braham. Brother Eugene,

working at the time at the Maytag plant in Newton, Iowa, spent his vacation that year helping the firm get off the ground. He never returned to Iowa.

Shortly after the first beater was launched, Bernard took over marketing for the budding firm, which consisted of towing a small trailer behind his car throughout the Midwest, selling the mixer to hardware store owners.

What a mixer it was, according to an early newspaper ad *(fig. 16-2):* "ACTS TWO WAYS! TWICE AS EFFECTIVE. THE NEW HIGHSPEED WILL DO IT … TIME and LABOR SAVING — two important merits which place this beater and whipper in a class by itself.

"The 'Acts 2 Ways' feature is the reason for this saving in time and labor. This feature doubles the agitation with each turn — thus performing faster work in less than half the time required in operating the ordinary mechanism."

The ad ended with the motto "Made by home folks for home folks."

On March 8, 1932, Eugene A. Aurelius was granted his own eggbeater patent *(fig. 16-3)* and presented the kitchenware world with one of the most desirable twentieth century kitchen collectibles around.

FIG. 16-1

Bernard E. Aurelius patent
Nov. 9, 1926
Pat. No. 1,606,684

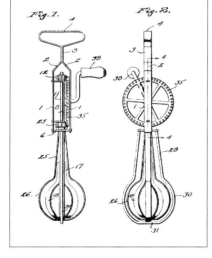

FIG. 16-2

Braham Journal
1929 ad

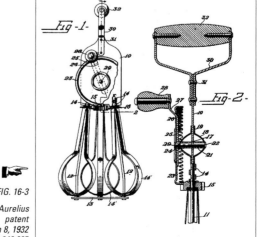

FIG. 16-3

Eugene A. Aurelius
patent
March 8, 1932
Pat. No. 1,848,925

The MASTER eggbeater is believed to be one of the few American triple dasher beaters ever manufactured. Another triple, by Paul Hazzard of Chicago, was patented Aug. 28, 1923 *(fig. 16-4)* but apparently was never made.

In his patent specifications, Eugene said his device "includes triple beater elements, whereby the time necessary for beating eggs or whipping cream will be materially reduced, novel means being provided for driving the beater elements."

Following his return home from service in World War II, Wendell Nelson went to work for the two brothers as their first real employee in 1945, and recalled that at the time it took 75 different steps to make an eggbeater.

He also recalled that although overshadowed by the HIGHSPEED and the MASTER, the firm also produced two other notable mixers, the FAVORITE and the IDEAL *(fig. 16-5)*.

And therein lies another story.

"Shortly after World War II when stainless steel in coils became available for purchase from the steel mills, the demand for IDEAL and FAVORITE eggbeaters was greater than the production capability of Aurelius," Nelson said in a correspondence in 1991.

"An arrangement was made with Mr. Joe Fladebo of Isle, Minnesota, the owner of Mille Lacs Spinner Company, to cooperate with Aurelius in an endeavor to satisfy this demand."

And thus Nelson solved a beater mystery — why MILLE LACS appears on two Aurelius mixers.

"Aurelius purchased materials and 'stamped' all the parts for both beaters. 'Stamped' refers to a process whereby steel strips or coils are fed into a machine called a punch press, and were cut, shaped and formed to provide the configuration of parts which when properly assembled became an eggbeater.

"To prevent rusting and corrosion, and to provide a pleasing appearance, all parts, with the exception of stainless steel parts, were nickel plated before assembly. Plating is a special process which Aurelius was not equipped to perform. Mille Lacs Spinner Company had a plating department for their fishing tackle products, and could provide this service.

"Aurelius made parts, Mille Lacs plated, assembled and finished the product, packaged and distributed it. Mr. Aurelius allowed Mille Lacs to distribute the product under their own name. This arrangement was successful but short lived, as the market for hand beaters soon disappeared."

By 1949 Aurelius Brothers had turned to other markets. It offered a device for tightening sagging clothes lines, an electric sharpener for push lawn mowers, and a shotgun shell holder and dispenser that clipped to the jacket of a hunter. There were other outdoor sports items, including a line of fishing tackle.

In 1964, Wendell Nelson purchased the company, following the deaths of the two brothers.

And it was Wendell Nelson who over the years guided the firm as it adapted to survive. For example, when the Dahlman Company, with its potato pickers and combines, relocated to Braham, Aurelius moved quickly to fill the firm's need for something new — hydraulic cylinders.

The business today is still hydraulic cylinders, under the direction of Conrad and Loren Nelson, who took over after their father's retirement.

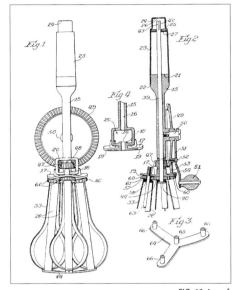

FIG. 16-4

Paul Hazzard patent Aug. 28, 1923 Pat. No. 1,465,940

FIG. 16-5

Aurelius beaters (left to right):

AURELIUS BROS. BRAHAM, MINN. PAT. NOV. 9, 1926
11-1/2" —$100—

MASTER EGG BEATER MFD. BY AURELIUS BROS. BRAHAM, MINN. PAT. APPLD. FOR
11-1/2" —$450—

FAVORITE MFG. BY MILLE LACS LAKE SPINNER CO.
11-3/4" —$35—

IDEAL MILLE LACS MFG.
10-3/4" —$50—

D G Simons

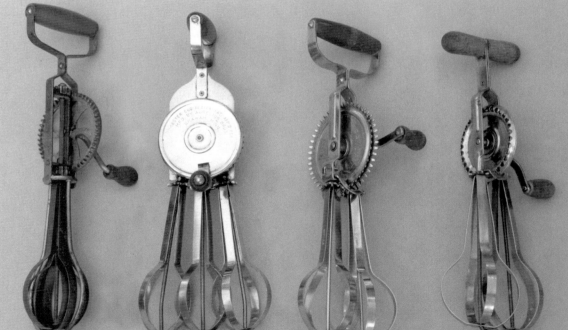

Chapter 17

Androck

A real mix.

The full name of this firm should include The Wire Goods Company, Andrews Wire and Iron Works, Cassady-Fairbank Manufacturing Company, The Washburn Company and Androck.

The birthplace was once again Worcester, Massachusetts. The time, the Fall of 1880. Charles G. Washburn started producing wire goods for cotton and woolen machinery.

In 1882 he incorporated under the name The Wire Goods Company and by 1889 the firm offered 4,400 different articles made from wire, including screw eyes, screw hooks, gate hooks, belt hooks, hitching rings, hammock hooks and garment hangers.

Another Washburn, Reginald, took over as president in 1906 and four years later was instrumental in offering one of the firm's first beaters. On Feb. 8, 1910 *(fig. 17-1)*, Reginald obtained a patent for a handheld beater made of bent wire *(See Chapter 24, Handheld Cousins, page 274)*. Five years later on April 6, 1915 *(fig. 17-2)* he was granted a patent for another one. Both are still available today, along with similar models with such names ELECTRIC EGG WHIP, CHECKER EGG WHIP and the CROSS-CUT EGG WHIP (fig. 17-3).

FIG 17-3

Circa 1927 Washburn Company catalog sheet

FIG. 17-1

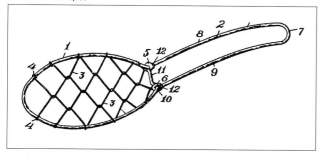

Reginald Washburn patent
Feb. 8, 1910
Pat. No. 948,750

FIG. 17-2

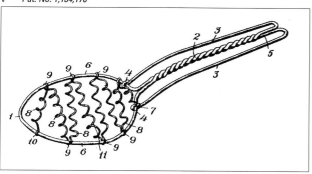

Reginald Washburn patent
April 6, 1915
Pat. No. 1,134,170

ANDROCK

Applicant claims ownership of Registration No. 101,728.
FOR MECHANICAL EGG BEATERS AND WHIPS,
SPATULAS, CAKE TURNERS, APPLE CORERS, PAS-
TRY BLENDERS, POTATO MASHERS; SPOONS,
FORKS, LADLES AND SCOOPS MADE OF BASE
METAL; JAR OPENERS, FLOUR SIFTERS, MEAT AND
VEGETABLE CHOPPERS; HAND-OPERATED BEATER
AND BOWL SETS FOR MIXING FOODS; PLATE
SCRAPERS; ICE PICKS, MELON BALLERS; ASH
SIFTERS, ASH LADLES AND TONGS FOR USE AS
FURNACE TOOLS; AND LAWN RAKES.
Claims use since Mar. 1, 1908.

FIG. 17-4

U.S. Patent & Trademark Office Official
Gazette, Nov. 7, 1950, The Washburn
Company trademark

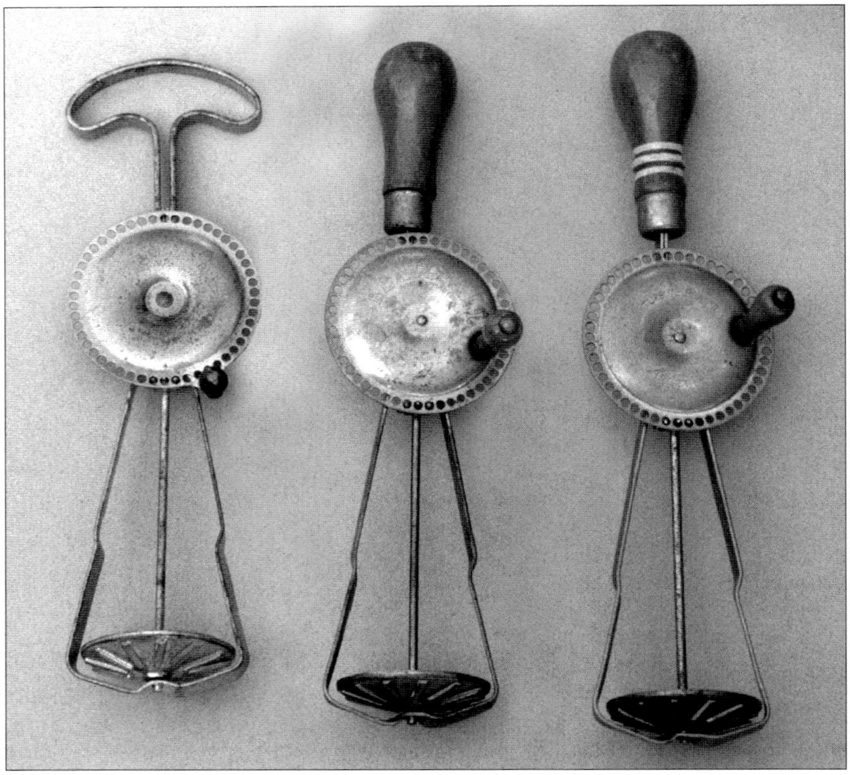

FIG. 17-5

Turbines (left to right):

**TURBINE EGG BEATER
PAT. AUG. 20, 1912
THE WASHBURN CO.**
10-1/2″ —$25—

**BEATS-ALL
PATENT APPLIED FOR
THE WASHBURN CO.**
11″ —$20—

**TURBINE BEATER ANDROCK
MADE IN U.S.A.**
11-1/2″ —$20—

Over the years, The Wire Goods Company absorbed several other firms, including the E. Jenckes Company of Pawtucket, Rhode Island, and the Woods-Sherwood Company of Lowell, Massachusetts.

But the biggest acquisition came in 1914 with the purchase of the Cassady-Fairbank Manufacturing Company of Chicago, and its fine line of kitchen products.

Meanwhile, in Rockford, Illinois, Charles Andrews in 1885 founded Andrews Wire and Iron Works. He combined his name with 'Rockford' to come up with its famous trademark, ANDROCK, which graces several different models of outstanding beaters and other kitchen products.

Andrews and Washburn merged in 1917, taking the name Associated Companies. The name changed to The Washburn Company in 1922 and the firm became well known for its ANDROCK and TURBINE beaters.

However, by 1967 the Rockford plant was closed and the name of the firm was changed once again, to the Androck Company, by the new owners, Robin Steel Company of Buffalo, New York.

In 1975, the Androck Company died.

The plant and its equipment sold at auction — appropriately enough where it all began, Worcester. Over the years the firm produced a variety of items, spelled out in a 1950 trademark (fig. 17-4).

Included in the mix, starting with turbines (fig. 17-5):

▶ The TURBINE EGG BEATER was an all-metal turbine, manufactured by The Washburn Company in Chicago, dated Aug. 20, 1912. The patent (fig. 17-6) by Evelyn P. Sperry of Oak Park, Illinois, said one "object of the invention is to provide a beater which is adapted to thoroughly beat, mix and aerate efficiently, and with substantially the highest possible degree of facility, comparatively small or large quantities of eggs, cream batter or other materials."

▶ The same model came with a vertical wood handle, including the BEATS-ALL and another marked TURBINE BEATER BY ANDROCK.

FIG. 17-6

Evelyn P. Sperry patent
Aug. 20, 1912
Pat. No. 1,036,159

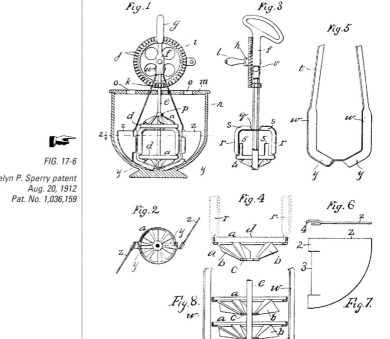

THE WASHBURN COMPANY

MAIL ORDERS DIRECT TO

→ Chicago (Cassady-Fairbank) Division
Chicago, Illinois
EACH FACTORY OPERATES AS A SEPARATE UNIT

Items Underscored Are Best Selling Numbers

Egg Beaters and Can Openers

The New Whirlwind Turbine Beater
Nickel Plated
New Drive Crank Construction
Ivory White Handle
BEATS—one or two eggs in one minute.
WHIPS—one-half pint of cream in two minutes.
MIXES—oil and vinegar for French dressing in two minutes
BEST BY TEST
For Mixing Batter, Beating Fudge, Mixing Mayonnaise and many other ingredients.

Easy to Operate—Easy to Clean
Length overall, 10½ in.

No. 232 Whirlwind Turbine. Per gross................$48.00
Packed in Individual Boxes. Twelve boxes in carton
Weight per carton, 10 lbs.

A New Androck Special

1326 TURBINE BOWL SET
Per gross $48.00
Packed: Six French gray glazed bowls and six turbine beaters in a shipping carton.
Weight per carton, 16 lbs.

Turbine Egg Beater

Retinned—10½ in. Overall
No. 132 Per gross...........$30.00
Weight per gross, 41½ lbs.
One dozen in a corrugated carton

Page 34—SECTION II

Dover Egg Beaters

| No. 100 | Finish Bronzed | Length 10½ in. | Per Gross $18.45 |
Weight per gross, 60 lbs.

Center Drive
| No. 450 | Finish Bronzed | Length 10½ in. | Per Gross $26.00 |
Weight per gross, 72 lbs.
One dozen in box

Batter Beater

Length overall 11 in.
Nickel Plated Wires
Ivory White Handle
No. 250 Per gross.........$22.00
Weight per gross, 2½ lbs.
One dozen in a display box

Can Openers

Length overall 8½ in.
Blade—Steel Nickel Plated
Ebony Handle
No. 35 Per gross...........$9.60
Weight per gross, 24 lbs.
1 dozen in display box

Ivory White Finished Handle
Tool Steel Blade
Length overall 6¼ in.
No. 1 Per gross.............$9.00
Weight per gross, 18½ lbs.
One dozen in a box

Length overall 7 in.
Steel, Nickel Plated
No. 7 Per gross.............$21.00
Weight per box, 3 lbs.
One dozen in a display box

FIG. 17-7

c. 1927 Washburn Company catalog sheet

Practically every portion of the device can be made of sheet metal and thus produced cheaply …

— THOMAS E. JONES IN HIS 1917 PATENT

In addition to the TURBINE EGG BEATER, Washburn made the WHIRL-WIND TURBINE BEATER with center-gear drive. It was featured in a circa 1927 catalog sheet along with the TURBINE, and a coveted TURBINE BOWL SET. The same sheet also features Dover and Taplin beaters *(fig. 17-7)*.

The next patent date in the turbine family is Nov. 13, 1917 for an all-metal model by Thomas E. Jones of Hammond, Indiana *(fig. 17-8)*. There were two versions of this beater manufactured, both marked TURBINE EGG BEATER and listing The Cassady-Fairbank Manufacturing Company. One has the regular turbine bottom and the other the so-called paper clip bottom *(fig. 17-9)*.

FIG. 17-8

Thomas E. Jones patent Nov. 13, 1917 Pat. No. 1,246,104

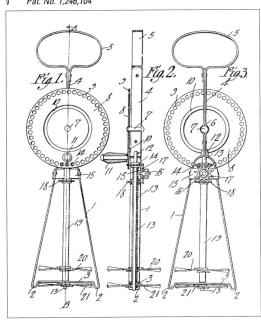

FIG. 17-9

Turbines (left to right):

TURBINE EGG BEATER MFGD BY CASSADY-FAIRBANK CO. CHICAGO
10″ —$25—

TURBINE EGG BEATER MFGD BY CASSADY-FAIRBANK CO. CHICAGO
10″ —$150—

D G Simons

CHAPTER 17: ANDROCK

At this point, Charles Andrews Jr. of Rockford entered the picture. He was granted a patent Feb. 15, 1927 (fig. 17-10) for a longtime mainstay of the Androck mixing line. It's a handheld model with wire dasher in a fan shape and embossed in the metal securing the dasher, BEATS EGGS, CREAM, BATTER, ETC on one side and NO 825 ANDROCK on the other. A catalog sheet described it as "a new mixer designed to meet the suggestions of expert cooking teachers" (fig. 17-11). It's probably the easiest of Androck handhelds to find, with others a bit more scarce (fig. 17-12).

Another handheld mainstay is a mixer, or pastry blender, patented (fig. 17-13) by Elmer L. Dennis of Rockford, assignor to the Washburn Company. It is marked ANDROCK with Dennis' patent number 1,735,236, and came with a wood or sometimes Bakelite handle (See Chapter 24, Handheld Cousins, page 282).

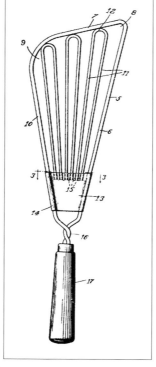

FIG. 17-10

Charles Andrews Jr.
patent
Feb. 15, 1927
Pat. No. 1,617,787

FIG. 17-11

c. 1927 Washburn
Company catalog sheet

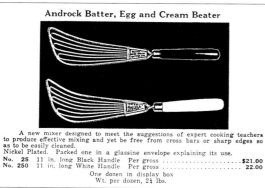

Androck Batter, Egg and Cream Beater

A new mixer designed to meet the suggestions of expert cooking teachers to produce effective mixing and yet be free from cross bars or sharp edges so as to be easily cleaned. Nickel Plated. Packed one in a glassine envelope explaining its use.
No. 25   11 in. long Black Handle   Per gross $21.00
No. 250 11 in. long White Handle   Per gross 22.00
One dozen in display box
Wt. per dozen, 2¼ lbs.

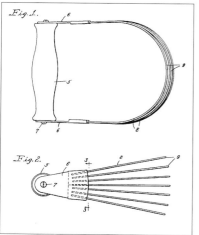

FIG. 17-13

Elmer L. Dennis patent
Nov. 12, 1929
Pat. No. 1,735,236

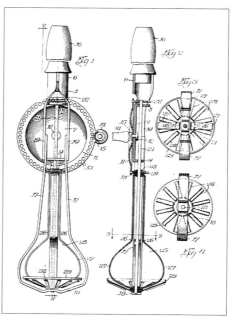

FIG. 17-14

Charles Andrews Jr.
patent
June 17, 1930
Pat. No. 1,764,597

FIG 17-12

R S Arnold

Androck handhelds
(left to right):

**BEATS EGGS, CREAM,
BATTER, ETC
NO. 825   ANDROCK**
11"   —$5—

ANDROCK
all metal   13"   —$15—

**ANDROCK
MADE IN U.S.A.,**
Bakelite handle
11"   —$10—

FIG. 17-15

**BEATS-ALL
PAT APPLIED FOR
THE WASHBURN CO.**
12-1/2"   —$35—

D G Simons

THE EGGBEATER CHRONICLES

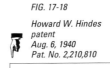

On June 17, 1930, Andrews was granted a patent *(fig. 17-14)* for a rotary beater with both dashers and a turbine *(fig. 17-15)*. Andrews said the primary object of his invention was to provide a beater with "two rotatable members, one of which delivers the material to the other and the other beats air into the material delivered thereto, the two members cooperating together in an efficient manner."

It was in the 1930s and 1940s that the Androck line of mixers was established, based on different patents *(figs. 17-16 through 17-18)* by three Worcester inventors.

The three patents accounted for a variety of rotary cranks *(figs. 17-19 through 17-21)*, some with prized Bakelite handles and at least one atop a Pyrex measuring jar, making Androck one of the dominant beaters on the market at that time.

FIG. 17-16

Samuel T. Hobbs patent
June 24, 1930
Pat. No. 1,767,454

FIG. 17-18

Howard W. Hindes patent
Aug. 6, 1940
Pat. No. 2,210,810

R S Arnold

FIG. 17-19

ANDROCK
10"   —$10—

FIG. 17-17

Levi E. Wheeler patent
April 10, 1934
Pat. No. 1,954,507

FIG. 17-20

Androcks (left to right):

ANDROCK
with Bakelite handle 11"   —$20—

ANDROCK 11"   —$15—

ANDROCK 12-1/2"   —$15—

ANDROCK 11"   —$15—

ANOTHER ANDROCK PRODUCT
PAT. NO. 2210810
10-3/4"   —$15—

ANOTHER ANDROCK PRODUCT 12-1/2" —$20—

ANOTHER ANDROCK PRODUCT 12"   —$15—

ANOTHER ANDROCK PRODUCT
with mesh dasher 12"   —$90—

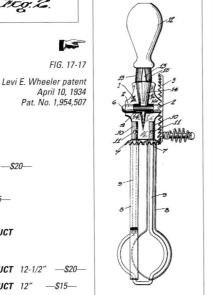

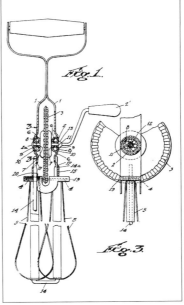

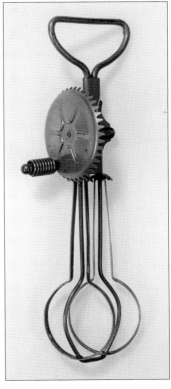

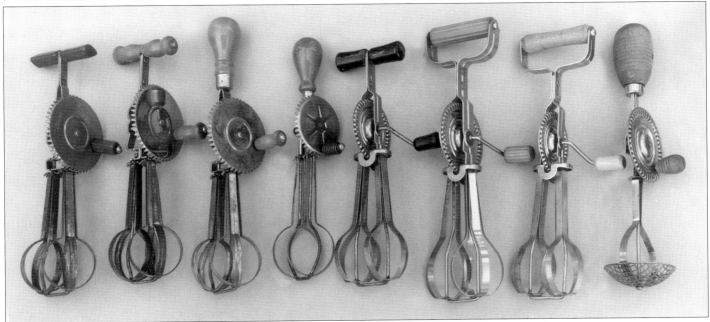

D G Simons

CHAPTER 17: ANDROCK

Androck bowl beaters, known for their mesh dashers, came on the market in the 1940s, based on a patent by John R. Lawrence of Worcester *(fig. 17-22)*.

According to Lawrence, the "principal object" of his device was "to mount the beater and a cover for the bowl as a single unit in such a way that pressure on the handle will hold the beater element in the lower most portion of the bowl and will hold the cover in place on the bowl. In this way any splashing of the material being whipped or beaten is prevented and at the same time the beater element is close enough to the bottom of the bowl to assure a complete beating of the material."

As an assignor to Washburn, Lawrence also was granted a patent April 25, 1950 *(fig. 17-23)* for a sleek rotary crank mixer.

The bowl beaters came in three sizes and a variety of colors *(fig. 17-24)*.

FIG. 17-21

ANOTHER ANDROCK PRODUCT
MADE IN UNITED STATES OF AMERICA
PATENT NO. 2,210,810
(on gear wheel)
FITS PYREX No. 532
ONE QUART MEASURE
(on apron)
11" overall   —$30—

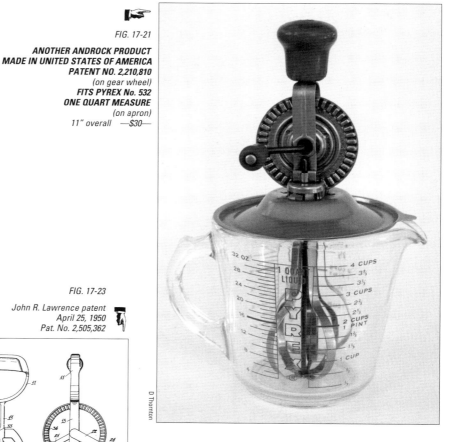

FIG. 17-23

John R. Lawrence patent
April 25, 1950
Pat. No. 2,505,362

FIG. 17-22

 John R. Lawrence patent
Dec. 9, 1941
Pat. No. 2,265,533

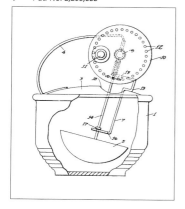

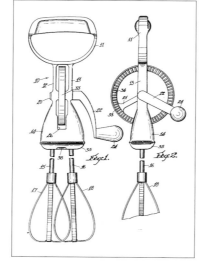

FIG. 17-24

Androck bowl beaters (left to right):

ANOTHER ANDROCK PRODUCT
clear glass 5-1/2"   —$35—

ANOTHER ANDROCK PRODUCT
orange bowl 5-1/2"   —$35—

ANDROCK PAT PENDING MADE IN UNITED STATES OF AMERICA
clear glass 6-3/4"   —$40—

ANOTHER ANDROCK PRODUCT
MADE IN UNITED STATES OF AMERICA PATENT PENDING
red plastic coating on beater handle and bowl   —$45—

D Thornton

Rotary Beaters with Containers

The railroad connection.

FIG. 18-1

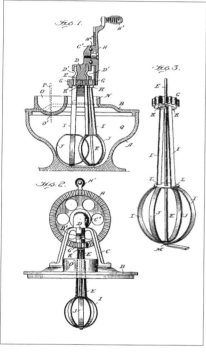

Job Hutchinson patent
Sept. 2, 1913
Pat. No. 1,071,747

Another mixed up story — but the truth is embossed in the glass of the S&S bowl.

Patented Sept. 2, 1913 *(fig. 18-1)* by Job Hutchinson of New York, assignor to the National Indicator Company, the S&S — Scientific & Sanitary — is a very desirable mixer that came in two sizes.

Contacted about the National Indicator Company of Long Island City, manufacturer of the S&S Hutchinson mixer, the reply from the Queens Borough Public Library was cordial, and right to the point.

"I assume that you have, or have handled, an example of the jar mixer bearing the company's name and patent date," wrote Robert C. Friedrich, senior librarian of the Long Island Collection.

Friedrich, with a hint of amazement, disclosed that the firm was listed in early publications as a manufacturer of "train indicators," and noted its existence was "most incongruous with a kitchenware product." But he didn't stop there.

"I have contacted a researcher on local railroad lore, who has suggested that the 'indicators' were the rectangular metal signs printed with route names, etc. used on N.Y. City subway cars."

The *Directory of Manufacturers of Queens Borough New York City* 1918, (Published by the Chamber of Commerce of the Borough of Queens, New York City — Price One Dollar) listed the National Indicator Co. under the category of "train indicators" and the address as 852 Vernon Ave., Long Island City. That same address is embossed on the bottom of one of the S&S mixers.

The larger S&S is unique in that the cast-iron rotary crank is mounted in the glass lid of the mixing vessel. The big wheel is marked two ways: S&S *(fig. 18-2)* and on a rarer model HUTCHINSON *(fig. 18-3)*. The HUTCHINSON indicates that Job Hutchinson tried on his own to manufacture the mixer before turning it over to National Indicator.

FIG. 18-2

**S&S HUTCHINSON NEW YORK
PAT. APPL. FOR**
(on gear)
**S&S TRADE MARK
REG. U.S. PAT. OFF.
852 VERNON AVE.
LONG ISLAND
CITY, N.Y.** (embossed on jar)
9-1/2"   —$400—

FIG. 18-3

**HUTCHINSON NEW YORK PAT.
APLD. FOR** (on gear)
**130 WORTH ST. NEW YORK
J. HUTCHINSON
S&S TRADE MARK**
(embossed on jar)
9-1/2"   —$550—

D G Simons

D G Simons

GRIFFITHS COLLECTION

MOFFET COLLECTION

FIG. 18-4

S&S HUTCHINSON NO. 2 NEW YORK PAT. SEPT. 2, 1913 (on gear) **NATIONAL INDICATOR CO. NO. 2 S&S TRADE MARK LONG ISLAND CITY** (embossed on jar)
9-1/2"
—without funnel: $450;
   value of funnel: $125—

FIG. 18-5
Early S&S
brochure

PATENTED SEPT. 2, 1913

S & S BEATER No. 2

"IT BEATS EVERYTHING!"

Combination
Mayonnaise Mixer, Cream Whipper,
Egg Beater and Butter Churn

The smaller S&S, marked NO. 2, is a rotary crank with metal wheel and metal apron. This model came with a glass funnel *(fig. 18-4)* which is nearly impossible to find.

The 1913 patent tells the story behind the unusual design: "It is well known that in making mayonnaise dressing and the like a great amount of beating is required while certain ingredients are very slowly added, since otherwise the product is inferior.

"With this object in view, I provide an inexpensive and effective apparatus which includes with beating devices means for supplying oil automatically at such rate that each drop of oil is thoroughly incorporated with the other ingredients while the operation is very rapid and the labor slight."

A S&S brochure, featuring the NO. 2 on the cover *(fig. 18-5),* said the mixer "is an ideal holiday gift, suitable for any time of year. It is invaluable to the housekeeper when making the Thanksgiving and Christmas delicacies and in the hot summer months for the cool beaten frostings and whipped desserts. It is in service all the year for omelets, salad dressing, desserts and refreshing beverages."

How did a railroad sign company end up manufacturing an eggbeater? The answer is Hutchinson. As a prolific inventor from 1908 to 1960, he was awarded at least 46 patents, most while associated with National Indicator as their assignor.

Hutchinson, who died at the age of 92 in 1966, started his patent career with a railway electric signaling device in 1908 and over the years produced dozens of indicators. And he still had time for an ice pick, an internal combustion engine, a washing machine and a vacuum cleaner *(fig. 18-6).* He apparently was quite proud of his eggbeater — it was the only invention for which he registered a trademark *(fig. 18-7).*

FIG. 18-6

Job Hutchinson patents

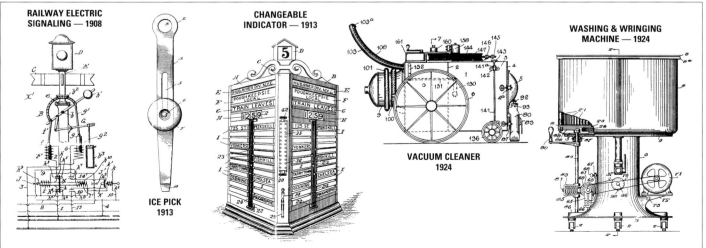

RAILWAY ELECTRIC
SIGNALING — 1908

ICE PICK
1913

CHANGEABLE
INDICATOR — 1913

VACUUM CLEANER
1924

WASHING & WRINGING
MACHINE — 1924

FIG. 18-7

U.S. Patent & Trademark Office Official Gazette, July 9, 1912 Job Hutchinson's S&S trademark

D G Simons

GRIFFITHS COLLECTION

FIG. 18-8

THE E-Z MIXER REGISTERED 1902 PAT'D JUNE 30, 1903 32 OZ.

13" —$675—

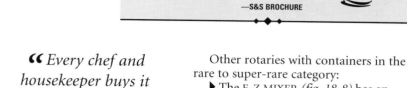

Three-Minute Mayonnaise

Yolk of 1 egg, 1/3 teaspoon salt, 1/3 teaspoon mustard, few grains cayenne, 1 tablespoon vinegar, 1/2 cup oil.

Method — Put all the ingredients except the oil in the S&S bowl, beating for a few seconds until well blended. Add the oil, 1 teaspoon at a time, through the receptacle on the cover, beating rapidly. When 4 teaspoons have been added this way, keep the receptacle filled with oil, beating rapidly until the 1/2 cup has been used. If the ingredients and bowl are cold, this amount can be made in 3 minutes without any danger of curdling.

This recipe makes enough for 6 people. Olive or cottonseed oil may be used.

—S&S BROCHURE

> " *Every chef and housekeeper buys it on sight.* "
>
> — E-Z MIXER AD

Other rotaries with containers in the rare to super-rare category:

▶ The E-Z MIXER (*fig. 18-8*) has an unusual hold-down or push-down handle top and a pedestal jar embossed REGISTERED 1902, PAT'D JUNE 30, 1903, 32 OZ.

In a 1905/06 catalog, the F. B. Mills Mail-Order House, said of the E-Z: "It has no equal for beating eggs, whipping cream, custards or any kind of batter, special sauces, salad dressings, etc. Price … $1.25."

The National Mfg. & Supply Company of Pittsburgh said in a *House Furnishing Review* ad (*fig. 18-9*) that "Fifteen-thousand dealers will be selling the E-Z mixer before the close of 1904." It also boasted that the "glass vessel has no seams or corners in which the mixture can escape the whirling dasher, and no leakage is possible."

The E-Z was patented (*fig. 18-10*) by Luther E. Shinn of Pittsburgh, who also noted the glass vessel, saying that "owing to the tapering egg-shaped bottom all the material will gravitate to the bottom and be mixed by the beaters, which conform to the shape of the bottom."

FIG. 18-9

December 1903 House Furnishing Review ad

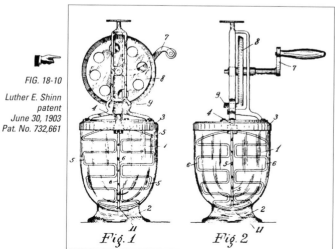

FIG. 18-10

Luther E. Shinn patent June 30, 1903 Pat. No. 732,661

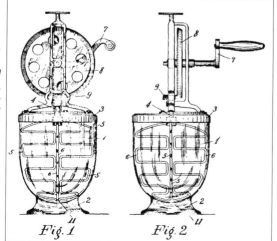

Fig. 1   *Fig. 2*

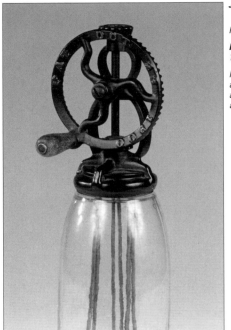

FIG. 18-11

PAT. OCT. 23 1900
14-3/4" designed for two-quart fruit jar —$2,000—

Note: This mixer comes in a smaller size, 12-1/2" for use in a one-quart fruit jar. One brought $3,450 at a 1999 Internet auction, the result of a rare beater coming on the market and two bidders determined to get it.

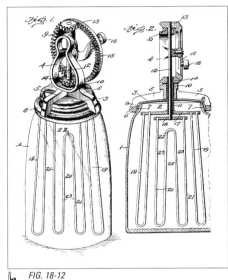

R S Arnold   ALLEN COLLECTION

FIG. 18-12

John M.C. Jones patent
Oct. 23, 1900
Pat. No. 660,513

D G Simons

FIG 18-13

*Kapheim jar beaters
(left to right):*

**GLOBE CREAM BEATER
PAT JUNE 11, 1907**
8-1/2" including vertical wood knob
—$1,500+—

Note: This jar attachment model brought $2,600 at a 1999 Internet auction, the result of a rare beater coming on the market and two bidders determined to get it.

**STANDARD SPECIALTY CO.,
MILWAUKEE, WISCONSIN
PAT'D JUNE 11, 1907**
12-1/4" —$900—

Note: This model is also marked:
**STANDARD SPEC CO.
MIL WIS PAT JUNE 11 1907**

MOFFET COLLECTION

▶ John M. C. Jones of Gibson City, Illinois called his jar beater, with figure-8 back brace *(fig. 18-11)*, "a combined egg beater, cream-whipper and churn." The Oct. 23, 1900 patent *(fig. 18-12)* said the bent wire dashers "will be revolved in reverse directions, and their construction and relative arrangement are such that as each beater cuts through and whips or beats up the cream or eggs it throws the same into the path of the other beaters and at the same times vibrates rapidly…"

▶ The STANDARD SPECIALTY CO. mixer (not related to the Standard hand-held rotary) is marked as such on the gear wheel *(fig. 18-13, right)*. It has unique dashers which patentee Frederick W. Kapheim of Milwaukee described as "a plurality of arms … made of wires which are twisted or coiled around the lower end of the shaft" *(fig. 18-14)*.

▶ The same patent was used for the GLOBE CREAM BEATER *(fig. 18-13, left)*. The GLOBE has a unique horizontal rotary wheel that sits atop the jar lid. The dashers of the two mixers are nearly identical.

Standard Specialty first appeared in the *Milwaukee City Directory* in 1908, located at the home of Kapheim. The next year it was listed at a different address as a division of the W. N. Durant Company, a manufacturer of counting machines.

According to Thomas Tomczk at the Milwaukee Public Library, "Mr. Kapheim continued to manufacture 'novelties and special machinery' at his home address under the name New Era Manufacturing Company. These listings continued in 1910. In the 1911 and later directories, there is no mention of New Era, and Kapheim is listed as a laborer. Standard Specialty also disappears as a separate entity. It would seem that Mr. Kapheim's invention was not a rousing commercial success."

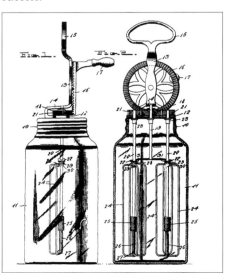

FIG. 18-14

Frederick W. Kapheim
patent
June 11, 1907
Pat. No. 856,469

THE EGGBEATER CHRONICLES

D G Simons

MOFFET COLLECTION

FIG. 18-15

JUDELL MFG. CO.
MILWAUKEE, WISC.
PAT. PEND.
12"   —$675—

FIG. 18-16

Catalog sheet from
The Jesse L. Edgren Co.
Household Specialties,
Milwaukee, Wisconsin

Mason Jar Egg Beater, Cream Whipper, Ice Cream Freezer and Mixer Combined

THIS wonderful device is manufactured to take the place of the expensive devices of this kind now on the market. Articles of this kind for the same purpose sell from   Every purchaser is obliged to purchase an extra expensive glass vessel to which the beater is attached. Now our *Mason Jar Beater* can be attached to any *Mason Jar* and it will do the same work better than the expensive beater. It is a very good article to sell with our *Fruit Jar Holder and Opener.* A trial will convince you we have struck another big winner.

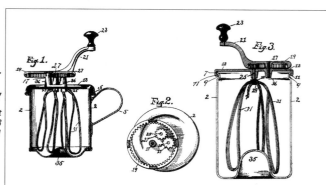

FIG. 18-17

Henry F. Juergens patent
June 20, 1893
Pat. No. 499,741

FIG. 18-18

Jewels (left to right):

THE HOUSEHOLD JEWEL
EGG BEATER
CAKE BEATER AND
ICE CREAM FREEZER
JUERGENS BROS.
MANUFACTURERS &
PATENTEES
MINNEAPOLIS, MINN.,
with concave glass
bottom designed to aid in
the mixing.
7-1/2"   —$900—

JEWEL BEATER MIXER
WHIPPER & FREEZER
MADE BY JUERGENS
BROS. MINNEAPOLIS,
MINN.
7-1/2"   —$800—

C Meeker

▶ Milwaukee also was the home of another cast-iron rotary atop quart jar: A mixer embossed on the wheel, JUDELL MFG. CO. MILWAUKEE, WISC. PAT. PEND. (fig. 18-15). This mixer also was called the MASON JAR EGG BEATER in an old catalog by The Jesse L. Edgren Co. Household Specialties of Milwaukee (fig. 18-16). "Now our Mason Jar Beater can be attached to any Mason jar and it will do the work better than the expensive beater," the catalog said.

▶ The JEWEL beater, patented June 20, 1893 by Henry F. Juergens of Minneapolis (fig. 18-17), is a heavy-duty model described in the patent application as "an egg or cake beater, a drink mixer, a cream whipper, an ice-cream freezer or a churn ..." The JEWEL (figs. 18-18 & 18-19) was manufactured by Juergens Brothers of Minneapolis. The jar is embossed: FLOUR 2 LB., SUGAR 3 LB., LIQUID 1 1/2 QT.

FIG. 18-19

Top view of JEWELS,
showing different
design of spokes in
main rotary gears

MEEKER COLLECTION

D G Simons
D Thornton

GRIFFITHS COLLECTION

FIG. 18-20

Butter-Flys (left to right):

BUTTER-FLY CHURN
THE WARE-STANDARD MFG. CO.
NEW YORK U.S.A.
11"   —$850—

THE BUTTER-FLY MIXER
14-1/2"   —$650—

FIG. 18-21   MOFFET COLLECTION

"ONE-MINUTE CHURN"
STANDARD CHURN MFG. CO.
NEW YORK, USA
PAT. SEPT. 19, '05
OTHER PATENTS PENDING
10"   —$450—

FIG. 18-22

TURN-A-MINIT CHURN CO.
METROPOLITAN TOWER, NEW YORK
PAT. APP'D FOR
with tin container,
one quart, 5" in diameter   —$800—

▶ It's the snake-spokes on the big front gear that make the BUTTER-FLY so recognizable. This beater came in two sizes with different dashers *(fig. 18-20).* They were made by the Ware-Standard Manufacturing Company of New York.

▶ Very similar to the small BUTTER-FLY is the ONE-MINUTE CHURN and the TURN-A-MINIT. The ONE-MINUTE *(fig. 18-21)* was made by the Standard Churn Manufacturing Company of New York. It has a wood dasher.

The TURN-A-MINIT *(figs. 18-22 & 18-23)* was made by the Turn-A-Minit Churn Company, 2804 Metropolitan Tower, New York City. It has a porcelain dasher and comes with a glass jar or a tin container. A larger model comes in a one-gallon porcelain jar. A *Good House-keeping* magazine ad listed the one quart glass size at $2.50 and the one gallon at $9. "There are lots of machines that will make milk mush by merging butter with milk. The Turn-A-Minit makes butter — real butter — and it takes only 1 minute," the ad said in part. There is a good possibility the same manufacturer made the BUTTER-FLY, ONE-MINUTE and TURN-A-MINIT mixers.

R S Arnold

KEHRER COLLECTION

THE EGGBEATER CHRONICLES

R S Arnold

FIG. 18-23

Glass and porcelain (left to right)

**TURN-A-MINIT CHURN CO.
METROPOLITAN TOWER, N.Y.
PATENT APPLIED FOR** *(on cast-iron top)*
TURN-A-MINUTE *(embossed on glass
one-quart container)*
—$850—

**TURN-A-MINIT CHURN CO.
METROPOLITAN TOWER, N.Y.
PATENT APPLIED FOR** *(on cast-iron top),*
with one-gallon porcelain container
7-1/2" high —$1,000+—

ALLEN COLLECTION

R S Arnold

FIG. 18-24

**BEATS-ALL
MADE BY** *(first three
letters unreadable)*
**XXXSEN
SPECIALTY CO.
LOS ANGELES, CAL.
USA**
*This mixer was found
with a Ladd tumbler jar
and the fit is perfect
17-1/2"* —$850—

Two rotaries with containers in the super rare to one-of-a-kind category are in the collection of Bruce Johnson:

▶ The clamp-on BEATS-ALL, measuring in at 17-1/2", was made in Los Angeles *(fig. 18-24).*

▶ No I.D., but believed patent model with brass handle and complex twisted flat wire dasher *(figs. 18-25 & 18-26).*

BRUCE JOHNSON COLLECTION

FIG. 18-25

*J. P. McLean and P. A. Morley patent
June 19, 1860
Pat. No. 28,760*

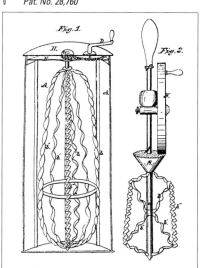

R S Arnold

BRUCE JOHNSON COLLECTION

FIG. 18-26

*No I.D. but believed McLean
patent model,
missing container,
6-1/2" high,
top 3-7/8" in diameter*
—$500—

**The April 1889, *Iron Age*
magazine featured the
13-1/2" WALKER'S
BEVERAGE-MIXER, made
by the Erie Specialty
Manufacturing Company
of Erie, Pennsylvania.
The mixer, which came
with three jars,
has not surfaced.**

D G Simons

 FIG. 18-27

Prestos (left to right):

PRESTO (on underside of metal, screw-on top)
PRESTO SUPREME MASON MANUFACTURED BY OWENS-ILLINOIS GLASS COMPANY (embossed on jar)
10-3/4″ —$190—

PRESTO (on underside of metal, screw-on top)
PRESTO SUPREME MASON MANUFACTURED BY OWENS-ILLINOIS GLASS COMPANY (embossed on jar)
13″ —$190—

R S Arnold

BOEDEKER / ALLEN COLLECTIONS

FIG. 18-28

SCHMIDT BROS. LANCASTER, PA
12″ to top of gear —$300—

SCHMIDT BROS. LANCASTER, PA PRESTO
13″ to top of gear —$400—

R S Arnold

FIG. 18-29

Fruit jar mixers
(left to right):

PEERLESS
11-1/2″ —$150—

No I.D.
14-1/4″ —$150—

BALL
13-1/2″ —$150—

**BUTTERCUP
GREENFIELD, MISSOURI**
11″ —$150—

ALLEN COLLECTION

Other rotary cranks in jars:

▶ The PRESTO (marked on the underside of the screw-on top) has an adjustable rotary that can be used on two different size jars, one- and two-quart *(fig. 18-27)*. The dasher shaft can be extended for the deeper two-quart.

▶ Like the PRESTO, one Schmidt Bros. mixer *(fig. 18-28)* has metal paddle dashers. It was manufactured in Lancaster, Pennsylvania and apparently was designed to fit any large fruit jar. In fact there is a Schmidt Brothers with the metal, screw-on lid embossed PRESTO.

▶ Very scarce fruit jar mixers include the PEERLESS, the BUTTERCUP, the BALL and an unmarked top designed for a pint jar *(figs. 18-29 & 18-30)*.

▶ The Metal Goods Manufacturing Company of Boston made at least two beaters with different dasher bottoms — a loop dasher with coiled wire and one with three dasher springs at the bottom of the rod *(figs. 18-31 & 18-32)*. The three-dasher spring model came in one-pint and one-quart jar sizes, according to the 1924 Montgomery Ward catalog, and sold for 49¢ and 89¢.

A 1920s ad *(fig. 18-33)* called this mixer the DELIGHT EGG-BEATER AND CREAM-WHIP and said it was "scientifically designed as a labor-saving device for the housewife." The DELIGHT name was trademarked by Metal Goods Manufacturing Company in 1923 *(fig. 18-34)*.

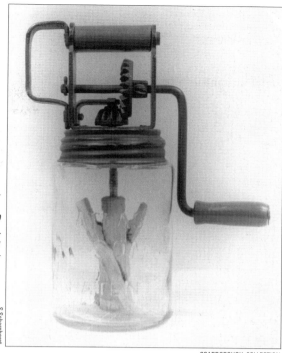

FIG. 18-30

No I.D., designed for one-pint jar
8-1/2" overall
—$500—

S Scharnhorst

SCARBOROUGH COLLECTION

FIG. 18-33

1924 Delight ad

The Delight
Egg-Beater and
Cream-Whip

Given for
Four Subscriptions

THIS egg-beater and cream-whip has been scientifically designed as a labor-saving device for the house-wife. One single turn of the handle will cause the coiled spring to strike the contents eight times. It holds one quart but is so constructed that one egg, or a small quantity of cream can be beaten as well as a pint or more —simply incline the jar, and the very tip end of the spring will strike the contents. What an improvement this is over the old type of egg-beater, with its exposed gears and parts which soon worked loose! There are no exposed gears here to collect grease and dirt, and no spattering— the top is absolutely spatter-proof. It surely is a pleasure to use this cream-whip when the desired result can be obtained with but a few turns of the handle. When ordering please mention **Gift No. 6900.**

FIG. 18-34

U.S. Patent & Trademark Office Official Gazette,
Jan. 9, 1923, Metal Goods Manufacturing Co.
trademark for the Delight

Ser. No. 167,050. (CLASS 23. CUTLERY, MACHINERY, AND TOOLS, AND PARTS THEREOF.) METAL GOODS MANUFACTURING CO., Boston, Mass. Filed July 18, 1922.

DELIGHT

Particular description of goods.—Egg Beaters and Cream Whip.
Claims use since May 17, 1922.

FIG. 18-31

METAL GOODS MANUFACTURING CO.
(embossed on top of gear mount)
7-1/2"   —$125—

D G Simons

FIG. 18-32

No I.D. but advertised as the DELIGHT
by Metal Goods Manufacturing Co.
7-1/2"   —$140—

D G Simons

MOFFET COLLECTION

▶ The MIN-IT-MAID *(fig. 18-35)* was manufactured by Pratt Automatic Machine Company, Chicago, and is very hard to find with the original jar.

▶ There are at least three rotary top, small jar models — one of which has its own patent *(fig. 18-36)* — that are very collectible. The most recognizable of the three *(fig. 18-37)* is the TIP 'N WHIP, the paper label of which says in part: "Tips & beats at any angle. Comfortable, restful motion … Easy to clean. No splash. No splatter. Takes very little space. A kitchen necessity."

▶ There are two jar rotaries with exceptional dashers and dasher movements — the ROTO-MIX and MINIT-MIXER. With five vertical dashers that all rotate in unison, the ROTO-MIX is a very novel mixer *(fig. 18-38)*. Relatively new, dating from the 1950s, it was made in Dayton, Ohio. The MINIT-MIXER *(fig. 18-39)*, which is also a combination reamer, was made in Germany and distributed in the United States by the Nutmeg Supply Co. of New Britain, Connecticut. It has four V-shaped dashers that revolve two ways. There are two similar mixers — the all plastic WHIP-O-MATIC manufactured by Popeil Brothers of Chicago, probably from the 1970s, and MIX-MATIC made by the E-Z Por Corporation, with plastic top and glass jar, from about the 1960s.

☞

FIG. 18-35
MIN-IT-MAID
PRATT AUTOMATIC
MACHINE CO.
PAT PN'D CHICAGO
9"   —$105—

D G Simons

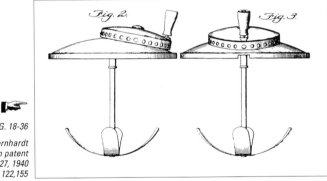

☞

FIG. 18-36

Rudolph Bernhardt
design patent
Aug. 27, 1940
Design Pat. No. 122,155

FIG. 18-37

Small jar rotaries (left to right):

No I.D. fancy jar
4-1/2"   —$30—

No I.D. circular jar with graduated bubble design
4"   —$25—

TIP 'N WHIP with paper label
4 -1/2"   —$40—

D G Simons

A mystery beater is the CLIPPER SANITARY EGG & CREAM WHIPPER *(fig. 18-40)*. The top, believed to be rotary, has never been found. Embossed the H. S. GEER CO., the jar is 4-1/2" in diameter with four ridges on top for an attachment. The H. S. Geer Company was listed in the 1910 *Troy, New York, City Directory* as "Soda Fountain Specialties." The next year, 1911, was the last directory listing for H. S. Geer but in 1912 the Clipper Fountain Supply Co., was listed, and continued in the directory until 1918. Around 1915 Geer became a "commercial traveler" (traveling salesman).

A large, cast-iron gear wheel with heart cutouts is the main feature of 'THE MOLLER CHURN' *(fig. 18-41)*. This mixer was made in New Rochelle, New York and is considered very rare.

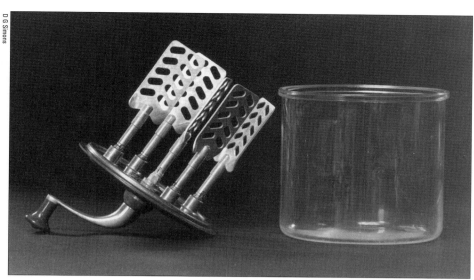

ALLEN COLLECTION

FIG. 18-38
ROTO-MIX DAYTON, OHIO PAT PEND.
8 3/4" —$250—

FIG. 18-39
THE ORIGINAL MINIT-MIXER PATENTED MADE IN GERMANY
(embossed on bottom of plastic jar)
9" to top of crank handle —$20—

FIG. 18-40
THE CLIPPER SANITARY EGG & CREAM WHIPPER (PATENT PENDING) MANF. BY THE H. S. GEER CO. TROY N.Y.
5-1/2"
—jar alone: $100;
value with top undetermined—

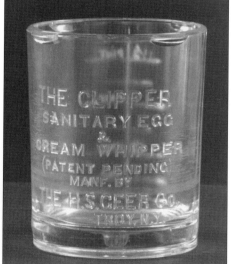

D G Simons

D G Simons

FIG. 18-41
'THE MOLLER CHURN' NEW ROCHELLE, N.Y. U.S.A PATENTS PEND'G
8" —$1,000—

SEIDEL COLLECTION

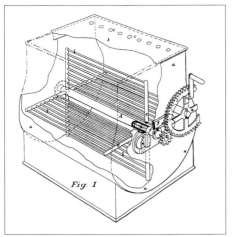

FIG. 18-42

Sarah A. Ulmer patent
Feb. 3, 1880
Pat. No. 224,117

FIG. 18-43

PATENTED FEB. 3, 1880
7" high, 9-1/2" long, 5" wide
—$475—

C Badger   BADGER COLLECTION

FIG. 18-44

WOOD & SELICK N.Y. *(embossed on brass plate)*
14-1/2" high, 14" long, 9" wide
—$450—

R S Arnold

MAIR COLLECTION

▶ The oldest known and thus most wanted tin container rotary mixer is one marked only PATENTED FEB. 3, 1880 *(figs. 18-42 & 18-43)*. It is known to collectors as the ULMER. The patent, by Sarah A. Ulmer of Portland, Maine, said in part:

"It is the result of my observation that eggs are most thoroughly and quickly beaten by subjecting them to the blows, in rapid succession, of smooth-surfaced wires, and that anything of a sharp cutting nature destroys the fiber of the egg, which should be preserved. This principle is embodied in my device ..."

Similar in design to the ULMER, but almost twice as high, is the WOOD & SELICK, with four cast-iron feet *(fig. 18-44)*. The WOOD & SELICK name is embossed on a brass plate soldered on the top of the mixer.

Detail of
WOOD & SELICK
brass plate

R S Arnold

Other metal container models include:

▶ The CREAM CITY (*figs. 18-45 & 18-46*), with paper label, was patented Sept. 17, 1907 (*fig. 18-47*) by Frank Reed of Milwaukee. He described the device as a "liquid agitator" for whipping cream, beating eggs, etc.

FIG. 18-45

***CREAM CITY
TURN SLOWLY
PAT. SEPT. 17, 1907***
11" —$350—

D G Simons

MOFFET COLLECTION

FIG. 18-46

CREAM CITY
15-1/2" extended

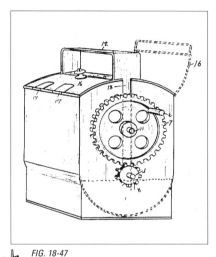

FIG. 18-47

*Frank Reed patent
Sept. 18, 1907
Pat. No. 866,067*

The Lincoln Chemical Works of Chicago offered Madam Blumer's Egg Saver in a small envelope, with a pinch equal to "one fresh hen's egg."

Conkey Egg Separator

3-1/4" diameter
—$25—

COOPER COLLECTION

FIG. 18-48

FRIES
10-1/2" —$90—

ULMER COLLECTION

FIG. 18-50

**HODGES
PAT. APLD FOR**
(on ice chamber)
10-1/2"
—$160—

FIG. 18-49

Thomas Mills & Brother catalog

FIG. 18-51

Detail of
**RICHARDSON'S
MARSHMALLOW
BEATER**
10-1/2"
—$150—

Egg Beater, Batter Mixer and Cream Whip

No. 1—	3	pt. .	$1.85
No. 2—	6	pt. .	2.25
No. 3—	9	pt. .	2.50
No. 4—	18	pt. .	5.00

▶ The FRIES cream whip (*fig. 18-48*) came in several sizes. According to an early catalog of Thomas Mills & Brother of Philadelphia featuring ice cream manufacturers' equipment, the FRIES was offered in 3-, 6-, 9-, and 18-pint sizes (*fig. 18-49*). One model featured a compartment for ice, when making ice cream (*fig. 18-50*), and another model was offered as marshmallow beater, under the name RICHARDSON'S (*fig. 18-51*).

The FRIES was made by George Fries' Sons, wholesale manufacturers located at 909 Filbert Street, Philadelphia, Pennsylvania. According to an early letterhead, the firm offered tin and Japanned ware, stamped ware, grocers' fixtures, scales, house furnishing goods, and dash board and station lanterns.

▶ Of a bit heavier metal is the clamp-on NUCOA MIXER (*figs. 18-52 & 18-53*) and the MIN-ET MIX-ER, a cast-metal device with its own four legs (*fig. 18-54*).

▶ Outfitted with what was believed a tin cup, the KWIKMIX is a milk shake mixer with its own wooden stand (*fig. 18-55*) and was available with two different dashers (*fig. 18-56*). The dasher slides up, allowing the insertion of a tin cup just under 4" high. The large, 5-1/4" diameter gear gives it super dasher speed.

The KWIKMIX was patented (*fig. 18-57*) by Mathew Black of Brooklyn, New York, who described his invention as a "mixing device with independently-adjustable stirring-rod." Black said one of the objects of his invention was to "permit the stirring member to be raised or moved independently without moving the driving mechanism therewith."

BRUCE JOHNSON COLLECTION

R S Arnold

 FIG. 18-52

NUCOA MIXER
PAT. APPLIED FOR
11" from clamp to handle,
5" in diameter
—$55—

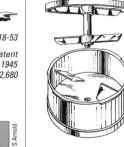

R S Arnold

 FIG. 18-53

Ray Swanson patent
Oct. 23, 1945
Pat. No. D-142,680

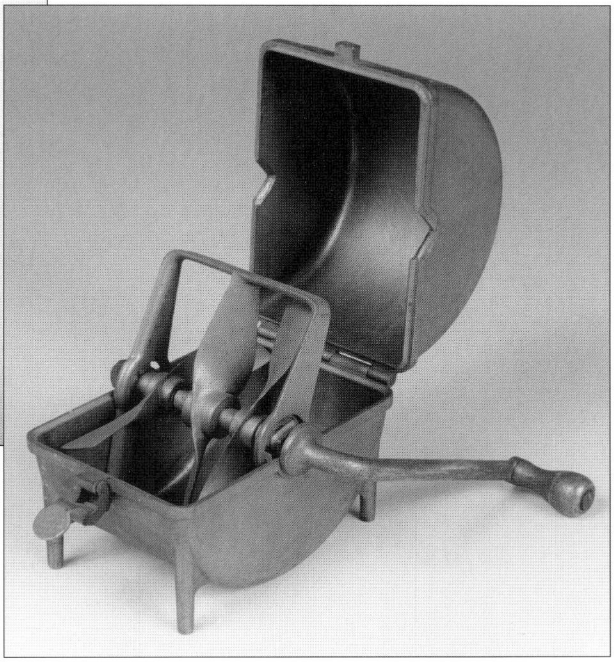

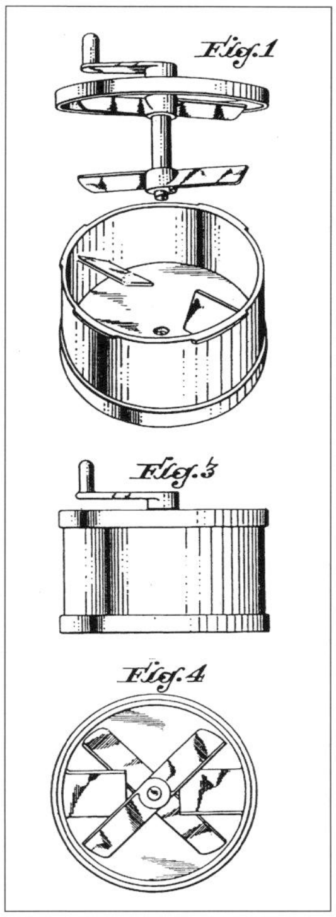

R S Arnold

 FIG. 18-54

MIN-ET MIX-ER (on top)
PAT. PEND (on bottom),
three rotating blades inside
a 5" diameter body
—$200—

BRUCE JOHNSON COLLECTION

R S Arnold

FIG. 18-55

KWIKMIX
PAT APPL'D FOR
RUST PROOF
10-1/2" overall
—$350—

FIG. 18-57

Mathew Black patent
March 9, 1920
Pat. No. 1,333,379

FIG. 18-56

Detail of different
KWIKMIX dasher

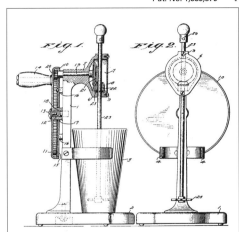

D Thornton

MEEKER COLLECTION

CHAPTER 18: ROTARY BEATERS WITH CONTAINERS

201

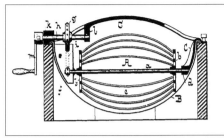

FIG. 18-58

Jacob L. Newcomer patent
May 26, 1885
Pat. No. 318,786

Larger container beaters that are
known to exist:

▶ THE NEWCOMER EGG AND SPONGE
CAKE BEATER was patented May 26, 1885
by Jacob L. Newcomer of Baltimore,
Maryland *(fig. 18-58)*. The Aug. 1, 1885
Scientific American magazine noted the
wooden box "prevents the contents of
the pan coming in contact with the chain
or wheels. The apparatus requires but
little effort to operate it, each revolution
of the beater agitates or lifts the whole
batch, and there is no danger of splashing." The mixer was manufactured by
J. L. Newcomer of Baltimore *(fig. 18-59)*.

▶ IVES' CELEBRATED SPONGE CAKE
BEATER was patented Sept, 8, 1885 by
George H. Ives of New Haven, Connecticut *(fig. 18-60)*. Although the patent lists
it as a "mixing machine for bakeries,"
an 1885 ad *(fig. 18-61)* said it was for
the "family baker."

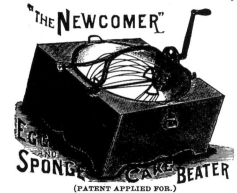
FIG. 18-59

Ad in the February, 1885
Confectioners' Journal

FIG. 18-60

George H. Ives patent
Sept. 8, 1885
Pat. No. 325,933

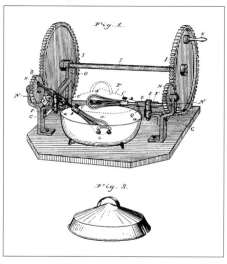

FIG. 18-61

Ad in The Household
Guide and Family
Directory of 1885

▶ VICKER'S EGG BEATER was featured in the Oct. 10, 1886 *Scientific American* (*fig. 18-62*). "The revolving frame consists of two sets of spokes and cross bars which are arranged to revolve one inside and one outside the stationary frame," the article said in explaining the beating process for this machine patented in 1886 by William Vickers of Jersey City, New Jersey (*fig. 18-63*).

▶ The PATENT EGG AND SPONGE BEATER came in three sizes and proclaimed in an ad: "It can be operated by any boy, and will beat five dozen of eggs in from ten to fifteen minutes" (*fig. 18-64*).

▶ COLES SHAKER (*fig. 18-65*) for soda fountains stands 24-1/2" high and is the ultimate rotary shake maker. Manufactured in Philadelphia, this heavy-duty mixer with two malt jars came with holes drilled in the bottom support so it could be secured to a counter.

FIG. 18-62
Drawing in the Oct. 30, 1886
Scientific American

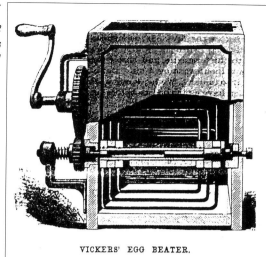

VICKERS' EGG BEATER.

FIG. 18-63
William Vickers patent
Oct. 12, 1886
Pat. No. 350,708

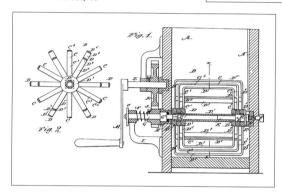

FIG. 18-64
Thomas Mills & Brother
ad in February, 1885,
Confectioners' Journal

FIG. 18-65
**COLES SHAKER
COLES MFG. CO.
PHILADELPHIA PA.
24-1/2" —$950—**

3 SIZES.

Patent Egg and Sponge Beater.
THE BEST IN USE.

This machine is the only practical one in use, the frame being made entirely of iron. The beater is made of stout wire, and has a crank motion, which is the same as beating by hand. It is simple in its construction. The can and beater may be removed from the machine in less than half a minute. It can be operated by any boy, and will beat five dozen of eggs in from ten to fifteen minutes. Those who are using them say they can save the price of a machine in a short time, as there is no waste.

D Thornton

▶ A giant "whisking machine" could be hand or belt driven. This machine came with a six gallon bowl *(fig. 18-66)*. "Beater, mixer and masher for eggs, cream, vegetables, &c.," is how William Sturma of Philadelphia described his device *(fig. 18-67)*.

❖

The proper ending on this chapter of eggbeater history: An "animated mixer and drinking tumbler combination for children."

In his Nov. 15, 1966 patent *(fig. 18-69)*, Adolph E. Goldfarb of North Hollywood, California, said in part:

"Many products which are healthful for children are in the form of dry powders which must be mixed with a liquid, such as milk or the like, before being consumed by a child. Some of these products do not mix satisfactorily with the liquid medium with a spoon."

I still wish I had one.

FIG. 18-66

Thomas Mills & Brother catalog page

Whisking Machine

HAND POWER

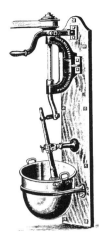

POWER MACHINE, FRICTION DRIVE

This is an excellent machine for all kinds of egg whites, sponges, creaming pound cake, white mountain cake, Spanish bunn, layer cake, kisses and icing. The large fly-wheel, revolving in a horizontal position, causes the machine to work very easily, and the beater to rotate with great rapidity, in exact imitation of hand whisking. The beater can be set higher or lower, and also to take a larger or smaller circle, being thus adapted to large or small mixings, and different size mixing pans as required. The beater can be removed, and the flour, etc., added to the mixture in the same pan in which the beating is done.

It can be fixed to a wall or upright post. It is a strong and durable machine and gives satisfaction wherever used.

The bowl is made of copper and holds 6 gallons.

FIG. 18-67

William Sturma patent Feb. 5, 1907 Pat. No. 843,309

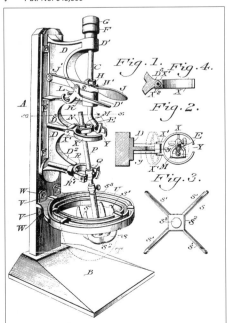

Here's a container beater you won't find in the kitchen. It's a promotional item for Oil-Mate featuring two eggbeaters in two compartments in an enclosed plastic case. It asks the gas station customer of the 1960s to "Turn for 40 second test" of regular oil and oil with Oil-Mate. The one with Oil-Mate does appear to be more effective, as the oil climbs up the dasher on the right.

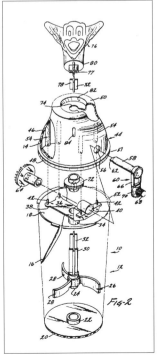

FIG. 18-69

Adolph E. Goldfarb patent Nov. 15, 1966 Pat. No. 3,285,584

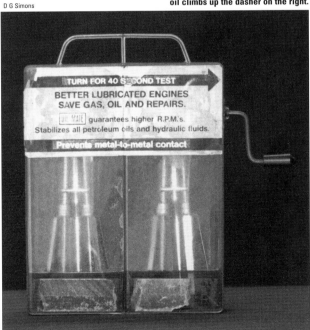

D G Simons

TURN FOR 40 SECOND TEST

BETTER LUBRICATED ENGINES SAVE GAS, OIL AND REPAIRS.

OIL MATE guarantees higher R.P.M.'s Stabilizes all petroleum oils and hydraulic fluids.

Prevents metal-to-metal contact

Chapter 19

Syllabub Churns, Shakers & Plungers

"Stiff enough to cut with a knife."

Syllabub: A dessert made
of a mixture of whole milk
or cream with wine or cider,
usually slightly sweetened,
and often including eggs,
nutmeg and cinnamon.

FIG. 19-1

Syllabub churns with heights to top of cylinders (left to right):

LIGHTNING CREAM WHIP & EGG BEATER
5-1/2"   —$50—

THE WONDER CREAM WHIP & EGG BEATER ABSOLUTELY UNEQUALED
5-1/2"   —$55—
Note: There is a very similar model marked **BADGER EGG CHURN**

No I.D. but believed to be **BROOKLYN EGG BEATER AND CREAM WHIP**
6-1/4"   —$60—

SALTSMAN'S COLUMBIA EGG BEATER ALBANY, N.Y. PATENTED GREAT BRITAIN & U.S.A JULY 10, 1894
6-1/4"   —$55—

 ECONOMICAL EGG BEATER AND CREAM WHIPPER PATENT APPLD FOR
6-1/2"   —$45—

This family of mixers, including syllabub churns, cream shakers, whip churns, and churn dashers, is still fertile ground for collectors. Most of these items are not in the same league with the rarer cast-iron rotary crank beaters, and are available to the determined collector.

Recommended by Fannie Farmer in her 1896 *The Boston Cooking-School Cook Book* for whipping thin cream, the syllabub churn consists of a plunger with a perforated disk and an open ended, or closed cylinder. The open cylinder, often perforated around the bottom, was placed on the bottom of a bowl containing eggs or cream. Holding it still with one hand, the cook pushed the plunger up and down with the other.

Small, tin syllabubs include *(fig. 19-1):*

▶ The LIGHTNING CREAM WHIP & EGG BEATER is described in an 1890 catalog as "a simple contrivance, durable and easy to clean, but surprisingly in its results." The catalog boasted: "The white of an egg can be beaten in one minute to a froth stiff enough to cut with a knife."

▶ An early ad *(fig. 19-2)* for a very similar syllabub, THE WONDER CREAM

WHIP AND EGG BEATER, proclaimed: "Nothing to get out of order. No cog wheels or other mechanical arrangements to get out of adjustment … It will beat from one to twenty eggs in half the time ordinarily required."

▶ The BROOKLYN EGG BEATER AND CREAM WHIP SILVER'S PATENT features the same hollow plunger as in the SILVER'S EGG BEATER *(See Chapter 9, Keystone and Silver, page 92).* "It aerates the eggs or other mixtures by forcing the air through them," said a catalog. Silver also made a BROOKLYN NO. 2, a larger model with a T-top plunger like the glass SILVER plunger.

▶ SALTSMAN'S COLUMBIA EGG BEATER, ALBANY, N.Y. was patented by Aaron J. Saltsman who also patented two other mixers, both slotted spoon devices *(See Chapter 24, Handheld Cousins, page 280).*

▶ The ECONOMICAL EGG BEATER AND CREAM WHIPPER is probably the most common of the small tin syllabub churns.

☞

FIG. 19-2

Unidentified kitchenware and recipe booklet

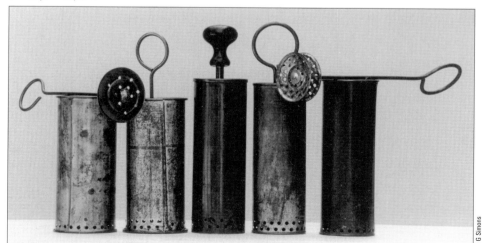

D G Simons

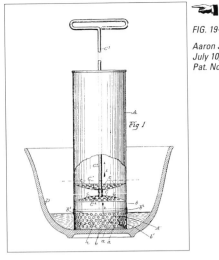

FIG. 19-3

Aaron J. Saltsman patent
July 10, 1894
Pat. No. 522,944

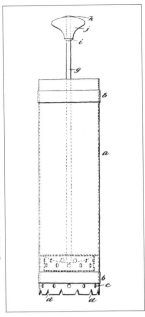

In addition to the Saltsman patent (*fig. 19-3*), there are several other patents related to syllabubs, dating into the 1920s (*figs. 19-4 through 19-6*).

Three of the more rare open-end syllabubs are the New Jersey-made SURPRISE (*fig. 19-7*) with exceptional bottom cylinder perforations, a mixer marked only PAT. PEND. (*fig. 19-8*), which can be used in any mixing bowl, and another with a special air vent (*fig. 19-9*).

FIG. 19-4

Hartwell A. Dalrymple and Patrick C. McGrath patent
June 30, 1896
Pat. No. 563,139

Fig. 19-6

William Schramm patent
Jan. 13, 1925
Pat. No. 1,523,085

C Badger

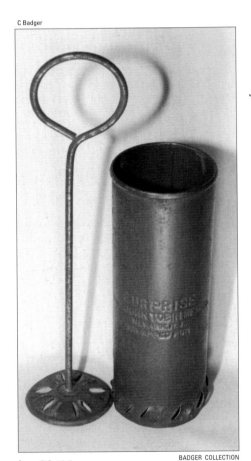

FIG. 19-5

John H. Gourlie patent
June 30, 1914
Pat. No. 1,101,693

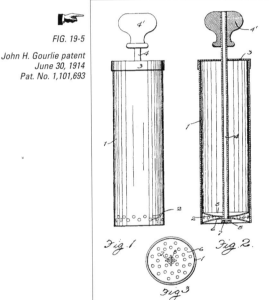

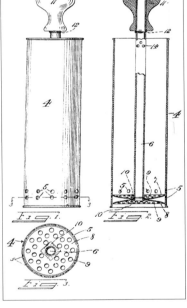

BADGER COLLECTION

FIG. 19-7

SURPRISE
THE JOHN TOBIN MFG. CO. NEWARK, N.J.
PAT. APPLD FOR
6-1/4" cylinder —$150—

R S Arnold

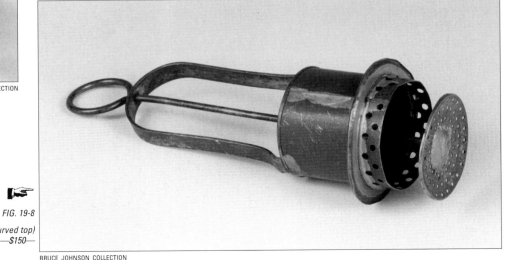

FIG. 19-8

PAT. PEND. (on one side of curved top)
8-1/2" —$150—

BRUCE JOHNSON COLLECTION

THE EGGBEATER CHRONICLES

FIG. 19-9

No I.D., tin churn with flat dasher and side air vent
8" cylinder   —$150—

Beating Eggs

Aero-Whip brochure

Place the Aero-Whip tube into the bowl and break the eggs into it. Insert the plunger and operate in the same manner as whipping cream. The eggs will be whipped to a delightfully foamy consistency in practically no time at all.

Although the syllabubs run mostly five to six inches high, there is one model nearly twice that size. This skinny mixer is also unusual in that the cylinder and the bottom itself are perforated *(fig. 19-10).*

The syllabub churn even made it into the 1950s, with a plastic cylinder and spring loaded plunger model called the AERO-WHIP *(fig. 19-11).*

"The plunger can be operated with either the palm of the hand or the fingers, pushing it down against the spring as far as it will go. The spring then returns the plunger to its original position. The action is simple and the entire operation can easily be done with one hand," said a brochure for the manufacturer, The Fletcher-Terry Company of Forestville, Connecticut.

FIG. 19-10

No. I.D.
1-1/2" in diameter,
11-1/2" high
—$75—

❝ *The faster the plunger is operated the sooner the cream will whip.* **❞**

—AERO-WHIP BROCHURE

FIG. 19-11

AERO-WHIP
IT'S SPATTER PROOF
CREAM WHIPPER
with box and brochure
8"   —$35—

MOFFET COLLECTION

I am the champion of the world. My motto is to always beat, spoon or crank that can be whirled till ever with my shake compete. —PAPER LABEL, THE TILDEN

A cousin of the syllabub churn is the egg or cream shaker, a closed tin cylinder container with a snug fitting top, and a spinning disk or other contrivance inside. The best known shaker is TILDEN'S PATENT AUG. *1, 1865 (figs. 19-12 & 19-13)*. This model has a removable, winged disk inside that when shaken hastens the whipping process.

Howard Tilden of Boston said in his patent application: "The nature of my invention consists in a long case or box of convenient size to be taken in the hands and shaken, and provided with a revolving wheel midway between the ends, with floats arranged diagonally to its axis, so that the wheel will be turned by the eggs or liquid in the box as it flows back and forth when the box is shaken."

A year earlier, on Nov. 22, 1864, Tilden patented a churn dasher *(fig. 19-14)* which is worth mentioning just for the name of one of the witnesses who signed the patent, Greenleaf Stackpole.

Charles M. Drennan of Boston patented a shaker *(figs. 19-15 & 19-16)* similar on the outside to Tilden's. However, Drennan's Sept. 18, 1866 device had in the center "a diaphragm, composed of wire-gauze or its equivalent material." The implement, Drennan said, is "grasped in the hand and shaken back and forth briskly for a few seconds, when the eggs will be found to be thoroughly beaten by being forced through the diaphragm."

Drennan's mixer was offered as a "Family Egg-Beater, with no machinery. Price only 30 cents" (60 cents by mail), by W. P. & I. Gannett, proprietors and manufacturers, 50 Bromfield St., Boston, in an 1866 magazine ad. In addition, there is an English version in the collection of Guy and Sheila DiAmbrosio, marked with a brass seal embossed: 10 SECOND EGG BEATER NO. 1256 ROBERT WILSON 50 KINGS ST. MANCHESTER.

R S Arnold   MAIR COLLECTION

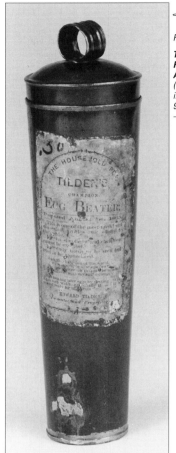

FIG 19-12

TILDEN'S PATENT AUG. 1, 1865
(marked on inside disk)
9"
—$225; with paper label, $350—

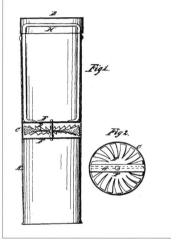

FIG. 19-13

Howard Tilden patent
Aug. 1, 1865
Pat. No. 49,176

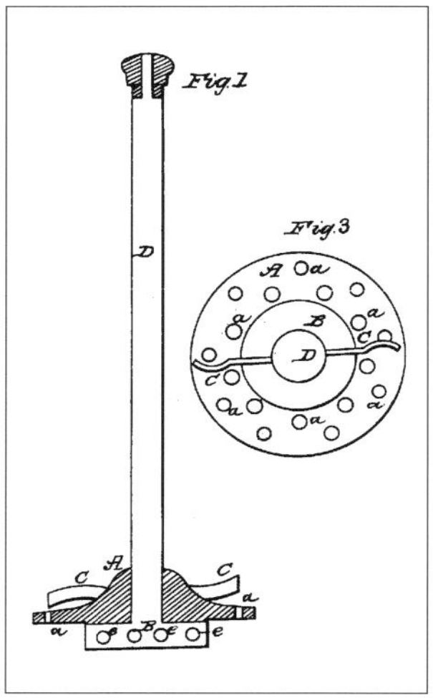

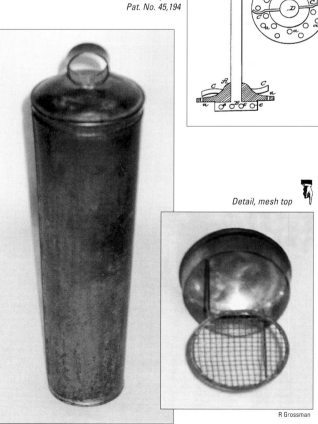

FIG. 19-14

Howard Tilden patent
Nov. 22, 1864
Pat. No. 45,194

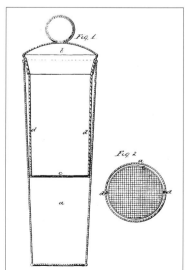

FIG. 19-15

Charles M. Drennan patent
Sept. 18, 1866
Pat. No. 58,165

GROSSMAN COLLECTION

FIG. 19-16

No. I.D., but Drennan patent shaker with wire strainer
9" —$250—

Detail, mesh top

R Grossman

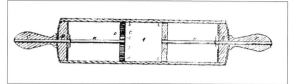

FIG. 19-17

George G. Carver patent
Dec. 3, 1867
Pat. No. 71,696

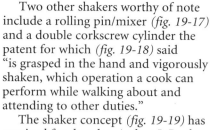

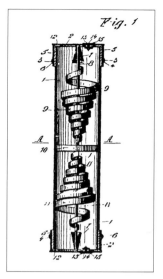

FIG. 19-18

Ernest R. Godward patent
July 10, 1900
Pat. No. 653.233

Two other shakers worthy of note include a rolling pin/mixer *(fig. 19-17)* and a double corkscrew cylinder the patent for which *(fig. 19-18)* said "is grasped in the hand and vigorously shaken, which operation a cook can perform while walking about and attending to other duties."

The shaker concept *(fig. 19-19)* has survived for decades. Arthur J. Rochow patented his SWIRL MIXER July 16, 1940 *(fig. 19-20)*. Taking shaking to new heights, Rochow said his device has "a closed elongated body and end walls including a sheet metal bottom having a central reentrant exterior cavity stamped therein forming pitched surfaces on the interior projecting internally of the container and oppositely inclined on opposite sides of the geometric center in a circumferential direction in the manner of a propeller to produce a swirling motion in the liquid."

FIG. 19-19

Various shakers (left to right)

LOFT
(in script on aluminum top and
bottom of jar,
which is marked in ounces)
7-3/4"   —$12—

**SMOOTHIE MIXER AND
MEASURE ALUMINUM**
one-cup, 3-7/8"   —$5—

**HEMO THOMPSON'S
DOUBLE MALTED MILK
WITH BEEF AND IRON**
4"   —$10—

**SWIRL MIXER PAT. NO 2,208,431
ROCHESTER, N.Y.**
one-cup, 4"   —$5—

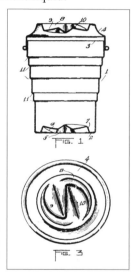

FIG. 19-20

Arthur J. Rochow patent
July 16, 1940
Pat. No. 2,208,431

R S Arnold

For Extra Good Measure

Patented July 13, 1880, the one-quart FAMILY MEASURING JAR stands 7-3/4" high at its tallest point. In addition to FAMILY MEASURING JAR , the jars are embossed vertically, MANUFACTURED BY THE SHINN MANUFACTURING CO. (left) and MANUFACTURED BY THE ROCHESTER TUMBLER CO. (right). The different measurements include liquid pints and ounces, up to a pound sugar powdered, tea cups, and up to a pound flour. The patent was obtained by Thornton A. Shinn of Remington, Pennsylvania. With his invention, Shinn said "culinary operations … may be greatly facilitated by substituting for the slow and tedious process of weighing the various ingredients the more speedy operation of measuring them by the use of a graduated vessel…"

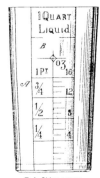

T. A. Shinn patent
July 13, 1880
Pat. No. 230,075

D Thornton

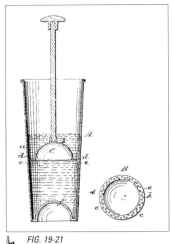

FIG. 19-21

E. L. Pratt patent
Nov. 6, 1866
Pat. No. 59,449

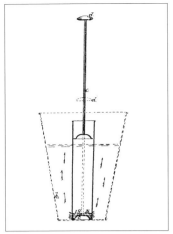

FIG. 19-22

E. L. Pratt patent
Sept. 10, 1867
Pat. No. 68,788
(described as an
improvement to 59,449)

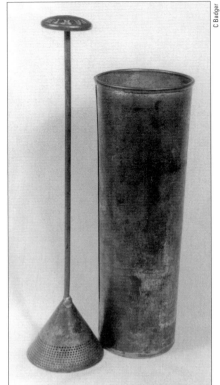

C Badger

FIG. 19-23

PRATTS EGG BEATER
PAT. NOV. 6, 1866
(on top of plunger)
9-1/2" cylinder   —$275—

BADGER COLLECTION

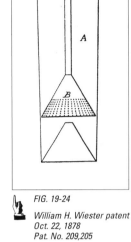

FIG. 19-24

William H. Wiester patent
Oct. 22, 1878
Pat. No. 209,205

FIG. 19-27

AUTOMATIC EGG BEATER NO. 2
PATENTED OCTOBER 22, 1878
11-1/2"   —$350—

R S Arnold

FIG. 19-25

AERATING EGG BEATER
PRATT'S PATENT
NOV. 6, 1866 AND SEPT. 10, 1867...
WIESTER & CO. MANUFACTURERS
AND DEALERS IN USEFUL INVENTIONS
17 NEW MONTGOMERY ST
(GRAND HOTEL BUILDING)
SAN FRANCISCO
patent model 11"   —$1,000—

BRUCE JOHNSON COLLECTION

FIG. 19-26

Detail of paper label

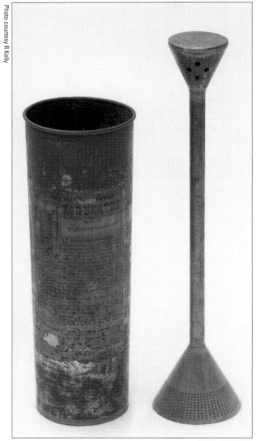

Photo courtesy R Kelly

KELLY COLLECTION

THE EGGBEATER CHRONICLES

Another cousin is the tin cylinder with plunger action. Some have flat bottoms and others have an inward cone bottom which fits right into the perforated cone-end dasher.

One of the first tin plungers with cone-bottom patents went to E. L. Pratt of Boston for his Nov. 6, 1866 "improved apparatus for aerating and mixing substances" *(figs. 19-21 through 19-23)*.

Manufactured by Woods, Sherwood & Company of Lowell, Massachusetts, the PRATT mixer came in three sizes. At least four of the NO. 2 size, holding two pints, exist in collections. However, the No. 1 at 1 pint, and the NO. 3 at 3-1/4 pints, are waiting to be discovered.

Edward P. Woods and Daniel Sherwood organized the firm of Woods, Sherwood & Company in 1861 to manufacture white lustral wire ware. By 1897, more than 75 men were employed. Both men were inventors, with Sherwood being granted a patent for a wire hand-held mixer *(See Chapter 24, Handheld Cousins, page 273)*, and Woods winning a patent for improvements in bench hooks and clamps.

Woods, Sherwood & Co. also made the DUDLEY-BRYANT PATENTED EGG BEATER *(See Chapter 12, Archimedes,*

page 116). The firm later became part of Androck.

William H. Wiester of San Francisco borrowed on Pratt's two plungers and in 1878 patented what is believed the earliest West Coast beater *(figs. 19-24 through 19-26)*. This is how Wiester described his improvement: "In Pratt's device the concavity of the plunger alone is depended upon for conveying air into the body of the material to be mixed and aerated, but I have discovered that by combining a hollow plunger-rod and valve with the concave perforated plunger or dasher, so as to force air into the concavity of the plunger at every stroke, I can greatly increase the efficiency of the device." A later

version of Wiester's patent was called the AUTOMATIC EGG BEATER NO. 2, and did not mention Pratt's patents *(fig. 19-27)*.

The patent model for a tin churn eggbeater *(figs. 19-28 through 19-30)* patented in 1865 by William B. Smith of New York City still exists today — although it's not known if the beater ever made it to market. According to Smith, this is how his "apparatus" works: "When the eggs (of course divested of their shells) are placed in the vessel and a reciprocating motion given to the rod the variously-shaped beating-blades at the bottom thereof will cut and agitate the liquid eggs and thus beat them to any desired consistency."

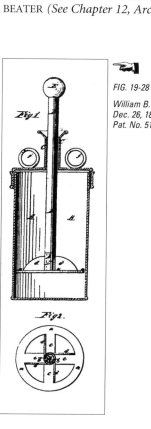

FIG. 19-28

William B. Smith patent
Dec. 26, 1865
Pat. No. 51,758

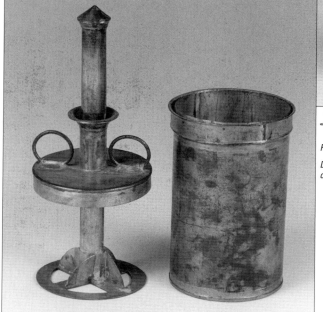

FIG. 19-29

William B. Smith patent model with original label 9" overall —$1,000—

R S Arnold

HOY COLLECTION

FIG. 19-30

Dasher arrangement of patent model

FIG. 19-31

**WM. REDHEFFER'S
LIGHTNING EGG BEATER
MANUFACTURED BY
W.H. & J.S. CHICK & E.R. THRELKELD
ST. LOUIS, MO.
PAT. JAN. 20, 1874**
10-1/2" cylinder —$475—

C Badger   BADGER COLLECTION

Two flat-bottom tin churns with brass labels and Kansas City connections are the LIGHTNING *(figs. 19-31 & 19-32)* and the WONDER VACUUM *(figs. 19-33 & 19-34)*. The LIGHTNING was patented in 1874 by William Redheffer of Kansas City, Missouri, and features triple conical dashers. Redheffer also utilized the same triple dashers in three similar patents. The other flat bottom is attributed to Mrs. L. B. Leagan, also of Kansas City, Missouri.

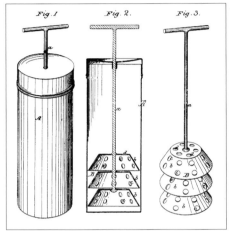

FIG. 19-32

*William Redheffer patent
Jan. 20, 1874
Pat. No. 146,710*

BRUCE JOHNSON COLLECTION   R S Arnold

FIG. 19-33

**THE WONDER VACUUM
BUTTER MAKER
MRS. L. B. LEAGAN
INVENTOR AND OWNER
KANSAS CITY, MO.**
6-1/2" —$225—

FIG. 19-34

*Detail of **WONDER VACUUM** brass label*

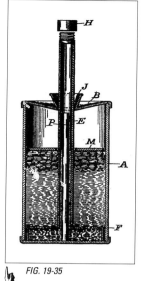

FIG. 19-35

James M. O'Neall patent
Aug. 1, 1905
Pat. No. 796,083

FIG. 19-36

PAT. NO. 796083
15" —$200—

In addition to Mrs. Leagan, James M. O'Neall of Dallas, Texas in 1905 patented *(fig. 19-35)* a tin butter maker. His device, O'Neall said, was "adapted to aerate the milk during the churning operation until the milk is all converted into butter and the butter is free from water or milk and is of a firm consistency…" The main feature of this churn is a screw-on air vent with regulator insert in the plunger *(figs. 19-36 & 19-37).*

Other flat bottom tin churns include the OVEE, SPEED-E-WHIPPER, and WONDER MERGER, with many more nameless *(figs. 19-38 & 19-39).*

FIG. 19-37

Detail of screw-on air regulator

R S Arnold

MAIR COLLECTION

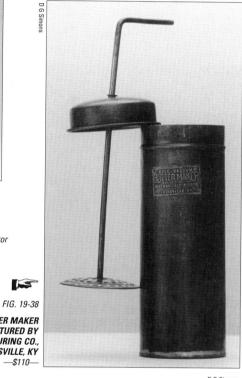

D G Simons

FIG. 19-38

**OVEE VACUUM BUTTER MAKER
MANUFACTURED BY
OVEE MANUFACTURING CO.,
LOUISVILLE, KY**
10-1/2" —$110—

FIG. 19-39

Flat bottoms with heights to top of cylinders (left to right):

No I.D.
6-3/4" —$45—

**SPEED-E-WHIPPER
PAT. PENDING**
7-1/2" —$35—

**WONDER MERGER
PAT. APLD. FOR**
9" —$45—

No I.D. tapers down
9-1/2" —$60—

No I.D.
8-1/2" and 4" in diameter
—$50—
Note: There is a smaller version of this mixer at 7-1/2" and 3-1/4" diameter marked:
SCHLAGSAHNEIN 1 MINUTE

D G Simons

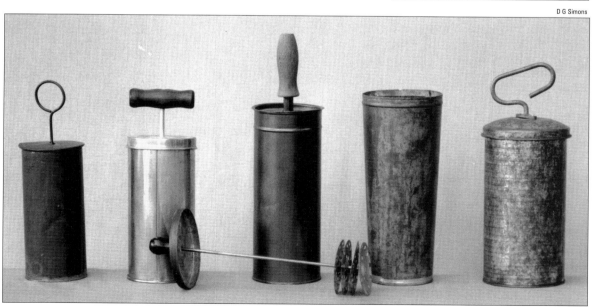

The unique feature of the flat-bottom STAR EGG BEATER *(fig. 19-40)* is that it has stars punched out of its three-layer disk dasher.

The STAR has two markings. One reads E. KUNKLE & BOSTICK MANUF'S PAT. SEP 5 '71, FT. WAYNE. The other reads STAR EGG BEATER MANUF'D BY KUNKLE & BOSTICK FT. WAYNE, IND. PAT. OCT, 3 '71.

Erastus B. Kunkle of Fort Wayne, Indiana, won his tin plunger patent *(fig. 19-41)* Sept. 5, 1871, listing himself as assignor to Emanuel Bostick, also of Fort Wayne. Bostick on Oct. 3, 1871, was given the design patent, an improvement on the earlier one. Kunkle rates a page in *The Pictorial History of Fort Wayne, Indiana* by B. J. Griswold, subtitle: "A Review of Two Centuries of Occupation of the Region About the Head of the Maumee River." This 1917 book itself is a noteworthy example of early regional U.S. histories — always taking the biographical high road. For example, this prose opens the page on our inventor: "Erastus B. Kunkle was one of those strong and loyal men who always faced the right way with the right spirit, and by very nature and integrity of purpose he helped to carry the victorious attitude in all the relations of a signally earnest and useful career."

On Jan. 15, 1884, William G. Flanders of Troy, New York, patented a tin plunger *(fig. 19-42)* that a brochure *(fig. 19-43)* said "gives universal satisfaction and needs only to be seen to be appreciated, and besides, it is at all times ready for use."

The brochure called it FLANDERS' PATENT EGG BEATER, SWEET CREAM, CUSTARD WHIP AND FROSTING MAKER and boasted that "it will beat any number of eggs from one to six, in from one to two minutes." The brochure confirms its existence, yet it has proven elusive to collectors.

FIG. 19-40

STAR EGG BEATER MANUF'D BY KUNKLE & BOSTICK FT. WAYNE, IND. PAT. OCT. 3, '71
7-1/2" cylinder
—$220—

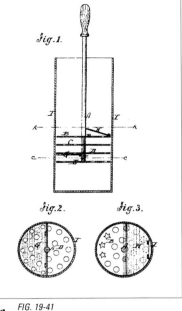

D G Simons

FIG. 19-41

Erastus B. Kunkle patent Sept. 5, 1871 Pat. No. 118,727

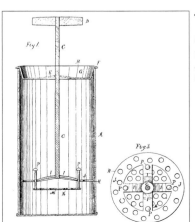

FIG. 19-42

William G. Flanders patent Jan. 15, 1884 Pat. No. 291,890

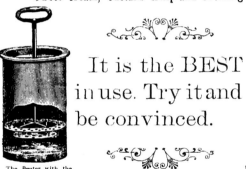

FIG. 19-43

G. Gerdom, West Troy, N.Y. early brochure

The UNIVERSAL EGG FOAMER (*fig. 19-44*) is the same category as the Flanders' claim of "needs only to be seen to be appreciated." This mixer has an unique wood plunger that measures nearly 11" high.

As for cone bottoms, there is one popular patent date: Sept. 14, 1875 (*figs. 19-45 & 19-46*). Friedrich E. Schonmeyer of Cleveland described it this way: "The operation of the device is as follows: The egg or other substance to be agitated is placed in the receptacle; it is then agitated by the dash. The conical form of this dash enables it to set down closely upon the conical project. As the dash is pressed down, the egg is, by the cone forced upward through the perforations in the dash and the egg or other substance is thoroughly cut and separated by the edges of the orifices through which it is forced."

R S Arnold

FIG. 19-44

UNIVERSAL EGG FOAMER
tin cylinder 6-7/8"
—$175—

Nulaid Egg Separator

3-1/4" diameter
—$22—

MAIR COLLECTION

D G Simons

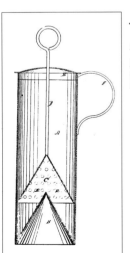

FIG. 19-45

*Friedrich E. Schonmeyer patent
Sept. 14, 1875
Pat. No. 167,696*

FIG. 19-46

*Sept. 14, 1875 cone bottoms
with heights to top of
cylinders (left to right):*

PAT. SEP 14-75
9" —$60—

**BON TON EGG BEATER
PATENTED SEPT. 14, 1875**
11-1/2" —$95—

PAT SEP 14-75
11-1/2" —$70—

PAT SEP 14-75
15" —$65—

☞

FIG. 19-47

*Cone bottoms with
heights to top of
cylinders
(left to right):*

*No I.D.
tapers down
7-1/2"* —$55—

**THE HAMILTON
PAT. JAN. 22, 1901
AUG. 18, 1903
9"** —$60—

*No I.D.
9"* —$50—

*No I.D.
10"* —$50—

Other cone-bottoms were offered in a variety of sizes *(fig. 19-47)*.

The cone-bottom CHAMPION EGG BEATER came in four sizes: one, two, three and four-pints. Its existence is noted in a *House Furnishing Review* magazine ad *(fig. 19-48)* that listed the manufacturer as The Reid-Edelmuth Mfg. Co. of Brooklyn. "Beats up eggs or cream in one-fourth the time of any beater ever made," the ad said.

Another cone-bottom, noted in an early ad *(fig. 19-49)*, is a real Southern beauty. The tin AIR-O-MIXER was made by the Dixie Stamping Company in Birmingham, Alabama, beginning around 1920.

Like the FLANDERS, collectors are waiting for the Champion and AIR-O-MIXER to turn up.

☞

FIG. 19-48

*December 1908
House Furnishing
Review ad*

FIG. 19-49

Dixie Stamping Company ad

FIG. 19-50

Hamilton & Sons
Manufacturing Company
catalog sheet

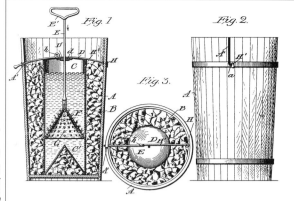

FIG. 19-51

Charles Richard
Hamilton patent
Jan. 22, 1901
Pat. No. 666,269

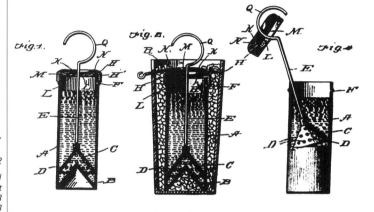

FIG. 19-52

Charles Richard
Hamilton patent
Aug. 18, 1903
Pat. No. 736,723

FIG. 19-53

Taller tin churns, cone and flat bottom, with heights to top of cylinders (left to right):

PAT'D JAN 22-01 AUG. 18-03
Hamilton patents, cone bottom, 11-3/4" —$75—

No I.D., 10-3/4" rounded bottom —$65—

PAT SEP 14 no year listed but Schonmeyer 1875 patent, 11" cone bottom, 5" in diameter —$85—

No I.D., possibly homemade, 10-1/4" —$75—

No I.D. similar to Fig. 19-10, 10-1/2" drilled, flat bottom, 1-1/2" in diameter —$75—

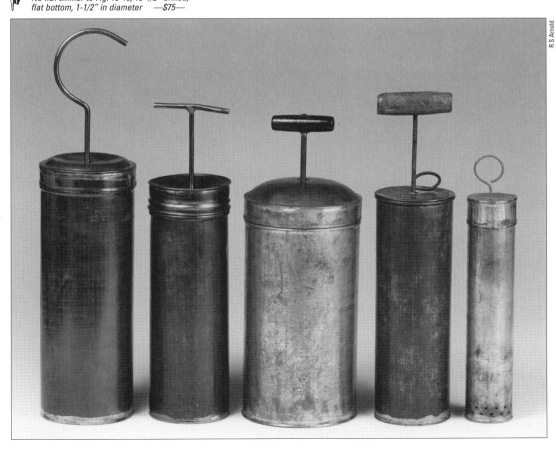

R S Arnold

Hamilton & Sons Manufacturing Company of Huntsville, Alabama (*fig. 19-50*), offered its cone-bottom tin churn in three sizes — two-quart, one-quart and miniature. They are marked with two patent dates (*figs. 19-51 & 19-52*) by Charles Richard Hamilton of Montgomery, Alabama, who identified the devices as ice cream freezers but said they could be used as churns "for working fine pastry, making various kinds of cake, floats, custards and dressings of all kinds."

The two-quart HAMILTON is 11-3/4" high to the top of the cylinder, one of the taller of all tin churns, but there are others that come close (*fig. 19-53*).

R S Arnold

☞

FIG. 19-54

Cone and flat bottom tin churns, with heights to top of the cylinders (left to right):

PAT APPLD
8-1/2" cone bottom —$75—

No I.D.
8-1/4" cone bottom with fine holes —$85—

SEP 14-75, *Schonmeyer patent*
8" cone bottom —$55—

No I.D. but brochure identifies it as the STERLING beater, made in England and "moulded in various colours," flat bottom
6"   —$45—

PAT'D JAN 22-01 AUG 18-03
Hamilton patents
6-1/4" cone-bottom —$75—

PAT FEB. 13 1877
4-3/4" flat-bottom   —$80—

☞

FIG. 19-55

Matthew C. Russell patent
Feb. 13, 1877
Pat. No. 187,417

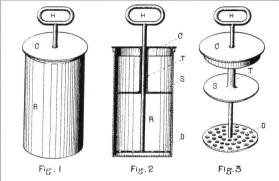

FIG. 19-56

**SPEED-E TRADE MARK
REG'D CREAM WHIPPER EGG BEATER
PAT APPLD FOR**
RICE MFG. CO. CLEVELAND, OHIO
8-1/4"   —$250—

FIG. 19-57

**BOYD
THREE MINUTE
BUTTER MAKER AND WHIP
FOR CREAM, EGGS AND
OTHER MIXTURES
WOOSTER, OHIO**
9"   —$300—

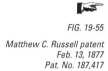

D G Simons   MOFFET COLLECTION   D G Simons   MOFFET COLLECTION

The miniature HAMILTON is only 6-1/4" high, and is probably the smallest of all cone-bottoms, although there is a flat bottom at 4-3/4" *(fig. 19-54)*. The tiny flat bottom was patented by Matthew C. Russell of Deposit, New York *(fig. 19-55)*.

Considered among the rarest of the glass jar plungers are the SPEED-E *(fig. 19-56)* with cone dasher and one-of-a-kind moulded glass cone bottom, and the BOYD THREE MINUTE BUTTER MAKER *(fig. 19-57)* with pedestal-like jar.

Two hard-to-find plungers with glass jars include the UMPIRE *(fig. 19-58)* and the LIGHTNING DASHER EGG BEATER *(fig. 19-59)*. The LIGHTNING was patented *(fig. 19-60)* by one of the few husband and wife inventing teams, Theron Spencer Stewart and Anna Maria Elizabeth Stewart of Toledo, Ohio.

FIG. 19-58

D Thornton

Umpires with height to top of jars (left to right):

UMPIRE GLASS CO.
PITTSBURGH   PAT APD FOR
(embossed on jar bottom)
UMPIRE MEASURING JAR NO. 1
(embossed vertically on jar, along with various measurements).
Replaced wood plunger handle.
7-1/4"   —$150—

No I.D., but UMPIRE
with identical jar measurements
7-1/4"   —$130—

FIG. 19-59

COOPER COLLECTION

Lightnings with heights to top of jars
(left to right):

THE LIGHTNING DASHER EGG BEATER
MADE IN U.S.A.
PAT. MARCH 27, 1888
one pint, 6"   —$200—

THE LIGHTNING DASHER EGG BEATER CO.
TOLEDO O PAT. MARCH 27, 1888
one quart, 7-1/2"   —$175—

FIG. 19-60

T. S. and
A. M. E. Stewart patent
March 27, 1888
Pat. No. 380,226

In their "churn dasher" patent they cited the "improved spring-dasher with disk attachments … designed to provide a beater or dasher that shall be adaptable to various household uses…"

The LIGHTNING, which came in two sizes, one-pint and one-quart, was made by the Lightning Dasher Egg Beater Company, Orange and Erie Streets, Toledo, Ohio. "It consists of a graduated glass jar, having a closely fitting cover, and a dasher, as in a churn. The eggs, cream or other substance to be beaten is put into the jar, the lid pressed into place and the dasher pushed down by the hand of the operator, the coiled spring re-returning it again," according to the July 1, 1893 issue of *The Metal Worker.*

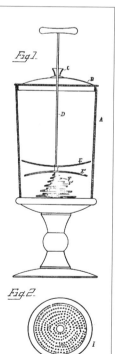

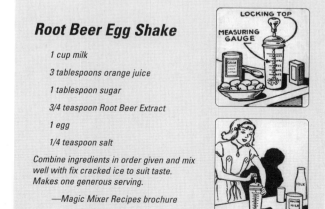

Root Beer Egg Shake

1 cup milk

3 tablespoons orange juice

1 tablespoon sugar

3/4 teaspoon Root Beer Extract

1 egg

1/4 teaspoon salt

Combine ingredients in order given and mix well with fix cracked ice to suit taste. Makes one generous serving.

—Magic Mixer Recipes brochure

Mayonnaise

*An egg, 2 tablespoons lemon juice or vinegar;
teaspoon each mustard, salt, sugar, dash of pepper.
Beat in thoroughly, as poured from bottle
1 pint Wesson Oil.*

— RECIPE EMBOSSED ON WESSON OIL JAR

Other glass plungers:

▶ The common but still quite collectible WESSON OIL MAYONNAISE MAKER (*fig. 19-61*) arrived on the market about 1933 as a premium for the Wesson Oil Company. It was offered direct by mail for 65¢ — including 16¢ for packing and shipping. The mixer came with a recipe folder and a pint can of Wesson Oil.

▶ Very similar to the WESSON but a bit harder to find is the Alabama-made AIR-O-MIXER (*fig. 19-61*). It's not known if this AIR-O-MIXER is related to the tin one (*page 216*).

▶ Bigger than both the WESSON and AIR-O-MIXER is an unmarked screw-on plunger and jar that is 17-1/2" tall and 4-5/8" in diameter (*fig. 19-62*).

FIG. 19-61

*Mayo makers with heights to
top of jars (left to right):*

**WESSON OIL
MAYONNAISE MAKER**
8-1/2"   —$25—

**AIR-O-MIXER
PAT APL'D FOR, MFG'D BY
BENTLEY-JONES INC.,
MONTGOMERY, ALA.
EGG BEATER, DRINK MIXER,
CREAM WHIPPER,
MAYONNAISE MIXER**
8-3/4"   —$65—

*And now you can
make perfect mayon-
naise every time this
new 1-1/2 minute
way … It's quick …
the new 'mesh' dasher
whips the mayonnaise
smooth and firm in
90 seconds.*

**— RECIPE FOLDER FOR THE
WESSON OIL MAYONNAISE
MAKER**

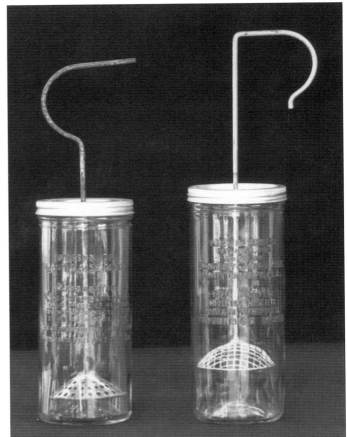

D G Simons

R S Arnold

FIG. 19-62

*No I.D., screw-on jar plunger
10-3/8" to top of jar*
—$150—

FIG. 19-63

**JONES WONDER
EGG BEATER
PAT PEND
MFG. BY JONES TOOL CO.
CLEVELAND, O.**
11-1/2"   —$150—

FIG. 19-64

*Louis W. Jones patent
June 29, 1926
Pat. No. 1,590,831*

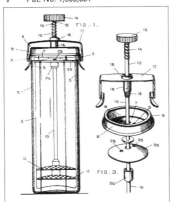

D G Simons

MAIR COLLECTION

THE EGGBEATER CHRONICLES

FIG. 19-65

RAPID FIRE
8" overall
—*$75 with label; $35 without label*—

Note: There is a very similar mixer, although about an inch shorter, that is marked **THE LARSON CO. GREEN BAY WIS., CON'T 14 OZ.**

▶ The JONES WONDER (*fig. 19-63*) cost $2 new, with a mailing tube 25 cents extra. Made by the Jones Tool Company of Cleveland, a paper label on the tube says: "The egg beater that's a world beater. It works like a charm. It's a drink mixer of the 'first order.' It's a milk shaker. It's a cream whipper. It's a butter maker. It's an egg beater."

Louis W. Jones of New York obtained the patent (*fig. 19-64*), saying the device was good for the "agitation, mixing and aeration of practically any liquid or semi-liquid substances…"

▶ Peter Neukirchen of Chicago obtained a Jan. 6, 1920 patent for his popular — and still out there — RAPID FIRE SANITARY BEATER (*figs. 19-65 & 19-66*). If you're lucky, the 16-sided jar will still have its paper label. If not, the only marking will be on the metal apron in the circle around the plunger hole, either the patent date or PATENT APPLIED FOR.

▶ The MAGIC MIXER, made by Acme Metal Goods Manufacturing Company of Newark, New Jersey, was touted in a brochure as "the modern way to mix,

" *Do not operate too fast.* "
— PAPER LABEL, RAPID FIRE

beat … unequaled for mixing and homeogizing [*sic*] baby foods. This mixer not only beats up the ingredients quickly but quickly beats the proper amount of air into the food to make it a light and digestible mixture."

The MAGIC MIXER is an Archimedes, but noted here because its jar and patent, Dec. 6, 1932, are also used for several plungers — the MALTED MILK MIXER and the HOME DRINK MIXER (*fig. 19-67*). The MALTED MILK MIXER, with its distinct tapered top, is also called the NATIONAL DAIRY MALTED MILK MIXER, KRAFT MALTED MILK MIXER and HORLICK'S MALTED MILK MIXER. Most of these are marked on the top of the dasher, MFG. BY WM. D. GIBSON CHICAGO, ILL SPECIALTY DEPT.

All of the jars are marked in ounces up to 12 ("Do not fill above this line"). On the bottom is the Hazel Atlas mark (H-over-A) and PAT PENDING OR PATENT NO. 1,890,307 (*fig. 19-68*). This same jar was used by A&J (*See Chapter 10, A&J, page 104*).

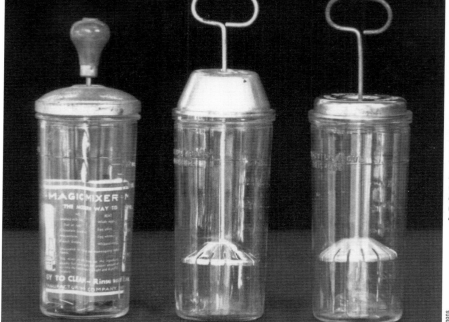

FIG. 19-67

Jar mixers with heights to top of jars (left to right):

MAGIC MIXER
(on paper label)
PATENT NO. 1890307
(embossed on jar bottom)
6-3/4"
—*$25 with brochure*—

MALTED MILK MIXER
(on top)
PATENT NO. 1890307
(embossed on jar bottom)
9" —*$20*—

HOME DRINK MIXER
(on top)
PATENT NO. 1890307
(embossed on jar bottom)
8-1/2" —*$20*—

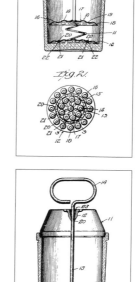

FIG. 19-66
Peter Neukirchen patent
Jan. 6, 1920
Pat. No. 1,327,568

FIG. 19-68
Philip B. Shailer and Harry P. Troendly patent
Dec. 6, 1932
Pat. No. 1,890,307

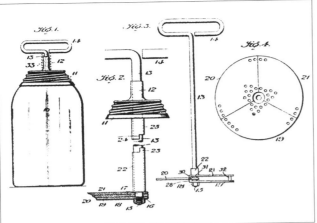

FIG. 19-69

Charles W. Ebeling patent
July 30, 1918
Pat. No. 1,274,021

FIG. 19-71

Later glass plungers
(left to right):

KWIK-WHIP 8″
—$25 with paper label—

**TODDY MIXER TAKES TEN
SECONDS** 9″ —$20—

**SPEED E WHIPPER
PAT. PEND.**
9-1/2″ —$15—

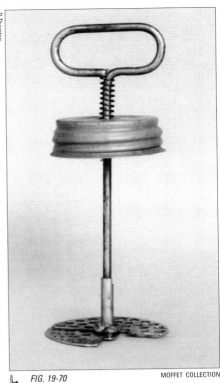

FIG. 19-70

**KRE-MO-BUTTER AGITATOR
PAT. ISSUED 7-30-1918**
8-1/4″ —$50—

MOFFET COLLECTION

D G Simons

▶ A plunger patented by Charles W. Ebeling of Elm Grove, West Virginia, was designed to fit any Mason jar *(figs. 19-69 & 19-70)*. Rotating the stem rod of the KRE-MO-BUTTER AGITATOR will collapse the dashers under each other for insertion into the jar. In the jar the stem is turned again and the dashers bloom out in a full circle.

▶ More common plungers include the KWIK-WHIP, the paper label of which says: "Beats Eggs, Whips Cream, Whips Egg-Whites, Mixes Water & Flour, Whips Mayonnaise;" the TODDY MIXER patented in 1931; and the sleek plastic and glass SPEED E WHIPPER with mixing instructions *(figs. 19-71 through 19-73)*.

▶ Other plungers include a boy's face, Hollywood and English connections and coiled springs *(figs. 19-74 through 19-76)*.

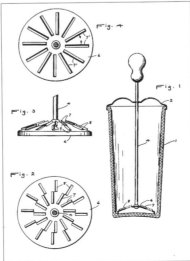

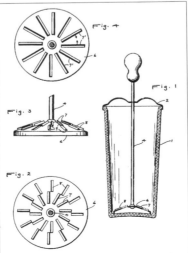

FIG. 19-72

William C. Pritchard patent
Sept. 29, 1931
Pat. No. 1,824,929

FIG. 19-73

SPEED E WHIPPER
brochure

This SPEED-E-WHIPPER has been designed to save many minutes in the kitchen. It beats, blends, whips, aerates, and homogenizes every time the plunger makes a complete cycle and you will enjoy using it to:

Whip Cream
Blend salad dressings
Mix malted milks
Beat eggs
Make smooth gravy
Make meringues
Mix cocktails
Blend smooth cake fillings
Mix delicious frostings
Children's formulas
Frozen Orange Juice

and many other uses you yourself will discover.

The SPEED-E-WHIPPER has been engineered to whip cream in a vacuum, forcing air into the cream which is the secret of the whipped cream staying durable for days without separating. (over)

L B SALES COMPANY
6301 CONDON AVENUE
LOS ANGELES 56, CALIFORNIA

Enclose $1.25 in check or money order and glass container will be mailed to you prepaid. Complete SPEED-E-WHIPPER $2.50 prepaid.

D G Simons

FIG. 19-74

Later glass plungers (left to right):

No I.D. but boy's face embossed in glass
11" —$15—

HOLLYWOOD MIXSTER 11" —$15—

HOLLYWOOD MIXSTER 9-1/2" —$10—

No. I.D. but FEDERAL PRACTICAL HOUSEWARES
10" —$15—

FIG. 19-75

More glass plungers (left to right):

No I.D. but SANITARY DAIRY CO.'S CREAM WHIPPER
one pint jar coil spring plunger
11-1/2" —$30—
Note: This model also comes in one-quart size

BING SERIAL 513,583
10" —$30—

**COLUMBUS EGG WHISK & EGG CREAM FREEZER
MADE IN ENGLAND**
11-1/2" —$35—

D G Simons

 FIG. 19-76

**LORRAINE METAL MFG. CO. INC.
NEW YORK CITY, N.Y.**
coil spring plunger
11-1/2" —$25—

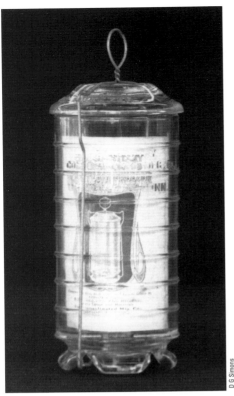

FIG. 19-77

**THE 'SANITARY' FREEZER
MFG'R'D BY CONSOLIDATED MFG. CO.
HARTFORD, CONN**
11" —$110—

FIG. 19-79

Ovaltines (left to right):

OVALTINE MIXER metal plunger
6" —$15—

OVALTINE MIXER plastic plunger
6" —$10—

FIG 19-78

**MARGY MAID
TRADE MARK
MIXER
MANUFACTURED BY FLOYD T. LOVENS
& ASSOCIATES SAN JOSE, CALIF.**
10" —$55—

There are related plunger items to always tempt the collector. They include ice cream makers, margarine makers and Ovaltine mixers *(fig. 19-77 through 19-79).*

A 1946 ad *(fig. 19-80)* for the MARGY MAID — price $3.95 — said in part: "Mixes and moulds in the same utensil … colors margarine, churns butter, whips cream, makes ice cream … whatever you wish." A patent design for the MARGY MAID was awarded in 1948 to George G. Green of San Jose, California *(fig. 19-81).*

FIG 19-80

House Furnishing Review December, 1946 ad

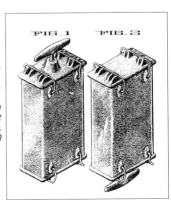

FIG. 19-81

George G. Green design patent Feb. 10, 1948 Pat. No. D-148,630

THE EGGBEATER CHRONICLES

Big Turbines & Blades

"It vibrates as it revolves."

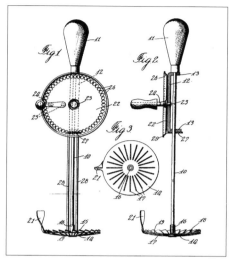

FIG. 20-1

Ernest D. Fahlberg patent
March 19, 1929
Pat. No. 1,705,639

This innovative family of beaters is made up of such models as the ATOM, DREAM CREAM WHIP, DUNLAP, DUPLEX, JIFFY, PRESTO WHIP and the WHIPPIT.

The story mix includes a university professor, a cousin called the S.O.S. pad, a famous roller skate manufacturer, and mostly-overlooked brown bowls.

The WHIPPIT, based on University of Wisconsin Professor Ernest D. Fahlberg's March 19, 1929 patent *(fig. 20-1)*, made its way through several companies, ending up the property of A&J *(See Chapter 10, A&J, page 95)* and its later parent, the giant EKCO *(See Chapter 11, EKCO, page 109).*

"… I have provided a simple and inexpensive beater which is efficient in operation and which will beat material such as cream and eggs in a very short time," said Fahlberg.

"The beater has unusual shearing powers and causes a large amount of foaming. All of the material being whip-ped or beaten is worked on uniformly, thereby resulting in a homogeneous and improved product," said Fahlberg's 1925 patent application, which although already being manufactured wasn't granted, for undetermined reasons, until four years later.

One of the first makers of the WHIPPIT *(fig. 20-2)* was the E. D. Fahlberg Manu-

FIG. 20-2

Whippits (left to right):

"WHIPPIT" CREAM & EGG WHIP PAT PEND MANUFACTURED BY WHITE AND HALLOCK MUSKEGON, MICH.
13-1/2"   —$20—
Note: A much rarer version of this model is marked:
"WHIPPIT" E.D. FAHLBERG MFG. CO. PAT. PEND. ILLINOIS SALES CO. CHICAGO, ILL. SOLE DISTRIBUTORS U.S.A.

"WHIPPIT" A&J CREAM WHIP MADE IN U.S.A. EKCO PRODUCTS CO. CHICAGO, ILL
13-1/2"   —$18—

"WHIPPIT" CREAM & EGG WHIP PATENT NO. 1705639 MANUFACTURED BY DURO METAL PRODUCTS CO. CHICAGO, ILL.
13-3/4"   —$20—

Original Whippet box from Indestro. Side of box said: "It has more than 500,000 enthusiastic users among women in the home. Why? Because it whips, beats and mixes perfectly, with incredible speed and ease. Because it saves time, temper and disappointments."

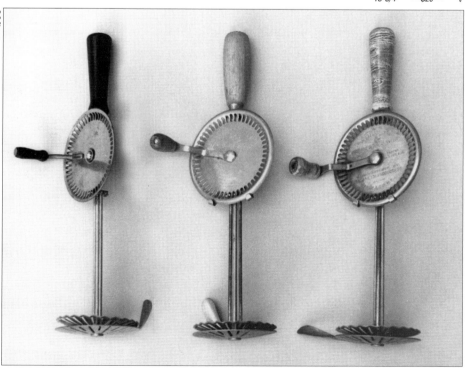

D G Simons

facturing Company, which apparently offered the beaters through a distributor, Illinois Sales Company of Chicago. The first major manufacturer was White & Hallock of Chicago and Oskaloosa, Iowa, which in 1928 obtained a trademark for the WHIPPIT (fig. 20-3).

On May 14, 1926, when White & Hallock announced it was moving its operations to Muskegon, Michigan, the local newspaper *The Muskegon* reported, "The company manufactures a line of hardware specialties for household use, the two principal items being patented devices sold under the trade names of Whippit and Skimit."

The SKIMIT, according to the newspaper, was "a device for removing the cream from a bottle of milk." And it disclosed that the "company also manufactures … a saponified steel wool sold under the trade name of 'S.O.S.'"

An ad in the May 1927 *Good Housekeeping* (fig. 20-4) offered the WHIPPIT at $1 and said in part: "You don't even need to put on your apron if you use a Whippit. With never a spatter, never a slip, you can whip whipping cream stiff in 15 seconds…"

White & Hallock is also known for its PRESTO WHIP (fig. 20-5), the name of which the firm trademarked in 1927 (fig. 20-6).

Patented Nov. 29, 1927 (fig. 20-7) by Arthur S. White (the White of White & Hallock) and Mark A. Wiseman, it is a very sturdy mixer. The patentees told of "a frame which is formed out of a single piece of metal, which can be cheaply and quickly manufactured, and which has baffle means and shearing edges for increasing the beating action."

FIG. 20-3

U.S. Patent & Trademark Office Official Gazette, July 3, 1928 White and Hallock's Whippit trademark

CLASS 23.
Cutlery, Machinery, and Tools, and Parts Thereof.

Ser. No. 257,209. WHITE AND HALLOCK, INC., Muskegon, Mich. Filed Nov. 7, 1927.

Whippit

For Beaters for Culinary Purposes Including Egg Beaters and Cream Whips.
Claims use since July 15, 1925.

FIG. 20-4

May 1927 Good Housekeeping

D G Simons

"….and Whipped Cream.. that's easy"

"Easy," you say? *Easy* to whip cream? How many women can say that?"

Are you interested? Would you like to find a new, sure way to whip cream, even ordinary milk-top cream, stiff and firm? Then, discover Whippit! It is a new development, which has taken away the worry of cream whipping for thousands of women.

You don't even need to put on your apron if you use a Whippit. With never a spatter, never a slip, you can whip whipping cream stiff in 15 seconds, coffee cream in 30 seconds, chilled milk-top cream in 30 to 60 seconds. It operates on a new principle; it is far superior to old-fashioned methods. No special bowl necessary. Can't slip or wobble. Easily cleaned.

Whippit Cream Whip

Whippit is $1.00; Skimit 50c. If your local dealer does not now carry them, send us his name, and we will arrange to have him deliver either or both to you, subject to your approval. Or send us price plus 10c for prepaid mailing.

WHITE and HALLOCK, Inc., Muskegon, Mich.

Skimit
AUTOMATIC CREAM SIPHON
Draws off all the rich top cream from the milk bottle. Starts and stops itself.
50c

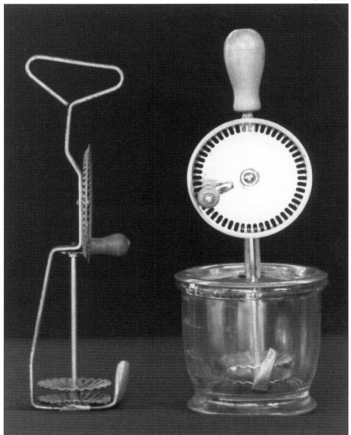

FIG. 20-5

Presto Whips (left to right):

PRESTO WHIP DURO METAL PRODUCTS CHICAGO, ILL REG. U.S. PAT OFF. PAT. APLD. FOR
11-3/4" —$30—
Note: An earlier version is marked **PRESTO WHIP WHITE AND HALLOCK INC. MUSKEGON, MICH. REG. U.S. PAT. OFF. PAT APP'D FOR,**
with a single bottom turbine.

PRESTO BOWL WHIP DURO METAL PRODUCTS CO. CHICAGO, ILL. REG. U.S. PAT. OFF. PAT. APLD. FOR
13" —$95—

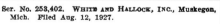

FIG. 20-6

U.S. Patent & Trademark Office Official Gazette, White and Hallock trademark October 25, 1927

Ser. No. 253,402. WHITE AND HALLOCK, INC., Muskegon, Mich. Filed Aug. 12, 1927.

No claim is made to the exclusive use of the word "Whip" apart from the mark shown in the drawing.
Particular description of goods.—Beaters for Culinary Purposes Including Egg Beaters and Cream Whips.
Claims use since July 12, 1927.

The same patent apparently was used for the DE LUXE BOWL WHIP, (fig. 20-8), which has a heavy-duty triple disk bottom with a large, dangerous-looking scraper.

A catalog sheet (fig. 20-9) touted both the PRESTO BOWL WHIP and the DE LUXE BOWL WHIP, saying, "As a merchandising or premium proposition, a satisfactory kitchen utensil cannot be equaled."

The WHIPPIT, PRESTO WHIP and DE LUXE, along with the whole line of White & Hallock, ended up with the Indestro Manufacturing Corporation of Chicago, which evolved into the Duro Metal Products Company, which is still in business today in Chicago.

A 1937 Indestro catalog sheet (fig. 20-10) said, "The Whippit with the turbine blade, slotted baffle plate, and infolder, combine exclusive patented features not found in any other whips. Whips cream in less than one minute. It is so universally known and used that it hardly needs a description." The catalog price was $1, but in an earlier ad the WHIPPIT was offered in a promotion with Pet Milk, for 60¢ and included 172 recipes featuring Pet.

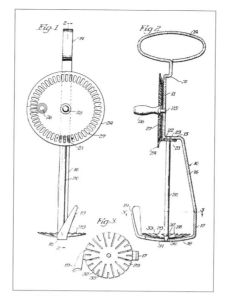

FIG. 20-7

Arthur S. White and
Mark A. Wiseman patent
Nov. 29, 1927
Pat. No. 1,650,777

D G Simons

FIG. 20-8

**DE LUXE BOWL WHIP
PAT. PEND.
MANUFACTURED BY
DURO METAL PRODUCTS
CHICAGO, ILL.**
(mismatch jar)
beater itself: 13-1/2"
—$35—
—with correct jar $100—

FIG. 20-9

Duro Metal Products
Company catalog sheet

FIG. 20-10

1937 Indestro Mfg. Corp. Chicago catalog sheet

CHAPTER 20: BIG TURBINES & BLADES

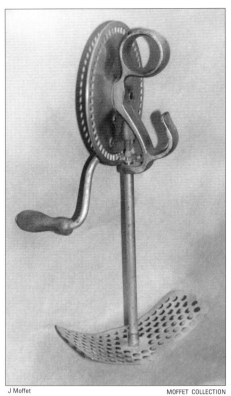

J Moffet

MOFFET COLLECTION

FIG. 20-11

DUNLAP'S SILVER BLADE CREAM & EGG WHIP
NO SPLATTER NO WASTE
J.S. DUNLAP CHICAGO USA
PAT'D MAY 15, 1906 FEB. 26, 1907 (on main gear)
MIDGET (embossed in cast-iron handle)
9-1/4"   —$150—

FIG. 20-12

John S. Dunlap patent
May 15, 1906
Pat. No. 820,405

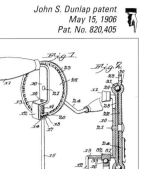

FIG. 20-13

John S. Dunlap patent
Feb. 26, 1907
Pat. No. 845,341

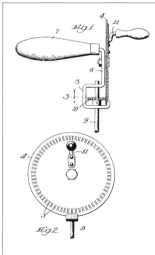

FIG. 20-15

John S. Dunlap patent
Sept. 26, 1916
Pat. No. 1,199,455

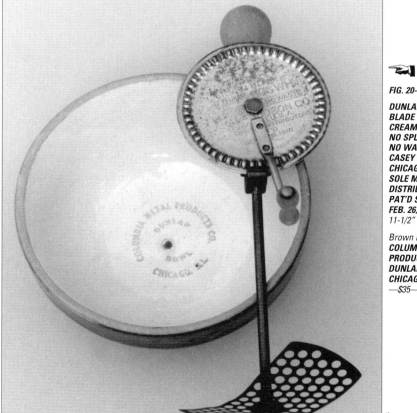

D G Simons

FIG. 20-14

DUNLAP'S SANITARY SILVER
BLADE
CREAM & EGG WHIP
NO SPLATTER
NO WASTE
CASEY HUDSON CO.
CHICAGO U.S.A.
SOLE MFRS &
DISTRIBUTORS
PAT'D SEPT. 26, 1916
FEB. 26, 1907 MAY 15, 1906
11-1/2"   —$30—

Brown bowl marked
COLUMBIA METAL
PRODUCTS CO.
DUNLAP BOWL
CHICAGO, ILL
—$35—

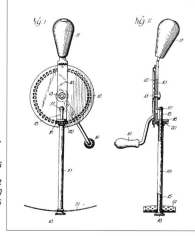

FIG. 20-16

William J. Casey patent
Jan. 21, 1930
Pat. No. 1,744,445

FIG. 20-17

DUNLAP'S
SANITARY CREAM & EGG WHIP
NO SPATTER NO WASTE
MFD BY DURO METAL PRODUCTS CO.
CHICAGO, ILL. USA
PAT. SEPT. 26, 1916,
FEB. 26, 1907, MAY 15, 1906
12-1/2"   —$75—

MAIR COLLECTION

Also ending up in the Indestro line were the DUNLAP turbines, the first of which was the very rare MIDGET *(fig. 20-11)*. The MIDGET is shorter than other DUNLAPS and is marked with two patent dates, MAY 15, 1906 *(fig. 20-12)* and FEB. 26, 1907 *(fig. 20-13)*. In his 1906 patent, John S. Dunlap said his device had "an improved form of resilient dasher adapted to conform to the shape of the interior of the bowl or other vessel in which it is being used." The MIDGET has an unusual cast-iron handle with a distinctive finger hole.

In addition to the J. S. Dunlap firm, DUNLAPS had another manufacturer, Casey Hudson Company, 357-61 East Ohio Street, Chicago. DUNLAP'S SANITARY SILVER BLADE CREAM & EGG WHIP *(fig. 20-14)* is marked with the May 15, 1906 and Feb. 26, 1907 dates, and a new patent, Sept. 26, 1916 *(fig. 20-15)*.

The Casey in the company was William J. Casey, who improved on the DUNLAP with his own turbine patent Jan. 21, 1930 *(fig. 20-16)*. Adding to its mixed-up past, at some point Casey Hudson became Columbia Metal Products Company, at the same East Ohio Street address before joining Indestro.

A later version of the DUNLAP had three vertical supports, instead of one *(fig. 20-17)* and was made by Duro.

The DUNLAPS had a unique and very collectible companion: Many of them came with brownware bowls. The bowls are quite distinctive in that they have an indenture in the center of the bottom of the bowl for the end of the beater to rest. They were usually marked, on the inside, with what appears to be ink under the glaze. Such marks include COLUMBIA METAL PRODUCTS CO. DUNLAP BOWL, CHICAGO ILL. and GENUINE DUNLAP CREAM WHIP BOWL.

A brochure *(fig. 20-18)* boasted of its "many exclusive features" and said: "What the Dunlap Silver Blade Cream Whip does sounds too good to be true. It does its work in a tenth the usual time. The blade in action has more than a yard of cutting edge. It vibrates as it revolves. A miniature whirlpool is caused."

After it became part of Indestro, the name changed somewhat. Said the 1937 Indestro catalog: "The Improved Dunlap Whip with the 'Little Brown Bowl' that a million housewives will testify is the best which they ever used." Price, with bowl: $1.

The DREAM CREAM WHIP came in two models *(fig. 20-19)*: One has a vertical wood handle, the other a novel behind-the-wheel handle, which, adding to the mix, lists the A. D. Foyer & Company of Chicago as the manufacturer.

The DREAM CREAM also came with its own brownware bowl marked NEW DREAM CREAM WHIP.

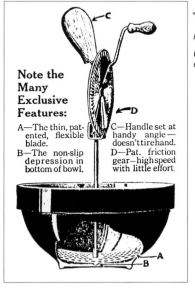

Note the Many Exclusive Features:

A—The thin, patented, flexible blade.
B—The non-slip depression in bottom of bowl.
C—Handle set at handy angle — doesn't tire hand.
D—Pat. friction gear—highspeed with little effort.

FIG. 20-18

Casey Hudson early brochure

FIG. 20-19

Dreams (left to right):

THE DREAM CREAM
TRADE MARK
WHIP
PATENT PENDING
KOHLER DIE & SP'LTY CO.
DEKALB, ILL U.S.A.
10-1/2"   —$35—

THE DREAM CREAM
TRADE MARK
WHIP
MANUFACTURED BY
A.D. FOYER & COMPANY
CHICAGO
10"   —$95—

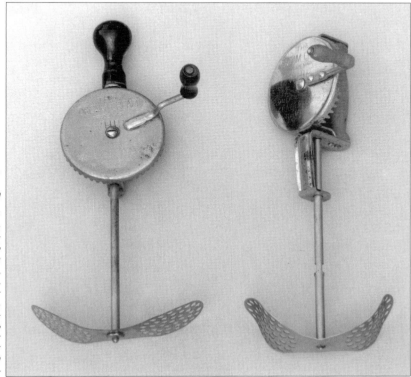

D G Simons

THE DREAM CREAM WHIP

For whipping cream, beating eggs, etc. With it you can whip single cream perfectly in one minute. It does not splash or spatter. Complete with special stone bowl. Sent, postpaid, for two (2) new subscriptions, or Cash Price, $1.50.

FIG. 20-20

American Cookery Magazine 1930 ad

The roller skate connection: A Jan. 26, 1924 *DeKalb* [Illinois] *Daily Chronicle* article said in part, "It is not generally known that roller skating as a popular sport dates back to 1760, but only during recent years is the volume of business reaching a point where sidewalk skates may be considered a stable item with the hardware and sporting goods trades. Roller skating is a healthful and wholesome sport that the medical authorities favor as one of the finest forms of outdoor exercise for the physical development of boys and girls."

The article was on Kohler Die & Specialty, described as the manufacturer of "a variety of staple articles and specialties, ranging from roller skates and kitchen utensils to hotel index equipment." The firm, the article said, was born in Chicago (817-825 Washington Boule-

FIG. 20-21

Jiffys (left to right):

JIFFY CREAM WHIP
PATENTED DEC. 12, 1922
KOHLER DIE & SP'LTY CO. DEKALB, ILL U.S.A.
with unmarked clear glass jar
12-1/2" —$100—

JIFFY CREAM WHIP
PATENTED DEC. 12, 1922
KOHLER DIE & SP'LTY CO. DEKALB, ILL U.S.A.
with unmarked green-tint glass jar
12-1/2" —$125—

vard) in 1902, but moved to DeKalb (1235 E. Lincoln Highway) in 1915.

Right behind roller skates in the article was an eggbeater: "The Dream Cream Whip has instant appeal to the housewife and the sale of the line has mounted into large figures during the few years it has been on the market.

"The secret of the construction that has made this the leading article of its kind on the market is the peculiar form of the perforated blade and the geared construction which gives five and one-half revolutions of the blade to one revolution of the hand. The handle is securely riveted to the frame and the device is intended for use with a special bowl which is so designed as to hold the point of the revolving shaft and prevent all possibility of splattering and waste."

American Cookery Magazine featured the DREAM CREAM WHIP as a premium (*fig. 20-20*) in 1930, offering one postpaid for two new subscriptions. Otherwise it had a cash price of $1.50.

Kohler also made the scarce JIFFY CREAM WHIP, with apron and 12-sided jar (*fig. 20-21*). This beater was patented (*fig. 20-22*) Dec. 12, 1922 by Stanley Orzchovski of DeKalb, assignor to Kohler, who brought to light an until now unknown fear that the beater operator's fingers were in possible danger. With his handle design, Orzchovski said "all danger of the fingers of the operator being caught in the gears is avoided, and by the location and arrangement of the gears, all danger of the gears getting out of mesh … is avoided."

FIG. 20-22

Stanley Orzchovski patent
Dec. 12, 1922
Pat. No. 1,438,716

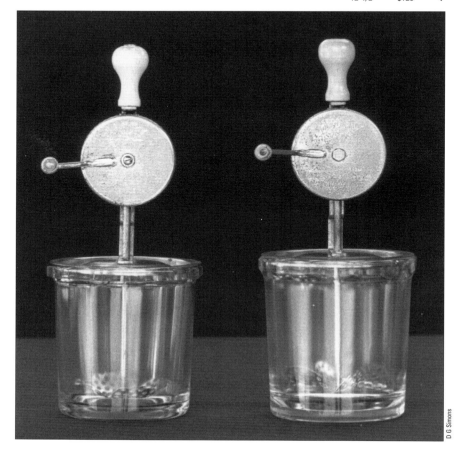

D G Simons

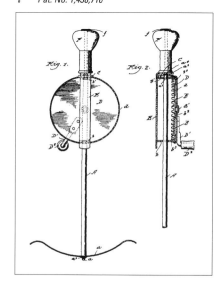

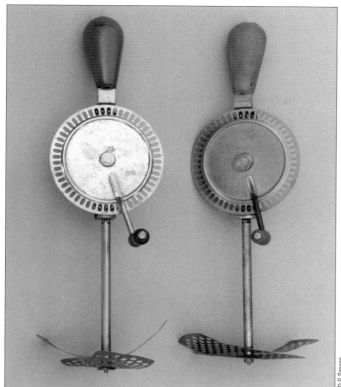

D G Simons

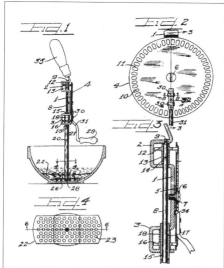

FIG. 20-23

Duplex Whippers (left to right):

DUPLEX CREAM & EGG WHIPPER MADE BY BRULL MFG. CO. OAK PARK, ILL. PAT'D NOV. 25, 1919
12-1/4″ —$20—

DUPLEX CREAM WHIPPER MFD. BY DUPLEX WHIPPER CORPORATION PATENT NUMBERS 1322874 1726977 MADE IN U.S.A.
12″ —$20—

FIG. 20-24

Eugene C. Brull patent Nov. 25, 1919 Pat. No. 1,322,874

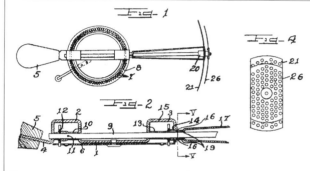

FIG. 20-25

Eugene C. Brull patent Sept. 3, 1929 Pat. No. 1,726,977

R S Arnold

FIG. 20-26

THE DUPLEX WHIPPER BOWL V.V. VALE CO. EVANSTON, ILL.
In addition to instructions, the bowl is marked:
USED BY MEMBERS OF ASSOC. OF INT'L MILK DEALERS
3-1/2″ high, 6-3/4″ in diameter —$55 with turbine—

Patented by Eugene C. Brull of Oak Park, Illinois, the DUPLEX *(fig. 20-23)* beaters feature a perforated double dasher. Brull, whose own firm first manufactured the mixers, obtained two patents for the DUPLEX *(figs. 20-24 & 20-25).* The Brull Manufacturing Company, located at 938 N. Austin Blvd. in Oak Park, later became the Duplex Whipper Corporation of Chicago. Later models of the DUPLEX could be purchased with a clear glass bowl, with an indentation in the bottom to accommodate the beater *(fig. 20-26).*

And there's another JIFFY — this one from the 1950s. The JIFFY WHIP was made by Krasberg & Sons of Chicago and patented by Rudolf Krasberg Aug. 14, 1951. Apparently not satisfied with the JIFFY WHIP, Krasberg offered the exact same mixer, but with smaller turbines. Obviously looking for a bigger market, he called it the ATOM WHIP *(fig. 20-27).*

FIG. 20-27

Krasberg whips (left to right):

ATOM WHIP PAT. 2,563,941 MADE IN U.S.A. CHICAGO, 47, ILL. KRASCO R. KRASBERG & SONS' MFG. CO.
11-3/4″ —$30—

JIFFY WHIP PATENT PENDING MADE IN U.S.A. CHICAGO, 47, ILL KRASCO R. KRASBERG & SONS' MFG. CO.
11-3/4″ —$25—

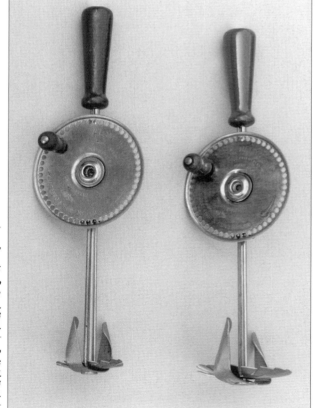

D G Simons

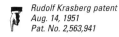

FIG. 20-28

Rudolf Krasberg patent
Aug. 14, 1951
Pat. No. 2,563,941

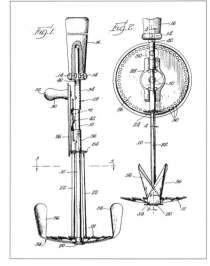

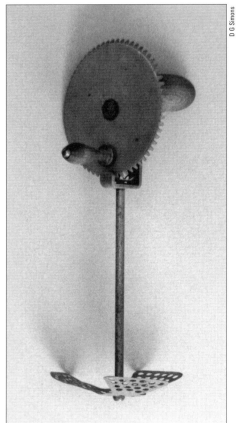

FIG. 20-29

**THE NECO
M. P. HOUGEN MINNEAPOLIS
PATENT PENDING**
10-1/2"   —$95—

BREON COLLECTION

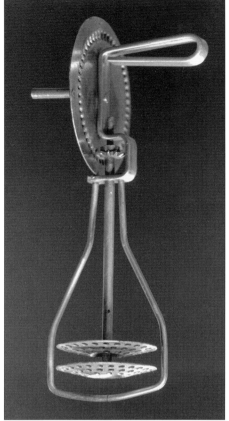

FIG. 20-30

No. I.D., but Viner patent,
possibly prototype
10"   —$185—

D G Simons

Krasberg boasted in his patent papers *(fig. 20-28)* that his device had "aerators of novel form which function to direct some of the liquid in a vertical circulatory path tangential to the whirling body of liquid, thereby to insure extremely rapid action and thorough aeration in the mixing or beating operation."

One of the rarer turbines is THE NECO *(fig. 20-29)* made in Minneapolis, and probably the rarest of all is a no-name *(fig. 20-30)* with an inventive off-center gearing in the main wheel that makes the turbines on the bottom go up and down as they spin around. This beater also has a Minneapolis connection. It was patented Sept. 5, 1922 *(fig. 20-31)* by John H. Viner of Minneapolis, who explained the gearing behind the up-and-down motion this way: "The circular row of slots ... is formed in eccentric relation with the center of the plate. Therefore, when the plate is rotated, by the crank, the pinion will follow the run of the slots, with the result that the mixing disks, which are secured to the lower end of the sleeve, will move up and down as well as rotate."

FIG. 20-31

John H. Viner patent
Sept. 5, 1922
Pat. No. 1,427,986

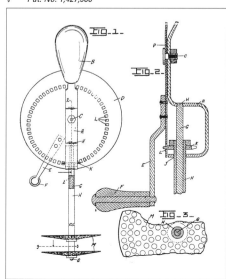

Cream Whips Better and more readily when at least 24 hours old. Cream which has been kept in a cool place for this length of time should be placed in a cool bowl or pan and in warm weather the whip should be chilled in cold water and dried before using. Eggs should also be cool to whip properly.

When using the Whippit for beating eggs it should be run in reverse direction for a few turns so as to pick up the eggs and get them started; then finish by turning in usual direction.

—SUGGESTIONS, FROM THE WHIPPIT BOX

Rotary Mix: The Later Years

"Runs Like a Thoro-bred and It Is."

The old cast-iron mixers always take the show but there are dozens of other rotaries that merit tribute and are the backbone of any good collection. They range from the common to the very rare.

Starting with A, for "aluminum," they include:

▶ The ALUMINUM BEAUTY *(fig. 21-1)*, is a favorite of the country's foremost kitchenware expert, Linda Campbell Franklin. In her book *300 Years of Kitchen Collectibles,* Franklin noted: "The Aluminum Beauty truly is a beauty, and works better than any eggbeater I've ever tried."

Also marked the INSTANT WHIP ALUMINUM BEATER and INSTANT WHIP PREMIUM BEATER *(fig. 21-2)* it was patented by Louis Ullman of New York City *(fig. 21-3)*. Ironically, Ullman

FIG. 21-1

Aluminum beaters (left to right):

ALUMINUM BEAUTY
PAT'D APRIL 20, 1920
VIKO THE GUARANTEED ALUMINUM
MADE IN U.S.A.
10-1/2" —$15—

INSTANT WHIP
PAT'D APRIL 20, 1920
ALUMINUM BEATER
MADE IN U.S.A.

10-1/2" —$15—

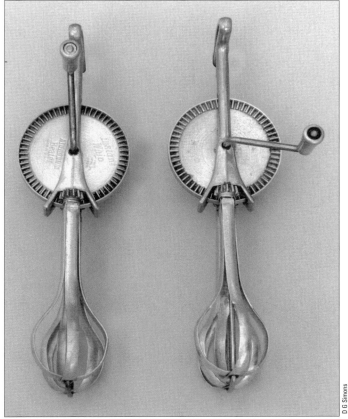

D G Simons

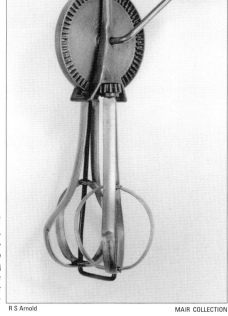

FIG. 21-2

INSTANT WHIP
PREMIUM BEATER
PAT'D APRIL 20, 1920
MADE IN USA
with stationary loops
inside dashers
10-1/2" —$35—

R S Arnold   MAIR COLLECTION

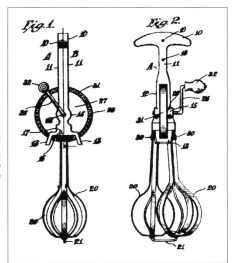

FIG. 21-3

Louis Ullman patent
April 20, 1920
Pat. No. 1,337,860

did not mention aluminum even once in his patent application. The May 1926 *Good Housekeeping* featured an ad *(fig. 21-4)* for the ALUMINUM BEAUTY, listing the price by mail at $1, and west of the Rockies $1.15. A few months later, the Ullman Aluminum Division, Long Island City, New York, trademarked the ALUMINUM BEAUTY logo *(fig. 21-5)*.

▶ The BENSON BEATER *(fig. 21-6)*, one of the few mixers that beats three ways, is a California classic. It has (1) inside dasher up and down movement combined with (2) circular disk movement, plus (3) adjustable dasher guards.

Frederick Benson's 1924 patent *(fig. 21-7)* drawing is a far cry from the beater that appeared on the market, although a March 2, 1926 Benson patent *(fig. 21-8)* is a much better match. The 1926 patent features the unique up-and-down rotary action for the lower disk.

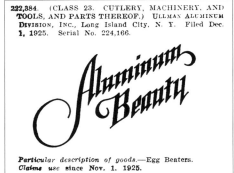

FIG. 21-4

May 1926 Good Housekeeping

FIG. 21-6

BENSON BEATER
253 POST ST. S.F. CAL.
PAT. OCT. 21, 24 PATS. PEND.
12" —$200—

FIG. 21-5

U.S. Patent & Trademark Office Official Gazette, Dec. 18, 1926 Ullman Aluminum Division's Aluminum Beauty trademark

222,384. (CLASS 23. CUTLERY, MACHINERY, AND TOOLS, AND PARTS THEREOF.) Ullman Aluminum Division, Inc., Long Island City, N. Y. Filed Dec. 1, 1925. Serial No. 224,166.

Aluminum Beauty

Particular description of goods.—Egg Beaters.
Claims use since Nov. 1, 1925.

FIG. 21-7

Frederick Benson patent Oct. 21, 1924 Pat. No. 1,512,669

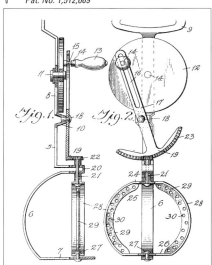

FIG. 21-8

Frederick Benson patent March 2, 1926 Pat. No. 1,575,090

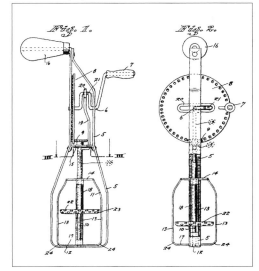

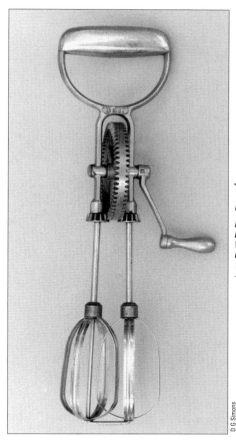

D G Simons

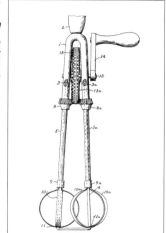

FIG. 21-10

Kenneth B. Van
Woert patent
Nov. 21, 1934
Pat. No.
1,981,531

FIG. 21-9

**BEST
MADE IN U.S.A.
V.W. MFG. CO.
OAKLAND CAL.**
11-1/2"
—$30—

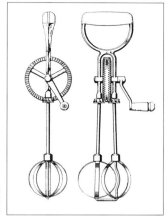

FIG. 21-11

Kenneth B. Van Woert design patent
Jan. 17, 1939
Pat. No. D-112953

▶ The BEST *(fig. 21-9)* is a beautifully designed mixer. The solid, stainless steel model was made by V. W. Manufacturing Company of Oakland and later Sunnyvale, California. Kenneth B. Van Woert, of Santa Clara County, California, said in his 1935 patent *(fig. 21-10)* that the "embodiment of the invention" was the inverted U-shaped bar forming the supporting body of the gadget, around which the dashers turn. Van Woert followed the 1935 patent with a design patent for the same beater in 1939 *(fig. 21-11)*.

**Albia Produce Co.
Egg Separator**

3-1/4" diameter
—$27—

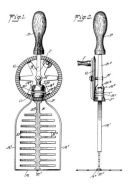

Frederick W. Ruckstuhl and Adele Pohlmann patent
Aug. 12, 1902
Pat. No. 707,019
Potato Creamer

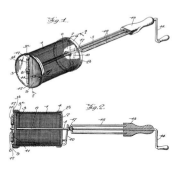

Sterling P. Pickett patent
Jan. 3, 1899
Pat. No. 616,964
Rotary Corn Popper or Coffee Roaster

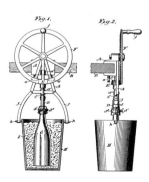

Israel J. Cobin and Adrian Hitt patent
Nov. 7, 1893
Pat. No. 507,996
Apparatus for Cooling Bottled Liquids

The rotary crank powered not only eggbeaters, but also potato creamers, corn poppers, and wine coolers, to name a few.

Frederick W. Ruckstuhl and Adele Pohlmann of New York City patented a "potato-creamer" Aug. 12, 1902. Their device came with a perforated bottom, like a regular potato masher, which did the initial mashing. As cream, milk or butter

was added, the rotary beater was engaged to insure a "creamy consistency."

Sterling P. Pickett of Woodlawn, Missouri patented his "rotary corn-popper or coffee-roaster" Jan. 3, 1899, saying his device would pop corn or roast coffee uniformly "without scorching or burning it."

Israel J. Cobin of New York City and Adrian Hitt of Jersey City, New Jersey, came up with a rotary device that would

spin a bottle of wine, or other beverage, in a bucket of ice for instant cooling. Cobin and Hitt were granted a patent Nov. 7, 1893 for their apparatus, which reportedly was made by the Cobin Manufacturing Company of New York. With rapid turning of the main, 12-inch in diameter gear wheel, the temperature of the wine or other contents "will be reduced nearly to freezing point in from two to three minutes."

Ser. No. 86,173. (CLASS 23. CUTLERY, MACHINERY, AND TOOLS, AND PARTS THEREOF.) ALEXANDER & LITTLEFIELD COMPANY, New York, N. Y. Filed Apr. 24, 1915.

BILTRITE

Particular description of goods.—Egg-Beaters. *Claims use* since Jan. 1, 1915.

FIG. 21-12

U.S. Patent & Trademark Office Official Gazette, July 23, 1918 Alexander & Littlefield Company trademark for Biltrite.

FIG. 21-14

George E. Alexander patent
March 23, 1920
Pat. No. 1,334,274

Waved beater blades resulting in 50% quicker results ... Built with beating blades so close to plate that one egg is drawn up from a flat plate. Impossible with other makes.

—BILTRITE AD IN THE 1919 HOUSE FURNISHING REVIEW

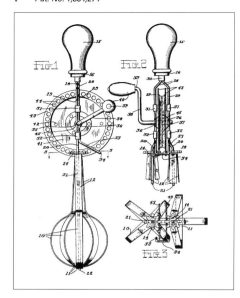

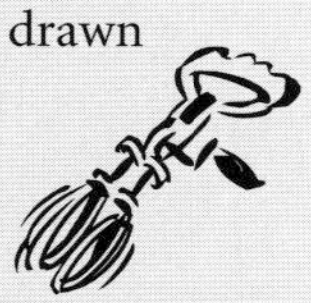

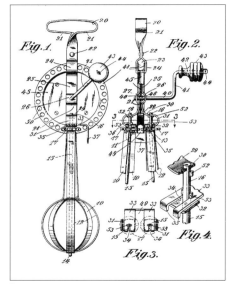

FIG. 21-13

George E. Alexander patent
Aug. 14, 1917
Pat. No. 1,236,814

FIG. 21-15

BILTRITE PAT. AUG. 14-17
(on guard on top of dashers)
9-3/4" —$45—

Note: This model also came with wavy dashers

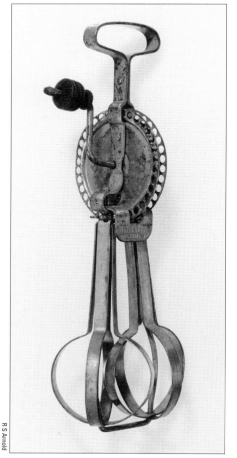

R S Arnold

▶ George E. Alexander of New York City was the person behind the BILTRITE and the WHIPWELL.

The Alexander & Littlefield Company of New York obtained a trademark for the BILTRITE name in 1918 *(fig. 21-12)*, saying it had been in use since 1915. Alexander patented the BILTRITE Aug. 14, 1917 *(fig. 21-13)* and the WHIPWELL March 23, 1920 *(fig. 21-14)*.

The original BILTRITE *(fig. 21-15)* was all metal with a wood knob on the turning handle, but over the years evolved with a vertical wood handle and wavy dashers *(fig. 12-16)*.

A funny flat knob on the top of the wooden handle distinguishes the WHIPWELL *(fig. 21-17)*. The knob, or button, marked WHIPWELL, makes the beater very easy to identify. When first manu-

FIG. 21-16

BILTRITE EGG BEATER
PATENTED
STUBER & KUCK PEORIA, ILL.
10-1/2" —$30—

Note: This model also is marked:
RM EGG BEATER NO. 50 PATENTED

D G Simons

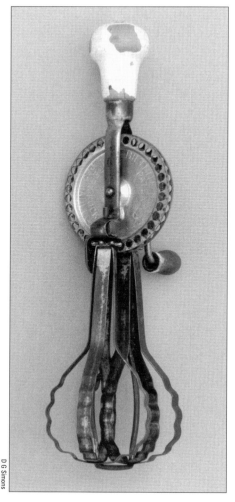

factured, these beaters were marked with Alexander's March 23, 1920 patent date. In later versions the top button was eliminated and another patent date added to the wheel — May 21, 1921, an Alexander patent for the novel wheel that propels both the BILTRITE and the WHIP-WELL. However, there's a problem in that the May 21 date is a typo — it should be May 24, 1921 *(fig. 21-18)*.

In later years, Stuber & Kuck Company of Peoria, Illinois, manufactured the BILTRITE and more than likely the WHIP-WELL. In fact, Henry G. Kuck, assignor to his Stuber & Kuck Company, obtained a patent related to the BILTRITE June 3, 1930 *(fig. 21-19)*. Kuck's patent featured an apron, or as he called it "a lid or cover for a receptacle wherein materials to be beater are contained…" Stuber & Kuck produced a very scarce apron model *(fig. 21-20),* but with gearing and a top handle different from the patent.

Kuck and Joseph Stuber, a native of Peoria, started out Dec. 1, 1887 with capital of only $250, offering tinware. Over the years business boomed, with the firm at one time employing nearly 200 people.

An ad in the 1920 *Peoria City Directory* said: "Large manufacturers of wash boilers, dairy pails, cream cans, flour shifters, tinware specialties, sanitary food cans, sweeping compound and cracker drums. Self-sealing fruit and paint cans … Samson brass and blind front cracker cans … Also, powder kegs."

D G Simons

FIG. 21-17

WHIPWELL
MADE IN U.S.A.
PAT. MCH 23, 1920
OTHER PAT PENDING
11"   —$20—

Note: A later version comes without the top button and with a second patent date, May 21, 1921 (which in fact should be May 24)

FIG. 21-18

George E. Alexander patent
May 24, 1921
Pat. No. 1,379,507

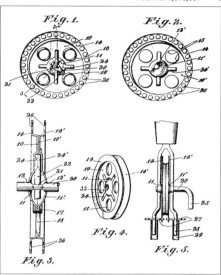

FIG. 21-19

Henry G. Kuck patent
June 3, 1930
Pat. No. 1,761,634

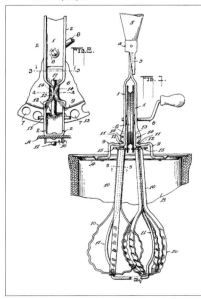

FIG. 21-20

BILTRITE
EGG BEATER
PATENTED
STUBER & KUCK
PEORIA, ILL.
9-/3/4"
pitcher believed to be original
—$110—

D Thornton

CHAPTER 21: ROTARY MIX: THE LATER YEARS

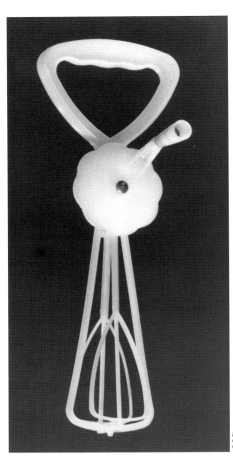

FIG. 21-21

BLISSCRAFT OF HOLLYWOOD, PAT. USA PEND.
12"   —$75—

D G Simons

▶ Only in Hollywood: A plastic egg-beater. In fact, except for two metal pins, the BLISSCRAFT (*fig. 21-21*), is all plastic. It's also, believe it or not, very hard to find. Charles O. Bliss of Los Angeles received a design patent in 1964 for the BLISSCRAFT (*fig. 21-22*).

▶ The nicknamed CHICO beaters (*figs. 21-23 through 21-25*), including a scarce stand-up model, date back to 1936. The CHICO designation comes from the Chico, California, hometown of the patentee, Axel H. Roos and his Roos Manufacturing Company.

The Jan. 28, 1936 patent (*fig. 21-26*) says in part: "The principal objects of my invention are to provide a device of this character arranged so that a very efficient beating action is obtained; one which may be supported and manipulated by either the right or left hand from different points relative to the axis of the beater at the option of the operator…" Roos followed that one up with another patent five years later (*fig. 21-27*).

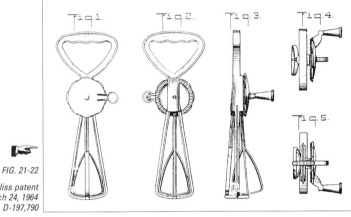

FIG. 21-22

Charles O. Bliss patent
March 24, 1964
Pat. No. D-197,790

R S Arnold

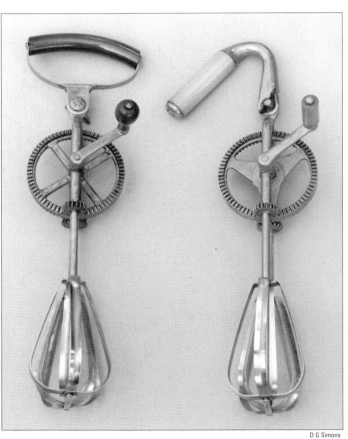

FIG. 21-23

Chicos (left to right):

"WONDER"
(on inside of adjustable D-handle)
12-1/4"
—$30—

No I.D.
adjustable V-handle
12-1/2"
—$40—

Note: Some models marked on dasher:
ROOS MFG. CO. CHICO, CALIF. or just **CHICO, CALIF.**

D G Simons

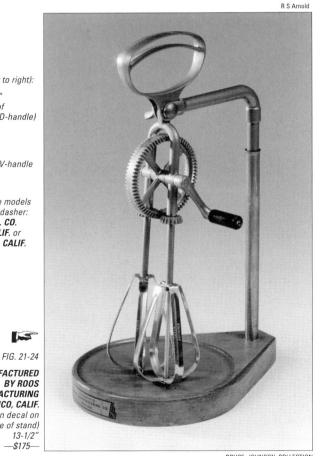

FIG. 21-24

MANUFACTURED BY ROOS MANUFACTURING CO. CHICO, CALIF.
(on decal on base of stand)
13-1/2"
—$175—

BRUCE JOHNSON COLLECTION

THE EGGBEATER CHRONICLES

R S Arnold   STOREY COLLECTION

☞
FIG. 21-87

**DUPLEX EGG AND CREAM WHIP
PAT APPLIED FOR U.S.A.**
10-1/4″   —$1,000—

T he main object of this invention is to provide an egg beater in which the drive wheel and the pinions in engagement therewith are encased in a graspable housing which also serves as the beater handle …

—SAM LEBOWITZ, IN HIS 1980 PATENT

▶ Another wire bottom was considered the show stopper at the 1999 KOOKS convention in Dublin, Ohio. This mechanical marvel is marked DUPLEX EGG AND CREAM WHIP PAT APPLIED FOR U.S.A. *(fig. 21-87)*. The unusual dashers push in and out from the center in a remarkable mixing motion. This beater does not appear to be part of the DUPLEX CREAM WHIPPER family of turbine beaters *(See Chapter 20 Big Turbines & Blades, page 231)*.

❖

The rotary mix peaked in the 1940s and 1950s, but the patent ideas continued for the next 30 years. One of the last, if not the very last, rotary crank beater patents went to Sam Lebowitz of New York City on March 18, 1980 *(fig. 21-88)*. Lebowitz' device features a unique encasing of the gears, the housing of which also serves as the handle, thereby lessening the overall size of the beater, which gives the operator much firmer control.

☞
FIG. 21-88

*Sam Lebowitz
patent
March 18, 1980
Pat. No. 4,193,697*

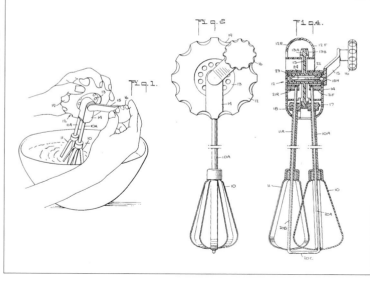

**1924
Wesson Oil ad**

**Egg Baking
Powder, c.1902
recipe booklet**

There are good dogs and bad dogs. A good dog is one of the best friends of mankind. He will protect his mistress from harm just as EGG BAKING POWDER will protect her from disappointment in baking. A bad dog, like bad baking powder, is not worth the room it takes up.

▶ To bring this chapter to a close, we go to Iowa for two connections worthy of note, both spinoffs on the always-popular rotary beater.

The first is a device found on display at the Gowrie Historical Depot Museum on Beek Street in the town of Gowrie (population 1,028).

It was the invention of a Gowrie farmer who had lost everything in the Great Depression. Edward V. Johnson was 63 years old when he patented his innovative device Jan. 13, 1931 (fig. 21-89).

"Beaters for whipping cream, beating eggs and the like are very tedious to operate due to the fact that they must be held in one hand an operated with the other hand," Johnson said in his patent application. "I have overcome this objective by providing a stand that will rigidly hold the egg beater in the proper position inside the container having the cream or eggs to be agitated."

Nikolas Telleen, a fourth-generation Gowrie farmer, tells this story about his great grandfather, who was born Aug. 12, 1868 and died Jan. 7, 1959:

E. V. Johnson was a very successful farmer who was financially ruined by the Depression. "The story my dad [Vernon Telleen] told was he [Johnson] really scrapped and skimped and saved his pennies to get enough money to work out a patent and make a form for his eggbeater holder (figs. 21-90 & 21-91). Just as he spent all of his money on these forms and got into production, the electric beater came out. It was just wrong timing. If it had been five to 10 years earlier it would have been very successful. As a result he ended up with all his investment gone," Telleen said.

On his death, Johnson left all the beater holders that had not sold to Vernon Telleen, and over the years "when Dad needed a piece of metal, he used a base of one of the holders. If he needed to repair a hole in a wagon, or a hole in the corn crib, he would use a base and nail it up."

Nik Telleen described his great grandfather as a special person. "I remember his as a kind man who made wooden toys for us kids. Older people who remember him describe him to me as 'the kind of man who whistled while he worked.'"

[The Gowrie Historical Depot Museum houses the collection of the Gowrie Historical Society in the community's original railroad depot in Laurel Park. The museum is open Sunday and holidays, Memorial Day through Labor Day.]

The second Iowa connection is Eugene D. McGrath of New Hampton, a master craftsman who produces unique artifacts in wood, including giant eggbeaters (fig. 21-92).

McGrath, who turned 77 on Pearl Harbor Day in 1998, is a retired farm equipment dealer. In addition to giant eggbeaters, his wood working projects have included 15" paddle locks, giant chains and large wristwatches with bands.

"I like to fool around with wood," he said. "I don't like TV. It (wood) is my pastime and my hobby."

Asked how he came about creating a 41-1/2" high, center-gear mixer, he replied, "I was just wondering if I could make an eggbeater. And I did it."

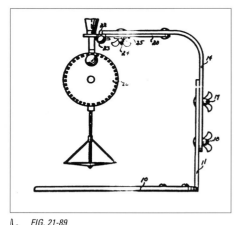

FIG. 21-89

Edward V. Johnson patent
Jan. 13, 1931
Pat. No. 1,788,675

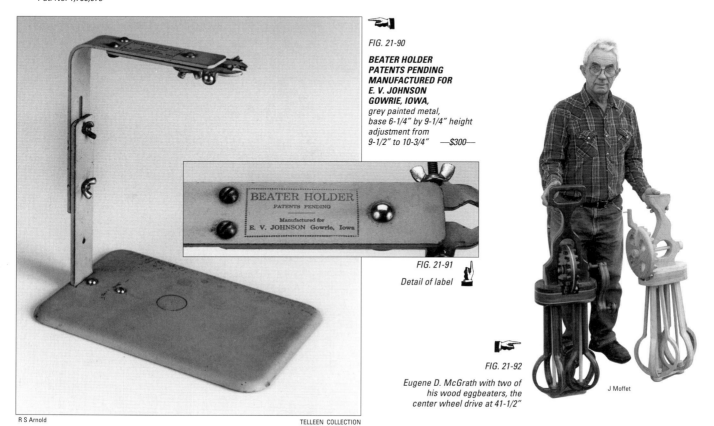

FIG. 21-90

BEATER HOLDER PATENTS PENDING MANUFACTURED FOR E. V. JOHNSON GOWRIE, IOWA, grey painted metal, base 6-1/4" by 9-1/4" height adjustment from 9-1/2" to 10-3/4"   —$300—

BEATER HOLDER
PATENTS PENDING
Manufactured for
E. V. JOHNSON Gowrie, Iowa

FIG. 21-91

Detail of label

FIG. 21-92

Eugene D. McGrath with two of his wood eggbeaters, the center wheel drive at 41-1/2"

J Moffet

R S Arnold

TELLEEN COLLECTION

Ratchet, Push, Pull & Squeeze

From ratchet power to rope power.

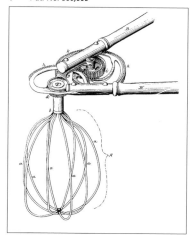

FIG. 22-1

Harry Jaquette patent
Nov. 28, 1893
Pat. No. 509,665

FIG. 22-2

Jaquettes (left to right):

PAT., *only I.D.*   20" $1,500+

JAQUETTE BROS NO. 2 8-3/4" —$850—

JAQUETTE BROS
PHILA PA PATENTED NO. 3
10-1/2" —$800—

JAQUETTE BROS NO. 1 7-1/2" *(broken handle)*
$1,000+ in good condition

"The object of my invention is to so construct an implement for beating or stirring materials in performing different culinary operations that said implement can be conveniently handled and the maximum amount of power exerted in order to cause the rotation, first in one direction and then in the opposite direction, of the beating or stirring device.

"This object I attain by providing said beating or stirring device with two handles pivoted together so as to be movable one in respect to the other, and with gearing whereby when the outer or free ends of the handles are moved toward or from each other the back and forth rotations of the beater or stirrer will be effected…"

That was how Harry Jaquette of Philadelphia described his cast-iron, scissorstype eggbeater in his Nov. 28, 1893 patent *(fig. 22-1)*. The JAQUETTE BROS came in five sizes, ranging from one with scissors handles 7-1/2" long, which can be oper-

ated with one hand in a pinch, to the largest with wooden handles at about 20 inches *(fig. 22-2)*.

It's best to stick to the measurements in identifying the different sizes because the lines between those marked NO. 2, NO. 3 and NO. 4, are sometimes mixed up. For example, there is a NO. 2 the same size as the NO. 3 at 10-1/2" *(fig. 22-3)*. For the record, the sizes are 7-1/2", 8-3/4", 10-1/2", 11-1/2" (not pictured) and 20 inches. Some models have filigreed handles and others are plain. Some have wire dashers and others have wire strip dashers.

Nearly all the models are marked JAQUETTE BROS on the underside of the handles. But the only Jaquette appearing in Philadelphia city directories off and on from 1895 to 1910, was Harry Jaquette, listed as a manufacturer of hardware specialties and an inventor, at 1710 Barker.

D G Simons

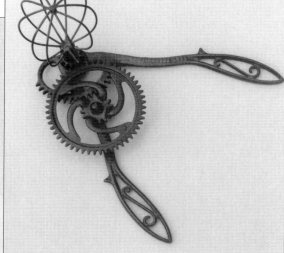

FIG. 22-3

Although marked
JAQUETTE BROS   PHILA PA
PAT. ALD.   NO. 2
This mixer is the same length as the No. 3, 10-1/2"

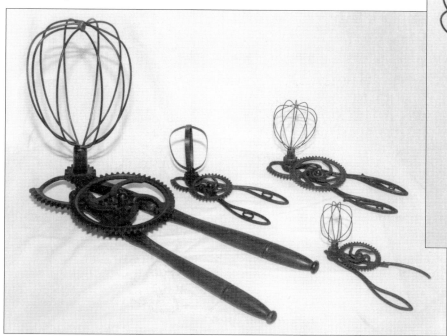

C Badger

WILLIS / BADGER COLLECTIONS

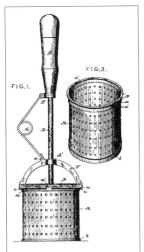

FIG. 22-4

*Uriah D. Seltzer patent
Nov. 29, 1892
Pat. No. 487,024*

FIG. 22-5

Lebanons (left to right):

PATENT PENDING
*fine mesh cylinder
13" —$500—*

PATENT PENDING
*coarse mesh cylinder
13" —$500—*

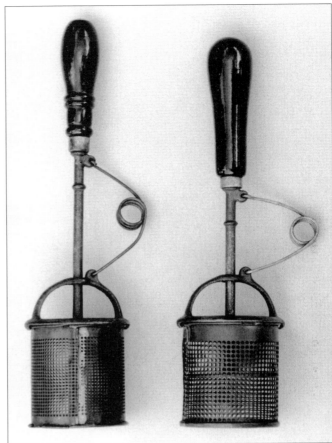

D G Simons

FIG. 22-6

*Early Lebanon Beater
trade card*

LEBANON BEATER
FOR
Mashing Potatoes, Beating Eggs, Etc.
MANUFACTURED BY
SELTZER SPECIALTY COMPANY,
LEBANON, PA.
PATENTS PENDING.

EGGS   POTATOES
Price with 2 Cylinders, 50 cts.
FOR SALE BY ALL DEALERS.

 FIG. 22-8

No I.D.   9-1/2"   —$100—

R S Arnold

Other ingenious egg beating solutions, in random order, include:

▶ Uriah D. Seltzer put Lebanon, Pennsylvania, on the map as far as kitchenware collectors are concerned. But local Lebanon historians just don't have that much information on what perhaps could be the city's most famous inventor son.

Seltzer patented his exceptional LEBANON BEATER Nov. 29, 1892 *(fig. 22-4),* boasting a bit that "the advantages and utility of my device are apparent. It has a wide range of usefulness, for it may be used as well for an eggbeater, fruit-press &c., as for a potato-masher. Combined with the efficient manner in which these operations are performed make it a very desirable object for kitchen use. Its simplicity, too, is a feature. Its parts, being few and easy to manufacture, will enable me to make it at a cost within the reach of everyone."

Seltzer Specialty Company manufactured the black-handled gadget, which came with two interchangeable, perforated cylinders, one with coarse holes, the other fine *(fig. 22-5).* A cast-iron plunger/piston fits within the cylinder and a looped wire on the handle gives it a spring action. An early trade card *(fig. 22-6)* listed the price, with two cylinders, at 50¢.

According to the Lebanon County Historical Society, Seltzer was a "heating engineer" in Washington, D.C., before he settled in Lebanon, marrying Barbara Elizabeth Light. In the 1900 Census his occupation was listed as "cigar store." He apparently lived on North 9th Street and had his business on North 10th Street. He was not listed as having a business in 1901.

A similar beater was patented Sept. 26, 1893 by George W. Huber of Philadelphia *(fig. 22-7).* It was a simple device with its spring power within the perfor-

FIG. 22-7

*George W. Huber patent
Sept. 26, 1893
Pat. No. 505,766*

THE EGGBEATER CHRONICLES

FIG. 22-9

No I.D.
9" —$125—

BADGER COLLECTION

C Badger

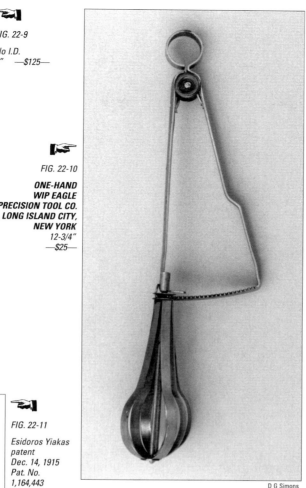

FIG. 22-10

**ONE-HAND
WIP EAGLE
PRECISION TOOL CO.
LONG ISLAND CITY,
NEW YORK**
12-3/4"
—$25—

D G Simons

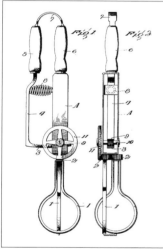

FIG. 22-11

Esidoros Yiakas
patent
Dec. 14, 1915
Pat. No.
1,164,443

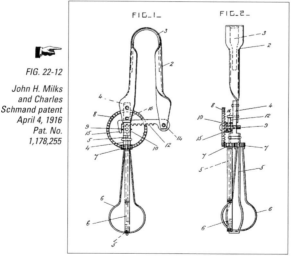

FIG. 22-12

John H. Milks
and Charles
Schmand patent
April 4, 1916
Pat. No.
1,178,255

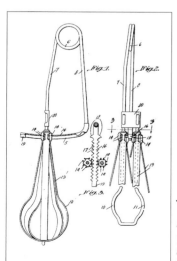

FIG. 22-13

William W. Crocker patent
Dec. 18, 1923
Pat. No. 1,477,943

FIG. 22-14

No I.D.
11-3/4"
—$55—

HOY COLLECTION

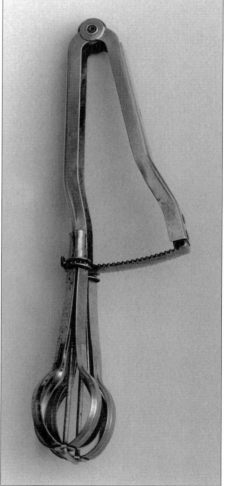

D G Simons

ated cylinder. A possible match to the patent *(fig. 22-8)* has the spring on the outside and a squatter apparatus, but the principle is the same.

▶ Another push beater is a simple but effective all-wire model with no markings and featuring a coil spring, push bottom *(fig. 22-9)*.

▶ The ONE-HAND WIP *(fig. 22-10)* was manufactured by the Eagle Precision Tool Company, Long Island City, New York. It is one of the better-known squeeze beaters.

Of the three known one-hand squeeze eggbeater patents *(figs. 22-11 through 22-13)* on file, the Dec. 18, 1923 design by William W. Crocker of Salina, Kansas, appears the best match. The primary object of his invention, said Crocker, was to provide a device "which may be efficiently controlled by one hand of the operator, leaving the other hand free to add material to the egg or material being agitated."

▶ Crocker's patent also appears to apply to a heavy-duty, no-name model *(fig. 22-14)*.

CHAPTER 22: RATCHET, PUSH, PULL & SQUEEZE

D G Simons

FIG. 22-15

No I.D. but FAVORITE, composition ratchet bar —$125—

FIG. 22-16

No I.D. but FAVORITE, back and forth metal handle —$175—

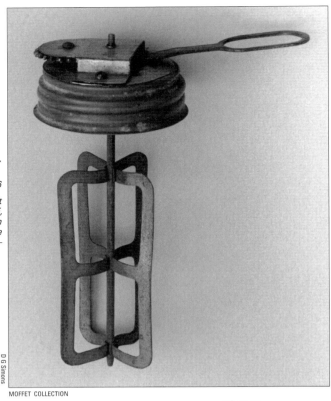

D G Simons

MOFFET COLLECTION

FIG. 22-18

Harry J. Favorite and Donald B. O'Neal patent Oct. 24, 1916 Pat. No. 1,202,415

FIG. 22-17

August, 1917 House Furnishing Review ad

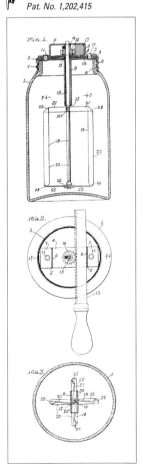

▶ The FAVORITE CREAM WHIPPER was made for any quart fruit jar. There are two models: (1) a back-and-forth ratchet with a detachable composition or metal ratchet bar about 7-3/4" long with a tin loop handle *(fig. 22-15)*, and (2) a side-to-side, non-detachable metal ratchet arm with loop *(fig. 22-16)*.

A 1917 *House Furnishing Review* magazine ad *(fig. 22-17)* said: "The Favorite whips cream, beats eggs, churns butter, and does the mixing for the kitchen in a jiffy! Attaches to any regular screw top quart fruit jar. No special jar needed. Cannot leak or splash out! Retails at 50 cents with a good margin of profit for the dealer!"

The July 21, 1917 issue of the *Tippecanoe (Ohio) Herald* said: "The Favorite Products Company, a local concern located on South Street, is meeting with great success with their cream whipper, of which H. J. Favorite is the patentee. Agencies have been established in a number of states, and it is difficult to turn out the article fast enough. The Ohio distributor sold nearly 1,000 of them to Dayton dealers last week."

Harry J. Favorite and Donald B. O'Neal, both of Tippecanoe, said in their Oct. 24, 1916 patent *(fig. 22-18)* that their invention would "eliminate wabbling and give a steady movement to the rotating parts of a churn or the like."

The *Favorite* Cream Whipper

Is new both in design and principle. Examine the illustration closely. Note its simple, strong, durable construction, also its easy method of operation.

The Favorite whips cream, beats eggs, churns butter, and does the mixing for the kitchen in a jiffy!

Attaches to any regular screw top quart fruit jar. No special jar needed. Cannot leak or splash out!

Retails at 50 cents with a good margin of profit for the dealer!

Made of strong coated material, eyelet bearings and has a reversible rack and pinion movement. Weighs only 3½ ounces complete, as every home furnishes the jars.

Write us today for prices!

Tested and Approved by the Good Housekeeping Institute Conducted by Good Housekeeping Magazine 1690

The Favorite Products Co.
Tippecanoe City
Ohio

Two of the earliest American beaters patented employed the same push-pull principle as the Favorite.

Harvey Miller of Cincinnati, Ohio, said in his Dec. 1, 1857 patent (*fig. 22-19*), "My invention consists of a cast iron frame having a ratchet bar and revolving beater in combination with a jar or can; this forming an egg beater cheaper in construction and more convenient than any heretofore known."

John B. Heich, also of Cincinnati, said in his Dec. 15, 1857 patent (*fig. 22-20*) that his beater was operated "by the motion backward and forward of the grooved bar" against "a disk of India rubber or other elastic material" attached to the top of the dasher drive.

Heich's mixer was written up in the Feb. 27, 1858 *Scientific American*. "The process of egg-beating is a tiresome one; many a cook, with aching wrist, will be glad to hear of this invention, which will beat six eggs in ten seconds," the article said. "It is one of the most useful and compact aids to domestic economy that we have ever seen, and can be made of any size from one quart to five gallons."

The article indicated the beater was not in production — that only the patent rights were being sold.

▶ In a similar back-and-forth mode is the May 11, 1880 eggbeater patented (*fig. 22-21*) by Edward Morse of Boston and Lychurgus Burham of Woburn, Massachusetts. This beater is powered with two fingers and an arch-shaped ratchet which is moved back and forth. Marked only MATCHLESS, this mixer (*fig. 22-22*) stands 7-5/8" tall and is very, very rare.

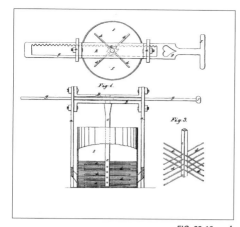

FIG. 22-19
Harvey Miller patent
Dec. 1, 1857
Pat. No. 18,759

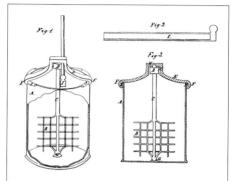

 FIG. 22-20

John B. Heich patent
Dec. 15, 1857
Pat. No. 18,849

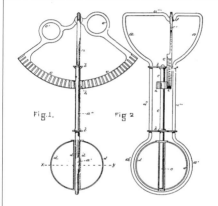

FIG. 22-21

Edward Morse and
Lychurgus Burham patent
May 11, 1880
Pat. No. 227,378

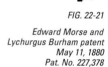 FIG. 22-22

MATCHLESS
7-5/8"
—$1,000+—

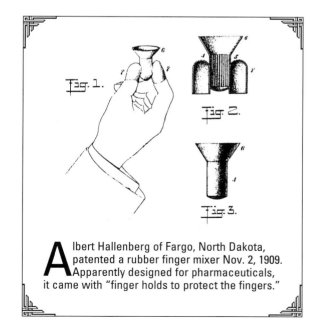

Albert Hallenberg of Fargo, North Dakota, patented a rubber finger mixer Nov. 2, 1909. Apparently designed for pharmaceuticals, it came with "finger holds to protect the fingers."

FIG. 22-23

Double Action Mfg. Co. catalog sheet

FIG. 22-24

D-over-**A**
12-1/2"
—$95—

▶ Another ratchet is the D-OVER-A, the two letters stacked on top of each other, standing for DOUBLE ACTION. A catalog sheet *(fig. 22-23)* from Double Action Manufacturing Company of Grand Rapids, Michigan, said it "can be operated with one hand or one finger. Will not move bowl as all pressure is straight downward."

The 1926 *Grand Rapids City Directory* listed the firm as "Double Action Electric Co., H.C. LeVine Mgr, Mfrs of Electric toasters, heaters and small appliances, 30-32 Market Ave. NW."

The name changed in the 1931 directory. "Double Action Mfg Co (Harry C. LeVine) household appliances, 30 Michigan NW," was the new listing, which continued for at least two more years.

The DOUBLE ACTION beater *(fig. 22-24)* utilizes a spring in its handle for back-stroke power. A patent that it could have been based on, but with the spring on the main shaft, was granted Nov. 19, 1929 *(fig. 22-25)* to Thomas J. Madigan of Brooklyn.

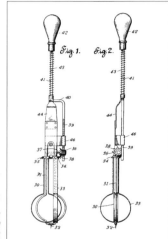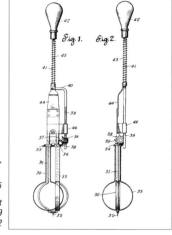

FIG. 22-25

*Thomas J. Madigan patent
Nov. 19, 1929
Pat. No. 1,736,542*

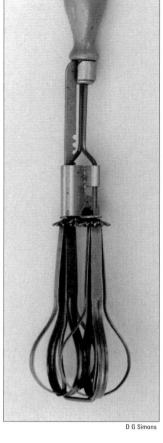

D G Simons

**"Primrose"
Egg Separator**

*3-1/4" diameter
—$20—*

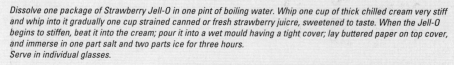

The Kewpies' Recipe for Apple Snow

Dissolve one package of Strawberry Jell-O in one pint of boiling water. When partly cold, turn into sherbet glasses, fillling three-quarters full. When firm, pile apple snow on top. Apple Snow: White of one egg, one grated apple, one-half cup sugar. Beat till light and feathery. In making this Apple Snow, either Raspberry or Cherry Jell-O can be used instead of the Strawberry flavor, if desired or if more convenient.

Jell-O's Kewpies can be seen in a 1915 Jell-O recipe cookbook helping out around the house: setting the table, helping with Mom's embroidery, and bringing Jell-O to little Dorothy who is sick in bed.

Mrs. Lincoln's Strawberry Mousse

*Dissolve one package of Strawberry Jell-O in one pint of boiling water. Whip one cup of thick chilled cream very stiff and whip into it gradually one cup strained canned or fresh strawberry juicre, sweetened to taste. When the Jell-O begins to stiffen, beat it into the cream; pour it into a wet mould having a tight cover; lay buttered paper on top cover, and immerse in one part salt and two parts ice for three hours.
Serve in individual glasses.*

—1915 JELL-O RECIPE COOKBOOK, GENESE PURE FOOD COMPANY, LEROY, NEW YORK

From ratchet power to rope-power is only a small jump. At least a dozen rope or chain powered beaters were patented in the U.S. from 1859 to 1935 — just about all of them real engineering beauties.

Five good examples came in the years 1869, 1909, 1910, 1922 and 1935 *(figs. 22-26 through 22-30)*, with the 1922 one possibly making it to market.

▶ Le Roy J. Dekin of Ilion, New York said in his 1922 patent that his device "operated through successive pulls upon a cord being used to rotate a weighted wheel or balance wheel..." Although the balance wheel is at the top and not in the middle, there is a model *(fig. 22-31)* that could be a match.

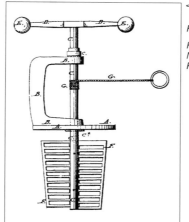

 *FIG. 22-26*
H.G. and A.C. Fougen patent
Nov. 30, 1869
Pat. No. 97,379

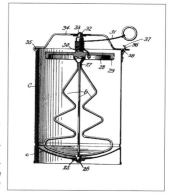

FIG. 22-27
Frederick P. Burr patent
Sept. 28, 1909
Pat. No. 935,088

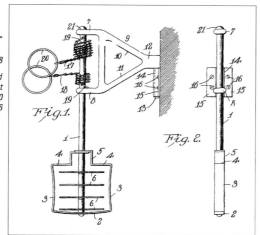

FIG. 22-28
John W. Horner and
George L. Patterson patent
May 31, 1910
Pat. No. 959,536

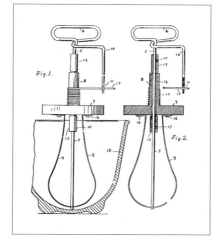

FIG. 22-29
Le Roy J. Dekin patent
Nov. 28, 1922
Pat. No. 1,437,133

FIG. 22-30

 Ralston R. Smith patent
June 4, 1935
Pat. No. 2,003,521

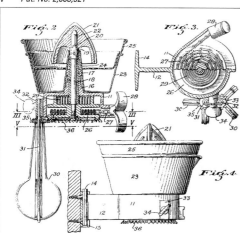

R S Arnold

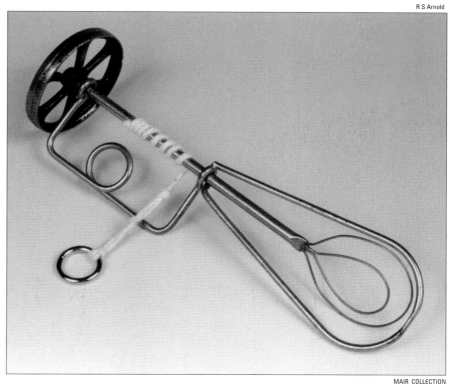

 *FIG. 22-31*
No I.D., but possibly Dekin 1922 patent
10-1/8" —$195—

MAIR COLLECTION

▶ A German rope model, LUGULLUS, is marked with the German patent DRGM DRP and a symbol with the letters GBN and BAVARIA *(fig. 22-32)*. It has a loop handle on the top, three sturdy metal legs and a brace at the bottom to support the bullet-shaped jar. There is also a tube that can be used to feed liquids into the mix. A similar model, with the same top design but one that screws onto a jar, and with a wood dasher, was also made by GBN *(fig. 22-33)*.

On both models, pulling the rope spins the fly wheel. At the end of the pull (and the end of the rope), the rope feeds back, rewinding on the knob of the spinning fly wheel. When it is rewound, slowly pulling it back out reverses the direction of the dashers and starts the process again.

▶ A tin churn operates on the same principle, but with a wire bow *(figs. 22-34 & 22-35)*. The 16-3/4" heavy twisted wire bow is worked back and forth against the thread spool mounted on the top of the churn to turn the dashers.

S Scharnhorst

D G Simons

FIG. 22-32
LUGULLUS
DRGM DRP
GBN BAVARIA
12" —$750—

SCARBOROUGH COLLECTION

FIG. 22-33
GBN
BAVARIA
11-3/4"
—$800—

FIG. 22-34

No I.D., tin churn
11-1/4" overall height
—$400—

FIG. 22-35

Detail of bow operation

R S Arnold

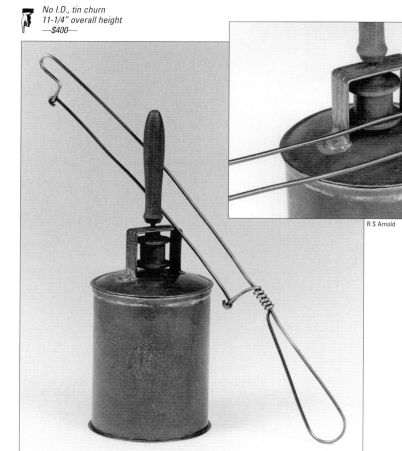

MAIR COLLECTION

Rumford Egg Separator

3-1/4" diameter
—$50—

THE EGGBEATER CHRONICLES

Muncie, Indiana was the hometown of Ray V. Sowers and it was in Muncie that a prototype *(fig. 22-36)* of his squeezer's delight was found. This is how Sowers described his mixer in his Nov. 10, 1931 patent *(fig. 22-37)*: "A manual device for converting reciprocative motion into rotary motion…" The prototype utilizes a recycled Ladd main wheel but otherwise matches the patent perfectly *(See Chapter 15, Ladd, p. 176)*.

▶ The QUIK-WHIP *(fig. 22-38)* is another one-hand marvel. Squeezing with two fingers, with the end of the beater braced in your palm, sets off the spring action which sends the disk dasher spinning. The patent for this one has so far proven elusive. However, there are other notable squeeze patents *(figs. 22-39 & 22-40)*, including the first and perhaps last trigger-powered eggbeater.

▶ A squeeze also powers the KORENA, a rare beater made in New York *(fig. 22-41)*. This device could be propelled by palm or thumb.

FIG. 22-36

No I.D. but Sowers patent despite Ladd main wheel
12-3/4"   —$500—

ULMER COLLECTION

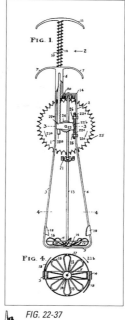
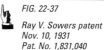

FIG. 22-37

Ray V. Sowers patent
Nov. 10, 1931
Pat. No. 1,831,040

FIG. 22-38

**QUIK WHIP
REG. U.S. PAT. OFF
PATENT PENDING**
11-1/4"   —$110—

FIG. 22-39

Fred C. Booth patent
Nov. 11, 1947
Pat. No. 2,430,600

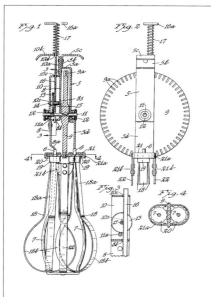

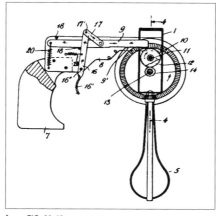

FIG. 22-40

Albert Kelley patent
July 9, 1935
Pat. No. 2,007,249

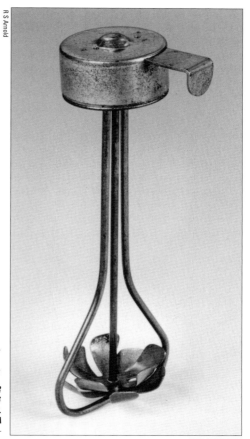

FIG. 22-41

**KORENA EGG & CREAM WHIPPER
PAT-PENDING
KEB MFG. CORP.
NEW YORK, NY, USA**
7"   —$750—

MAIR COLLECTION

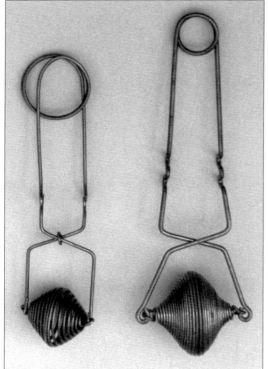

FIG. 22-42

No I.D. but Nifty Sifter
6-1/2" —$20—

8" —$5—

FIG. 22-43

Bror N. Carlson patent
Feb. 25, 1930
Pat. No. 1,748,830

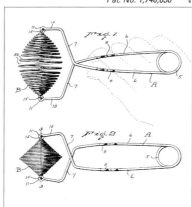

▶ There is another squeeze that
should be mentioned because it is often
mistaken for an eggbeater, but it isn't
an eggbeater. Described on the patent as
a "material receptacle and sifter" it is a
flour, or sugar, pincher that comes in
two sizes *(fig. 22-42)*.

Patented Feb. 25, 1930 *(fig. 22-43)*
by Bror N. Carlson, it was marketed
under the name NIFTY SIFTER. Carlson
described his device as "an improved
cooking utensil adapted for use in sifting
small amounts of flour and other ingredients of a similar nature into gravies,
batters and like dishes where it is desirable to add the ingredients gradually as
to prevent lumping."

▶ Winding up this chapter is a windup mixer. Samuel I. Berger of Newark,
New Jersey, patented his mixer July 9,
1935 *(figs. 22-44 & 22-45)*. "This invention relates to devices especially adapted
for mixing various liquids, such as malted
milk, iced drinks, eggnog, or for beating
various substances, such as whipped
cream, eggs or the like," Berger said.

This clever device has a spring motor
which is wound up with the top knob
and controlled with a switch.

▶ Another wind-up was patented
nearly 50 years earlier. Mary F. Bishop
of Bridgeport, Connecticut, said in her
June 19, 1888 patent *(fig. 22-46)* that
"a great number of eggs may be beaten
simultaneously, while at the same time
the operation of beating is
accomplished automatically and
in a very short space of time."

FIG. 22-44

No I.D. windup mixer
12" —$55—

FIG. 22-45

Samuel I. Berger patent
July 9, 1935
Pat. No. 2,007,361

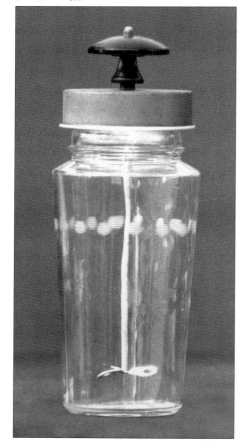

D G Simons

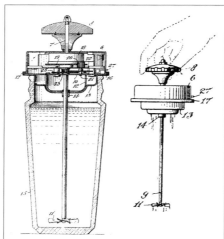

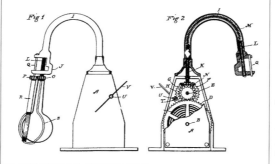

FIG. 22-46

Mary F. Bishop patent
June 19, 1888
Pat. No. 384,674

D G Simons

THE EGGBEATER CHRONICLES

Chapter 23

Water Power

"Turn the Faucet and it Starts!"

It's the most common substance on Earth.

It makes up about 65 percent of your body, 80 percent of an earthworm, and 95 percent of a tomato. It covers more than 70 percent of the Earth's surface. It can be a solid, a liquid or a gas. And it can power eggbeaters.

Few and far between, water-powered eggbeaters do exist — if only in early patents, ads and catalog sheets.

The first water-power patent idea came in 1917, and several models have been patented since.

Probably the most common — although far from common on the collectors market — is THE WORLD BEATER (*fig. 23-1, left*).

Herbert L. Thompson of Elgin, Illinois, said in his April 29, 1924 patent (*fig. 23-2*) that "the device shall be adapted for convenient use, being preferably arranged for actuation by a water motor and to that end capable of being mounted on an ordinary faucet."

Six months later Thompson patented the mixer's "power wheel" (*fig. 23-3*). Thompson, who was born in 1882 and died in 1954, is credited with dozens of patents for mechanical devices, including a gasoline-powered lawn mower, an electric corn popper, a wire weaving machine and a one-half horsepower gasoline engine for a washing machine, which he sold to Maytag.

An ad in the October, 1922 magazine *Modern Priscilla* (*fig. 23-4*) said THE WORLD could be "sent parcel post prepaid, $2.75 east of Rockies."

FIG. 23-1

Water beaters (left to right)::

**THE WORLD BEATER
MFRD BY THE WORLD NOVELTY CO.
ELGIN, ILL.   PAT. APLD. FOR**
8-1/2"   —$110—
Note: A later model is marked:
**THE WORLD BEATER DELUXE
PATENT APRIL 29, 1924 - OCT. 14, 1924
WORLD NOVELTY CO.
ELGIN, ILL.   OTHER PAT. PENDING**

**3-MINUTE MAY-O-NAZE MAKER
WESTERN ALUMINUM MFG. CO.
OAKLAND, CALIF.   PAT APPLIED FOR**
7"   —$175—

D G Simons

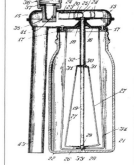

FIG. 23-2

Herbert L. Thompson patent April 29, 1924 Pat. No. 1,492,229

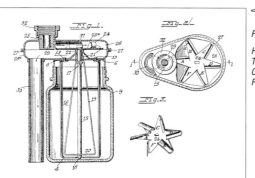

FIG. 23-3

Herbert L. Thompson patent Oct. 14, 1924 Pat. No. 1,511,541

FIG. 23-4

October, 1922 Modern Priscilla magazine ad

▶ The 3-MINUTE MAY-O-NAZE MAKER (*fig. 23-1, right*) was manufactured in Oakland, California, probably in the 1930s. It has a rubber hose with an aluminum fitting with rubber center nuzzle that attaches to a faucet. The water exhaust is from bevel cuts in the top.

This advice is embossed on the aluminum top: FOR BEST RESULTS USE PRIMROSE SALAD OIL.

▶ Frank H. Parker and Kenneth H. Kolpien of Cleveland, Ohio, not only patented what they called a "culinary mixer" — the NIAGARA — but also the action behind it — a "fluid motor." Both patents (*fig. 23-5*) were granted on the same day, Dec. 24, 1929. The patents listed Parker and Kolpien as assignors to the Niagara Mixer Company of Cleveland, which as far as can be determined produced only the NIAGARA mixer (*fig. 23-6*).

A brochure that came with the NIAGARA said it "runs forever," and "works while you rest." The brochure listed the firm's address as 215 The Arcade Building, Cleveland, Ohio, Phone Main 1906. The retail price was $4.85. The brochure also gave this advice: "Regulate speed of the Mixer by turning the faucet handle. Always turn it on gradually at first until you find the speed best suited to the quantity and kind of substance in the bowl."

▶ There also is a stand-alone water-power beater (*fig. 23-7*). It was not made to fit on a particular jar or bowl, but rather it screwed onto the faucet and then a container with the ingredients to be mixed was lifted into position. Named the MARVEL WHIPPER, it was patented in 1925 by Israel P. Duncan and Thomas M. Gore of Los Angeles (*fig. 23-8*).

▶ Another stand-alone is the 7" HYDRO-MOTOR (*fig. 23-9*).

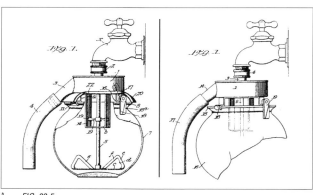

FIG. 23-5

Frank H. Parker and Kenneth H. Kolpien patent Dec. 24, 1929 Pat. No. 1,740,709

Frank H. Parker and Kenneth H. Kolpien patent Dec. 24, 1929 Pat. No. 1,740,710

MOFFET COLLECTION

R S Arnold

FIG. 23-6

GILSON COLLECTION

NIAGARA MIXER PAT APPLIED FOR THE NIAGARA MIXER CO. CLEVELAND OHIO U.S.A. (on mixer) No I.D. on 5-1/2" jar overall 8" —$450—

FIG. 23-7

PAT. PEND. 7-3/4" —$150— Note: Later models are marked: **MARVEL WHIPPER CO. LOS ANGELES, CAL. PAT'D 5-26-25**

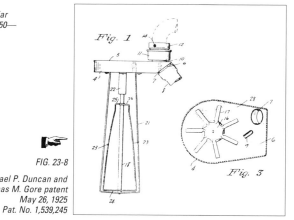

FIG. 23-8

Israel P. Duncan and Thomas M. Gore patent May 26, 1925 Pat. No. 1,539,245

THE EGGBEATER CHRONICLES

FIG. 23-9

HYDRO-MOTOR
PAT'D
NEW YORK
7" —$200—

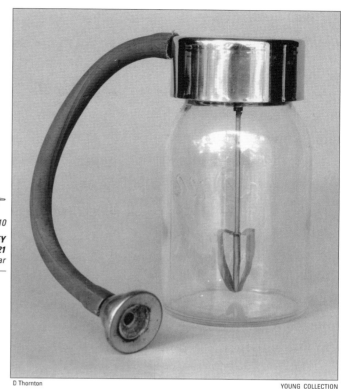

FIG. 23-10

JERSEY
PAT. APR. 19-21
fits on quart jar
—$200—

D Thornton

YOUNG COLLECTION

R S Arnold

BOHN COLLECTION

FIG. 23-11

*Jersey Manufacturing
Company brochure*

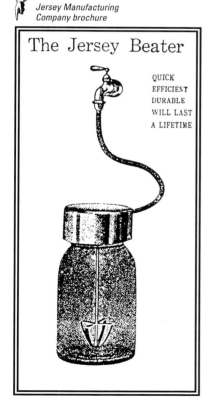

The Jersey Beater

QUICK
EFFICIENT
DURABLE
WILL LAST
A LIFETIME

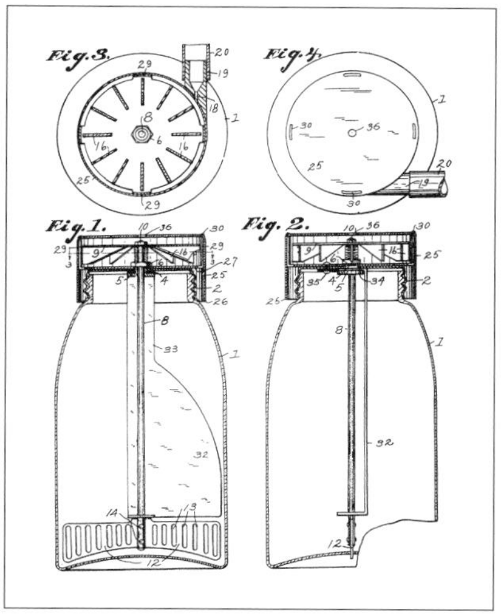

FIG. 23-12

*Otto P. Werner and
Theodore W. Arntz
patent
April 19, 1921
Pat. No. 1,375,338*

Fig. 3. *Fig. 4.*
Fig. 1. *Fig. 2.*

FIG. 23-13

*Mid-City
Manufacturing
Company catalog
sheet*

SPEEDS

PRICE
ONLY
$1.50

KASKAID

Cooled by
Water
OUTSIDE

Rotary
Agitator
INSIDE

▶ THE JERSEY BEATER *(fig. 23-10)*
featured a tube for easy placement of the
jar near the faucet. Made by the Jersey
Manufacturing Company of Sussex,
Wisconsin, it was listed at $2.50. An
early brochure *(fig. 23-11)* called it "a
world beater" that "whips cream; beats
eggs; mixes salad dressing, batters,
malted milk, and all other liquids or
semi-liquids that should be thoroughly
mixed for best cooking results."

It also boasted that "from one to a
dozen eggs can be beaten to a fine froth,
preparing excellent omelettes, icings, etc."
It even noted the water flow had an added

an advantage: "Escape water flows over
outside of jar, keeping contents cold."
THE JERSEY was patented in 1921 by Otto
P. Werner and Theodore W. Arntz of
Milwaukee, Wisconsin *(fig. 23-12)*.

▶ The KASKAID WHIPPER, made by
Mid-City Manufacturing Company,
Chicago, claimed that "there are many
unusual features … chief among them is
the cooling and heating system which is
supplied by the water overflow."

Early catalog sheets *(figs. 23-13 & 23-
14)* listed the price at $1.50 and crowed:
"Water cooled, water powered, and
water lubricated."

FIG. 23-14

Mid-City Manufacturing
Company catalog sheet

KASKAID
REG. U.S. PAT. OFF.
WATER POWERED
WHIPPER

*"Cools as
it Whips"*

▼

WHIPS
CREAM

▼

BEATS
EGGS

Children mix their own Milk Drinks

MIXES MAYONNAISE,
MALTED MILK, EGG NOGS,
GELATIN DESSERTS,
WAFFLE BATTER,
SWEET BUTTER, ETC.

Water Cooled, Water Powered,
and Water Lubricated

◆

MANUFACTURED BY

MID-CITY MANUFACTURING CO.
1161 W. Madison Street
Chicago

A Magic Egg Beater
6 *WONDERS* IN 1

I Do you want a **magic egg** beater which will beat eggs, whip cream or salad dressing by itself while you attend to other things?

II Do you want to clean bottles, tumblers and lamp chimneys automatically?

III Do you want a perfectly noiseless and effective cooling fan in the kitchen to make the hot season bearable?

IV Do you want a self-operating emery wheel on which to sharpen and clean your knives, scissors and edged tools?

V Do you want a splendid cotton polishing wheel revolving so fast that you can make your silverware and cutlery shine as it never shone before?

"Turn the faucet—that's all"

VI Do you want a powerful little motor for 20 useful ends about the home, to run sewing machine, meat chopper, small dynamo, cooling fan, etc.?

If interested in any of these remarkable claims you want our "Little Wonder" WATER MOTOR which will attach to your water faucet, smooth or threaded, in a jiffy. A line from you brings our attractive FREE descriptive booklet telling all about it. Don't be deceived by cheap, worthless imitations.

WARNER MOTOR COMPANY
Dept. J, Flatiron Bldg.,   New York City
Mfrs. of Water Motors 1-16 to 10 H.P. Water Fans and Accessories

FIG. 23-15

Good Housekeeping,
June 1906 ad

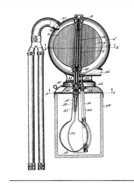

FIG. 23-16

Edward Schubert patent
Aug. 21, 1917
Pat. No. 1,237,707

Russell L. Long patent
April 20, 1920
Pat. No. 1,337,478

Henry S. Walter patent
Sept. 28, 1920
Pat. No. 1,354,230

Christian E. Jensen patent
May 22, 1923
Pat. No. 1,456,448

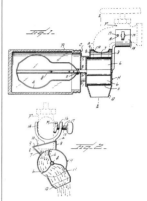

Ser. No. 182,257. (CLASS 23. CUTLERY, MACHINERY, AND TOOLS, AND PARTS THEREOF.) THE P-K MANUFACTURING COMPANY, Cleveland, Ohio. Filed June 20, 1923.

PE KAY

Particular description of goods.—Water-Power Beater and Whipper.
Claims use since May 1, 1923.

FIG. 23-17

U.S. Patent &
Trademark Office
Official Gazette,
Sept. 11, 1923
P-K Manufacturing
Company trademark

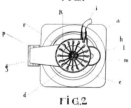

▶ Another water-power beater — with five other uses, including cooling fan — was billed as the LITTLE WONDER, manufactured by the Warner Motor Company of New York City.

A June, 1906 *Good Housekeeping* ad (*fig. 23-15*) warned: "Don't be deceived by cheap, worthless imitations."

▶ There are at least four other patents and one trademark for water-power beaters (*figs. 23-16 & 23-17*), insuring that the search will continue.

Probably the only source of power that could eclipse water as the most unique way of beating eggs would be hot air.

Air not only powers his device, said Curtis Riedel of New Brighton, Pennsylvania, in his Feb. 6, 1934 patent (*fig. 23-18*), but also provides an important bubble action: "compressed air … not only stirs or agitates the material, but … delivers air under pressure to the lower portion of the material to form bubbles therein…"

Riedel's "compressed air cream and egg whip" apparently never made it past the patent stage.

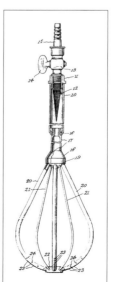

FIG. 23-18

Curtis Riedel patent
Feb. 6, 1934
Pat. No. 1,945,915

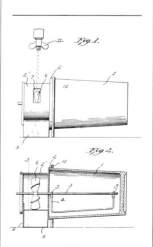

Chapter 24

Handheld Cousins

The ridiculous to the super utilitarian.

*S*hake hands with another member of the mixer family, although a poor cousin of sorts.

These are the non-mechanical, non-rotary, you-do-all-the-work handheld beaters. Handhelds, always the low-budget beater, range from the ridiculous to super utilitarian.

They include intricate and sometimes silly wire devices, extra pronged forks, slotted spoons, and the whisk.

The first handheld eggbeater patented in America is believed to be by Francis L. King of Worcester, Massachusetts. The Jan. 2, 1866 patent *(fig. 24-1)*, gave a detailed description of the device and then reaffirmed what all hardcore rotary crank collectors believe about handhelds, no matter how intricate: "The instrument is used in the same way that a person would use a fork or a spoon to beat up an egg."

Other American inventors went for the spiral spring bottom. William H. Peirce of Bangor, Maine, patented one March 24, 1868 *(fig. 24-2)* which has survived in one form or another for decades. Peirce's original has the patent date stamped in the wood handle *(fig. 24-3)*.

Said *Practical Housekeeping, A Careful Compilation of Tried and Approved Recipes,* Minneapolis, Minnesota, Buckeye Publishing Company, 1883: "This is a very useful implement in the kitchen, cheaper though not so good as the 'Dover.' The spiral beater does the work well, but not so easily or quickly as the more costly machine."

A green-handle model *(fig. 24-4)* is obviously from the mid-20th century — and a long lost son of the 1868 patent.

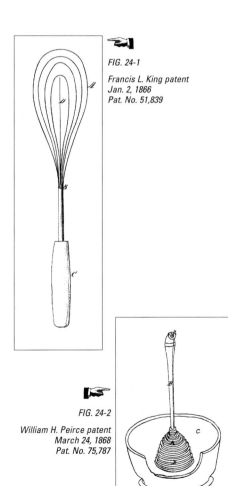

FIG. 24-1

Francis L. King patent
Jan. 2, 1866
Pat. No. 51,839

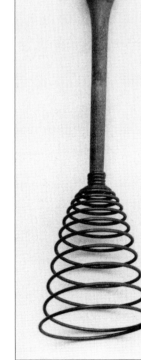

FIG. 24-2

William H. Peirce patent
March 24, 1868
Pat. No. 75,787

FIG. 24-3

MARCH 24, 1868
9-1/2"   —$35—

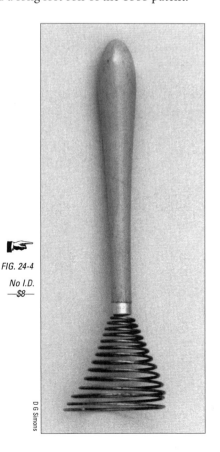

FIG. 24-4

No I.D.
8"   —$8—

D G Simons

D G Simons

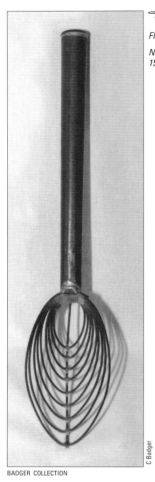

FIG. 24-5

No I.D., but Munson patent
15"   —$85—

C Badger

BADGER COLLECTION

FIG. 24-6

No. I.D., but Munson patent
10"   —$85—

C Badger

BADGER COLLECTION

Wire bent in the shape of a spoon was a popular theme for early handhelds, including an all-metal beauty *(fig. 24-5)* and a similar one with wood handle *(fig. 24-6)* offered in Montgomery Ward & Company's Catalog No. 57: "Spoon Egg Whip, with wood handle. Ea $0.05. Per dozen .40." Both were based on the March 5, 1872 patent *(fig. 24-7)* by David Munson of Indianapolis.

Early handhelds also utilized bent wire in various shapes, including fingers, as over the years the handles shifted from woven wire and tin to wood *(figs. 24-8 through 24-13).*

FIG. 24-7

David Munson patent
March 5, 1872
Pat. No. 124,375

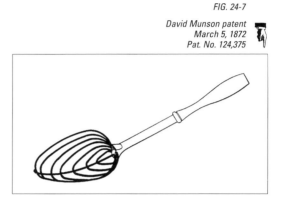

FIG. 24-10

No. I.D., wire spiral
with decorated
tin handle
13"   —$110—

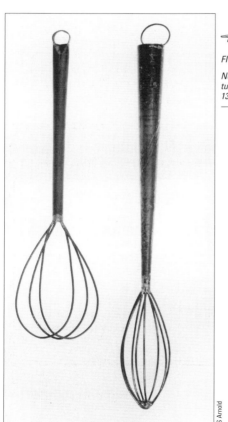

FIG. 24-8

No I.D., bent wire with
tubular tin handles
13" and 14"
—$95 each—

R S Arnold

MAIR COLLECTION

FIG. 24-9

No. I.D., heavy
wire with
woven wire
handle
10-1/4"
—$85—

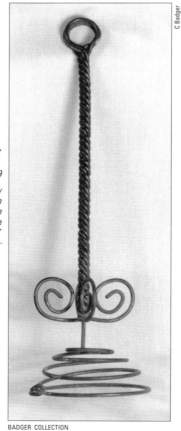

C Badger

BADGER COLLECTION

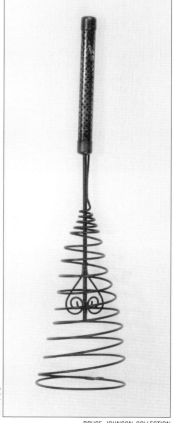

R S Arnold

BRUCE JOHNSON COLLECTION

THE EGGBEATER CHRONICLES

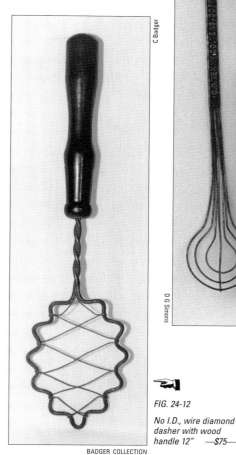

The June 6, 1882 patent *(fig. 24-14)* by Daniel Sherwood of Lowell, Massachusetts, is the mainstay of all stretched wire mixers, the design of which he described as a "truss."

It was followed by similar patents, most notably the March 22, 1887 one *(fig. 24-15)* by William Johnson of Newton, Massachusetts, assignor to the National Manufacturing Company of Worcester, for which he also had patented a dandy rotary mixer *(See Chapter 7, National Manufacturing Co., page 68).*

Sherwood's beater is known as the SURPRISE, one of the few beaters that had its own trade card *(fig. 24-16).*

The SURPRISE was featured in Montgomery Ward and Linington catalogs. Montgomery Ward listed the price at 5¢ each, or 35¢ a dozen. Linington said: "The Surprise. Frame made of heavy wire, with fine wire in center of spoon part; all well retinned; the most popular beater on the market. Put up 1 dozen in package … \$.42."

Over the years, Androck produced similar handhelds, with the added attraction of several being patented by members of the families whose firms evolved into Androck *(See Chapter 17, Androck, page 181).*

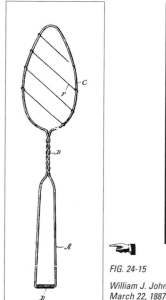
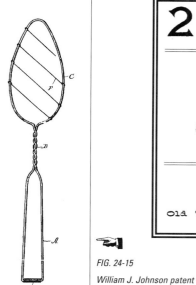

FIG. 24-14

*Daniel Sherwood patent
June 6, 1882
Pat. No. 259,056*

FIG. 24-15

*William J. Johnson patent
March 22, 1887
Pat. No. 359,976*

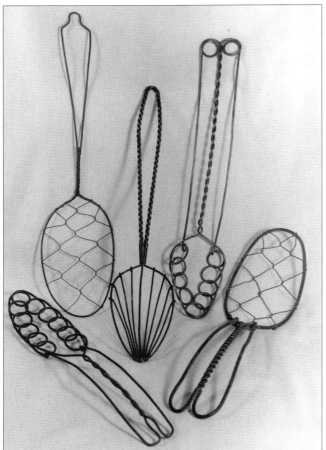

C Badger

BADGER COLLECTION

FIG. 24-17

SURPRISE (far right) and other early wire handhelds —$10 to $65—

The SURPRISE is the best known, but there are dozens of other wire handhelds *(figs. 24-17 through 24-23)*, many in the very rare category and many that are readily available, including a 1959 model with its own patent *(fig. 24-24)*.

R S Arnold

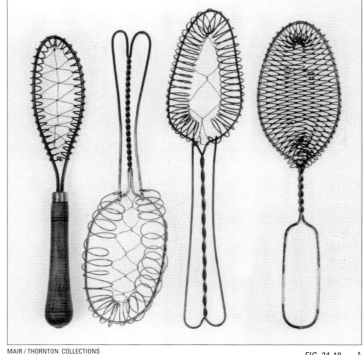

MAIR / THORNTON COLLECTIONS

FIG. 24-18

Wire handhelds (left to right):

No. I.D. spring bottom with diamonds	10-3/8"	—$20—
No. I.D. spring bottom with diamonds	10-1/2"	—$15—
No I.D. spring bottom with diamonds	11-1/4"	—$15—
No I.D., interlocking spring mix	11"	—$15—

D G Simons

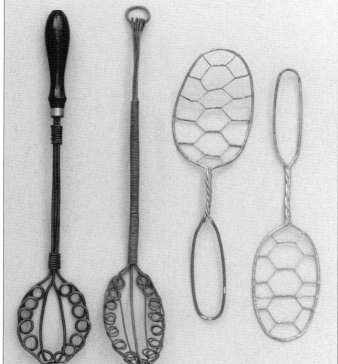

FIG. 24-19

Wire handhelds (left to right):

*No I.D.
13"   —$25—*

*No I.D.
13"   —$35—*

*No I.D. all wire with plastic coated handle
10-1/2"   —$5—*

*No I.D. all wire
10-1/2"   —$5—*

FIG. 24-20

Wire and wood handhelds (left to right)

*No I.D., three fingers
10-3/4"   —$15—*

*No I.D., spring dasher
10-1/4"   —$10—*

**COCOA WHISK
BOURNVILLE**
9-1/4"   —$20—

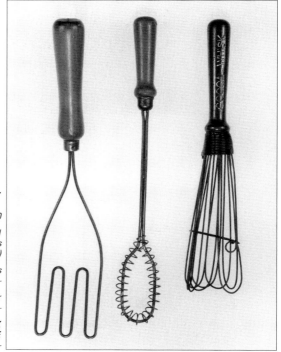

R S Arnold

R S Arnold

MAIR COLLECTION

FIG. 24-21

Wood and woven wire handhelds (left to right)

No I.D.   9-1/4"   —$25—

No I.D.   9-3/4"   —$20—

No I.D.   10-1/2"   —$30—

No I.D., ornate woven wire 10-1/2"   —$75—

No I.D., woven wire 13"   —$45—

R S Arnold

FIG. 24-22

No I.D. but similar design to Cocoa Whisk 14-1/4"   —$45—

MAIR COLLECTION

FIG. 24-23

Tight diamonds, springs and circles and a plastic handle marked **PATENT NO. 2906510** *10-1/4" to 12-1/2" —$5 to $25—*

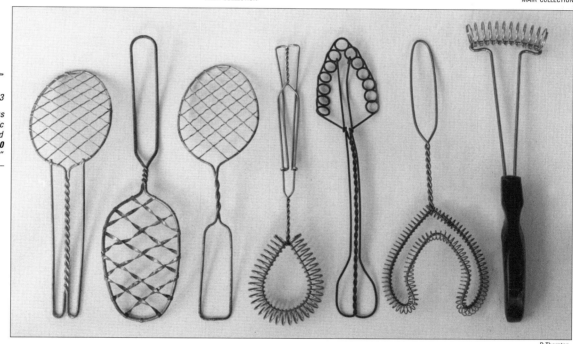

D Thornton

FIG. 24-24

Victoria P. Harris patent Sept. 29, 1959 Pat. No. 2,906,510

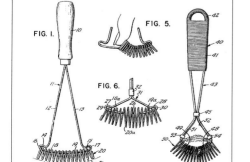

Egg Baking Powder Co. recipe booklet

Ladies! Use that King of baking powders—EGG BAKING POWDER, and you will soon learn that the economy on baking powder and eggs will enable you to use the best of all other material and still be money in pocket.

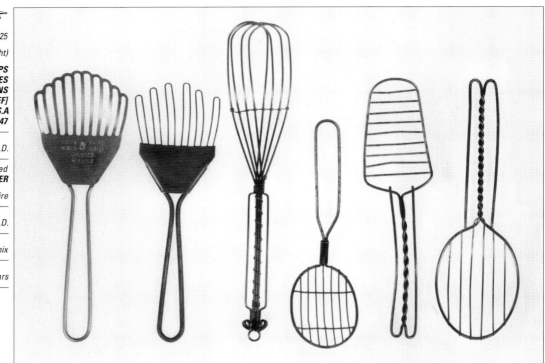

☞

FIG. 24-25

Different mixing designs (left to right)

LIFTS WHIPS
MIXES MASHES
CRUSHES STRAINS
[PICTURE OF INDIAN CHIEF]
MADE IN U.S.A
PAT. NO. D-109,647
10-3/4" —$9—

PAT PEND, *only I.D.*
10-1/4" —$12—
Note: This model is also marked
FORMAY HELPER

No I.D. ornate woven wire
12-1/2" —$45—

No I.D.
9-1/4" —$7—

No I.D., heavy wire, horizontal mix
10-1/2" —$10—

No. I.D. vertical bars
10-12" —$18—

R S Arnold

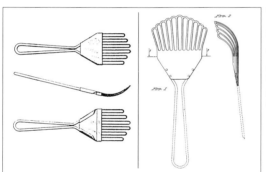

☞

FIG. 24-26

Charles A. Rowley patents (left to right):

Jan. 26, 1937
D-102,959

May 10, 1938
D-109,647

FIG. 24-27

Early wire designs,
all with dish towel holders
13-1/2" to 16"
—$60 to $95— ☞

R S Arnold

MAIR COLLECTION

The variations of design for hand-helds seems endless, including the continuing "finger" theme, vertical and horizontal beating wires, and woven springs as the main mixing elements (*fig. 24-25*). Charles A. Rowley of Los Angeles protected his "finger" design mixers with design patents granted in 1937 and 1939 (*fig. 24-26*).

Continuing the variations of design, simple springs and circles were the basic mixing element for many of the primitive beaters, considered by some collectors to be the most beautiful of all handhelds (*figs. 24-27 & 24-28*).

The bigger, more contemporary, handhelds (*fig. 24-29*), in the 14–15" range, include a spring bottom advertiser, a novel three finger and an all-wire model that could have resulted from a 1949 patent (*fig. 24-30*).

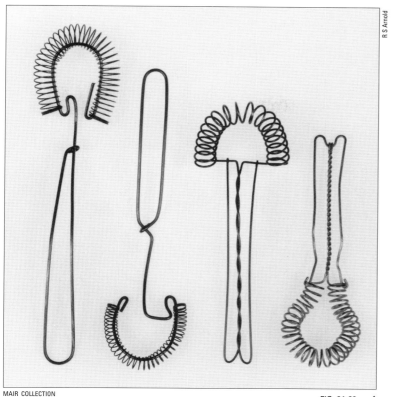

MAIR COLLECTION

R S Arnold

FIG. 24-28

Twisted wire with spring circles
9" to 12-3/4"
—$15 to $30—

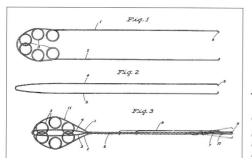

FIG. 24-30

Dewey C. Hughes patent
Sept. 20, 1949
Pat. No. 2,482,587

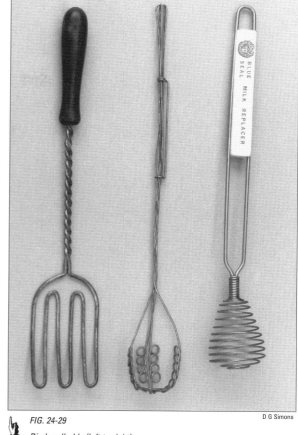

D G Simons

FIG. 24-29

Big handhelds (left to right):

No I.D.   14-1/2"   —$25—

No. I.D. all wire   15"   —$30—

BLUE SEAL MILK REPLACER   *14"   —$20—*

Wesson Oil magazine ads
(left to right):

1921, 1923, 1928

CHAPTER 24: HANDHELD COUSINS

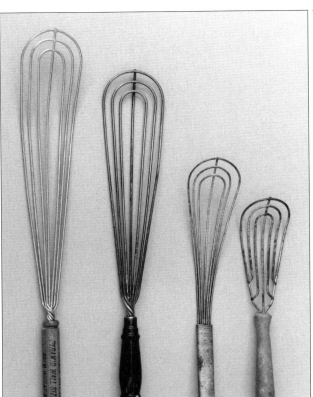

D G Simons

Other long johns include those employing the fan principle. The biggest around, at nearly 17", is partially marked on the wooden handle: PYRAMID DRY PASTE, PYRAMID WALL SIZE, PALM WHEAT PASTE. Yes, a mixer for wall-paper paste.

But as the fans get smaller, it's obvious they are for eggs (*fig. 24-31*), especially the SENSIBLE (*figs. 24-32 & 24-33*), touted as "neat and novel in its construction, superior in workmanship and durability, and embraces all the conveniences of the time-honored spoon and fork, and is far better than either."

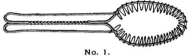

Another popular handheld is the slotted spoon, which was first patented by Eugenia Kilborn of Cedar Rapids, Iowa, on Aug. 5, 1884 (*fig. 24-34*). The slots, Kilborn said, enhanced her device because they allowed the mixing "material ready passage through them."

The oldest slotted spoon is THE VANDEUSEN EGG WHIP (*fig. 24-35*) patented March 13, 1894 by William A. Van Deusen of Brooklyn (*fig. 24-36*).

It was manufactured by C. A. Chapman of Geneva, New York, which was first listed in the *Geneva City Directory* in 1901: "Chapman, Charles A., manufacturer of house-furnishing specialties, 386 Exchange, residence, same." Chapman was last listed in the 1931 directory.

Chapman also offered "Mrs. Van Deusen Cake Molds" in several sizes. And those who purchased a whole set got a bonus, a copy of *The Chapman Scientific Rules and Recipes for Cake Making* pamphlet, which offered the following advice:

"Always use a whip for beating the whites of the eggs, when they are to be used in the cake — rotary beaters will not fill the mass with air cells, and thus make it light — therefore the cake will not rise to the required lightness, and will be heavy. This will be shown more especially in making Angel, Sunshine and Sponge cakes, for these cakes cannot be made successfully when a rotary beater is used for beating the whites of the eggs, used in making same."

Still available are the RUMFORD handhelds (*fig. 24-37*), featuring horizontal and vertical slots. The model with the horizontal slots is the rarer one, but the vertical slot model marked with advertising other than Rumford is also scarce.

The Rumford Chemical Works of Providence, Rhode Island, which made Rumford Baking Powder, took its name from renowned chemist Count Rumford.

Count Rumford was really scientist and political figure Benjamin Thompson (1753-1814), a native of Woburn, Massachusetts, who embraced the Tory cause. He abandoned America the first week of the Revolution and sailed for England, where his war service was recognized later via knighting by George III. But it was his service in Bavaria, for England, that resulted in his title. It was in 1791 that the title Count Rumford was granted. Thompson apparently chose his new name from his wife's American hometown, Rumford (now Concord), New Hampshire.

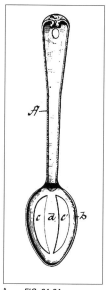

D Thornton

FIG. 24-34

Eugenia Kilborn patent
Aug. 5, 1884
Pat. No. 303,022

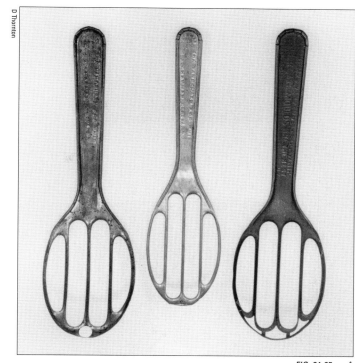

FIG. 24-35

Vandeusens (left to right)

**THE MRS. VANDEUSEN EGG WHIP
HER CAKE MOUNDS ARE THE BEST
C.A. CHAPMAN NY   PATD MAR 13, 1894**
12-/4"   —$30—

**THE VANDEUSEN EGG WHIP
C.A. CHAPMAN, GENEVA, N.Y.   MAR 13 1894**
11"   —$15—

**THE MRS. VANDEUSEN EGG WHIP
HER CAKE MOUNDS ARE THE BEST
C.A. CHAPMAN NY   PATD MAR 13, 1894**
with more open end   12-/4"   —$30—

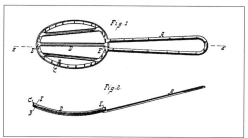

FIG. 24-36

William A. Van Deusen patent
March 13, 1894
Pat. No. 516,415

FIG. 24-37

Slotted handhelds (left to right)

**RUMFORD CAKE MIXER
CREAM WHIP AND EGG BEATER
SALTSMAN'S PAT. APRIL 27 97**
11-1/2"   —$20—

**RUMFORD CAKE MIXER
AND CREAM WHIP
SALTSMAN'S PAT. OCT. 6-08,
IMPROVED ROYAL**
11"   —$35—

VETERAN DUTCH PROCESS COCOA
11-1/2"   —$25—

Note: This model is also marked:
E-A-CO FLOUR WASECA, MIN.

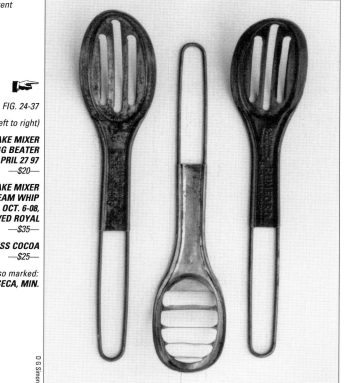

D G Simons

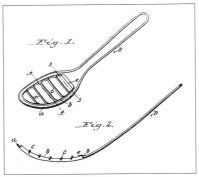

FIG. 24-38
Aaron J. Saltsman patent
April 27, 1897
Pat. No. 581,493

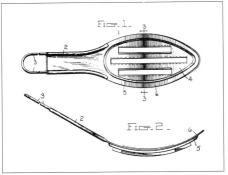

FIG. 24-39
Aaron J. Saltsman patent
Oct. 6, 1908
Pat. No. 900,210

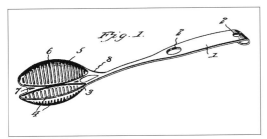

FIG. 24-40
Carrie Bentley patent
March 31, 1903
Pat. No. 724,246

FIG. 24-41
*Handheld utility and swivel head
mixers (left to right)*

IDEAL BEATER
MAR. 31, 1903 9-1/4" —$20—

B-M SPOON CO. PAT. APRIL 21, 1908
HAVERHILL, MASS. 12" —$25—

"WHIRLPOOL" PAT PEND 11-1/2" —20—

**SNOW-MELLOW
BEAT VERY STIFF BEFORE ADDING SUGAR**
11-3/4" —$15—

PAT. 11-24-14
**FROM E. J. BRODELL GROCERY 880 NATIONAL AVE.
MILWAUKEE, WIS.,** *with bottle opener*
11" —$25—

**THE NEW STIRRING SPOON PAT. JAN. 22, 1901
AMERICAN MFG. CO. ANOKA MINN. U.S.A.,**
nicknamed the "stand up spoon" 12" —$55—

*No I.D., swivel head masher and mixer.
With disk in horizontal position, it is a masher.
With disk in vertical position with handle,
it stirs and mixes*
10-3/4" —$30—

The Rumford firm offered various premiums into the 1930s, including its cake mixer, cream whip and eggbeater patented April 27, 1897 *(fig. 24-38)* by Aaron J. Saltsman, who listed his home towns over the years as Albany, Buffalo and Chicago.

Saltsman had two other mixer patents. One was granted Oct. 6, 1908 *(fig. 24-39)*, another spoon model with vertical slots, which Saltsman noted could also be used as a fish-scaler, and the other July 10, 1894, a syllabub churn *(See Chapter 19, Syllabub Churns and Other Plungers, page 206)*.

The so-called "skeleton" spoon is marked IDEAL BEATER. It was patented March 31, 1903 *(fig. 24-40)* by Carrie Bentley of Lincoln, Illinois, who said the "transversely-extended slots" mean the mixing "material is thus soon finely divided, and the labor of beating the egg is reduced to the minimum." The IDEAL BEATER is at the top of the list of utility handheld mixers, which include the B-M SPOON, WHIRLPOOL, SNOW-MELLOW and swivel heads *(fig. 24-41)*.

R S Arnold

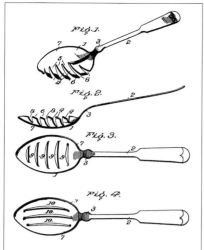

FIG. 24-42
Alonzo W. Cram patent
April 21, 1908
Pat. No. 885,444

FIG. 24-43

1876 Haverhill City
Directory ad

The B-M SPOON was patented in 1908 by Alonzo W. Cram of Haverhill, Massachusetts (fig. 24-42). His device, Cram said, "is provided with blades or fingers set at an angle to the body of the spoon and causing a greater agitation of the material being mixed." Cram, who died at the age of 73 in 1913, was a prolific inventor, as evidenced by an ad in the 1876 *Haverhill City Directory (fig. 24-43).*

SNOW-MELLOW mixtures were offered for cake fillings, meringues for pies, pudding and desserts, frostings and candies. A 1913 recipe booklet for the Chicago firm *(fig. 24-44)* offered the SNOW-MELLOW beater as a premium for a 2 cent stamp.

A 1914 patent date *(fig. 24-45)* graces a slotted spoon mixer given as a premium by E. J. Brodell Grocery, and, for that matter, by any other business that purchased them in bulk. The design patent by John L. Sommer of the J. L. Sommer Manufacturing Company of Newark, New Jersey, was for a "combined bottle opener and cake turner" but apparently adapted to a slotted spoon.

Luther C. Farmer of Minneapolis, Minnesota in 1901 patented what he called a "kettle or dish cleaner &c." *(fig. 24-46)* with a swivel disk that "readily adjusts itself ... to reach any desired portion of the surface" to be cleaned. The American Manufacturing Company of Anoka, Minnesota took Farmer's concept and made it into a stand-up spoon. With the bottom disk locked into a horizontal position, the spoon stands by itself. With the disk shifted to a vertical position with the handle, it is THE NEW STIRRING SPOON.

John A. Swope Jr. of Union Deposit, Pennsylvania, took the spoon mixer (this one without slots) to new heights in the trademark he obtained in 1928 *(fig. 24-47).* His trademark was for "cake beaters and mixers" and the trade name — HUMAN HAND CAKE BEATER — was obviously truth in advertising for the time period.

FIG. 24-44
1913 Snow Mellow "Goodies"
recipe booklet

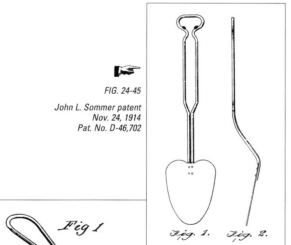

FIG. 24-45
John L. Sommer patent
Nov. 24, 1914
Pat. No. D-46,702

FIG. 24-47
U.S. Patent & Trademark Office
Official Gazette, July 17, 1928
Human Hand Cake Beater Co.
trademark

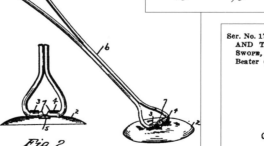

FIG. 24-46
Luther C. Farmer patent
Jan. 22, 1901
Pat. No. 666,633

Ser. No. 177,333. (CLASS 23. CUTLERY, MACHINERY,
AND TOOLS, AND PARTS THEREOF.) JOHN A.
SWOPE, Jr., doing business as Human Hand Cake
Beater Co., Union Deposit, Pa. Filed Mar. 12, 1923.

Particular description of goods.—Cake Beaters and
Mixers.
Claims use since Oct. 25, 1922.

One of the best ever handhelds was patented Dec. 19, 1922 (fig. 24-48) by Agnes C. Hayward of Chicago.

"I am aware that many different forms of beaters for the purpose specified have been devised and some of them have come into very extensive use, among the best and most widely known beaters being those known to the trade as the 'Dover' and the 'Universal.' I have found in practice, however, that both of these beaters are ineffective as regards the number and size of the air bubbles which it is possible to incorporate into the material by means thereof — or, in other words, as regards the 'lightness' of the material produced thereby."

Her invention? Hayward said it could be "described as a fork, comprising tines arranged to form series positioned in intersecting planes, said planes diverging from each other at an obtuse angle, a desirable angle for general use being about 140 degrees."

As she said, a fork.

And it wasn't the first. Alonzo W. Cram, the inventor behind the B-M SPOON, patented a fork-like device Feb. 19, 1907 (fig. 24-49), which was followed five months later by a similar patent (fig. 24-50) by Mary E. French of Clyde, Ohio This mixer (fig. 24-51) made it to the marketplace but substantially different than the patent.

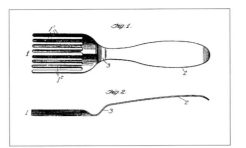

 FIG. 24-48

Agnes C. Hayward patent
Dec. 19, 1922
Pat. No.. 1,439,102

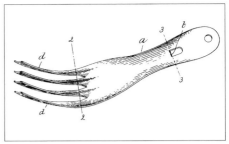

FIG. 24-49

Alonzo W. Cram patent
Feb. 19, 1907
Pat. No. 844,499

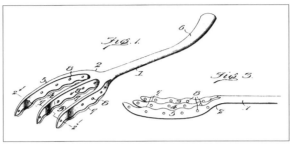

 FIG. 24-50

Mary E. French patent
July 2, 1907
Pat. No. 858,970

 FIG. 24-51

FRENCH EGG BEATER
PAT'D JULY 2, 1907
CLYDE, OHIO
12-3/4"   —$45—

R S Arnold

OLIVARES COLLECTION

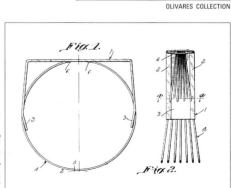 FIG. 24-52

Pastry blenders
(from bottom clockwise):

ANDROCK MADE IN U.S.A.
PAT. 1735236   5-3/4"   —$5—

RAPID SHORTENING MIXER
PAT. PEND.   5-1/4"   —$7—

THE IDEAL PASTRY MIXER
PAT. APLD FOR   5"   —$10—

A&J DOUGH BLENDER
TO BLEND FLOUR WITH
SHORTENING
PATS. NOS. 1486255
1645062 1724356
4-3/4"   —$7—

ANDROCK
MADE IN U.S.A.
5-3/4" —$5—

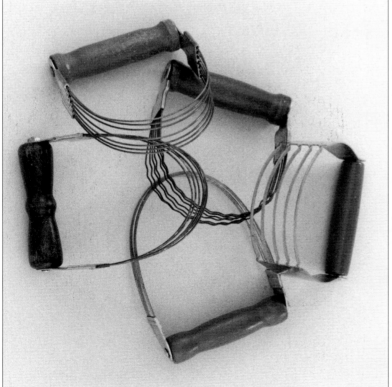

D G Simons

 FIG. 24-53

Clara Birchard
Lambert patent
March 11, 1924
Pat. No. 1,486,255

A whole family of handhelds includes pastry mixers/blenders *(fig. 24-52)*. Clara Birchard Lambert of Pasadena, California, patented three blenders *(figs. 24-53 through 24-55)*, including an all metal model that is very collectible *(fig. 24-56)*. Most of the Lambert metal models are not marked, but there are a few inscribed Lambert Pat. 1486255. In addition to that blender, all three patent dates appear on an A&J blender. Another blender, with diamond wire bottom *(fig. 24-57)* was patented by William L. Hood of Lexington, Massachusetts in 1927 *(fig. 24-58)*.

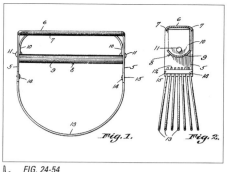

FIG. 24-54

Clara Birchard Lambert patent
Oct. 11, 1927
Pat. No. 1,645,062

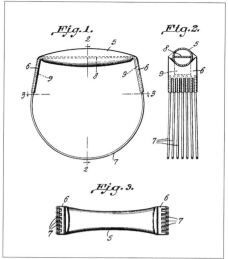

FIG. 24-55

Clara Birchard Lambert patent
Aug. 13, 1929
Pat. No. 1,724,356

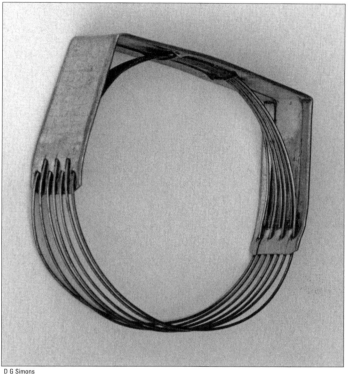

D G Simons

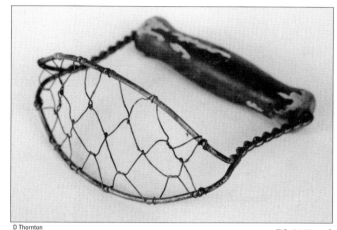

D Thornton

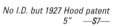

FIG. 24-57

No I.D. but 1927 Hood patent
5"   —$7—

FIG. 24-56

No I.D. but 1924 Lambert patent
4-1/4"   —$15—

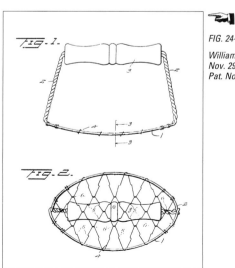

FIG. 24-58

William L. Hood patent
Nov. 29, 1927
Pat. No. 1,651,276

Australians William V. Paley and Thomas H. Bussey patented their chain-bottom handheld in the United States and England. The U.S. patent, No. 771,088, Sept. 27, 1904, noted a truly unique feature — a support disk with a sharp edge against which eggshells could be broken. This mixer probably was made in Queensland, Australia, but apparently didn't make its way to the U.S.

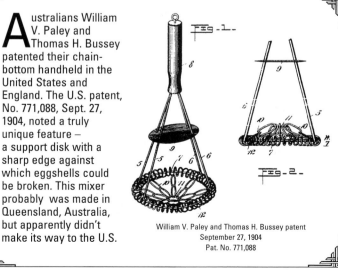

William V. Paley and Thomas H. Bussey patent
September 27, 1904
Pat. No. 771,088

Other blender patents stretched from 1929 to 1944 (figs. 24-59 through 24-63).

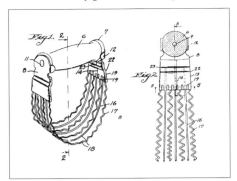

FIG. 24-60
☛ Stewart E. Baker patent
Jan. 31, 1933
Pat. No. 1,895,833

FIG. 24-61
Stewart E. Baker patent
May 23, 1933
Pat. No. 1,910,229 ☛

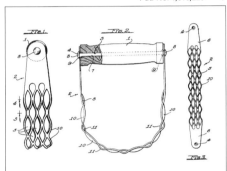

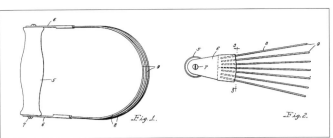

☛ FIG. 24-59
Elmer L. Dennis patent
Nov. 12, 1929
Pat. No. 1,735,236

FIG. 24-62
☛ Charles A. Rowley patent
March 21, 1933
Pat. No. 1,902,525

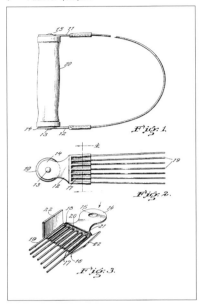

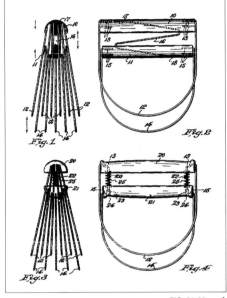

FIG. 24-63 ☛
Homer Gamache patent
Sept. 12, 1944
Pat. No. 2,357,886

FIG. 24-64
☛ Otto A. Hensel design patent
Aug. 13, 1895
Pat. No. D-24,545

R S Arnold

☛ FIG. 24-65
PAT. AUG. 13, 95
9-3/4" —$55—

BOHN COLLECTION

Egg Whips

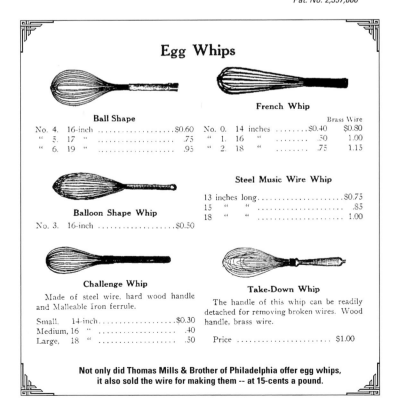

Ball Shape

No. 4.	16-inch	$0.60
" 5.	17 "	.75
" 6.	19 "	.95

Balloon Shape Whip

No. 3. 16-inch $0.50

Challenge Whip

Made of steel wire, hard wood handle and Malleable Iron ferrule.

Small,	14-inch	$0.30
Medium, 16	"	.40
Large,	18 "	.50

French Whip

			Brass Wire
No. 0.	14 inches	$0.40	$0.80
" 1.	16 "	.50	1.00
" 2.	18 "	.75	1.15

Steel Music Wire Whip

13 inches long		$0.75
15 " "		.85
18 " "		1.00

Take-Down Whip

The handle of this whip can be readily detached for removing broken wires. Wood handle, brass wire.

Price $1.00

Not only did Thomas Mills & Brother of Philadelphia offer egg whips, it also sold the wire for making them -- at 15-cents a pound.

MAIR COLLECTION

R S Arnold

FIG. 24-66

AKRON EGG WHIP CO.
PATENT NO. 61421
AKRON, OHIO U.S.A.
11″ —$40—

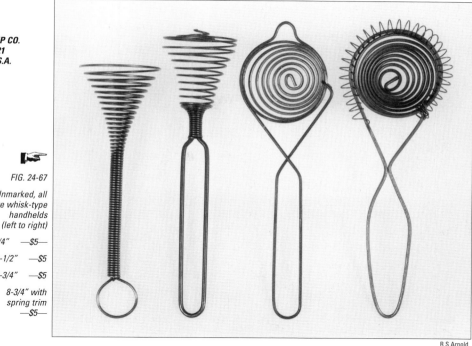

R S Arnold

FIG. 24-67

Unmarked, all
wire whisk-type
handhelds
(left to right)

7-1/4″ —$5—

8-1/2″ —$5—

8-3/4″ —$5—

8-3/4″ with
spring trim
—$5—

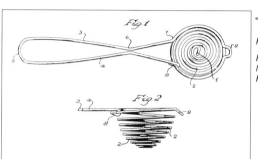

FIG. 24-68

Herbert M. Taylor patent
Nov. 22, 1927
Pat. No. 1,649,874

"The leading feature of my design consists in the form of the propeller-shaped blades at the bottom of a cylindrical shank," said the design patent *(fig. 24-64)* by Otto A. Hensel of Pittsburgh, Pennsylvania. Described as an "egg beater or agitator," at least one was marketed *(fig. 24-65)*.

The Akron Egg Whip Company made its own aluminum handle whisk *(fig. 24-66)* and other all-wire mixers *(fig. 24-67)* have proved popular over several generations, including one patented in 1927 *(fig. 24-68)*. Herbert M. Taylor of Rochester, New York, said his device was "capable of being employed in the kitchen for a large number of different purposes, as for instance, an egg separator, a ladle, a strainer for separating solids from liquids, as a coffee or tea strainer, or for separating fruits and vegetables from liquids and also as a beater for beating up cakes, eggs or whipped cream or the like."

Later handhelds were perfect premium or advertising vehicles *(fig. 24-69)*, a cross-over for collectors, especially with the many dairy ads. A typical one was: "Commemorating Our 25th Anniversary — Rothermel's Dairy." A later handheld featured a spiral bottom and wood handle and was designed to stand by itself *(fig. 24-70)*. It also could be used as a masher *(See Chapter 10, A&J, page 96)*.

D Thornton

FIG. 24-70

MADE IN U.S.A.
(on tin rivet)
9-1/2″ —$7—

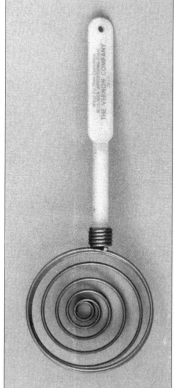

D G Simons

FIG. 24-69

WHIP UP NEW CUSTOMERS
With IDEA ADVERTISING From
THE VERNON COMPANY
8-1/2″ —$5—

FIG. 24-71

No I.D. propeller spoon
11" —$500—

FIG. 24-72

James H. Collins patent
Aug. 3, 1909
Pat. No. 929,917

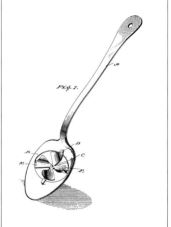

FIG. 24-73

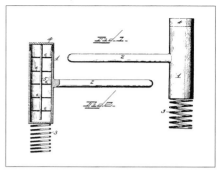

Samuel E. Chapman patent
Aug. 29, 1899
Pat. No. 632,044

The king of handhelds *(fig. 24-71)* was patented Aug. 3, 1909 *(fig. 24-72)* by James H. Collins of Harrisburg, Pennsylvania.

"The beater … consists of a spoon in the bowl of which is pivoted an agitator wheel … formed like a propeller … This construction is such that when the implement is moved rapidly in the operation of beating, the liquid acts upon the vanes to cause the wheel to rotate and thus assist in the beating operation," said the patent.

The propeller spoon has to rank as one of the more offbeat handhelds. But there is a patent for another model that takes the cake *(fig. 24-73)*.

The best description for the Aug. 29, 1899 patent by Samuel E. Chapman of Napa, California, is spring loaded. According to the patent this is how it worked: The hammer part of the beater was a container with a screw-on top.

The eggs were put in and the top screwed down.

"By grasping the handle and rapidly striking the coiled spring on any suitable object the contents of the receptacle will be rapidly and efficiently mixed or agitated. The said spring prevents any injury to the device by reason of the blows struck and also causes the receptacle to rebound after the blows have been struck."

The premier issue of the quarterly **Hardware Buyers Directory** came out in January of 1922. Self-described as the "recognized reference medium of the hardware and allied trades," the directory listed the manufacturers of all kinds of hardware, including beaters. It is interesting to note that even in 1922 the name Dover was used by several companies, despite protests and litigation by the original Dover. It also is interesting to note there are yet to be discovered beaters, including the "Kollins," "Cosmos" and "Rover's." The list, under the heading BEATERS and WHIPS , Egg:

A.&J. Mfg. Co., Binghamton, N.Y. "A.&J."

Air-O-Mix Corp., 51 Beaver, New York, N.Y. "Whip-all"

Bridgeport Wire Goods Co., East Port Chester, Conn.

Browne (W.G.) Mfg. Co., Kingston, N.Y. "Cyclone"

Casey-Hudson Co., 361 E. Ohio, Chicago, Ill. "Dunlap"

Cassady-Fairbanks Mfg. Co., 6126 S. La Salle, Chicago, Ill. "Turbine"

Chapman Co., Geneva, N.Y.

Christy Knife Co., Fremont, O.

Continental Co., Penobscot Bldg., Detroit, Mich.

Darby (Edw.) & Sons Co., 412 N. 18th, Philadelphia, Pa.

Dawson (J.R.) Mfg. Co., Fairhill Sta., Philadelphia, Pa. "Surprise"

Dover Stamping & Mfg. Co., Cambridge, Mass. "Leviathan Dover" "New Dover"

Dunlap, J.S., 334 S. Clinton, Chicago, Ill.

Fries (Geo.) Sons, 222 S. Front, Philadelphia, Pa.

Gilbert (A.C.) Co., New Haven, Conn. "Polar Cub"

Giles & Nielsen Nickel Works, Troy, N.Y. "Clipper"

Hamblin & Russell Mfg. Co., Worcester, Mass. "Dover"

Hollow Cable Mfg. Co., Hornell, N.Y. "Only Perfect"

Holt-Lyon Co., Tarrytown, N.Y. "Holts Improved Dover" "Lyon"

Kohler Die & Specialty Co., De Kalb, Ill.

Landers, Frary & Clark, New Britain, Conn. "Dover"

MacLoed Mfg. Co., 2640 Greenview Av., Chicago, Ill. "Kollins"

Meek Mfg. Oven Co., Newburyport, Mass.

Meyers (Fred J.) Mfg. Co., Hamilton, O.

National Indicator Co., 852 Vernon Av., Brooklyn, N.Y. "S.&S."

National Mfg. Co., Worcester, Mass. "Dover," "French," "Natwire," "Superior," "Surprise"

Novelty Mfg. Co., Waterbury, Conn. "Cosmos"

Parker Wire Goods Co., Worcester, Mass. "Dover"

Parkesburg Stamping & Mfg. Co., Parkesburg, PA. "Up-to-Date"

Racine Iron & Wire Works, Racine, Wis.

Roberts Lightning Mixer Co., 39 Pearl, Boston, Mass. "Roberts"

Roseland Can & Specialty Co., Roxford, Ill. "Double Quick"

Silver & Co., 304 Hewes, Brooklyn, N.Y. "Silver"

Standard Wire Co., New Castle, Pa.

Star Specialty Co., Ashland, O.

Taplin Mfg. Co., New Britain, Conn. "Dover," "Light Running," "Tumbler"

Thurnauer (G.M.) Co., 6 E. 20th, New York, N.Y. "Rover's"

Turner & Seymour Mfg. Co., Torrington, Conn. "T.&S. Dover"

United Royalties Corp., 1133 Broadway, New York, N.Y. "Ladd"

Utility Mfg. Co., 1816 Lancaster, Baltimore, Md.

Wickwire-Spencer Steel Corp., Worcester, Mass. "Diamond"

Wire Goods Co., Worcester, Mass. "Dover"

Wire Hardware Co., 6126 S. La Salle, Chicago, Ill.

Woods-Sherwood Co., Worcester, Mass. "Sensible," "Surprise"

Chapter 25

Play Things

Little mixers for little hands

*E*ven today the eggbeater plays a role in the toy and novelty world. Since the 1920s it has been marketed for tots — and it still is.

There is a potpourri of toys out there for young cooks to-be, in addition to the BETTY TAPLINS *(See Chapter 4, Taplin, page 36)* and A&J BINGOS *(See Chapter 10, A&J, page 105)*. Ranging from battery powered to windup toys to salt and pepper shakers to miniature electric mixers, they can all add a special dimension to any collection *(figs. 25-1 through 25-8)*.

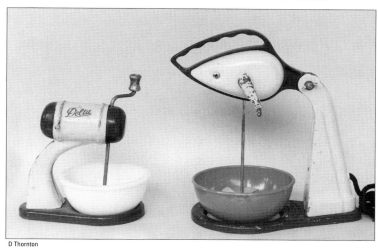

D Thornton

FIG. 25-1

Rotaries (left to right):

DELTA DETROIT
with white milk glass bowl
5" —$45—

LITTLE DEB   MIXER MAKER
NORTHWESTERN PRODUCTS CO.
ST. LOUIS, 3 MO.
PAT. PEND.
8" —$55—

D Thornton

FIG. 25-2

Battery power (left to right):

MIXIT MASTER JR.
1 FOLD 2 STIR 3 MIX 4 BEAT 5 WHIP
EXELO *(on detachable top)* **JAPAN** *(on base)*
battery powered with headlight
7-1/2" —$30—

MIXEE-MIXER *(on detachable top)*
JAPAN *(on top and base)*
pink and black; battery powered with headlight
6-3/4" —$35—

D Thornton

FIG. 25-3

Plastic mixers (left to right):

MADE IN CHINA *(on sticker)*
Pink plastic with lever for power
5-1/4" —$7—

SUZY HOMEMAKER
CAT. NO. 2014 D.L.T. CORP ©1968
MADE BY DE LUXE TOPPER CORPORATION
ELIZABETH, NEW JERSEY U.S. OF AMERICA PAT. PENDING
TOPPER *(on detachable top)*
turquoise and white battery powered
9" —$35—

D Thornton

FIG. 25-4 (left to right):

No I.D. relatively new windup
2-1/4" —under $5—

No. I.D. pewter mixers and beater from
relatively new doll house collection
7/8" to 1-1/4" —under $5—

No. I.D. relatively new windup
2-1/2" —under $5—

D Thornton

FIG. 25-5

Salt and pepper shakers

(left and right): **PAT. PEND.**
black and white salt and pepper
shakers in detachable dashers
(open & closed positions)
4-1/2" —$10—

(middle): **STYLE 485 FIVE & DIME 1987
WNY N.J. 07093**
pink and black salt and pepper shakers in
detachable dashers 6-1/2" —$25—

D Thornton

FIG. 25-6
WILTON WOODRIDGE
relatively new Big
Bird
10" —$35—

FIG. 25-8

**GOWI
MADE IN AUSTRIA**
7-1/2" —$5—

D Thornton

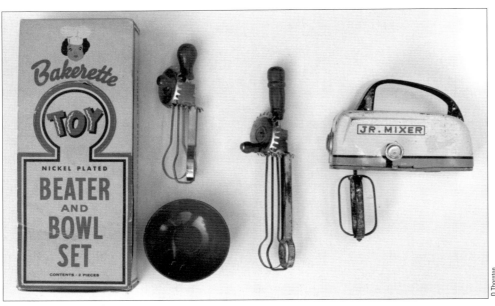

D Thornton

FIG. 25-7 (left to right):
**BAKERETTE TOY NICKEL PLATED BEATER AND BOWL SET
CONTENTS 2 PIECES BAKER MANUFACTURING COMPANY COLUMBIA, PENNSYLVANIA** (on box)
4-1/2" beater (next to box); 2-1/2" diameter bowl —$40—

BAL-SO 6-1/2" —$20—

JR. MIXER JAPAN push-button ratchet 5" —$10—

The Charles Wm. Doepke Manufacturing Company of Cincinnati, Ohio
produced the MARY MIX EGG BEATER
for kids two to five years old. The box
for this toy beater *(fig. 25-9)*, says in
part: "A child can whip up a lot of fun
in a hurry with this colorful wooden-toy
version of a fascinating kitchen tool.
Encourages imitative play, develops
wrist and hand muscle, illustrates
principles of gear action."

FIG. 25-9
DOEPKE
10-1/2"
—$10—

D Thornton

Chapter 26

International Mix

Bon appétit!

The rotary crank and the Archimedes weren't limited to the United States. Australian, Canadian, English, French, and German beaters continually turn up in the U.S. and become part of collections.

The market for foreign beaters is mixed, and prices can be tricky. A good guide would be to try to pay what you would for a similar American beater.

One of the rarest and most unique foreign beaters is a French water-power, a stand-up model with its own base (fig. 26-1).

Other, more common foreign rotaries are more wavy and wiggly than their American counterparts, and range from cast-iron to stamped metal to lots of heavy-duty wire to plastic/Bakelite and at least one English plunger (figs. 26-2 through 26-14).

D Thornton

FIG. 26-2

No I.D. wavy bottom twins   9-1/2"   —$45
Note: Some models are marked
GERMANY on the dashers

D G Simons

GRIFFITHS COLLECTION

FIG. 26-1
**BATTEUR
AUTOMATIQUE
CIGOGNE**
12"   —$900—

FIG. 26-3

Rotaries (left to right):

**"BUNNY"
MADE IN ENGLAND
REGD DES NO. 852764 PAT. APDD FOR**
9-1/2"   —$50—

**SKYLINE
MADE IN BURNEY, ENGLAND**
10-1/2"   —$10—

No I.D.   11-1/2"   —$12—

**"NUTBROWN"
MADE IN ENGLAND**
11"   —$25—

D G Simons

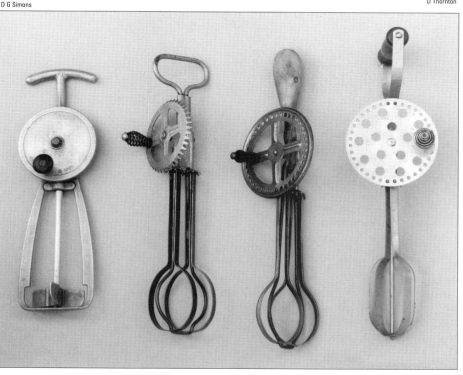

FIG. 26-5

French models (left to right):

No. I.D.
20″ —$600—

 No I.D.
12″ —$145—

☞

FIG. 26-6

Rotaries (left to right):

No I.D. believed German
14-1/2″ —$100—

No I.D. but French
12-1/2″ —$200—

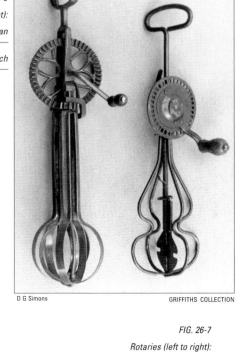

D G Simons   GRIFFITHS COLLECTION

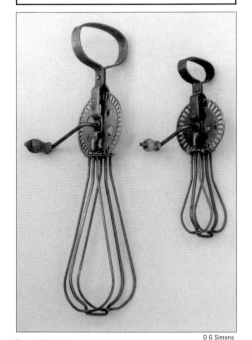

D G Simons

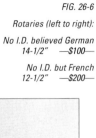 *FIG. 26-4*

French Quarters (left to right):

QUARTER BTE SGDG
11-1/2″ —$30—

No I.D., but smallest QUARTER
7″ —$100—

D G Simons

GRIFFITHS COLLECTION

FIG. 26-7

Rotaries (left to right):

**CBM BATTEURS EROIDES
SGDG BREVETE MAYONNAISE TOUJOUR
CREME CHANTILLY REUSSIS**
12″ —$45—

NEIGE ROK 11-1/2″ —$18—

BTE SGDG 1921 11-3/4″ —$25—

Unreadable markings on wheel, fork bottom
12″ —$35—

No I.D. but markings on main shaft 13″ —$75—

No I.D. but markings on main shaft 13″ —$75—

MARDUE DEICSEE
11-1/2″ —$30—

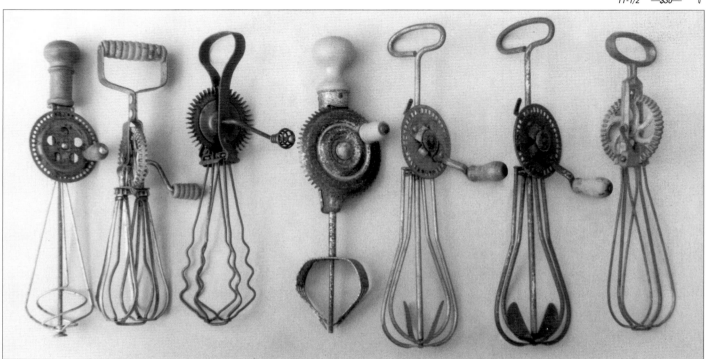

D G Simons

THE EGGBEATER CHRONICLES

FIG. 26-8

D G Simons

Rotaries (left to right):

HIGH SPEED CENTRE DRIVE MADE IN ENGLAND PAT. APLD FOR 12-1/4" —$10—

BEATRICE EGG BEATER MADE IN ENGLAND NO. 2999 10-1/2" —$35—

FISHER PATENT PENDING MADE IN CANADA 12-1/2" —$15—

SWIFT WHIP A PROPERT PRODUCT MADE IN AUSTRALIA PATENT BALL DRIVER 13" —$40—

BREVETE BATTEUR "ELSA" MARQUE DEPOSEE S.G.D.G. 11" —$30—

BEMAR 11-1/2" —$15—

PAT. NO. 706803/8 only I.D. but Canadian 10-3/4" —$35—

FIG. 26-11

No I.D., wire frame
10-3/4" —$45—

FIG. 26-9

**GOODALLS
IMPROVED EGG WHISK**
9-1/2" —$150—

FIG. 26-10

No I.D., heavy brass
beater with funnel
attached, wire
dashers look French,
but could be English
or American
16-1/2"
—$550—

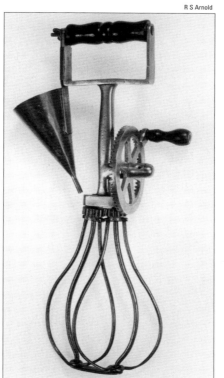

R S Arnold

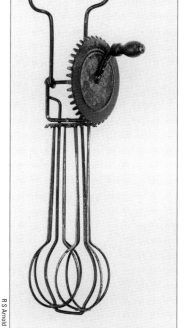

R S Arnold

D G Simons

GRIFFITHS COLLECTION

MAIR COLLECTION

OLIVARES COLLECTION

R S Arnold

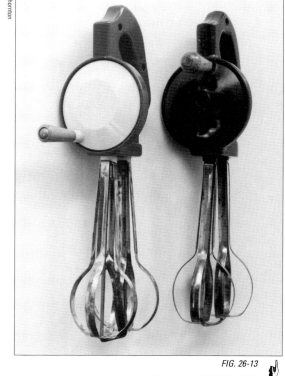

D Thornton

 FIG. 26-12

Canadian and English (left to right)

MASTER MIX MADE IN CANADA 12-1/2" —$12—

MACDONALD MADE IN CANADA 11-1/2" —$6—

U.K. DESIGN REGISTRATION NO. 1013301 10" —$10—

FIG. 26-15

Archimedes (left to right):

No I.D. but believed English with plastic handle
10-1/4" —$7—

No I.D., but English, early paper label
says **ONE HAND UTILITY WHIP**
12" —$10—

STEELCRAFT, GERMANY, BRITISH ZONE
9-1/2" —$10—

 **THE WHIP-IT HARTLEY PRODUCT
MADE IN ENGLAND REG. DES 848217**
10-3/4" —$12—

FIG. 26-13

German plastic (left to right):

GLORIA EVPW.50M, purchased new
in East Germany in 1982
10" —$20—

GLORIA D.A.P. WFW, same GLORIA family
but much earlier version
with Bakelite-type plastic
10" —$55—

FIG. 26-14

**THE "LIGHTNING" EGG-BEATER
GRAFTON'S SIZE 1 PATENT 11075**
white porcelain container
9" high —$75—

R S Arnold

MAIR COLLECTION

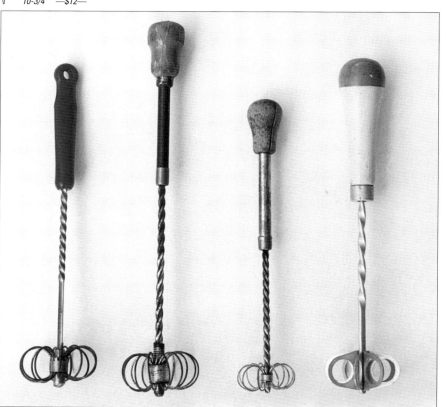

D Thornton

THE EGGBEATER CHRONICLES

The French and the English were partial to Archimedes beaters, producing models ranging from the simple to the exotic, including the NUTBROWN (figs. 26-15 through 26-18).

☞

FIG. 26-16

*Circle dashers
(left to right):*

No I.D.
11″   —$55—

No. I.D.
9-1/4″   —$55—

FIG 26-18

Archimedes (left to right):

DRGM
12″   —$35—

No I.D.
10-3/4″   —$25—

BATVIT BTE S.G.D.G.
12″ fully extended   —$35—

No I.D.
13-3/4″   —$20—

No I.D.
11-1/2″   —$20—

MADE IN FRANCE
12-1/4″   —$40—

No I.D. Archimedes side handle
12-1/2″   —$65—

**NUTBROWN INSTANT WHISK
REG. DES. NO. 888928
MADE IN ENGLAND**
13-3/4″   —$70—

FIG. 26-17

No I.D.
11″   —$95—

BADGER COLLECTION

C Badger

D G Simons

GRIFFITHS COLLECTION

D G Simons

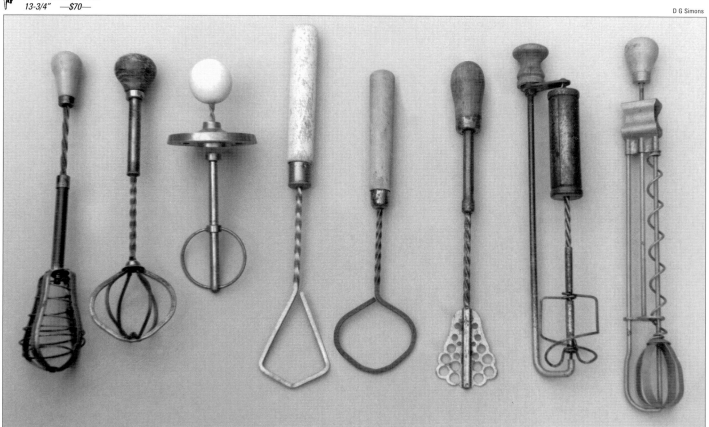

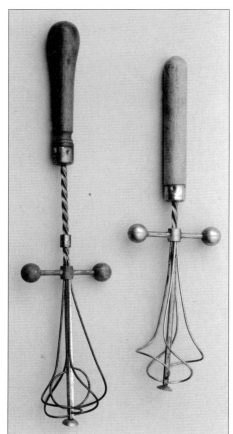

FIG. 26-19

Fly-wheels (left to right):

CORDON BLEU BTE. S.G.D.G.
15" fully extended   —$100—

No I.D.
15" fully extended   —$100—

D G Simons

FIG. 26-20

House Furnishing Review ad August, 1938

Courtesy Jos. Import Co.

Springless Eggbeater
Automatic action, no springs, free ratchet movement are features of "Spirit" eggbeater.

The CORDON BLEU *(fig. 26-19)* was imported to America by Joseph Import Company of New York City under the name SPINIT. A 1938 *House Furnishing Review (fig. 26-20)* look at new products said: "Light downward strokes on handle spin the wires with two solid balls giving swing and power."

The English patent *(fig. 26-21)* for the PROBUS *(fig. 26-22)* was granted to William and Henry Probert March 30, 1922. The two men, apparently brothers, said they were associated with Aero Works, Smith Street, Hockley, Birmingham, and that their device "comprises improvements in whisks of the archimedean type." Their Aero Works is believed responsible for the HORLICK'S AERO *(See Chapter 12, Archimedes, page 137).*

FIG. 26-23

VITUS
11"   —$210—

D G Simons

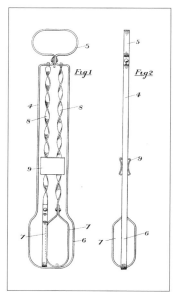

Fig 1   Fig 2

FIG. 26-21

William and Henry Probert English patent March 30, 1922 Pat. No. 177,384

FIG. 26-22

"PROBUS"
PATENT 177,384
MADE IN ENGLAND
11"   —$100—

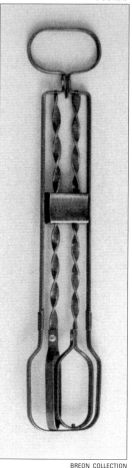

BREON COLLECTION

MAIR COLLECTION

FIG. 26-24

English Archimedes (left to right:)

PAT APPLD FOR MADE IN ENGLAND
9" —$45—

No I.D.
12" —$65—

D G Simons

MOFFET COLLECTION

R S Arnold

FIG. 26-25

MADE IN ENGLAND
disks with star cutouts
8-3/4" —$55—

OLIVARES COLLECTION

A heavy-duty ratchet model from France, the VITUS, featured an unusual center gear *(fig. 26-23)* and other English Archimedes came with floppy disks with circle and star cutouts *(figs. 26-24 through 26-26).*

The English also are believed to be manufacturers of elegant mayonnaise makers with bone china bowls and tin tops *(fig. 26-27).* These came in two sizes with the smaller version, with the bowl 3-1/4" high, featured in an early sales booklet by The Boston Cooking School Magazine Company *(fig. 26-28).*

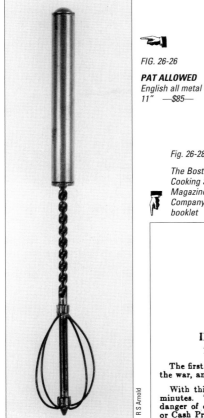

FIG. 26-26

PAT ALLOWED
English all metal
11" —$85—

Fig. 26-28

The Boston Cooking School Magazine Company sales booklet

R S Arnold

MAIR COLLECTION

Fig. 26-27

No I.D. on the two sizes of mayo mixers, but believed to be English 4-1/2" & 3-1/4" to top of containers —$150 each—

D Thornton

GRIFFITHS COLLECTION

IMPORTED MAYONNAISE MIXER

Nickel Plated with Decorated China Bowl

The first time we could offer this beautiful and useful article since the war, and at a lower price.

With this mixer you can make an excellent mayonnaise in five minutes. The oil is added automatically, drop by drop, avoiding all danger of curdling. Sent, prepaid, for two (2) new subscriptions or Cash Price, $1.50.

Early Pacific Egg Food trade card

FIG. 26-29

No I.D. but
"ROCKINGHAM" GLASS CHURN
according to instruction sheet
11-1/4" —$75—

BECKWITH COLLECTION

FIG. 26-30

Paper label says in part: **FUPA "VITESSE-MAYONNAISE"**
MADE IN FRANCE *(embossed on jar)*
funnel has unique wire stirrer
10" overall —$500—

English, French and German glass bottom churns have proven popular with American collectors *(See Chapter 13, Dazey and Other Churns),* and a small English churn — designed to turn one-half pound of butter into one pound — is no exception. An instruction sheet that came with the unmarked churn identified it as the "ROCKINGHAM" GLASS CHURN *(fig. 26-29)* The instruction sheet said in part: "Cut 1/2-pound of butter into thin slices and put this with 1/2-pint of milk into the jar, adding 1/2-tea-spoon full of fine salt or according to taste … fix on the lid and turn the handle quickly until the butter and milk are thoroughly mixed."

Smaller than the ROCKINGHAM is a French mayo mixer, the FUPA "VITESSE-MAYONNAISE" *(fig. 26-30).* It stands only 10" high (the jar is 5"), but it commands a hefty price, with one of the attractions being the heart cutouts on the main gear. The jar is embossed MADE IN FRANCE, meaning it met then requirements for importation to the U.S.

This heavy-duty bread mixer is of English or Australian origin. Marked only PAT ALLOWED, it is 14" high fully extended and fits on a bowl 11" in diameter.

Pineapple Bavarian Cream

Dissolve a package of Lemon Jell-o into mixer bowl with a half pint of boiling water and add a half pint of pineapple juice. When cool and just as Jell-o starts to set, beat to consistency of whipped cream and quickly fold in one cup of the crushed pineapple, add 2 cups whipped and sweetened cream. Pour into mold and set in a cool place to harden. Turn from mold and garnish with sliced pineapple and cherries or grapes.

—NIAGARA MIXER COMPANY BROCHURE, 1928

The Soufflé

For 4 to 6 servings, smoothly blend 2 tablespoons butter or margarine, 3 tablespoons flour, 1/4 teaspoon powdered mustard, 1/8 teaspoon pepper and 3/4 teaspoon salt in a pint saucepan. Gradually add 1 cup milk; stir until boiling. Cool 5 minutes. Add 3/4 cup minced cooked chicken, ham, luncheon meat or tuna, or use 3/4 cup graded or processed sharp American cheese.

Separate 5 eggs: beat the yolks until creamy. Mix with the sauce. With an egg beater, beat the 5 egg whites stiff, then beat in 1/2 teaspoon baking powder. Fold the egg-yolk mixture into the beaten whites. Turn into an ungreased 2-quart baking dish; bake 1 hour in a very moderate oven (325°-350°F). Serve at once with a thin tomato sauce.

—ALL ABOUT EGGS, BY IRMA BAILY ALLEN, 1956

Chapter 27

Electric Mixers

The shocking end.

A hint of the beginning of the end came as early as Nov. 17, 1885 when Rufus M. Eastman of Boston was granted a patent *(fig. 27-1)* for a "mixer for creams, eggs and liquors."

Unbeknownst to Eastman, his patent No. 330,829 is believed to be the first for an electric mixer.

"My invention has for its object the construction of a device, which may be connected to a table or other convenient structure and operated by a motor, for mixing in a suitable vessel creams, eggs, liquors, &c.

"My invention does not include any particular motor for furnishing power, as I can use any of the well-known motors — either spring, weight, water or electric — as may be most convenient or desirable."

Neither spring, weight, water nor electric for this particular invention came about. Eastman's patent ended up only a patent.

It wasn't until the turn of the century that the real glut of electric beater patents came about.

The first few are worth noting:
▶ Michael W. Hall of San Francisco patented an electric mixer April 6, 1909 *(fig. 27-2)* that obviously was and is, the world's highest. If a regular eggbeater is a one-story motel, this model would be an eight-story hotel.

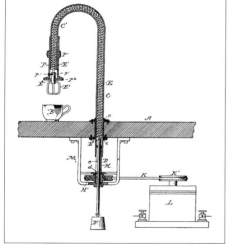

FIG. 27-1

Rufus M. Eastman patent
Nov. 17, 1885
Pat. No. 330,829

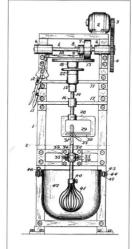

FIG. 27-2

Michael W. Hall patent
April 6, 1909
Pat. No. 917,289

▶ The heavy-duty mindset was continued with the Aug. 9, 1910 killer *(fig. 27-3)* by Harry Read of York, Pennsylvania.

▶ And on the same date, Wilhelm Wenk of Switzerland presented his elaborate "whisking machine" *(fig. 27-4)*.

Since these mixer behemoths never made it to the market, the field was left wide open for three men who got their start with an electric vibrator company. It was in 1910 that Chester A. Beach, L. H. Hamilton and Fred Osius founded the Hamilton Beach Manufacturing Company in Racine, Wisconsin.

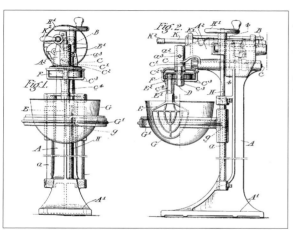

FIG. 27-3

Harry Read patent
Aug. 9, 1910
Pat. No. 966,765

FIG. 27-4

Wilhelm Wenk patent
Aug. 9, 1910
Pat. No. 966,501

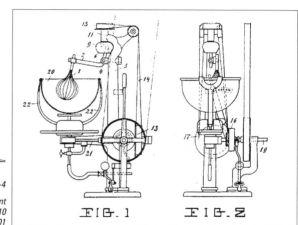

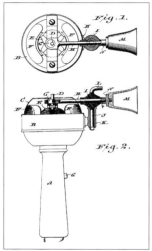

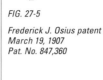

FIG. 27-5

Frederick J. Osius patent
March 19, 1907
Pat. No. 847,360

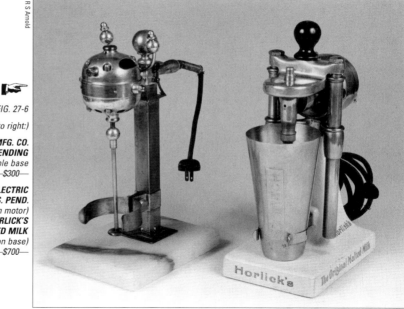

R S Arnold

FIG. 27-6

Early malt mixers (left to right:)

HAMILTON-BEACH MFG. CO.
RACINE, WIS. PATENTS PENDING
(on motor), with marble base
13-1/2" —$300—

DUMORE WISCONSIN ELECTRIC
RACINE WIS. PATS. PEND.
(on motor)
HORLICK'S
THE ORIGINAL MALTED MILK
(on base)
14" —$700—

MAIR COLLECTION

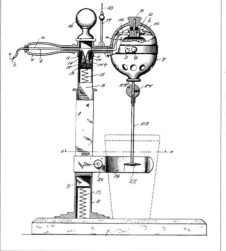

FIG. 27-7

Frederick J. Osius patent
Oct. 10, 1911
Pat. No. 1,005,653

FIG. 27-8

U.S. Patent & Trademark Office
Official Gazette, Feb. 10, 1920
Hobart Manufacturing Company
trademark for FountainAid

U.S. Patent & Trademark Office
Official Gazette, April 6, 1920
Hobart Manufacturing Company
trademark for KitchenAid

U.S. Patent & Trademark Office
Official Gazette, July 20, 1920
Hobart Manufacturing Company
trademark for BakersAid

Ser. No. 125,751. (CLASS 21. ELECTRICAL APPA-RATUS, MACHINES, AND SUPPLIES.) THE HOBART MANUFACTURING COMPANY, Troy, Ohio. Filed Dec. 9, 1919.

FountainAid

Particular description of goods.—Electrically-Driven Beating and Mixing Machines.
Claims use since Oct. 14, 1919.

Ser. No. 126,517. (CLASS 21. ELECTRICAL APPARA-TUS, MACHINES, AND SUPPLIES.) THE HOBART MANUFACTURING COMPANY, Troy, Ohio. Filed Dec. 27, 1919.

KitchenAid

Particular description of goods.—Electrically-Driven Beating and Mixing Machines.
Claims use since Nov. 25, 1919.

Ser. No. 133,144. (CLASS 21. ELECTRICAL APPARA-TUS, MACHINES, AND SUPPLIES.) THE HOBART MANUFACTURING COMPANY, Troy, Ohio. Filed June 1, 1920.

BakersAid

Particular description of goods.—Electrically-Driven Beating and Mixing Machines.
Claims use since Apr. 27, 1920.

The three, all at one time associated with the Arnold Electric Company, a vibrator concern, are believed to be the first to produce an electric drink mixer.

Osius, apparently the mechanic brains behind the firm, was granted one of the first patents for an electric vibrator, or massaging implement, as he called it. His device, he said in his March 19, 1907 patent *(fig. 27-5)*, would "provide simple, economical, compact, light, durable, and efficient portable massaging implements each organized to have the manipulating device thereof either oscillative and reci-procative or simply oscillative, as may be preferred from time to time in practice."

Osius' mixing triumph *(fig. 27-6)* came with his Oct. 10, 1911 patent *(fig. 27-7)*. "The primary object of my invention is to provide a portable electric motor-driven mixing implement for liquid beverages, compounds or the like, the construction and arrangement of the implement being such that the stem of an agitator disk is directly and rigidly coupled to a protrud-ing end of the motor-shaft …"

By 1920, the Hobart Manufacturing Company of Troy, Ohio, was producing electric beaters, and at the same time covering all its bases. In that year it received trademarks for the names of three "electrically-driven beating and mixing machines" *(fig. 27-8)*.

One prolific electric mixer inventor got his start with a handheld shaker. Raymond B. Gilchrist of Newark, New Jersey, assignor to the Gilchrist Com-pany, patented a shaker Oct. 17, 1916 *(fig. 27-9)*, saying his mixer had "an improved egg-breaking device which is simple in construction and which can be readily cleansed so that it will be sanitary and which efficiently serves to disinte-grate and mix the contents of the receptacle."

Gilchrist later went on a patent ram-page, being granted seven on Aug. 21, 1923 *(fig. 27-10)*, all for his drink mixer.

A major electric beater patent date is Nov. 21, 1933 *(fig. 27-11)* for an "electric cream whipper and drink mixer" by Irving Nachumsohn of Chicago.

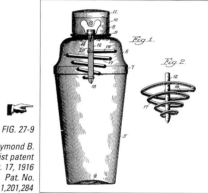

FIG. 27-9

Raymond B. Gilchrist patent Oct. 17, 1916 Pat. No. 1,201,284

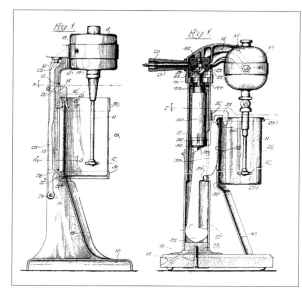

FIG. 27-10

Raymond B. Gilchrist patent
Aug. 21, 1923
representative of all seven patents
on the same date
Pat. Nos. 1,465,629 through 1,465,635

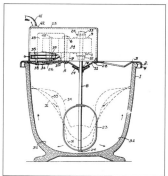

FIG. 27-11
Irving Nachumsohn patent
Nov. 21, 1933
Pat. No. 1,935,857

One object of his patent was "to provide a device of the character described which obviates the necessity of employing different mixing attachments for mixing substances of different consistencies; for, by virtue of the size and shape of the mixing paddle and particularly certain power characteristics of the driving motor, only one simple and easily cleaned paddle need be provided."

Long winded, but at least two manufacturers agreed — Vidrio of Cicero, Illinois, and Knapp Monarch of St. Louis, both citing that patent date for their early mixers.

An ad *(fig. 27-12)* for another model based on the same patent listed the price at $1.98 and encouraged you to say "goodbye to the old-fashioned egg-beating!"

The subsequent patents and products *(figs. 27-13 through 27-26)* over the years by Vidrio, Knapp-Monarch, Hamilton Beach, General Electric, Consolidated Electric and many others meant the beginning of the shocking end of the popularity of the rotary hand crank eggbeater.

FIG. 27-12

1930s newspaper ad

FIG. 27-13

Joseph M. Vogel patent
Feb. 10, 1925
Pat. No. 1,525,967
(This for an improvement in the "commutator connection," or revolving part in a motor that carries the current)

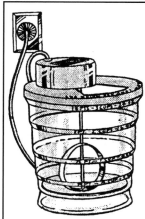

Electric Mixers

—a new model
—a new size
—at a new price

$1.98

Made to Sell for $2.98

Good-bye to the old-fashioned egg-beater! Here's a new little mixer that's going to be a big help in beating mayonnaise, dressings, whipped cream, beverages and other liquids that need mixing! Stainless steel, with a green glass bowl.

(Fifth Floor & Thrift Ave.)

FIG. 27-15

Early electrics (left to right):

110-120 VOLTS 60 CYC AC ONLY   MADE IN U.S.A.
on transparent green measuring cup
5"   —$55—

No I.D.   Bakelite top
7"   —$40—

VIDRIO PRODUCTS CORP. CICERO, ILL NO. E
(embossed on bottom of transparent green jar)
7-1/2"   —$45—

FIG. 27-14

Harry L. Stiles patent
Dec. 27, 1949
Pat. No. D-156,679

D G Simons

FIG. 27-16

Electrics (left to right):

THE MASTER ELECTRIC CO. DAYTON, OHIO U.S.A.
7-1/2"   —$25—

VIDRIO PRODUCTS CORP.
PAT. NO. 1935857   CAT. # E-30
7"   —$25—

THE NELSON MACHINE & MFG. CO. ASHTABULA, OHIO
9"   —$30—

FIG. 27-18

*The Master Electric Company,
Dayton, Ohio, catalog sheet*

FIG. 27-17

*Eugene Newhampt patent
Jan. 27, 1931
Pat. No. 1,790,242*

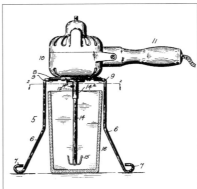
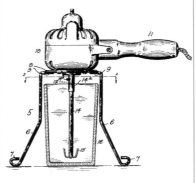

MASTER MIXER

•

MOTOR
The same high quality, trouble free motor (110 volt, 60-50 cycle. A. C.) that is used in the famous Master Fan. powers the Master Mixer.

BOWL
The heavy clear glass graduated bowl has a 1½ pint (3 cup) capacity.

FINISH
The motor housing and cover are finished in attractive two color green and ivory lacquer.

BEATER
The specially designed beater is detachable for cleaning.

MANY PRACTICAL USES
Whipping Cream
Beating Eggs
Mixing Ovaltine, Eggnogs
French Dressings and Mayonnaise
And Many General Utility Kitchen Purposes

PACKING
Packed in individual cartons, twelve to a shipping case—weight 45 lbs.

GUARANTEED BY THE MANUFACTURER

THE MASTER ELECTRIC COMPANY
DAYTON, OHIO, U. S. A.

FIG. 27-19

*Oscar P. Erhardt
(assignor to A. C. Gilbert) patent
Feb. 28. 1922
Pat. No. 1,407,789*

FIG. 27-21

ESKIMO KITCHEN MECHANIC PATENT NO. 1525967 110 VOLTS AC OR DC UNITED ELECTRICAL MFG. CO. ADRIAN, MICH. U.S.A.
with adjustable stand-up base
13"   —$50—

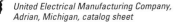

FIG. 27-20

*United Electrical Manufacturing Company,
Adrian, Michigan, catalog sheet*

Attachment for mixing drinks.

Attachment for beating and whipping.

Aluminum cup. For mixing cool drinks, chocolate, malted milk, etc.

Graded 1 quart glass bowl. For beating eggs, cream, batters, etc.

Saves Time, Saves Labor
The ESKIMO TWIN MIXER beats eggs, whips cream, mixes light batters or makes mayonnaise in a quarter of the time that it can be done by hand, and does them all much better.

ESKIMO
TWIN MIXER

The ESKIMO TWIN MIXER is a useful and valuable addition to any home, for with its two attachments it can be put to so many different uses that daily require both time and labor. It will not only mix drinks but also beats eggs and mayonnaise, whips cream and mixes light batters. Simply turn on the switch and the Eskimo does the rest.

Finished in lettuce green and white enamel with nickeled trimmings, it is attractive as well as useful.

Complete, with adjustable stand and seven feet of cord. Toggle switch and two-piece plug. Graded glass mixing bowl holding 1 quart and aluminum cup for mixing drinks. Also two attachments—a twin beater and a mixer. Shipped in standard packages, 6 mixers each. Formerly sold at $11.75.

New List price $8.95

UNITED ELECTRICAL MFG. COMPANY
Adrian, Michigan, U. S. A.

FIG. 27-22
HAMILTON BEACH "GOLD STAR" FOOD MIXER
PAT. NO. 1738112
MADE IN U.S.A. BY HAMILTON BEACH MFG. CO.
with black Bakelite handle   11"   —$50—

D Thornton

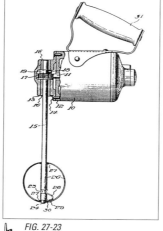

FIG. 27-23

Thomas B. Meyers patent
Dec. 3, 1929
Pat. No. 1,738,112

FIG. 27-24
LANDERS, FRARY & CLARK
NEW BRITAIN, CONN. U.S.A.
UNIVERSAL ELECTRIC MIXABEATER
12-1/2"   —$155—

D Thornton

R S Arnold

FIG. 27-25

Electrics (left to right):

LONG-MARCH COMPANY
BOSTON, MASS
9-1/2"   —$100—

No I.D., screw-on top
10"   —$95—

WEINIG MADE-RITE CO.
CLEVELAND, OHIO
MADE-RITE
9"   —$55—

D G Simons

MAIR COLLECTION

FIG. 27-26

Electrics (left to right):

ESKIMO KITCHEN MECHANIC
BERSTED MFG. CO.
ONTARIO CANADA
handheld with cast-iron stand
11-1/2"   —$55—

KNAPP MONARCH ST. LOUIS U.S.A.
CAT NO. 6-500
6 AMP 60 CY 115 V PAT. NO. 1935857
9-1/2"   —$30—

KNAPP MONARCH
ST. LOUIS U.S.A.
PAT. NO. 1935857
9-1/2"   —$35—

The A.C. Gilbert Company for decades thrilled the youth of America with American Flyer toy electric trains, microscope and chemistry sets, radio kits, tool chests and Erector Sets before it went out of business in the 1960s. Alfred Carlton Gilbert launched the Mysto Manufacturing Company in New Haven, Connecticut, in 1909 after graduating from Yale Medical School. Gilbert did not begin a medical practice but instead produced a variety of items for magicians.

Three years later, inspired by the trolley lines and industrial scene in New Haven, he came up with an altogether new toy — the Erector Set. Composed of small metal girders, plates, nuts and bolts, the Erector Set allowed its youthful owner to construct bridges, cranes, and merry-go-rounds, among other things. It was an instant success. Gilbert's first patent for his Erector Set was granted July 8, 1913 (fig. 27-27). "This invention relates to an improvement in toy construction blocks, the object being to provide blocks by which toy structures of various kinds may be erected, the blocks simulating what is known as steel construction…" the patent said.

In 1916 Mysto became the A.C. Gilbert Company and the toy line was expanded to all sorts of boxed kits for young scientists. In 1939, Gilbert purchased the small firm of American Flyer Company of Chicago, the maker of American Flyer toy electric trains, and built the line into one of the most popular in the country.

In 1956, with sales in the $20 million range, Gilbert passed the presidency to his son, Albert C. Gilbert Jr., and assumed the title of chairman of the board. Gilbert died in Boston in 1961, and shortly thereafter the A.C. Gilbert Company closed its doors, the victim of ever-changing toy tastes and fads.

Gilbert, who attributed his success to being a boy at heart all his life, will be remembered for his dazzling hobby, science and educational sets that generations of American youth grew up with. He also will be remembered for his invention and manufacturing of electric eggbeaters. Gilbert's first of 15 electric mixer patents came on Nov. 14, 1922 (fig. 27-28) and his last March 3, 1936 (fig. 27-29).

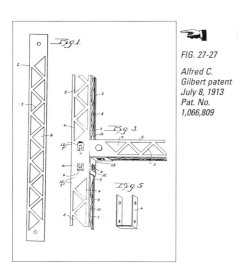

FIG. 27-27

Alfred C. Gilbert patent July 8, 1913 Pat. No. 1,066,809

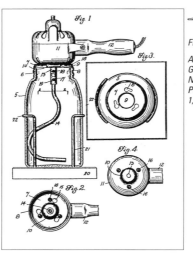

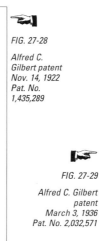

FIG. 27-28

Alfred C. Gilbert patent Nov. 14, 1922 Pat. No. 1,435,289

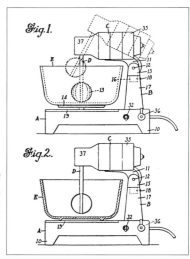

FIG. 27-29

Alfred C. Gilbert patent March 3, 1936 Pat. No. 2,032,571

FIG. 27-30

Alfred C. Gilbert patent Jan . 8, 1929 Pat. No. 1,698,363

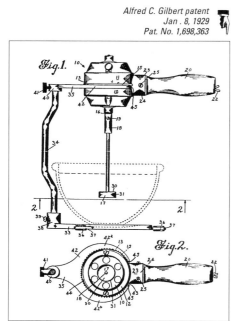

FIG. 27-31

Alfred C. Gilbert patent June 10, 1930 Pat. No. 1,763,301

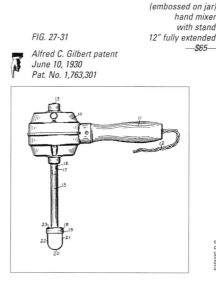

FIG. 27-32

POLAR CUB AC GILBERT (on mixer) **POLAR CUB** (embossed on jar) hand mixer with stand 12" fully extended —$65—

D G Simons

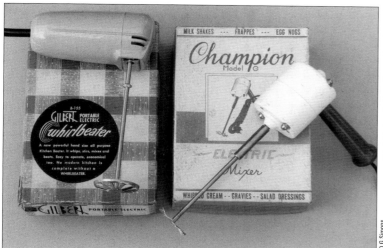

FIG. 27-33

Handheld electrics (left to right):

WHIRLBEATER
A.C. GILBERT COMPANY OF NEW HAVEN, CONN.
"Developed at the Gilbert Hall of Science...
Beats anything in the kitchen" *(on box)*
5" handle   —$30—

CHAMPION MIXER
HEINZE ELECTRIC CO. LOWELL, MASS.
"Use any jar, glass or bowl!" *(on box)*
5-1/2" handle   —$35—

FIG. 27-34

November, 1930
Good Housekeeping ad

FIG. 27-35

NO. X GILBERT
KITCHENKIT
THE A.C. GILBERT CO.,
NEW HAVEN, CONN.
PATENT NO. 2007500
OTHER PATS. PENDING
13" to top of reamer bowl
—$120—

FIG. 27-36

SUNBEAM MIXMASTER JR.
CHICAGO FLEXIBLE SHAFT CO.
CHICAGO U.S.A.
9-1/2" high to top of handle
—$200—

Gilbert's Jan. 8, 1929 *(fig. 27-30)* and June 10, 1930 patents *(fig. 27-31)* were the basis of the then-popular POLAR CUB *(fig. 27-32)*, which was followed by other mixers, including small, more modern handhelds *(fig. 27-33)*.

"Madame, here is news to brighten every corner of your kitchen. Mixing, beating, whipping are now merely a matter of clicking a switch," said a 1930 ad *(fig. 27-34)* for the POLAR CUB.

As Gilbert's and other patents evolved, reamers and tip-up tops were added, as all chrome and brass *(fig. 27-35)* and enamel models, even junior sizes *(fig. 27-36)* became popular in the 1930s.

The STAR-RITE MAGIC-MAID (fig. 27-37 & 27-38), which also was introduced in the 1930s, was, according to a catalog ad, "the choice of the modern housewife because of its simplicity and ease of operation. To watch its smooth effortless performance makes one marvel at is efficiency."

The Fitzgerald Manufacturing Company of Torrington, Connecticut offered the MAGIC-MAID. The mixer motor could be used as a tip-up mixer and reamer and could be detached to be used as a handheld beater, elements typical of many electric mixers of that era.

The electric evolution of milk shake makers was more pronounced. The first electric drink mixers (fig. 27-39) did not have on-off switches, but went on when plugged in.

Grandma's Old-Fashioned Molasses Cake

2 cups molasses
1 cup butter
3 eggs
3 cups flour
1 teaspoon ginger
1 teaspoon cinnamon
1/2 teaspoon cloves
1 teaspoon salt
1 cup boiling water
3 teaspoons soda

Heat butter and molasses together. Add to well beaten eggs, beating with the MAGIC MAID at medium speed. Sift together flour, salt and spices. Combine with butter mixture. Dissolve soda in boiling water and add to batter. Beat until well mixed. Use large loaf pan and bake for 1 hour in a very moderate oven (350°F) ... so rich it needs no frosting.

—MAGIC MIXER RECIPE BOOKLET, 1932

« With the multi-speed power of the STAR-Rite MAGIC MAID and its superior beater-unit and revolving bowl, every mixing task is scientifically and quickly done. »

—MAGIC MAID RECIPE BOOKLET, 1932

FIG. 27-37

STAR-RITE MAGIC-MAID
IT'S PORTABLE
in tip-up position, 13"
—$145—

FIG. 27-38

MAGIC-MAID reamer attachment, 18" across from end of mixing bowl to end of reamer bowl

FIG. 27-39

Electrics without switches (left to right):

No I.D.
8-3/4" —$30—

THE MADE-RITE CORP. CLEVELAND, OHIO, U.S.A. MADE-RITE FOR USE ONLY ON A.C. 110-115 VOLTS 60 CYCLES
8" —$35—

D Thornton

1932 Magic Maid recipe booklet

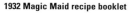

NEW STAR-Rite MAGIC MAID

MODEL C — No. 804

The new MAGIC MAID Mixer-Beater-Juice Extractor offers every advantage for convenient and efficient use.

(1) **Portable** — Remove from support and use anywhere.

(2) **Height Adjustor** — Instant adjustment for beverage mixing in any container.

(3) **Tilts Back** — to three positions: (1) to drain in bowl; (2) for removal of beaters; (3) for instant extractor attachment at new low level.

Complete with 2 sizes of revolving bowls of heavy Jade Green glass — Juice Extractor and extra Beverage Mixer. Now ready, at slight extra cost — Vegetable Slicer, Shredder, Meat Grinder and Food Chopper, Knife Sharpener, Silver Polisher, Coffee Roaster and Grinder.

★ ★ ★ ★ ★

R S Arnold

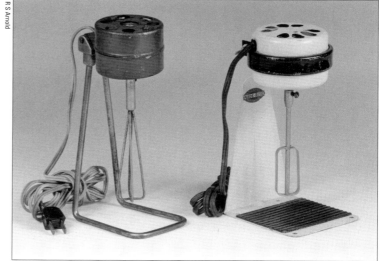

TRAVERSO COLLECTION

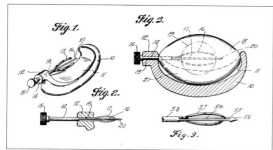

FIG. 27-40

Oliver Hansen patent
April 20, 1943
Pat. No. 2,316,861

FIG. 27-41

Murry D. Harper patent
Aug. 28, 1956
Pat. No. 2,760,763

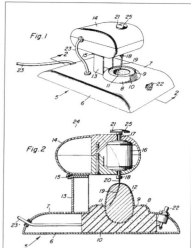

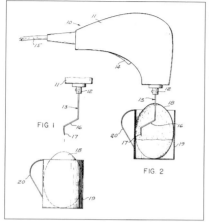

FIG. 27-42

Carl Djuvik patent
March 12, 1974
Pat. No. 3,796,512

FIG. 27-43

Benjamin H. Stansbury patent
April 28, 1981
Pat. No. 4,264,216

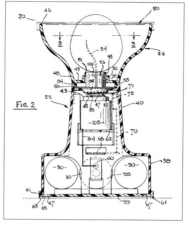

Nothing electric, of course, can match the ingenuity of the handheld rotary crank eggbeater. But four electric mixer patents come close:

▶ Oliver Hansen of Detroit said in his April 20, 1943 patent *(fig. 27-40)*: "The purpose of my invention is to provide a simple and effective device for scrambling eggs without the need for any cups or containers, as the scrambling is effected within the shell of the egg itself. This feature eliminates the need of washing of containers which otherwise would have to be used for the purpose."

Hansen went on to say that "an agitator or scrambler comprising a shank" is inserted into the egg and "both the yolk and the white of said egg may now be thoroughly mixed or scrambled …"

▶ Murry D. Harper of Dunbar, West Virginia, said in his Aug. 28, 1956 patent *(fig. 27-41)* that his device "is adapted to thoroughly and rapidly mix or scramble eggs while still in the shell, after which said eggs may, if desired, be boiled in the usual manner or opened and cooked." Another plus, according to Harper, is that "only a very small hole will be left in one end of the shell after the egg has been mixer or scrambled, which hole may be readily sealed or patched preparatory to boiling said egg."

▶ Carl Djuvik of Sun City, Arizona, used the same in-shell principle, but on a super simple basis. In his March 12, 1974 patent *(fig. 27-42)*, Djuvik said:

"A motor held kitchen aid in the form of a pointed, bent wire is inserted into an egg and rotated. The beaten contents are then delivered directly from shell to cooking or baking mix."

▶ Benjamin H. Stansbury Jr. of Beverly Hills, California, said in his April 28, 1981 patent *(fig. 27-43)* that his "device for scrambling an egg within its shell" had such low power requirements it "may be battery powered, fully self-containing and portable."

At least two models of the scramble-in-the-shell made it to market , THE EGGstir, and THE EGG SCRAMBLER *(fig. 27-44)*. THE EGG SCRAMBLER was made by Ronco of Elk Grove Village, Illinois, in 1981 and one of the boasts it made on the box was: "Makes food look and taste better or your money back!"

FIG. 27-44

THE EGGstir (on front of base)
A BRISE-LOVELL PRODUCT PAT PEND
(on bottom)
plug-in 8″   —$30—

THE EGG SCRAMBLER (on base)
5-1/2″   —$25 in box—

R S Arnold

C H A P T E R 2 7 : E L E C T R I C M I X E R S

FIG. 27-45

**DORMEYER ELECTRIC BEATER HAMILTON BEACH
MOTOR US PAT MARCH 22, 1921 FOREIGN PATS. PEND.**
removable motor
14-1/4" —$55—

**DORMEYER ELECTRIC BEATER HAMILTON BEACH
MOTOR US PAT MARCH 22, 1921 FOREIGN PATS. PEND.**
removable motor
12-1/2" —$55—

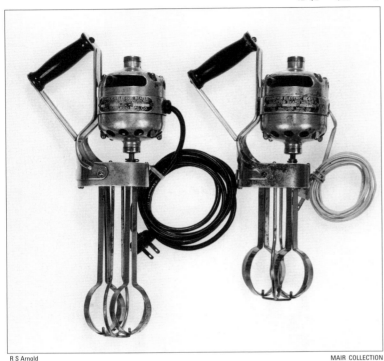

R S Arnold

MAIR COLLECTION

FIG. 27-47

DORMEYER ELECTRIC FOOD MIXERs
with different casing designs
13-1/4" —$60 each—

R S Arnold

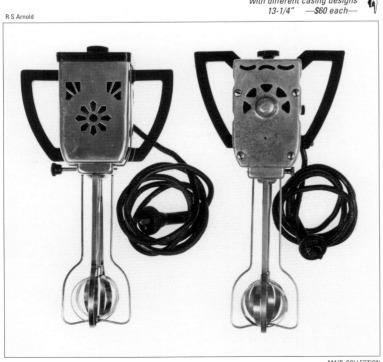

MAIR COLLECTION

Finally, the popular DORMEYER ELECTRIC FOOD MIXER *(figs. 27-41 through 27-43)* and the weasel factor — a 1930 magazine ad *(fig. 27-44)*.

The ad says in part: "How appropriate, too, that you an expert cook, should give the new bride this efficient instrument to help her become a good cook." And then in bigger type: "Makes cooking an art instead of a drudgery."

Others would argue the electric eggbeater took the art out of cooking and made mixing a drudgery. A sad, slow death for America's greatest invention.

FIG. 27-46

*Lathrop Collins patent
March 22, 1921
Pat. No. 1,372,279*

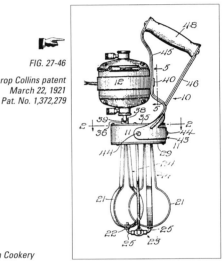

FIG. 27-48

*1930 American Cookery
Magazine ad*

THE EGGBEATER CHRONICLES

Patent Directory

American Patent History: *Novelty, Invention, Utility*

Each colony of what became the United States granted patents independent of each other, resulting in conflict and confusion. The Constitution tried to address the problem, in Articles I Section 8, which empowered Congress "to promote the progress of science and the useful arts by securing for limited times to authors and inventors, the exclusive rights to their respective writings and discoveries."

Congress passed its first patent law in 1790 and it was signed that year on April 10 by President George Washington. It established an examining board authorized to grant patents. The board was composed of the secretary of state, the secretary of war and the attorney general. The board members, however, did not have time to study the increasing number of applications and because the states could no longer grant patents, the 1790 law was very unpopular.

In 1793, Congress passed its second patent law, which allowed the issuance of patents without examination. Anyone who swore to the originality of his invention and paid the fees could get a patent. The Act of 1836 repealed the 1793 law and set the stage for the nation's present patent process, creating the Patent Office, a commissioner of patents, and a system to closely examine each application.

Until 1836 and the new patent law, patents were not numbered when they were issued, making research difficult. And compounding the problem, many of the original records of the earliest patents were destroyed in a Dec. 15, 1836 fire at the Patent Office. From 1790 to 1836, 9,957 patents were issued. Patent number 1,000,000 was issued in 1911, with 2,000,000 coming in 1935.

Patents gave the inventor a legal monopoly of his or her invention for 14 years until 1870, when a new law extended it to 17 years. Those caught at the tail end of the 14 year period, before the 17 year time period went into effect, could be granted "extensions," with only a notation in the recording books, as compared to the more common "reissues," which are numbered and have full drawings and patent facts.

Patent researchers will find very few "extensions," but they do exist and they will usually cause immediate questions because they do not have to fall on patent Tuesdays. For researchers, the first thing to check is whether a date falls on a Tuesday because 99.9% of all patents, design patents and reissues were and are issued on Tuesdays. It now takes a special act of Congress to renew a patent after its 17 year run. Meanwhile, a design patent, basically covering the appearance of an article, lasts 14 years.

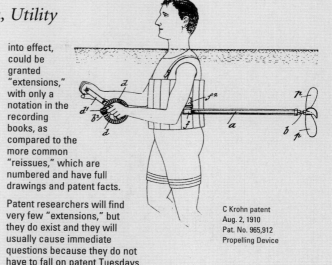

C Krohn patent
Aug. 2, 1910
Pat. No. 965,912
Propelling Device

Inventors have one year from the date of publication or sale of their invention to apply for a patent. Many manufacturers over the years marked their products "Patent Pending" or "Patent Applied For" while waiting for issuance of a patent. Such markings have no legal value but probably discouraged imitation.

B E A T E R   P A T E N T S

Date	Pat. No.	Inventor	Type	Beater Name / Company
1856-12-23	16,267	Collier, Ralph	rotary w/c	
1857-12-01	18,759	Miller, Harvey	ratchet w/c	
1857-12-15	18,849	Heich, John B.	ratchet w/c	
1858-03-23	19,738	Mihan, P.	ratchet w/c	
1858-04-27	20,032	Borrman, W.	rotary w/c	
1858-07-27	21,042	Yerby, E.	rotary	
1859-04-19	23,694	Monroe, J.F. & E.P.	rotary mount	Monroe, Star / Monroe Mfg
1859-04-26	23,814	Nicolai, John L.	rotary	
1859-05-03	23,843	Jones, Samuel F.	rope power	
1859-05-24	24,134	McBean, Thomas	rotary w/c	
1859-08-09	25,038	Parker, J. J.	rotary w/c	
1859-11-15	26,123	Pyne, John	rotary w/c	
1860-01-24	26,958	Walker, Sylvenus	ratchet	
1860-02-07	27,054	Jay, James M.	rotary w/c	Globe (cast-iron ball)
1860-04-17	27,908	Jay, James M.	rotary w/c	Globe (cast-iron ball)
1860-05-01	28,047	Ashley, Frederick	Archimedes	Ashley
1860-06-19	28,760	McLean, James P.	rotary w/c	
1860-09-18	30,053	Drott, H. F.	tin shaker	
1860-09-25	30,152	Nicholson, William T.	rotary mount	Christy
1860-10-16	R-1,062	Monroe, J. T. & E. P.	rotary mount	Monroe, Star / Monroe Mfg.
1860-10-23	30,453	Baker, Uriah	Archimedes	
1861-03-12	31,663	Hart, William	Archimedes	
1861-07-23	32,886	Nicholson, William T.	rotary	Heart
1862-07-29	36,030	Shive, David	hand rotary	
1863-07-07	39,134	Earle, Timothy	Archimedes	Earl's

Date	Pat. No.	Inventor	Type	Beater Name / Company
1863-10-06	40,188	Schildecker, Peter	rotary w/c	
1864-05-03	42,603	Sallade, William	rotary w/c	
1864-12-06	45,309	Bliss, J. W.	glass shaker	
1865-04-18	47,264	Adamson, William	rotary rags	
1865-07-04	48,525	Crane, Moses G.	rotary	
1865-08-01	49,176	Tilden, Howard	tin shaker	Tilden's
1865-12-26	51,758	Smith, William B.	plunger	
1866-01-02	51,839	King, Francis L.	handheld	
1866-02-13	52,518	Blasse, Alfried R.	rotary w/c	
1866-03-20	53,260	Billings, Jerome	rotary in cabinet	
1866-03-27	53,429	Felthouse, H. D. & J. H.	tin shaker	
1866-04-17	53,965	Fisler, Thomas	syllabub	
1866-04-24	54,134	Earle, Timothy	rotary	
1866-05-01	54,388	Moore, Samuel C.	tin shaker	
1866-05-15	54,761	Pangborn, Samuel B.	plunger	
1866-05-15	54,776	Robinson, Alexander	tin shaker	
1866-06-19	55,625	Crane, Moses G.	rotary	Monitor
1866-06-26	55,802	Ashley, Frederick	Archimedes	Ashley
1866-06-26	55,807	Bemis, William A.	tin shaker	
1866-07-17	56,382	Davis, Joshua	rotary w/c	
1866-07-31	56,845	Alden, Leonard B.	ratchet w/c	
1866-08-28	57,596	Strange, Emerson C.	syllabub	
1866-09-18	58,165	Drennan, Charles M.	tin shaker	
1866-10-16	58,750	Arnold, Varnum G.	tin shaker	
1866-10-16	58,770	Butterfield, Charles	jar shaker	
1866-10-16	58,882	Pinder, Charles	tin shaker	
1866-11-06	59,449	Pratt, E. L.	plunger	

w/c = with container   D = Design Patent   R = Reissue

Date	Pat. No.	Inventor	Type	Beater Name / Company
1867-01-22	61,494	Westover, George C.	rotary w/c	
1867-01-29	61,679	Oakley, Frederick	rotary w/c	
1867-04-09	63,774	Wickersham, William	rotary	
1867-05-21	64,928	Williams, Marvin T.	rotary w/c	
1867-06-18	65,916	King, Francis L.	rotary w/c	
1867-07-16	66,855	Klepper, P.	rotary w/c	
1867-07-30	67,218	Rosenberry, Christian	rotary w/c	
1867-08-27	68,037	Bridger, George E.	rotary w/c	
1867-09-10	68,788	Pratt, E. L.	plunger	Pratt's
1867-12-03	71,696	Carver, George G.	rolling pin/shaker	
1867-12-10	72,136	Webster, Dudley	handheld	
1868-02-25	74,837	Louden, Henry W.	rotary w/c	
1868-03-10	75,340	Wilson, Sylvanus C.	tin plunger	
1868-03-24	75,787	Peirce, William H.	handheld	
1868-04-21	76,970	Angus, William N.	rotary	
1868-07-28	80,440	Blake, Lewis T.	rotary w/c	
1868-12-29	85,460	Mackay, D. D.	Archimedes	
1869-04-06	88,672	Seitz, C. F. Augustus	rotary w/c	
1869-11-09	96,604	Miller, C.J. Jr.	churn	
1869-11-30	97,397	Fougen H. G. & A. C.	rope power	
1869-12-21	98,168	Laurie, Linn	rope power	
1870-01-04	98,533	Williams, Lewis	tin shaker	
1870-01-25	99,173	Earle, Timothy	rotary	
1870-02-01	99,337	Miller, Nathaniel C.	rotary	
1870-02-15	99,883	Haines, William H.	handheld	
1870-02-22	100,155	Krandelt, Frank	rotary w/c	
1870-03-29	101,281	Lehmann, Charles	rotary w/c	
1870-05-31	103,811	Williams, Turner	rotary	Dover
1870-06-14	104,174	Marsh, Thomas	rotary	
1870-07-05	105,057	Earle, Timothy	rotary	
1870-07-26	105,655	Dearborn, Gilbert K.	rotary	
1870-08-09	106,182	Marsh, Thomas	rotary	
1870-09-20	107,515	Marsh, Thomas	rotary	
1870-09-27	107,673	Earle, Timothy	rotary	
1870-10-11	108,203	Swartz, Daniel M.	rotary w/c	
1870-10-18	108,498	Maltby, Harriet S.	rotary w/c	
1871-06-13	115,862	Marsh, Thomas	rotary	Centripetal/Jenks
1871-08-15	117,982	Clayton, Daniel B.	rotary w/c	
1871-09-05	118,727	Kunkle, Erastus B.	tin plunger	
1871-10-03	D-5,296	Bostick, Emanuel	tin plunger	Star Egg Beater / Kunkle & Bostick
1872-01-23	122,997	Dane, John Jr.	rotary	
1872-02-06	123,353	Miller, Harvey	ratchet	
1872-03-05	124,375	Munson, David	handheld	
1872-06-18	128,013	Burdict, Arthur	handheld	
1872-08-06	130,297	Hood, Harrison P.	handheld	
1872-08-20	130,591	Peirce, Charles, R.	rope power	
1872-09-10	131,283	Lehmann, Charles	rotary (soap)	Lehmann's Patent
1872-09-24	131,600	Crocker, William O.	rotary	
1872-10-22	132,483	Muth, Henry	beater blades	
1873-04-22	138,094	Miller, Nathaniel C.	rotary mount	
1873-05-06	138,647	Hadley, Ethan	rotary	Dover
1873-06-17	140,067	Munson, David	handheld	
1873-07-15	140,891	Condon, John W.	rotary w/c	
1873-11-11	144,567	Rote, John F.	rotary w/c	
1874-01-20	146,710	Redheffer, William	tin plunger	Lightning
1874-02-10	147,412	Lehmann, Charles	rotary (soap)	Lehmann's Patent
1874-06-09	151,761	Crocker, William O.	rotary	
1874-06-09	151,784	Landis, Jacob F.	rotary w/c	
1874-08-18	154,263	Mackay, Donald D.	rotary	
1874-08-25	154,411	Monroe, J. F. & E. P.	rotary	
1874-10-27	156,357	Jones, George W.	rotary churn	
1874-12-08	157,456	Mackay, Donald D.	Archimedes	
1875-03-16	160,815	Cline, Martin	syllabub	
1875-06-13	R-6,542	Earle, Timothy	ratchet	Dover Stamping Co.
1875-06-15	164,491	Silver, William H.	churn dasher	Silvers (first)
1875-07-13	165,585	Howes, John	syllabub	
1875-07-13	165,615	Redheffer, William	ice cream freezer/syllabub	
1875-07-27	166,143	Redheffer, William	tin plunger	
1875-08-03	166,412	Rote, John F.	rotary w/c	
1875-08-17	166,893	Redheffer, William	syllabub	
1875-09-14	167,696	Schonmeyer, F. E.	tin plunger	Bon Ton
1875-10-05	168,506	Lampton, William R	rotary churn	
1875-10-05	168,510	Lozo, Martin	rotary w/c	
1876-02-22	174,015	Seymour, Frederick J.	rotary	T&S cast-iron

Date	Pat. No.	Inventor	Type	Beater Name / Company
1876-05-15	177,574	Seymour, Frederick J.	rotary	T&S cast-iron
1876-09-05	181,903	Boon, Alonzo T.	tin plunger	
1876-09-26	182,639	Brothwell, John G.	rotary	Family / Turner & Seymour
1876-10-24	183,589	Nichols, William B.	rotary w/c	
1877-01-16	186,278	Sisson, George P.	rotary	
1877-02-13	187,417	Russell, Matthew C.	tin plunger	
1877-05-01	190,238	Monroe, James F.	rotary mount	
1877-05-08	190,628	Scofield, James H.	rotary	Victor
1877-06-19	192,157	Dulje, Eustache R.	rope power	
1877-07-24	193,493	Eberhart, Lloyd	rotary	
1877-10-02	195,695	Borcher, Thomas	Archimedes	
1877-11-13	197,135	Hunting, George H.	egg forks	
1877-12-18	198,363	Duty, Michael K.	churn	Dazey Churn (first)
1878-02-12	200,290	Harrison, Reuben N.	handheld	
1878-04-30	203,081	Silver, William H.	plunger	Silver Dessert Maker
1878-04-30	203,153	Hughes, James R.	Archimedes	
1878-06-04	204,498	Mooney, George	rotary	Vortex
1878-07-09	205,859	Hamble, Melvin D.	rotary w/c	
1878-08-06	206,742	Mann, Harry C.	rotary	
1878-10-22	209,205	Wiester, William H.	tin plunger	Pratt's, Automatic
1879-04-29	214,936	Marchand, Henry E.	tin plunger	
1879-06-03	216,053	Mooney, George	rotary	Vortex
1879-10-07	220,272	Burry, William C.	rotary	
1879-10-28	221,016	Backmire, George H.	rotary w/c	
1880-02-03	224,117	Ulmer, Sarah, A.	rotary w/c	
1880-03-02	225,003	Earle, Timothy	rotary holder	
1880-03-23	225,693	Emmert, John	Archimedes	
1880-05-11	227,378	Morse, Edward	ratchet	Morse
1880-06-29	229,372	Brown, Thomas W.	rotary	Standard, Manhattan, Hub
1880-07-13	230,075	Shinn, Thornton A.	measuring container	Family Measuring Jar / Shinn & Rochester
1880-09-07	232,018	Foss, L. Bacon	rotary holder	Dover Stamping Co.
1880-09-14	232,125	Henry, Frank	rotary	
1880-09-21	232,328	Brown, Thomas W.	rotary	Standard
1880-09-21	232,358	McCool, Horace, B.	tin plunger	
1880-10-12	233,287	Schmidt, George A.	rotary w/c	
1880-12-07	235,245	Hughes, James R.	rotary	Advance
1880-12-21	235,620	Carroll, Philip F.	rotary w/c	
1881-02-01	237,150	Williams, Linus H.	mixed drink shaker	
1881-02-15	237,741	Gill, George W.	rotary	
1881-03-01	238,393	Howson, Henry Jr.	rotary w/c	American Machine Co.
1881-03-08	238,565	Brown, Thomas W.	rotary	Standard, Duplex
1881-03-22	R-9,615	Condon, John W.	rotary w/c	
1881-05-24	241,784	Brooks, Heman P.	Archimedes	Globe
1881-10-11	248,004	Allen, D. H.	Archimedes	
1881-11-01	249,044	Hawkins, Elisha D.	rotary w/c	
1882-01-24	252,800	Richardson, Gus W.	Archimedes	
1882-03-07	254,540	Deis, Charles	rotary w/c	
1882-04-11	256,310	Fowler, George F.	rotary w/c	
1882-06-06	259,056	Sherwood, Daniel	handheld	Surprise
1882-08-01	261,857	Kitterman, George M.	Archimedes	
1882-10-31	266,679	Doll, Arnold	rotary w/c	
1882-10-31	R-10,228	Harrison, Reuben N.	handheld	
1882-11-14	267,491	Carley, James T.	rotary	
1882-11-28	268,185	Caufman, Abraham	rotary pot	
1883-01-02	270,015	Carter, William W.	rope power	
1883-01-16	270,642	Doll, Arnold	rotary w/c	
1883-02-27	273,173	Short, Samuel	rotary	
1883-04-24	276,290	Schrebler, Charles	rotary w/c	
1883-05-08	277,218	Burnham, Lycurgus	rotary	
1883-05-08	277,219	Burnham, Lycurgus	rotary	
1883-06-26	280,019	Earl, Francis	tin shaker	
1883-08-07	282,738	Livingood, Katherine	rotary w/c	
1883-11-20	288,775	Cherry, Peterson H.	lemonade shaker	
1884-01-15	291,890	Flanders, William G.	tin plunger	Flanders' Patent
1884-02-05	292,821	Johnson, Willis	rotary w/c	
1884-02-19	293,648	Gibson, Hannah Z.	rotary mount	
1884-04-22	297,115	Deis, Charles	rotary w/c	
1884-05-13	298,375	Henderson, William B.	rotary w/c	
1884-05-13	298,503	Rex, Alfred C	rotary w/c	King Egg Beater
1884-06-03	299,884	Willing, John Edward	tin plunger	
1884-08-05	303,022	Kilborn, Eugenia	handheld	
1884-08-05	303,080	Weissenborn, Oscar	rotary drink mixer	
1884-12-09	308,901	Kitchell, Oscar	rotary w/c	
1885-05-12	317,755	Fletcher, Theodore	tin shaker	
1885-05-26	318,786	Newcomer, Jacob L.	rotary w/c	Newcomer's Improved

Date	Pat. No.	Inventor	Type	Beater Name / Company
1885-06-02	319,191	Bryant, Charles A.	Archimedes	Bryant
1885-06-30	321,327	Welling, John Edward	tin plunger	
1885-07-14	322,250	Brown, Thomas W.	rotary	Dover, Standard
1885-09-08	325,674	Haak, Thomas E.	rotary w/c	
1885-09-08	325,840	Hough, Earl F.	Archimedes	
1885-09-08	325,933	Ives, George H.	rotary mount	Family Baker
1885-09-29	327,109	Rider, John	Archimedes spoon	
1885-10-20	328,457	Burry, William C.	rotary w/c	
1885-11-03	329,859	Silver, William H.	egg poacher	
1885-11-17	330,829	Eastman, Rufus M.	electric	
1885-12-01	331,662	Thomas, George H.	rotary	PD&Co.
1885-12-15	332,375	Baltzley, Edwin	rotary/mount	New Keystone Beater / also table mounts North Brothers
1885-12-22	332,837	Rock, Daniel B.	rotary	
1886-05-11	341,697	Silver, William H.	plunger	Silver plunger
1886-07-20	345,709	Marsh, Edith A.	handheld	
1886-07-27	346,375	Laube, Godfried	plunger	
1886-09-28	350,023	Thomas, George H.	rotary	E-A-S-Y
1886-10-12	350,708	Vickers, William	rotary w/c	
1886-12-21	354,684	Carley, James T.	rotary	
1886-12-28	354,934	Raymond, Frances V.	rotary w/c	
1886-12-28	355,170	Houck, Frank A.	tin plunger	
1887-03-22	359,887	Platner, Marshal D.	rotary cake mixer	
1887-03-22	359,976	Johnson, William J.	handheld	National Mfg. Co.
1887-05-10	362,858	Stambaugh, Charles	Archimedes	
1887-06-28	365,624	Paine, George H.	Archimedes	
1887-08-02	367,569	Wikidal, La Fayette	rotary w/c	
1887-08-30	369,273	Brown, Thomas W.	Archimedes	Clipper / National Mfg. Co.
1887-09-20	370,335	Hunter, Rudolph M.	rotary cake mixer	
1887-09-27	370,406	Peters, Daniel	rotary w/c	
1887-10-25	371,976	Rice, David Hall	rotary	Cam Beater
1887-10-25	372,282	Winter, David T.	rotary mount	Express
1887-10-25	372,043	Pusey, Caroline S.	handheld	
1887-12-13	374,706	Rosenbranz, Louis	rotary w/c	
1887-12-20	375,274	Dodson, Wilson P.	rotary	
1888-03-06	378,863	Baltzley, Edwin	rotary mount	Keystone table mount
1888-03-27	380,200	Gerard, John	rotary	Landers, Frary & Clark
1888-03-27	380,226	Stewart, Theron S.	plunger	Lightning
1888-04-03	380,564	Hadley, Ethan	rotary	Dover
1888-05-29	383,489	Peters, Daniel	rotary w/c	
1888-06-19	384,674	Bishop, Mary F.	rotary spring	
1888-07-17	386,105	Bryant, Charles A.	rotary	
1888-07-17	386,424	Dudley, George D.	Archimedes	Dudley-Byrant / Woods, Sherwood & Co.
1888-08-07	387,214	Diell, John J.	rotary w/c	
1888-08-14	387,634	Fulton, Harmon	rotary beverage mixer	
1888-09-18	389,631	Baltzley, Edwin	rotary w/c	
1888-10-09	390,974	Jennings, Benjamin	rotary beverage mixer	
1888-10-17	391,150	Jennings, Benjamin	rotary beverage mixer	
1889-02-12	397,655	McDowell, John J.	rotary w/c	
1889-02-12	397,831	Charles, Robert S.	rotary mount	
1889-02-19	398,258	Hudson, Frederick W.	rotary	P D & Co. look-alike
1889-04-02	400,547	Crafton, Charles Baker	Archimedes	
1889-04-02	400,674	Haring, Peter Paul	rotary beverage mixer	
1889-04-09	401,058	Pfau, Christian F.	handheld	
1889-04-16	401,724	Williams, Robert S.	plunger	
1889-05-21	403,502	Baltzley, Edwin	rotary motor	
1889-06-18	405,683	Shepherd, Francis H.	rotary beverage mixer	
1889-07-02	406,321	Wiedersheim, John A.	rotary beverage mixer	
1889-07-09	406,653	Kirby, John L.	rotary	Dover
1889-08-20	409,616	Richardson, John	rotary mount	
1889-11-05	414,566	Nelleson, Lambert	rotary w/c	
1889-11-26	415,733	Perry, James A.	rotary w/c	
1889-12-03	416,636	Meyer, John W.	rotary beverage mixer	
1890-01-21	419,631	Brown, Thomas W.	rotary	Standard, Dover USA , Rival
1890-01-28	420,262	Boemermann, H.	glass plunger	
1890-03-04	422,462	Tatum, Charles A.	rotary beverage mixer	
1890-03-25	424,108	Hallam, Frank	rotary w/c	
1890-03-25	424,438	Stubbs, Joel	rotary beverage mixer	

Date	Pat. No.	Inventor	Type	Beater Name / Company
1890-05-06	427,473	Hauck, Charles J. Jr.	ratchet	
1890-05-27	428,999	Austin, Alvin Judd	Archimedes	
1890-12-09	442,429	Fletcher, John J.	tin plunger	
1891-03-31	449,187	White, Albert	Archimedes	
1891-06-09	453,998	Foster, George N.	handheld	American Machine Co.
1891-06-16	454,165	Dennison, William H.	rotary	
1891-06-16	454,194	Wilkinson, David A.	rotary fork	
1891-06-16	454,345	Hadley, Ethan	rotary	Lamb Knitting Machine
1891-07-07	455,479	Bruen, William	rope power drink mixer	
1891-09-15	459,668	Wood, Frances F.	Archimedes	
1891-09-29	460,265	Mulford, Charles J.	rotary w/c	
1891-11-24	463,818	Whitney, Edward H.	rotary	Dover
1891-12-29	466,178	Mitchell, Arobine C.	rotary w/c	
1892-01-19	467,328	Eichenberg, Edouard	rotary mount	
1892-03-01	470,005	Magin, Anna M.	handheld	
1892-04-05	472,092	Wheeler, William	rotary w/c	
1892-04-12	472,803	Brittain, Howard M.	ratchet wire	
1892-11-29	487,024	Seltzer, Uriah D.	plunger	Lebanon
1893-01-10	489,821	Leyburn, Edward J.	rope power drink mixer	
1893-01-31	490,730	Wiley, Frederick	rotary churn	
1893-02-14	491,583	O'Neill, John M.	rotary w/c	
1893-04-18	495,925	Albrecht, Antonius C.	rotary w/c	North Brothers Mfg
1893-06-20	499,741	Juergens, Henry F.	rotary w/c	Jewel Beater Mixer
1893-08-29	504,112	Paine, Frances E.	handheld	
1893-09-05	504,472	Hancock, Addison	belt wheel	
1893-09-26	505,692	Adancourt, William F.	mixed drink shaker	
1893-09-26	505,766	Huber, George W.	plunger	
1893-10-10	506,635	Harvey, Jennie	rotary mayo	
1893-10-10	506,636	Harvey, Jennie	rotary mount	
1893-11-07	507,996	Cobin, Israel Jones	rotary wine cooler	Cobin Mfg. Co.
1893-11-28	509,665	Jaquette, Harry	rotary scissor	Jaquette Bros.
1893-12-26	511,637	McDowell, Bartley D.	rotary mount	
1894-02-20	515,249	Renn, John F.	syllabub	
1894-03-13	516,214	Mohr, Leopold	rotary w/c	
1894-03-13	516,415	Van Deusen, W.A.	handheld	Vandeusen Egg Whip
1894-05-08	519,584	Mitchell, Arobine C.	rotary w/c	
1894-05-29	520,566	Hughes, John M.	vertical churn	
1894-07-10	522,944	Saltsman, Aaron J.	syllabub	Columbia Egg Beater
1894-11-06	528,688	Payne, William H.	drink shaker/ fruit squeezer	
1894-11-27	529,764	Weeks, Charles D.	Archimedes	
1894-12-04	530,268	Hensel, Otto A.	rotary combo	
1895-02-05	533,589	Hagley, William	rotary w/c	
1895-03-12	535,474	Warrington, Claude H.	rotary w/c	
1895-03-19	536,136	Ebel, John V.	rotary w/c	
1895-08-13	D-24,545	Hensel, Otto A.	dasher design	
1895-10-01	547,263	Hoyle, Ella L. D.	cake beater	
1895-10-08	547,488	Hunziker, James G.	combo, rotary mount	
1896-01-14	553,027	Eynon, Elizabeth J.	rotary w/c	The Eynon Mixer & Beater / Landers, Frary & Clark
1896-02-04	554,170	Cripe, Sara E.	rotary w/c	
1896-06-16	562,018	Nelson, John L.	rotary drink mixer	
1896-06-30	563,139	Dalrymple, Hartwell	syllabub	
1896-07-21	564,345	Stock, Harry A.	rotary w/c	
1896-08-04	565,260	Cook, George T.	handheld	
1896-09-15	567,684	Moody, Thomas A.	handheld	
1896-09-15	567,909	Mason, Herbert W.	rotary	Never Slip
1896-11-03	570,668	Kohlenberg, Ferdinand	Archimedes	
1896-12-15	573,208	Coombs, Stephen H	rotary	
1896-12-22	D-26,438	Steele, George H.	Archimedes	
1897-03-02	577,945	Davis, Arthur	rotary w/c	
1897-04-27	581,493	Saltsman, Aaron J.	handheld	Saltsman's Whip
1897-06-01	583,775	Swift, Willis S.	rotary w/c	
1897-07-06	585,703	Reedy, Edward E.	syllabub	
1897-08-10	588,112	Johnson, William J.	rotary	National Mfg Co.
1897-08-24	588,663	Smith, Charles F.	rotary	Landers, Frary & Clark
1897-09-07	589,795	Scopes, Edward John	rotary	Lyon (propeller)
1897-09-14	590,160	Mamugh, John S.	churn	graniteware churn
1897-09-28	590,782	Webber, Alexander	rotary w/c	
1897-10-26	592,708	Howe, Emma Jane	rotary w/c	
1897-12-14	595,354	Spilker, Bernard J.	rotary w/c	
1898-02-15	599,268	Spruin, William	tin creamer	

Date	Pat. No.	Inventor	Type	Beater Name / Company
1898-02-22	599,661	Scopes, Edward John	rotary	Perfection
1898-04-12	602,152	Bellanger, Frank S.	Archimedes	D. J. Barry & Co.
1898-09-16	609,270	Flaherty, James F.	push rotary	
1898-10-04	611,726	Wishart, Edward	rotary	
1898-12-27	D-29,873	Brown, Thomas W.	rotary	Standard
1899-01-03	616,964	Pickett, Sterling P.	rotary popcorn popper	
1899-01-03	617,093	Gipple, Rebecca A.	rotary	
1899-01-10	617,416	Ellis, Wilson R.	rotary	
1899-01-17	D-30,015	Rock, Peter J.	beater blade	
1899-01-17	618,029	Fitch, Gilbert M.	Archimedes	
1899-01-24	618,122	Nelson, John L.	rotary w/c	
1899-02-21	619,739	Emery, Benjiman F.	churn	The Monkey / B. F. Emery Des Moines
1899-07-11	628,471	Julier, Camilla	rotary w/c	
1899-07-25	629,608	Roberts, John C.	rotary w/c	
1899-08-01	630,009	Smalley, Albert G.	tumbler shaker attachment	
1899-08-22	631,715	Holt, Thomas	rotary	Holt-Lyon
1899-08-29	632,044	Chapman, Samuel E.	handheld	
1899-09-12	632,780	Crepeau, Henry T.	plunger	
1899-11-07	636,400	Friedman, Goste	rotary mount	
1899-11-07	636,559	Robinson, Richard	rotary w/c	
1899-11-07	636,737	Bagley, Charles H.	Archimdes	
1899-12-26	D-32,028	Munson, Samuel R.	beater frame	
1900-01-02	640,369	Cross, Ranslar R.	rotary w/c	
1900-04-03	646,736	Holt, Thomas	rotary	Holt-Lyon
1900-04-10	647,341	Tutt, John C.	rotary	
1900-05-15	649,683	Spanier, Waldemar	ratchet	
1900-07-10	653,233	Godward, Ernest R.	tin shaker	
1900-07-24	654,426	Downing, Elmer T.	Archimedes	
1900-07-24	654,526	Downing, Elmer T.	Archimedes	
1900-10-09	659,558	Sturgis, Herbert M.	Archimedes	
1900-10-23	660,513	Jones, J. M. C.	rotary w/c	
1900-12-04	663,305	Tingley, Philo B.	rotary w/c	
1900-12-25	664,779	Rabiger, Robert G.	rotary w/c	
1901-01-22	666,269	Hamilton, Charles R.	tin churn	
1901-02-19	D-34,098	Fell, Pearl F.	handheld cream whip	
1901-03-26	670,834	Benedict, Allen S.	rotary w/c	
1901-04-09	671,516	Hegner, Stella B.	handheld	
1901-04-30	673,198	Coombs, Stephen H.	rotary killer	
1901-06-02	677,421	McRae, Kate Hatch	cake beater	
1901-06-04	675,475	Glover, Julia, B	handheld	
1901-06-25	D-34,690	Browne, William G.	rotary dasher	Cyclone/Browne Mfg
1901-07-16	678,456	Browne, William G.	rotary	
1901-08-13	680,229	Davis, Della	rotary w/c	
1901-10-22	684,966	Weisenback, A.	rotary w/c	
1901-11-05	685,986	Hill, John E.	rotary	The H-I-L-L
1901-12-03	688,201	Scopes, Edward John	rotary	Ball Bearing
1901-12-10	688,657	Leu, Frederick	rotary w/c	
1902-01-14	691,115	Cohnhoff, Louis	rotary w/c	
1902-02-04	692,479	Roberts, Emmett R.	Archimedes	Roberts
1902-06-03	701,432	Weed, Elisha L.	Archimedes	
1902-08-12	707,019	Ruckstuhl, Frederick W.	rotary potato creamer	
1902-08-19	707,404	Elward, John H.	rotary w/c	
1902-08-26	R-12,026	Browne, William G.	rotary	W. G. Browne Mfg Co.
1902-09-02	708,229	Hooper, Beekman D.	rotary w/c	
1902-10-14	711,185	Smith, William B.	rotary holder	
1902-12-23	716,840	Hooper, Beekman D.	rotary w/c	
1903-03-31	724,246	Bentley, Carrie	handheld	Ideal
1903-04-14	725,507	Taplin, Clarence A.	rotary	Taplin
1903-06-02	729,884	Munson, Samuel R.	mixing vessel	Landers, Frary & Clark
1903-06-30	732,661	Shinn, Luther E.	rotary w/c	E-Z Mixer
1903-07-14	733,621	Browne, William G.	rotary	W.G. Browne Mfg Co.
1903-08-04	735,353	Eifert, Robert August	rotary w/c	
1903-08-11	736,161	Smith, Morris	rotary w/c	
1903-08-18	736,723	Hamilton, Charles R.	tin churn	
1903-09-22	739,488	Galatius, Louis M.	handheld	
1903-10-06	740,751	Friedman, Goste	rotary mount	
1903-10-06	740,752	Goss, Daniel S.	rotary w/c	
1903-10-13	741,586	Maurer, Fred	rotary w/c	
1903-10-27	742,264	Weber, Bertha E.	rotary mount	
1903-10-27	742,773	Cain, Wesley R.	Archimedes	
1903-11-03	743,149	Collins, George E.	rotary w/c	
1904-02-09	751,601	Angerbower, George	rotary	Taplin
1904-04-12	757,144	Richardson, William	rotary w/c	

Date	Pat. No.	Inventor	Type	Beater Name / Company
1904-05-03	758,746	Ganfolfo, John F.	rotary w/c	
1904-06-07	D-36,957	Helmer, William	rotary in glass globe	Glass Whipper
1904-08-23	768,086	Sturma, William	rotary belt	
1904-09-27	771,088	Paley, William V.	handheld	
1904-11-15	775,102	Dudley, Walter J.	rotary	
1904-12-06	776,791	Morgan, Edward	rotary	
1904-12-20	777,675	Hillman, Shimer B.	rotary w/c	Hillman Mfg. Co.
1905-01-31	781,247	Washington, William	handheld	
1905-02-07	781,917	Smith, Harry Arthur	handheld	
1905-03-21	785,114	Munn, George M.	rotary	
1905-03-21	785,249	Burnham Naomi C.	rotary	
1905-04-18	787,774	Lamb, Joseph F.	rotary clamp	Landers, Frary & Clark
1905-05-09	789,172	Roeck, Emmanuel	cake mixer	
1905-07-04	793,843	Libbman, Louis	vessel clamp	
1905-07-04	793,844	Libbman, Louis	rotary w/c	
1905-07-18	795,082	Warner, Alonzo A.	rotary w/c	Landers, Frary & Clark
1905-08-01	796,083	O'Neall, James M.	tin churn	
1905-08-22	797,959	Hulvorsen, Martin	rotary w/c	
1905-09-05	798,613	Marie, Wallace R.	Archimedes	
1905-10-24	802,923	Farmer, Edwin T.	Archimedes	
1905-11-07	803,833	Lamb, Joseph F.	mixing vessel	Landers, Frary & Clark
1905-11-21	805,020	Laurick, Carl	rotary w/c	
1905-12-26	808,613	Parish, Graham C.	rotary	corrected to Brown / W. G. Brown Mfg. Co.
1906-01-23	810,417	Kadel, Dottie	rotary w/c	
1906-04-10	817,272	Persons, Ernest Leon	rotary holder	
1906-04-10	817,635	Flowers, George R.	Archimedes	20th Century, The Up to Date, The Hess, Flowers
1906-04-24	818,914	Perrin, Thomas H.	rotary	
1906-05-15	820,405	Dunlap, John S.	rotary	Dunlap
1906-07-17	826,223	Broadwell, Charles H.	rotary mount	Landers, Frary & Clark
1906-07-31	827,474	Stewart, Alexander T.	tin plunger	
1906-09-25	831,538	Crimp, Harvey M.	handheld	
1906-10-02	832,052	Fritz, Arthur	rotary	
1906-10-02	832,235	Braham, Harry L.	rotary w/c	
1906-10-02	832,504	Sandall, Arthur	rotary	
1906-10-09	833,069	Loll, Frederick W.	rotary w/c	F. W. Loll Mfg Co.
1906-10-16	833,518	Frank, Miles E.	handheld	
1906-10-30	834,876	Seaman, John Albert	rotary mayo	
1906-11-06	835,165	Shaw, Edward Payne	rotary w/c	
1906-12-04	837,432	Stromer, Nicholas	rotary	Express look-alike
1906-12-04	837,750	Sturma, William	handheld	
1907-01-15	841,320	Hill, John E.	rotary	The H-I-L-L / J. E. Hill Co.
1907-01-29	842,509	Woodruff, Oliver D.	rotary mount	
1907-02-05	843,309	Sturma, William	rotary belt	
1907-02-05	843,461	Husser, Jules	handheld	
1907-02-19	844,499	Cram, Alonzo W.	handheld	
1907-02-26	845,326	Bailey, George F.	beater holder	Taplin Mfg. Co.
1907-02-26	845,341	Dunlap, John S.	rotary	
1907-03-12	846,661	Godward, Ernest	rotary	
1907-03-12	846,662	Godward, Ernest	rotary brace	
1907-03-12	846,763	Thompson, Andrew J.	Archimedes	
1907-03-12	846,829	Danner, Samuel	rotary	
1907-04-02	849,273	Schuirmann, Ernst	rotary w/c	
1907-04-16	850,525	Dazey, Nathan P.	rotary churn	Dazey Churn
1907-04-23	850,991	Abbott, Frank E.	rotary keader	Buffalo Mfg. Co.
1907-06-11	856,469	Kapheim, Frederick	rotary w/c	Standard Specialty, Globe Cream Beater
1907-07-02	858,970	French, Mary E.	handheld	
1907-07-16	859,943	Holden, Elbridge	rotary w/c	
1907-07-30	861,603	Newton, Ann F.	Archimedes	
1907-09-10	865,620	Vasconcelles, Harvey	handheld	
1907-09-17	865,999	Coombs, Stephen	rotary w/c	
1907-09-17	866,067	Reed, Frank	tin churn	Cream City
1907-09-24	866,909	Brenner, Frank A.	handheld	
1907-10-15	868,124	Raymond, George L.	Archimedes	A&J
1907-10-29	869,736	Ruppel, William	rotary w/c	
1907-11-19	871,247	Tomlinson, Walter H.	handheld	
1907-11-26	871,895	Savage, George E.	rotary w/c	
1908-01-14	876,549	Hoffman, John A.	Archimedes	
1908-01-21	877,468	Overkamp, Charles H.	rotary belt	
1908-03-10	881,268	Tuson, Charles R.	handheld	
1908-04-07	884,085	Genge, Felix	handheld	
1908-04-21	885,444	Cram, Alonzo W.	handheld	
1908-05-19	887,790	Griswold, Harry J.	Archimedes	
1908-06-16	890,604	Chittenden, William	rotary w/c	

Date	Pat. No.	Inventor	Type	Beater Name / Company
1908-06-16	890,629	Erwin, James R.	Archimedes	
1908-07-07	892,856	Ladd, Earnest W.	rotary	Ladd
1908-07-28	894,459	Ovidi, Adolofo	rotary w/c	
1908-08-25	896,848	Mills, George M.	rotary w/c	
1908-08-25	896,919	Kamerrer, William C.	ratchet	
1908-10-06	900,210	Saltsman, Aaron J.	handheld	Rumford Cake Mixer
1908-11-10	903,515	Snyder, Geroge H.	rotary w/c	
1908-11-24	905,036	Wells, Harlan P.	rotary	Taplin Light Running
1909-02-23	913,398	Kier, John M.	rotary w/c	
1909-03-02	913,766	Rambeaud, Rene	rotary w/c	
1909-04-06	917,289	Hall, Michael W.	electric	
1909-04-27	919,625	Nicholas, Stella A.	rotary w/c	
1909-05-18	921,991	Hood, Thomas Hubert	ratchet	
1909-06-15	925,038	Schmitz, Ernst	rotary w/c	
1909-06-29	926,362	Speer, Fannie Hoyt	rotary w/c	
1909-07-13	927,952	Cooke, Walter L.	paint mixer	
1909-08-03	929,917	Collins, James H.	handheld	propeller spoon
1909-08-10	930,364	Edwards, Russell E.	rotary w/c	
1909-08-17	931,100	Valy, Maximillian A.	handheld	
1909-08-24	932,294	Kreuzberger, Bartlett	rotary	Master
1909-09-07	933,580	Preston, Henry C.	Archimedes	
1909-09-07	933,646	Hunkler, Benjamin	rotary w/c	
1909-09-14	934,169	Hawes, Benjamin N.	butter merger	Home Butter Merger / Family Butter Merger Co.
1909-09-14	934,217	Rowe, Robert M.	churn lever	
1909-09-28	935,088	Burr, Frederick P.	rope power	
1909-10-12	936,410	Chase, Ernest L.	rotary w/c	
1909-10-26	938,369	Christin, Manuel D.	Archimedes	
1909-10-26	938,407	Bean, Percy L.	rotary mount	
1909-11-02	939,017	Hallenberg, Albert	finger squeeze	
1909-11-23	941,075	Jackson, David B.	electric	
1909-12-07	942,116	Van Houten, Frank H.	electric	Dutchess Tool Co.
1909-12-28	944,621	Larock, Frederick J.	rotary w/c	
1909-12-28	944,781	Gienandt, Fritz L.	handheld	
1910-01-4	945,639	Taylor, J.E. & T.G.	vertical churn	Reliable Churn / Taylor Bros Churn Co.
1910-01-11	945,983	Poore, Alfred C.	rotary w/c	
1910-01-11	946,169	Sturma, William	rotary belt	
1910-01-11	946,521	Nichols, Charles A.	rotary w/c	
1910-02-01	948,214	Fisher, Charles W.	rotary w/c	
1910-02-08	948,750	Washburn, Reginald	handheld	Washburn / Wire Goods Co.
1910-02-22	950,152	Gaar, William J. C.	rotary churn	
1910-03-15	951,834	Nehr, Herman F.	Archimedes	
1910-04-19	955,672	Nielsen, Rasmus	rotary	
1910-05-24	959,420	Ashby, William H.	rotary w/c	
1910-05-31	959,536	Horner, John W.	rope power	
1910-05-31	959,606	Ramstad, John N.	rotary w/c	
1910-05-31	959,731	Gilmour, Hugh Kerr	rotary mount	
1910-06-14	961,272	Ward, James N.	rotary w/c	
1910-07-12	964,291	Mattern, August	tin plunger	
1910-07-12	964,306	Otten, Arthur H. Otten	rotary w/c	
1910-08-09	966,501	Wenk, Wilheim	electric	
1910-08-09	966,738	Fowler, Benjamin F.	tin plunger	
1910-08-09	966,765	Read, Harry	electric	
1910-08-16	967,232	Perez, Waldo F.	churn	
1910-08-30	969,120	Shapleigh, Marshall	rotary w/c	
1910-09-06	969,324	Bachman, Harry M.	rotary stand	Dutchess Tool Co.
1910-09-20	970,969	Taylor, Dorothy	handheld	
1910-10-25	973,554	Pearson, James H.	rope power	
1910-11-01	974,586	Morgan, Edward M.	rotary	
1911-01-03	980,824	Noakes, William	tin plunger	
1911-01-03	980,827	Osner, Charles	rotary w/c	
1911-04-11	989,418	Read, Ellis D.	rotary w/c	
1911-04-18	989,733	Townsend, Harry E.	rotary belt	
1911-05-02	991,253	Van Engelen, Lucy	rotary w/c	
1911-05-02	991,432	Dupre, Wilfred	Archimedes	
1911-05-11	991,883	Olsen, Mariues B.	Archimedes	
1911-05-30	993,821	Brown, Harold S.	rotary w/c	
1911-08-22	1,001,451	Ross, Ashton D.	rotary w/c, eggshake apparatus	
1911-08-29	1,001,949	Hanna, William A.	rotary w/c	
1911-09-05	1,002,434	Opdahl, Carl	rotary w/c	
1911-09-12	1,003,319	Barton, Charles T.	rotary w/c	
1911-09-19	1,003,425	Booth, Charles C.	rotary mount	
1911-10-03	1,004,786	Hess, George F.	handheld	
1911-10-03	1,004,821	Schenk, Charles	rotary w/c	
1911-10-10	1,005,653	Osius, Frederick J.	electric	Hamilton Beach
1911-10-17	1,005,847	Knapp, Edwin L.	rotary mount	
1911-11-07	1,007,798	Rogers, Ulysses J.	butter blender, rotary w/c	
1911-11-07	1,007,891	Read, Harry	handheld	
1911-11-28	1,007,930	Dehuff, Walter F.	electric	
1911-11-28	1,010,019	Christoph, Emil A.	Archimedes	McGill Mfg Co.
1911-12-19	1,012,489	Westby, Adolph C	ratchet	
1912-01-02	1,013,803	Nilson, Oliver C.	rotary w/c	
1912-01-09	1,014,382	Forth, Charles	rotary	
1912-01-16	1,014,909	Schenk, Charles	rotary w/c	
1912-03-05	1,019,055	Kyle, Hattie	rotary w/c	
1912-03-05	1,019,546	Spear, Fannie G.	Archimedes	20th Century/Spear's
1912-05-07	1,025,798	Fitch, Charles G.	Archimedes	
1912-05-14	1,025,982	Johnson, Edward H.	Archimedes	A&J
1912-05-14	1,026,355	Hudson, Mahal	rotary w/c	
1912-06-25	1,030,796	Turner, Rose Rice	tin plunger	
1912-07-09	1,032,029	Seifke, Herman A.	electric	
1912-07-16	1,032,551	Leger, Splandien	syllabub	
1912-08-06	1,034,908	Grant, Sidney, A.	Archimedes	
1912-08-20	1,036,159	Sperry, Evelyn P.	rotary	Turbine Egg Beater
1912-09-10	1,038,204	Roberts, Henry P.	Archimedes	Roberts Lightning
1912-10-01	1,039,735	Helken, Emil, W. H.	electric	
1912-12-10	1,046,648	Roberts, Henry P.	rotary w/c	
1913-03-04	1,054,797	Schneider, Lorenz	rotary	
1913-04-29	1,060,419	Benjamin, Robert	shaker	
1913-05-20	1,062,059	Toda, Sozaburo	rotary w/c	
1913-06-10	1,064,070	Gibbs, Howard W.	rotary w/c	Dorsey Mfg Co.
1913-06-17	1,064,729	Hickey, James	handheld	
1913-07-29	1,068,450	Roberts, Henry P.	Archimedes	Roberts Lightning / Dorsey Mfg Co.
1913-07-29	1,068,994	Endorf, Charles	electric	
1913-09-02	1,071,747	Hutchinson, Job	rotary w/c	S&S Hutchinson / National Indicator Co.
1913-09-02	1,072,251	Parham, William J.	handheld	
1913-09-16	1,073,133	Jennings, Nancy G.	rotary mount	
1913-09-30	1,074,397	Westby, Adolph C.	rotary mount	
1913-11-04	1,077,832	Holt, Thomas	Archimedes	Holt / Holt-Lyon Co.
1913-12-23	1,082,243	Shelton, William G.	electric	
1914-02-03	1,085,858	Fulton, William H.	electric	Fulton-Bell Co.
1914-03-17	1,090,148	Harr, John L.	rotary mount	
1914-03-17	1,090,567	Roberts, Henry P.	Archimedes	
1914-06-16	1,100,683	Sinclair, Harry R.	Archimedes	
1914-06-23	1,101,347	Spear, Fannie G.	Archimedes	Spear's 20th Century
1914-06-30	1,101,560	McKinlay, Alexander	Archimedes	
1914-06-30	1,101,693	Gourlie, John H.	syllabub	
1914-06-30	1,101,781	Bleuler, Norman	rotary	
1914-09-01	1,108,973	Covey, Harry A.	rotary w/c	
1914-10-27	1,115,287	Coughlin, Joseph D.	Archimedes	Progressive Mfg Co.
1914-11-03	1,116,230	Boyd, Martha I.	plunger	
1914-11-10	1,116,988	Burke, Thomas A.	handheld	
1914-12-15	1,120,716	Hirt, Clifford I.	electric	
1914-12-15	1,120,882	Anderson, Gustaf M.	rotary plate cleaner	
1914-12-15	1,121,107	Kress, John	rotary w/c	
1914-12-29	1,122,876	Doty, William H.	Archimedes	McLean Black, Boston
1915-01-12	1,124,567	Wickstrom, Maurice	ratchet	
1915-01-19	1,125,337	Jorgensen, Thorleif B.	electric	
1915-03-30	1,133,413	Stough, Turnet H.	Archimedes	Simplex, Borden's, etc.
1915-04-06	1,134,170	Washburn, Reginald	handheld	Washburn / Wire Goods Co.
1915-04-27	1,137,037	Warner, Alonzo A.	rotary w/c	Universal Mayo / Landers, Frary & Clark
1915-05-11	1,138,897	Sari, Mary	handheld	
1915-05-18	1,140,341	Johnston, Arthur W.	Archimedes	
1915-06-01	1,141,207	Parent, Ludger M.	rotary w/c	
1915-06-01	1,141,420	Shattuck, Burt E.	rotary belt	Dow Surgical Battery
1915-06-01	1,141,528	Cunningham, Andrew	rotary w/c	
1915-06-08	1,142,331	Lahiere, Eugene A.	rotary w/c	
1915-06-22	1,144,215	Landsberg, William	rotary w/c	
1915-06-29	1,144,749	Beck, Rufus L.	rotary w/c	
1915-07-06	1,145,275	Smith, Oliver, C.	ratchet	
1915-07-27	1,148,032	McLoy, Jesse J.	rotary w/c	
1915-08-24	1,151,372	Moore, Robert A.	rotary	The Moore Beater / Moore-Libby
1915-09-28	1,154,940	Schmidt, Ernst M.C.	rotary	
1915-09-28	1,155,215	Cooley, Edward H.	handheld	
1915-10-05	1,155,907	Frame, John	rotary	
1915-10-26	1,158,178	Clark Elmer A.	bowl holder	
1915-12-14	1,164,443	Yiakas, Esidoros	ratchet	

Date	Pat. No.	Inventor	Type	Beater Name / Company
1915-12-21	1,165,307	Baltzley, Edwin E.	Archimedes	
1915-12-28	1,165,423	Ladd, Earnest W.	rotary	
1916-01-04	1,166,568	Wilton, Ralph P.	rotary w/c	
1916-01-04	1,167,336	Clark, Elmer A.	rotary	
1916-01-11	1,168,127	Szlemko, Katherine	rotary	
1916-02-01	1,170,358	Sweeting, Harry W.	handheld	
1916-02-08	1,171,054	Keppeler, Adolph	electric	
1916-02-15	1,171,922	Bordwell, Lavern	rotary w/c	Ladd Mixers 1 & 2 / Ladd
1916-02-15	1,171,923	Bordwell, Lavern	rotary w/c	Ladd
1916-03-07	1,174,828	Copeland, Alonzo	drink mixer	
1916-03-14	1,175,598	Bush, James D.	rotary	
1916-03-21	1,176,409	Stump, Ira E.	Archimedes	
1916-04-04	1,178,255	Milks, John H.	ratchet	
1916-04-18	1,179,984	Vidinghoff, Charles	splash guard	
1916-05-02	1,181,142	Kirkpatrick, Orson F.	beater vessel	
1916-05-30	1,184,927	Condogeorge, N.	rotary	
1916-05-30	1,185,004	Ross, Antonio	rotary w/c	
1916-06-06	1,186,526	Sears, Augustus H.	rotary w/c	
1916-07-18	1,191,170	Free, John Sr.	rotary w/c	
1916-07-25	1,192,426	Hudson, James H.	rotary w/c	
1916-08-22	1,195,839	Moses, Albert	handheld	
1916-09-05	1,197,565	Taylor, William	handheld	
1916-09-26	1,199,455	Dunlap, John S.	rotary gear	Dunlap
1916-10-17	1,201,284	Gilchrist, Raymond B.	shaker	Gilchrist Co.
1916-10-24	1,202,415	O'Neal & Favorite	ratchet	Favorite / Favorite Products
1916-11-07	1,203,899	Myers, Frederick	electric	
1916-11-07	1,204,363	Knobel, Abraham	rotary	
1916-11-28	1,206,327	Hills, Sidney C.	rotary	T&S
1916-12-19	1,208,862	Velissarides, V.	handheld	
1916-12-26	1,210,192	Moses, Albert	handheld	
1917-01-09	1,211,426	Farrington, Richard	tin plunger	
1917-01-23	1,213,561	Walker, Lena E.	handheld	
1917-01-30	1,214,010	Conner, May	rotary	
1917-02-06	1,215,214	Stewart, Charles A.	small churn	Lightning Butter Machine / Stewart-Skinner Co.
1917-02-06	1,214,975	Usher, Frederick S.	Archimedes	
1917-02-27	1,217,832	Saito, Kohei	rotary	
1917-03-27	1,220,426	Kelly, Guy W.	mayo attach	
1917-03-27	1,220,862	Lewis, Samuel W.	Archimedes	
1917-03-27	1,220,928	Baltzley, Edwin & Louis	rotary w/c	Keystone
1917-03-27	1,220,929	Baltzley, Edwin E.	funnel	Keystone funnel
1917-04-24	1,223,839	Turner, William D.	rotary	
1917-05-15	1,225,907	Wikstedt, Frans F.	beater holder	
1917-05-22	1,227,327	Sheaffer, John E.	rotary	
1917-05-29	1,227,671	Robertson, William P.	electric	Borden's Condensed Milk
1917-05-29	1,227,935	Robertson, William P.	electric	
1917-06-05	1,228,823	Robertson, William P.	electric	
1917-07-17	1,233,748	Briscoe, Marion G.	rotary w/c	
1917-08-14	1,236,814	Alexander, George E.	rotary	Biltrite (early model)
1917-08-21	1,237,585	Tripke, Paul	Archimedes	
1917-08-21	1,237,707	Schubert, Edward	water power	
1917-08-28	1,238,461	Tripke, Paul	Archimedes	
1917-09-18	1,240,355	MacMoran, Henrietta	rotary mount	
1917-09-18	1,240,688	Drucker, William J.	rotary w/c	Drucker & Boss
1917-10-23	1,243,982	Rupp, Laurente	tin plunger	
1917-11-13	1,246,103	Joinette, Ernest A.	rotary mount	
1917-11-13	1,246,104	Jones, Thomas E.	rotary	Turbine, Cassidy Fairbank
1917-11-27	1,247,655	Frame, John	rotary w/c	
1917-11-27	1,248,327	Hoerburger, Alex	rotary cheese	
1917-12-18	1,250,539	Witherbee, Mary	rotary	
1917-12-18	1,250,810	Dazey, Nathan P.	rotary w/c	Dazey Churn
1917-12-18	1,250,889	Johnson, Edward H.	Archimedes	A&J
1918-01-15	1,253,785	Chaparro, Roberto	shaker	
1918-02-12	1,255,993	Dunning, Warren H.	rotary stand	Dover stand, tin
1918-02-12	1,255,994	Dunning, Warren H.	rotary spring	Dover stand, spring
1918-04-16	1,263,014	Alexander, George E.	rotary	
1918-06-04	1,268,284	Ryerson, Eugene H.	handheld	Hamblin & Russell
1918-06-04	1,268,586	Lawton, Jason Lee	Archimedes	
1918-07-16	1,272,506	Olander, Ernest V.	handheld	
1918-07-23	1,273,486	Hills, Sidney C.	rotary	T&S
1918-07-30	1,247,021	Ebeling, Charles W.	plunger	Kre Mo Butter
1918-08-06	1,274,634	Tripke, Paul	Archimedes	
1918-08-13	1,275,587	Musser, George R.	beater guard	
1918-10-15	1,281,603	Leyer, Amand	rotary w/c	
1918-10-22	1,282,148	Tripke, Paul	Archmiedes	
1918-10-22	1,282,537	Burkhart, Lucy	handheld	
1918-12-17	1,287,741	Pinkney, Bryan D.	dasher	
1918-12-31	1,289,545	Roberts, Maurice H.	Archimedes	
1919-01-21	1,292,141	Swigert, Joseph O.	rotary w/c	
1919-02-04	1,293,274	Werth, Reinhardt	rotary mount	
1919-02-25	1,295,684	Bouquin, Joseph	plunger	
1919-03-04	1,296,326	Scollon, Richard	plunger	
1919-07-08	1,308,953	Johnson, Erich	rotary w/c	
1919-07-22	1,310,861	Fowler, Benjamin F.	plunger	
1919-08-12	1,312,569	Paige, James H.	shaker	
1919-11-04	1,320,603	Collins, Frank R.	rotary	
1919-11-25	1,322,874	Brull, Eugene C.	rotary	Duplex
1919-12-23	1,325,509	Crane, William M.	tin plunger	
1920-01-06	1,327,568	Neukirchen, Peter	glass plunger	Rapid Fire
1920-01-13	1,327,900	Black, Mathew	rotary mount	
1920-03-09	1,333,379	Black, Mathew	rotary w/c	
1920-03-23	1,334,274	Alexander, George E.	rotary	Whipwell
1920-04-20	1,337,478	Long, Russell L.	water power	
1920-04-20	1,337,860	Ullman, Louis	rotary	Aluminum Beauty, Instant Whip
1920-05-18	1,340,849	Buckle, John V.	electric	
1920-05-25	D-55,340	Thompson, Milton O.	Archimedes	
1920-06-08	1,343,091	Shearer, John A.	rotary	butter maker
1920-08-17	1,350,098	Hessey, John L.	handheld	
1920-09-21	1,353,443	Wilson, Robert Grout	shaker	
1920-09-28	1,354,230	Walther, Henry S.	water power	
1920-11-16	1,359,208	Viers, Burr D.	electric	
1920-12-07	1,361,368	Dailey, James W.	mayo funnel	
1920-12-14	1,362,164	Karamanos, Demetrios	ratchet	
1921-01-22	1,372,279	Collins, Lathrop	electric	Dormeyer
1921-02-01	1,367,002	Awiszus, Adam	vacuum	
1921-02-08	1,368,180	Nakamura, Mitsutaro	handheld	
1921-03-22	1,372,578	Weber, Erwin	Archimedes	
1921-04-05	1,373,761	Rabin, Samuel	Archimedes	
1921-04-19	1,375,338	Werner, Otto P.	water power	
1921-05-24	1,379,507	George E. Alexander	rotary	Whipwell
1921-06-14	1,381,665	Rostocki, John M.	handheld	
1921-06-28	1,382,682	Shelton, William G.	electric	
1921-07-12	1,384,593	Brumford, James L.	rotary	
1921-07-26	1,385,605	Cazenove, James O. H.	rotary	
1921-08-02	1,386,405	Hills, Sidney C.	rotary	T&S
1921-09-20	1,391,013	Schwager, Joseph W.	rotary w/c	
1921-09-20	1,391,439	Williams, Nora	rotary mount	
1921-10-18	1,393,799	Laurick, Carl	push rotary	
1921-10-18	1,393,941	Bordwell, Lavern	rotary	Ladd
1921-12-06	1,399,296	Feeney, John M.	rotary	
1921-12-06	1,399,513	Nyberg, Albert F.	rotary	
1921-12-13	1,399,740	Bott, George R.	electric	
1921-12-13	1,400,309	Munsing, George D.	syllabub	
1921-12-27	1,401,408	Hull, Henry M.	rotary	
1922-01-03	1,402,380	Schaedler, John M.	electric	
1922-02-14	1,406,619	Dazey, Nathan P.	churn	Dazey Churn
1922-02-14	1,406,778	Teetsell, Ulysses G.	rotary	Holt-Lyon side handle
1922-02-28	1,407,789	Erhardt, Oscar P.	electric	A. C. Gilbert
1922-03-07	1,408,591	Hamilton, Charles H.	tin plunger	
1922-03-14	1,409,209	Wolfe, Rowland H.	rotary w/c	
1922-04-21	1,410,522	Ziemba, John	handheld	
1922-04-25	1,413,874	Roberts, Maurice H.	Archimedes	Harris Co.
1922-05-30	1,417,982	Fitzpatrick, George J.	rotary	
1922-08-08	1,425,026	Lower, Raymond S.	rotary w/c	Lower
1922-08-15	1,426,080	Holt, Edward E.	rotary	
1922-09-05	1,427,986	Viner, John H.	rotary	
1922-09-26	1,430,012	Heiser, Lucien	rotary w/c	
1922-09-26	1,430,040	Trust, Henry	handturn w/c	
1922-10-24	1,433,508	Hills, Sidney, C.	rotary	T&S
1922-10-31	1,433,710	Flink, Carl E.	rotary	
1922-11-14	1,435,289	Gilbert, Alfred C.	electric	A. C. Gilbert
1922-11-28	1,437,133	Dekin, Le Roy J.	rope power	
1922-12-05	1,437,957	Bordwell, Lavern	rotary	Ladd
1922-12-12	1,438,281	Westerman, Frederick	electric	
1922-12-12	1,438,716	Orzchovski, Stanley	rotary	Jiffy Cream Whip / Kohler Die & Specialty
1922-12-19	1,439,102	Hayward, Agnes, C.	handheld	
1923-02-13	1,444,910	Goetz, Joseph F.	paint mixer	
1923-02-13	1,445,342	Midorikawa, Edward	plunger	
1923-02-20	1,445,696	Lively, Elbert W.	bowl attach	
1923-05-01	1,453,761	Lange, William F.	syllabub	
1923-05-08	1,454,199	Weidlich, Kunz	rotary	Moha
1923-05-22	1,456,448	Jensen, Christian E.	water power	

Date	Pat. No.	Inventor	Type	Beater Name / Company
1923-06-19	1,459,148	Flynt, Anthony I.	rotary w/c	
1923-07-03	1,460,493	Leinan, Edwin S.	rotary	
1923-07-10	1,461,468	Trust, Henry	handturn w/c	
1923-07-17	1,461,962	Bevan, Alexander	rotary	
1923-07-31	1,463,493	Anderson, Agustus F.	rotary	United Royalties Corp
1923-08-21	1,465,629	Gilchrist, Raymond B.	electric	Gilchrist Co.
1923-08-21	1,465,630	Gilchrist, Raymond B.	electric	Gilchrist Co.
1923-08-21	1,465,631	Gilchrist, Raymond B.	electric	Gilchrist Co.
1923-08-21	1,465,632	Gilchrist, Raymond B.	electric	Gilchrist Co.
1923-08-21	1,465,633	Gilchrist, Raymond B.	electric	Gilchrist Co.
1923-08-21	1,465,634	Gilchrist, Raymond B.	electric	Gilchrist Co.
1923-08-21	1,465,635	Gilchrist, Raymond B.	electric	Gilchrist Co.
1923-08-28	1,465,940	Hazzard, Paul	rotary triple	
1923-09-04	1,467,205	Steele, Arthur G.	rotary	
1923-09-11	1,467,989	Jembrzcki, Stanley	electric	Racine Universal
1923-09-18	1,468,560	Diehl, Philip Jacob	bakery whip	
1923-09-25	1,468,826	Minney, Arthur W.	rotary w/c	
1923-10-09	1,470,169	Kail, Charles E.	rotary	A&J
1923-10-09	1,470,170	Kail, Charles E.	rotary	A&J
1923-10-16	1,470,882	Sauer, Lena	rotary w/c	
1923-10-30	1,472,292	Cazenove, James	rotary	
1923-11-27	1,475,767	Green, James A.	rotary	T&S cast-iron
1923-12-04	1,475,978	Westerman, Fred	electric	
1923-12-18	1,477,943	Crocker, William W.	hand squeeze	One Hand Wip
1924-01-15	R-15,746	Westerman, F.	electric	
1924-01-29	1,482,279	Trust, Henry	rotary w/c	
1924-03-11	1,486,255	Lambert, Clara, B.	wire blender	
1924-04-22	1,490,980	Minney, Arthur Wells	rotary w/c	
1924-04-29	1,492,229	Thompson, Herbert L.	water power	World Beater
1924-05-27	1,495,367	Wiltrout, Edgar I.	rotary mount	
1924-09-02	1,506,951	Soukup, Wenzl	electric	
1924-10-14	1,511,541	Thompson, Herbert L.	water power motor	
1924-10-21	1,512,669	Benson, Frederick	rotary	Benson Beater
1924-11-18	1,516,210	Samuels, Julius	rotary	
1924-11-25	1,516,792	Ruggles, Wells G.	rotary w/c	Whippo Super Whipper / Dover Stamping & Mfg.
1924-12-09	1,518,284	Wessell, George	rotary	Taplin
1924-12-09	1,518,285	Wessell, George	rotary	Taplin
1924-12-16	1,519,533	Dingle, Charles	rotary	
1924-12-23	1,520,375	Trust, Henry	handturn w/c	
1925-01-13	1,523,085	Schramm, William	syllabub	
1925-02-10	1,525,967	Vogel, Joseph M.	electric mixer motor improvement	Dormeyer
1925-03-24	1,530,716	Doerb, George W.	handheld	
1925-05-26	1,539,731	Hanson, Walter	rotary	
1925-06-26	1,539,245	Duncan, Israel P.	water power	Marvel Whipper Co.
1925-06-09	1,540,946	Moeller, Arturo F.	syllabub	
1925-06-16	1,542,574	Park, Watson	rotary	
1925-08-11	1,548,919	Ward, Paul S.	rotary w/c	Triumph Mfg.
1925-08-18	1,549,889	Moore, Robert A.	rotary	Ram Beaters / Ram Metal Products
1925-09-29	1,555,502	Knoblauch, Edward	handheld	
1925-10-13	1,557,364	Headley, Afton Rees	rotary w/c	
1926-02-02	1,571,591	Lockwood, Harry C.	rotary	
1926-02-02	1,571,851	Lyon, Ray W.	rotary mount	
1926-02-09	1,572,764	Chattin, John E.	syllabub	
1926-03-02	1,575,090	Benson, Frederick	rotary	Benson Beater
1926-03-23	1,577,615	Emery, Harry Le Roy	rotary	
1926-06-29	1,590,831	Jones, Louis W.	glass plunger	Jones Wonder
1926-10-26	1,604,513	Hoffer, Ivan L.	plunger	
1926-11-09	1,606,684	Aurelius, Bernard E.	rotary	Aurelius / Aurelius Brothers
1926-11-30	1,609,254	Humphrey, Ernest N.	rotary	Ladd / United Royalties Corp
1926-12-28	1,612,281	Goetz, Joseph F.	paint mixer	Columbia Metal
1927-01-25	1,615,386	Jackson, Richard W.	rotary mount	
1927-02-08	1,616,817	Maxwell, Robert G.	rotary	
1927-02-15	1,617,747	Douglas, Robert W.	holder mount	
1927-02-15	1,617,787	Andrews, Charles Jr.	handheld	Androck / Washburn Co.
1927-04-05	1,623,256	Lienhard, Richard B.	rotary	Taplin
1927-05-03	1,627,314	Boynton, Oliver R.	rotary	
1927-05-03	1,627,315	Boynton, Oliver	rotary	
1927-05-27	1,629,956	Kopenhaver, Anna A.	rotary	
1927-06-21	1,633,470	Ball, Charles M.	electric	
1927-07-26	1,637,103	Corwin, Frank E.	tin shaker	
1927-08-23	1,639,932	Ellis, Wilson R.	rotary convex	Konvex/Whirl Whip

Date	Pat. No.	Inventor	Type	Beater Name / Company
1927-10-11	1,645,062	Lambert Clara B.	pastry mixer	
1927-11-01	1,647,800	Humphrey, Ernest N.	rotary	Ladd / United Royalties Corp
1927-11-22	1,649,874	Taylor, Herbert M.	handheld	
1927-11-29	1,650,777	White, Arthur S.	rotary	Presto T Whip / White & Hallock Inc.
1927-11-29	1,651,276	Hood, William L.	handheld	
1928-03-27	1,663,961	Taylor, William J.	rotary	
1928-04-10	1,665,879	Graves, Scott S.	rotary	
1928-06-05	1,672,224	Lauterbur, Frank X.	syllabub	
1928-07-03	1,676,128	Bordwell, Lavern	rotary	Ladd / United Royalties Corp
1928-07-03	1,676,189	Humphrey, Ernest N.	rotary	Ladd / United Royalties Corp
1928-07-17	1,677,754	Earle, Lee Edgar	rotary	United Royalties Corp
1928-07-24	1,678,425	Ellis, Wilson R.	rotary w/c	Konvex, Whirl Whip
1928-10-02	1,686,280	Keller, Graydon, M.	plunger	
1928-11-13	1,691,282	Guhl, August C.	rotary	
1928-12-11	1,694,500	Cazenove, James O. H.	rotary	
1929-01-08	1,698,363	Gilbert, Alfred C.	electric	A. C. Gilbert
1929-02-12	1,701,605	Bordwell, Lavern	rotary	Saturn A & B / United Royalties Corp
1929-02-19	1,702,862	Byland, Lucile	rotary	
1929-03-19	1,705,639	Fahlberg, Ernest	rotary	Whippit / E.D. Fahlberg Mfg Co.
1929-04-02	1,707,789	Fitzpatrick, George J.	rotary	
1929-04-16	1,709,768	Bordwell, Lavern	rotary	Ladd Ball Bearing / United Royalties Corp
1929-04-16	1,709,769	Bordwell, Lavern	rotary	Ladd Tumbler / United Royalties Corp
1929-04-30	1,710,836	Nippert, Tessie M.	handheld	
1929-04-30	1,711,409	Goundry, William J.	handheld	
1929-05-07	1,712,156	Morgan, Edward M.	rotary	
1929-05-21	1,713,828	Herron, George A.	rotary	
1929-05-21	1,714,359	Gambon, Emile	rotary w/c	
1929-06-18	1,718,111	Carlson, Harry J.	rotary	
1929-07-02	1,718,989	Sydney, Minatojo	rotary	Sydney
1929-07-09	1,719,973	Frates, Thomas L.	rotary w/c	
1929-07-09	1,720,361	Harris, Lottie J.	handheld	
1929-07-23	1,722,187	Wetzel, Hugo A.	bakery whip	
1929-08-13	1,724,356	Lambert, Clara B.	pastry mixer	
1929-09-03	1,726,977	Brull, Eugene C	rotary	Duplex
1929-10-01	1,730,219	Killman, Thomas A.	tin plunger	
1929-10-08	1,730,506	Hoffer Ivan L.	rotary	
1929-11-12	1,735,236	Dennis, Elmer L.	doughblender	Androck / Washburn Co.
1929-11-19	1,736,542	Madigan, Thomas J.	ratchet	
1929-12-03	1,738,112	Myers, Thomas B.	electric	Hamilton-Beach
1929-12-24	1,740,709	Parker, Frank H.	water power	Niagara / Niagara Mixer Co.
1929-12-24	1,740,710	Parker, Frank H.	water power	Niagara / Niagara Mixer Co.
1930-01-07	1,742,230	Bushnell, Porter K.	rotary	
1930-01-21	1,744,445	Casey, William J.	rotary	Columbia Metal Products
1930-02-11	1,747,032	Schlageter, Frederick	paint mixer	
1930-02-25	1,748,830	Carlson, Bror N.	flour pincher	Nifty Sifter
1930-03-25	1,751,853	Buck, Edwina	handheld	
1930-04-01	1,752,650	Pardini, Julian A.	rotary	
1930-04-01	1,752,832	Brumder, William C.	rotary w/c	
1930-04-15	1,755,132	Round, Albert W.	rotary	T&S
1930-05-13	1,758,111	Henderson, Frederick	rotary	Minute Maid / Henderson Corp.
1930-06-03	1,761,634	Kuck, Henry G.	rotary w/c	Biltrite Beater / Stuber & Kuck Co.
1930-06-03	1,762,081	Schleicher, George	electric	
1930-06-10	1,762,421	Pyle, Virgil Matthew	rotary w/c	
1930-06-10	1,763,301	Gilbert, Alfred C.	electric	A.C. Gilbert
1930-06-17	1,764,597	Andrews, Charles Jr.	rotary	Beats All, Washburn / Washburn Co.
1930-06-17	1,765,129	Cooke, Hugh	shaker	
1930-06-24	1,766,171	Hetherington, John	handheld	
1930-06-24	1,767,454	Hobbs, Samuel T.	rotary	Androck / Washburn Co.
1930-06-24	1,768,012	Stone, Randolph	plunger	
1930-07-01	1,768,926	Peters, James	paint mixer	Turbo-Mixer Corp.
1930-09-09	1,775,566	Lacey, Robert	rotary w/c	MIN-IT Products Inc.
1930-11-11	1,781,381	Gilbert, Alfred C.	electric	A. C. Gilbert
1930-12-09	1,784,575	Carlson, Gustav A.	handheld	Boyle Needle Co.
1930-12-16	1,785,563	Schiff, Sigmund	handheld	J. H. Day Co.
1931-01-13	1,788,479	Bell, John Wesley	ratchet	
1931-01-13	1,788,675	Johnson, Edward V.	beater holder	
1931-01-13	1,789,224	Edlund, Henry J.	rotary	Edlund
1931-01-27	1,790,242	Newnham, Eugene	electric	Galvin Electric Mfg.

Date	Pat. No.	Inventor	Type	Beater Name / Company
1931-02-24	1,793,934	Hommel, Susanna C.	rotary w/c	
1931-03-31	1,798,757	Roberts, Henry P.	Archimedes	
1931-04-14	1,801,154	Grommet, Katie Annie	table mount	
1931-06-23	1,811,499	Gilbert, Alfred C.	electric	A. C. Gilbert
1931-07-07	1,813,862	Madigan, Thomas J.	ratchet	
1931-07-28	1,816,046	Johannes, Hubert G.	plunger	Albert Pickbarth Co.
1931-08-04	1,817,665	Bailey, Thomas L.	rotary w.c	
1931-09-01	1,820,909	Drucker, Samuel B.	electric mayo	
1931-09-29	1,824,929	Pritchard, William C.	plunger	Toddy Mixer / Toddy Inc.
1931-09-29	1,825,450	Halse, Edwin	rotary	
1931-10-06	1,826,356	Mahony, William Jay	Archimedes	
1931-10-13	1,827,608	Pickard, Frank	rotary w/c	
1931-10-27	1,828,932	Kail, Charles E.	rotary	A&J
1931-11-10	1,831,040	Sowers, Ray V.	squeeze	
1931-12-29	1,839,082	Burgard, Louis C.	rotary w/c	
1932-03-01	1,847,226	Ringwald, Clarence	electric	Robbins & Myers Inc.
1932-03-01	1,847,563	Hjert, Andrew G.	rotary	
1932-03-08	1,848,925	Aurelius, Eugene A.	rotary	Aurelius Master / Aurelius Bros. Mfg.
1932-06-14	1,862,590	Dutt, Roller E.	stirrer (chips)	
1932-08-09	1,870,741	Nastrom, Nels	egg breaker	
1932-09-06	1,876,264	Tucker, James D.	bowl lock	
1932-10-04	1,881,361	Killman, Thomas A.	plunger	
1932-11-01	1,886,118	Pottsgrove, Philip N.	rotary w/c	
1932-12-06	1,890,307	Shailer, Philip B.	plunger	Magic Mixer, Malted Milk, Home Drink, A&J / Wm. D. Gibson Co.
1933-01-31	1,895,833	Baker, Stewart E.	pastry mixer	
1933-03-21	1,902,376	Purdin, Conn A.	electric	
1933-03-21	1,902,525	Rowley, Charles A.	handheld	
1933-03-21	1,902,678	Theodoropulos, A. A.	electric	
1933-04-04	D-89,565	Fitzgerald, Patrick J.	electric	Fitzgerald Mfg.
1933-04-11	1,903,527	Barnhisel, Walter B.	rotary w/strainer	Yankee Boy
1933-05-02	1,907,413	Anderson, Amers W.	electric combo	
1933-05-23	1,910,229	Baker, Stewart E.	pastry mixer	
1933-05-23	1,910,302	Maslow, Louis	handheld	
1933-05-23	1,910,303	Maynard, Mark	rotary	Maynard
1933-05-30	1,912,350	Gilbert, Alfred C.	electric	A. C. Gilbert
1933-06-06	1,912,525	Hotchkiss, Clarence	plumber's snake	Stow Mfg. Co
1933-06-20	1,915,017	Eck, Warren C.	rotary	
1933-06-20	1,915,190	Pauline Koment	massager	
1933-07-18	1,918,738	Burrell, Matthew	Archimedes	
1933-08-08	1,921,342	Bushnell, Porter K.	rotary	
1933-09-05	1,925,638	Killman, Thomas A.	rotary	
1933-09-12	2,926,910	Lynch, John W.	electric	Chicago Flexible Shaft Co.
1933-09-26	1,928,022	Little, Charles E.	rotary	
1933-09-26	1,928,032	Sack, Harry	rotary	
1933-10-17	1,930,948	Brewer, Everett	rotary w/c	
1933-10-31	1,933,439	Kuhn, Geroge	rotary	
1934-02-06	1,945,915	Riedel, Curtis	air power	
1934-02-20	1,948,431	Rolph, William	Archimedes	
1934-04-03	1,953,722	Pullen, Lester T.	rotary	Turner & Seymour
1934-04-10	1,954,507	Wheeler, Levi E.	rotary	Androck / Washburn Co.
1934-05-22	1,960,089	Rabb, Michael	Archimedes	Rabb
1934-07-10	1,965,650	Kail, Charles E.	rotary	A&J / EKCO
1934-07-10	1,966,352	Mahony, William J.	Archimedes	
1934-07-31	1,968,502	Nordby, Julius E.	rotary	
1934-08-07	1,969,162	Smith, Gertrude L.	handheld	
1934-08-21	1,971,257	Fitzgerald, Patrick J.	electric	Fitzgerald Mfg Co.
1934-10-16	D-93,596	Anderson, John	rotary	
1934-11-20	1,981,215	Alsop, Samuel	electric	
1934-11-20	1,981,531	Van Woert, Kenneth	rotary	Best
1934-11-27	1,982,531	Nash, Elizabeth F.	rotary w/c	
1934-12-18	1,984,557	Werner, Charles	Archimedes	Duroi Products Corp.
1935-01-01	1,986,163	Christina Rockwell	handheld	
1935-01-08	1,987,043	Andrews, James L.	rotary w/c	
1935-01-15	1,987,700	Muir, Herbert H.	Archimedes	
1935-02-26	1,992,564	Amdur, Alien	mix up	see 1,992,654
1935-02-26	1,992,654	Elliott, Clarence E.	rotary	K. C. side-handle
1935-03-05	1,993,338	Crowe, John M.	electric	
1935-05-28	2,003,259	Gilbert, Alfred C.	electric	A. C. Gilbert
1935-06-04	2,003,521	Smith, Ralston R.	rotary mount	
1935-06-04	2,003,829	Gilbert, Alfred C.	electric	A. C. Gilbert
1935-06-04	2,003,931	Gilbert, Alfred C.	electric	A. C. Gilbert
1935-07-09	2,007,249	Kelley, Albert	trigger	
1935-07-09	2,007,299	Gilbert, Alfred C.	electric	A. C. Gilbert

Date	Pat. No.	Inventor	Type	Beater Name / Company
1935-07-09	2,007,300	Gilbert, Alfred C.	electric	A. C. Gilbert
1935-07-09	2,007,361	Berger, Samuel I.	wind up	Wind up jar
1935-07-09	2,007,850	Drew, Clayton L.	tin plunger	
1935-08-06	2,010,534	Collins, Harold M.	drink mixer	
1935-09-03	2,013,615	Fontan, Le Roy H.	drink mixer	Napier Co.
1935-09-03	2,013,616	Rettenmeyer, F. W.	cocktail	Napier Co.
1935-09-03	2,013,617	Werfel, Harry A.	drink shaker	Napier Co.
1935-09-10	2,013,783	McLoughlin, James E.	electric	A.C. Gilbert
1935-09-10	2,013,887	Jeppsson, Ivar	electric	Chicago FlexibleShaft
1935-09-10	2,013,902	Tarrant, Marion A.	handheld	
1936-01-07	2,027,036	Gilbert, Alfred C.	electric	A. C. Gilbert
1936-01-28	2,028,921	Roos, Axel, H.	rotary	Roos' nickname Chico
1936-02-25	2,031,769	Gilbert, Alfred C.	electric	A. C. Gilbert
1936-02-25	2,031,770	Gilbert, Alfred C.	electric	A. C. Gilbert
1936-03-10	2,032,571	Gilbert, Alfred C.	electric	A. C. Gilbert
1936-03-10	2,033,453	Strief, Willie H.	Archimedes	
1936-03-17	2,034,214	Smith, Harold B.	electric	Robeson-Rochester
1936-04-07	2,036,262	Donahoe, Michael	rotary	
1936-04-21	2,038,256	Wright, Horace C.	electric	Chicago Flexible Shaft
1936-05-26	2,042,176	Hausman, Frederick	electric	
1936-06-02	2,042,791	Martinet, Eugene F.	electric	
1936-06-16	2,044,331	Rogers, Ivan	rotary	
1936-06-23	2,045,171	Wiegandt, Paul C.	Archimedes	
1936-06-30	2,046,109	Dunne, John J.	electric	
1936-07-14	2,047,841	Van Guilder, Walter	electric	General Electric
1936-08-04	2,049,727	Zimmer, Myron	gear hub	A&J / EKCO
1937-01-26	D-102,959	Rowley, Charles A.	handheld	
1937-07-13	2,086,658	Ames, George P.	electric can opener/mixer	
1937-08-31	2,091,786	Lienhard, Richard B.	rotary	Taplin
1937-09-07	2,092,353	Kyseth, George	drink stirrer	
1937-10-19	2,096,442	Whitmann, Joseph H.	Archimedes	
1936-11-24	2,061,868	Fitzgerald, Patrick J.	electric	
1938-03-15	2,11,407	Rommel, Paul J.	Archimedes spoon	Spoonomat / R. Wallace and Sons
1938-05-10	D-109,647	Rowley, Charles A.	handheld	Chief logo
1938-06-28	2,121,918	Leighty, Elroy Homer	rotary	
1938-07-05	2,123,118	Osborn, William L.	plunger	
1938-08-02	2,125,455	McLean, William A	electric	Geneva Processes Inc.
1938-08-16	D-110,899	King, Guy	mixer jar	A&J / EKCO cup
1938-12-13	D-112,531	Little, John M.	rotary	
1939-01-17	D-112,953	Van Woert, Kenneth B.	rotary	Best
1939-01-17	D-112,956	Hacmac, Edward R.	rotary	Worlbeater
1939-02-21	2,148,399	Crissey, Paul	rotary w/c	EKCO
1939-05-15	2,158,912	Piperi, Anthony J.	Archimedes	
1939-06-13	2,162,017	Illsche, Arthur	rotary	
1939-06-13	2,162,348	Hacmac, Edward R.	Archimedes	Johnston Cold Fudge / Na-Mac Products Co.
1939-06-20	D-115,335	Holister, Frank O.	rotary	Maynard Mixer / Note: Same as D-134,612
1939-07-18	2,166,437	Howie, Robert K.	tin plunger	
1939-08-15	2,169,607	Kelley, Albert	ratchet	
1939-11-21	2,181,078	Dehuff, Walter F.	electric	American Machine
1939-11-28	2,181,833	Palmieri, Cesare	Archimedes	Jiffy Whip
1939-12-12	2,182,921	Herter, Clarence	rotary	
1939-12-12	2,182,984	Hacmac, Edward R.	rotary	Deluxe Worlbeater / Na-Mac Products
1940-01-02	2,185,846	Hacmac, Edward R.	rotary	Worlbeater / Na-Mac Products
1940-03-12	2,193,461	Lienhard, Richard B.	rotary	Taplin
1940-04-09	D-119,841	Anstice, Mortimer R.	dasher design	
1940-04-09	D-119,842	Anstice, Mortimer R.	dasher design	
1940-05-28	D-120,771	Zimmer, Myron J.	rotary	Spinnit
1940-06-18	2,205,147	Madsen, Carl A.	container	
1940-07-09	2,207,335	Thomas, Louis R.	Archimedes	
1940-07-16	2,208,337	Maslow, Louis	handheld	
1940-07-16	2,208,431	Rochow, Arthur J.	shaker	Swirl Mixer
1940-08-06	2,210,608	Thinglum, Albert E.	rotary	Androck
1940-08-06	2,210,810	Hindes, Howard W.	rotary	Androck / Washburn Company
1940-08-27	D-122,155	Bernhardt, Rudolph	rotary w/c	
1940-09-06	2,210,810	Hindes, Howard W.	rotary	Washburn Company
1940-12-17	2,224,941	Weimer, Philip G.	egg venter	
1941-02-18	2,231,926	Leighty, Elroy Homer	rotary	
1941-04-29	2,240,237	Anderson, Selma	rotary potato	
1941-05-27	2,243,443	Sette, Frederick	rotary	Yoder, Simset
1941-06-24	2,246,517	Holister, Frank O.	rotary	Twin Speed /

Date	Pat. No.	Inventor	Type	Beater Name / Company
1941-12-09	2,265,533	Lawrence, John R.	rotary w/c	Holister Coil Spr Mfg
1941-12-23	2,267,424	Roos, Axel H.	rotary	Androck bowl beater / Washburn Co. Roos' nickname Chico
1942-03-31	2,277,986	Karp, Edward J.	bakery whip	
1942-03-31	2,278,398	Wittmann, Joseph H.	Archimedes	Wit Whip
1942-05-05	2,281,985	Morgan, Francis E.	handheld	
1942-08-04	2,291,708	Gluck, Henry	Archimedes	
1942-12-22	D-134,612	Maynard, Mark	rotary	Maynard Mixer / Note: Same as D-115,335
1943-03-23	2,314,522	Sette, Frederick E.	rotary	
1943-03-30	2,315,018	Lawrence, B.E.	electric	
1943-04-20	2,316,861	Hansen, Oliver	in shell	
1943-05-04	2,318,534	Seybert, Theodore	beater attach	
1943-09-21	2,330,012	Schlumbohm, Peter	handheld	
1944-05-23	D-137,946	Doner, Halbert C.	rotary in cabinet	
1944-09-12	2,357,886	Gamache, Homer	handheld	Acme Metal Goods
1945-05-01	2,374,831	Polcar, Marguerite	handheld	
1945-07-31	D-141,900	Latshaw, Fred F.	dasher design	
1945-10-16	D-142,550	Ford, George E.	electric	
1945-10-23	D-142,680	Swanson, Ray	rotary w/c	
1946-02-26	D-143,981	Maxson, William E.	electric	
1946-03-19	2,396,975	Verbrugge, Henry A.	Archimedes spoon	
1947-02-18	D-146,363	Jagow, Leroy J.	rotary	
1947-07-29	2,424,703	Morgan, Edward M.	rotary	
1947-11-11	2,430,600	Booth, Fred C.	squeeze	
1948-01-20	2,434,812	Roles, Duane	rotary w/c	
1948-02-10	D-148,620	Green, George G.	margarine mixer	Margy Maid
1948-02-24	D-148,770	Davis, John E.	rotary	
1948-03-16	D-149,011	Owens, Wayne F.	rotary	
1948-05-25	2,442,326	Pribil, Frank J.	handheld	
1948-08-31	2,448,174	Duvall, Walter J.	handheld	
1948-10-05	D-151,312	Zimmer, Myron	rotary	
1948-11-23	2,454,350	Shores, William P.	rotary	
1949-06-21	D-154,202	Hutton, Junius O.	rotary	
1949-08-09	D-154,752	De Martino, Alice	Archimedes	Possibly Boun-c-Beater
1949-08-30	2,480,482	Kirkpatrick, Orson	rotary	
1949-09-06	2,481,352	Sabatella, Vincent	plunger	
1949-09-20	2,482,587	Hughes, Dewey C.	handheld	
1949-09-27	2,483,280	Hansen, Harry	rotary mount	
1949-10-25	2,486,126	Dahnke, Marye	plunger	Kraft Foods Co.
1949-12-27	D-156,679	Stiles, Harry L.	electric with jar	
1950-02-28	2,499,074	Nordgarden, Ernest	handheld	
1950-03-07	2,499,371	De Vault, Ralph P.	rotary	
1950-04-04	2,502,571	Jones, Harry C.	rotary	
1950-04-25	2,505,362	Lawrence, John R.	rotary	Washburn Co.
1950-05-30	2,509,706	Szerenyi, Andrew	ratchet	
1950-07-18	2,515,713	Johnson, Andrew	Archimedes	
1950-08-22	2,520,075	Williams, Harry S.	rotary mount	

Date	Pat. No.	Inventor	Type	Beater Name / Company
1951-01-30	2,539,436	Kost, Alwin	rotary	
1951-06-05	2,555,756	Muehlhaus, Frank R.	plunger	
1951-07-31	2,562,380	Elliott, Clarence E.	rotary	K. C. rotary
1951-08-14	2,563,941	Krasberg, Rudolf	rotary	Jiffy, Atom Whip / Krasberg
1951-08-28	2,565,723	Euler, Donald J.	rotary	Boeing Airplane Co.
1951-09-18	2,568,318	Chester, Frank R.	rotary	
1951-11-20	2,575,978	Scheidecker, Wayne	Archimedes	
1951-12-04	2,576,947	Larson, Glen M.	electric	
1952-10-21	2,614,818	Bordwell, Lavern	rotary	United Royalties Corp.
1953-09-15	2,652,236	Lum, James	handheld	
1953-09-15	D-170,404	Elliott, Clarence E.	rotary	K .C. Rotary
1954-01-12	2,665,872	De Witt, Louis I.	bowl holder	
1954-03-02	2,670,938	Wittmann, Joseph H.	Archimedes	
1956-04-03	2,740,617	Ball, Howard L.	Archimedes spoon	
1956-06-05	2,749,098	Johnson, Albert H.	Archimedes	
1956-08-28	2,760,763	Harper, Murry D.	electric	
1957.02/19	2,782,014	De Vault, Ralph P.	rotary	
1958-02-04	2,822,009	Haus, Roy A.	egg venter	
1958-12-09	2,863,332	Maynard, Mark K.		Maynard (plastic enclosed gears)
1959-04-21	D-184,950	Maffel, Leo J.	handle for rotary	Taplin
1959-08-25	D-185,970	Latham, Richard S.	rotary	EKCO
1959-09-22	2,905,453	Wise, Clarence L.	attachment	
1959-09-29	2,906,510	Harris, Victoria P.	handheld	
1960/01/12	D-187,038	Hvale, James L.	rotary	EKCO
1960-08-16	2,949,284	Egedal, Lawrence	handheld	
1961/09/12	D-191,321	Latham, Ricahrd S.	rotary	EKCO
1961-11-21	3,009,686	Kaplan, Natham	Archimedes	
1962/05/15	D-192,812	Hvale, James L.	rotary	EKCO
1964/03/24	D-197,790	Bliss, Charles O.	rotary	Blisscraft of Hollywood
1964-05-12	3,132,849	Kritikson, John H.	pot stirrer	
1964-05-12	3,132,851	Tone, John W.	attachment	
1964-05-19	3,133,976	Gross, George E.	rotary	
1966-11-15	3,285,584	Goldfarb, Adolph E.	rotary w/c	
1968-11-26	3,412,983	Kesilman, Sol	handheld	
1973-07-10	D-227,646	Kelly, Roger L.	rotary	
1973-07-10	D-227,647	Kelly, Roger L.	rotary	
1973-07-10	3,744,767	Blasnik, William	Archimedes	
1974-03-12	3,796,512	Djuvik, Carl	electric	
1977-03-08	4,010,934	McCord, King S.	plunger	
1979-06-26	4,159,182	Adolfson, George	stirrer/pick	
1980-03-18	4,193,697	Lebowitz, Sam	rotary	
1981-04-28	4,264,216	Stansbury, Benjamin	electric	
1984-09-18	4,472,063	Eickelmann, Rolf W.	Archimedes	
1985-09-03	4,538,922	Johnson, William H.	Archimedes	
1988-04-05	4,735,510	Barbour, William P.	whisk	
1990-08-07	4,946,286	Purkapile, Emerson	Archimedes	Coca-Cola Co. Atlanta
1991-08-06	5,037,210	Bliss, William R.	Archimedes	industrial use

Inventor	Date	Pat. No.
Abbott, Frank E.	1907-04-23	850,991
Adamson, William	1865-04-18	47,264
Adancourt, William F.	1893-09-26	505,692
Adolfson, George	1979-06-26	4,159,182
Albrecht, Antonius C.	1893-04-18	495,925
Alden, Leonard B.	1866-07-31	56,845
Alexander, George E.	1917-08-14	1,236,814
Alexander, George E.	1918-04-16	1,263,014
Alexander, George E.	1920-03-23	1,334,274
Allen, D. H.	1881-10-11	248,004
Alsop, Samuel	1934-11-20	1,981,215
Amdur, Alien	1935-02-26	1,992,564
Ames, George P.	1937-07-13	2,086,658
Anderson, Agustus F.	1923-07-31	1,463,493
Anderson, Amers W.	1933-05-02	1,907,413
Anderson, Gustaf M.	1914-12-15	1,120,882
Anderson, John	1934-10-16	D-93,596
Anderson, Selma	1941-04-29	2,240,237
Andrews, Charles Jr.	1927-02-15	1,617,787
Andrews, Charles Jr.	1930-06-17	1,764,597
Andrews, James L.	1935-01-08	1,987,043
Angerbower, George	1904-02-09	751,601
Angus, William N.	1868-04-21	76,970
Anstice, Mortimer R.	1940-04-09	D-119,841
Anstice, Mortimer R.	1940-04-09	D-119,842
Arnold, Varnum G.	1866-10-16	58,750
Ashby, William H.	1910-05-24	959,420
Ashley, Frederick	1860-05-01	28,047
Ashley, Frederick	1866-06-26	55,802
Aurelius, Bernard E.	1926-11-09	1,606,684
Aurelius, Eugene A.	1932-03-08	1,848,925
Austin, Alvin Judd	1890-05-27	428,999
Awiszus, Adam	1921-02-01	1,367,002
Bachman, Harry M.	1910-09-06	969,324
Backmire, George H.	1879-10-28	221,016
Bagley, Charles H.	1899-11-07	636,737
Bailey, George F.	1907-02-26	845,326
Bailey, Thomas L.	1931-08-04	1,817,665
Baker, Stewart E.	1933-01-31	1,895,833
Baker, Stewart E.	1933-05-23	1,910,229
Baker, Uriah	1860-10-23	30,453
Ball, Charles M.	1927-06-21	1,633,470
Ball, Howard L.	1956-04-03	2,740,617
Baltzley, Edwin	1885-12-15	332,375
Baltzley, Edwin	1888-03-06	378,863
Baltzley, Edwin	1888-09-18	389,631
Baltzley, Edwin	1889-05-21	403,502
Baltzley, Edwin E.	1915-12-21	1,165,307
Baltzley, Edwin E.	1917-03-27	1,220,929
Baltzley,Edwin&Louis	1917-03-27	1,220,928
Barbour, William P.	1988-04-05	4,735,510
Barnhisel, Walter B.	1933-04-11	1,903,527
Barton, Charles T.	1911-09-12	1,003,319
Bean, Percy L.	1909-10-26	938,407
Beck, Rufus L.	1915-06-29	1,144,749
Bell, John Wesley	1931-01-13	1,788,479
Bellanger, Frank S.	1898-04-12	602,152
Bemis, William A.	1866-06-26	55,807
Benedict, Allen S.	1901-03-26	670,834
Benjamin, Robert	1913-04-29	1,060,419
Benson, Frederick	1924-10-21	1,512,669
Benson, Frederick	1926-03-02	1,575,090
Bentley, Carrie	1903-03-31	724,246
Berger, Samuel I.	1935-07-09	2,007,361
Bernhardt, Rudolph	1940-08-27	D-122,155
Bevan, Alexander	1923-07-17	1,461,962
Billings, Jerome	1866-03-20	53,260
Bishop, Mary F.	1888-06-19	384,674
Black, Mathew	1920-01-13	1,327,900
Black, Mathew	1920-03-09	1,333,379
Blake, Lewis T.	1868-07-28	80,440
Blasnik, William	1973-07-10	3,744,767
Blasse, Alfried R.	1866-02-13	52,518
Bleuler, Norman	1914-06-30	1,101,781
Bliss, Charles O.	1964/03/24	D-197,790
Bliss, J. W.	1864-12-06	45,309

Inventor	Date	Pat. No.
Bliss, William R.	1991-08-06	5,037,210
Boemermann, H.	1890-01-28	420,262
Boon, Alonzo T.	1876-09-05	181,903
Booth, Charles C.	1911-09-19	1,003,425
Booth, Fred C.	1947-11-11	2,430,600
Borcher, Thomas	1877-10-02	195,695
Bordwell, Lavern	1916-02-15	1,171,922
Bordwell, Lavern	1916-02-15	1,171,923
Bordwell, Lavern	1921-10-18	1,393,941
Bordwell, Lavern	1922-12-05	1,437,957
Bordwell, Lavern	1928-07-03	1,676,128
Bordwell, Lavern	1929-02-12	1,701,605
Bordwell, Lavern	1929-04-16	1,709,768
Bordwell, Lavern	1929-04-16	1,709,769
Bordwell, Lavern	1952-10-21	2,614,818
Borrman, W.	1858-04-27	20,032
Bostick, Emanuel	1871-10-03	D-5,296
Bott, George R.	1921-12-13	1,399,740
Bouquin, Joseph	1919-02-25	1,295,684
Boyd, Martha I.	1914-11-03	1,116,230
Boynton, Oliver	1927-05-03	1,627,315
Boynton, Oliver R.	1927-05-03	1,627,314
Braham, Harry L.	1906-10-02	832,235
Brenner, Frank A.	1907-09-24	866,909
Brewer, Everett	1933-10-17	1,930,948
Bridger, George E.	1867-08-27	68,037
Briscoe, Marion G.	1917-07-17	1,233,748
Brittain, Howard M.	1892-04-12	472,803
Broadwell, Charles H.	1906-07-17	826,223
Brooks, Heman P.	1881-05-24	241,784
Brothwell, John G.	1876-09-26	182,639
Brown, Harold S.	1911-05-30	993,821
Brown, Thomas W.	1880-06-29	229,372
Brown, Thomas W.	1880-09-21	232,328
Brown, Thomas W.	1881-03-08	238,565
Brown, Thomas W.	1885-07-14	322,250
Brown, Thomas W.	1887-08-30	369,273
Brown, Thomas W.	1890-01-21	419,631
Brown, Thomas W.	1898-12-27	D-29,873
Browne, William G.	1901-06-25	D-34,690
Browne, William G.	1901-07-16	678,456
Browne, William G.	1902-08-26	R-12,026
Browne, William G.	1903-07-14	733,621
Bruen, William	1891-07-07	455,479
Brull, Eugene C	1929-09-03	1,726,977
Brull, Eugene C.	1919-11-25	1,322,874
Brumder, William C.	1930-04-01	1,752,832
Brumford, James L.	1921-07-12	1,384,593
Bryant, Charles A.	1885-06-02	319,191
Bryant, Charles A.	1888-07-17	386,105
Buck, Edwina	1930-03-25	1,751,853
Buckle, John V.	1920-05-18	1,340,849
Burdict, Arthur	1872-06-18	128,013
Burgard, Louis C.	1931-12-29	1,839,082
Burke, Thomas A.	1914-11-10	1,116,988
Burkhart, Lucy	1918-10-22	1,282,537
Burnham Naomi C.	1905-03-21	785,249
Burnham, Lycurgus	1883-05-08	277,218
Burnham, Lycurgus	1883-05-08	277,219
Burr, Frederick P.	1909-09-28	935,088
Burrell, Matthew	1933-07-18	1,918,738
Burry, William C.	1879-10-07	220,272
Burry, William C.	1885-10-20	328,457
Bush, James D.	1916-03-14	1,175,598
Bushnell, Porter K.	1930-01-07	1,742,230
Bushnell, Porter K.	1933-08-08	1,921,342
Butterfield, Charles	1866-10-16	58,770
Byland, Lucile	1929-02-19	1,702,862
Cain, Wesley R.	1903-10-27	742,773
Carley, James T.	1882-11-14	267,491
Carley, James T.	1886-12-21	354,684
Carlson, Bror N.	1930-02-25	1,748,830
Carlson, Gustav A.	1930-12-09	1,784,575
Carlson, Harry J.	1929-06-18	1,718,111
Carroll, Philip F.	1880-12-21	235,620
Carter, William W.	1883-01-02	270,015

Inventor	Date	Pat. No.
Carver, George G.	1867-12-03	71,696
Casey, William J.	1930-01-21	1,744,445
Caufman, Abraham	1882-11-28	268,185
Cazenove, James	1923-10-30	1,472,292
Cazenove, James O. H.	1921-07-26	1,385,605
Cazenove, James O. H.	1928-12-11	1,694,500
Chaparro, Roberto	1918-01-15	1,253,785
Chapman, Samuel E.	1899-08-29	632,044
Charles, Robert S.	1889-02-12	397,831
Chase, Ernest L.	1909-10-12	936,410
Chattin, John E.	1926-02-09	1,572,764
Cherry, Peterson H.	1883-11-20	288,775
Chester, Frank R.	1951-09-18	2,568,318
Chittenden, William	1908-06-16	890,604
Christin, Manuel D.	1909-10-26	938,369
Christina Rockwell	1935-01-01	1,986,163
Christoph, Emil A.	1911-11-28	1,010,019
Clark Elmer A.	1915-10-26	1,158,178
Clark, Elmer A.	1916-01-04	1,167,336
Clayton, Daniel B.	1871-08-15	117,982
Cline, Martin	1875-03-16	160,815
Cobin, Israel Jones	1893-11-07	507,996
Cohnhoff, Louis	1902-01-14	691,115
Collier, Ralph	1856-12-23	16,267
Collins, Frank R.	1919-11-04	1,320,603
Collins, George E.	1903-11-03	743,149
Collins, Harold M.	1935-08-06	2,010,534
Collins, James H.	1909-08-03	929,917
Collins, Lathrop	1921-01-22	1,372,279
Condogeorge, N.	1916-05-30	1,184,927
Condon, John W.	1873-07-15	140,891
Condon, John W.	1881-03-22	R-9,615
Conner, May	1917-01-30	1,214,010
Cook, George T.	1896-08-04	565,260
Cooke, Hugh	1930-06-17	1,765,129
Cooke, Walter L.	1909-07-13	927,952
Cooley, Edward H.	1915-09-28	1,155,215
Coombs, Stephen	1907-09-17	865,999
Coombs, Stephen H	1896-12-15	573,208
Coombs, Stephen H.	1901-04-30	673,198
Copeland, Alonzo	1916-03-07	1,174,828
Corwin, Frank E.	1927-07-26	1,637,103
Coughlin, Joseph D.	1914-10-27	1,115,287
Covey, Harry A.	1914-09-01	1,108,973
Crafton, Charles Baker	1889-04-02	400,547
Cram, Alonzo W.	1907-02-19	844,499
Cram, Alonzo W.	1908-04-21	885,444
Crane, Moses G.	1865-07-04	48,525
Crane, Moses G.	1866-06-19	55,625
Crane, William M.	1919-12-23	1,325,509
Crepeau, Henry T.	1899-09-12	632,780
Crimp, Harvey M.	1906-09-25	831,538
Cripe, Sara E.	1896-02-04	554,170
Crissey, Paul	1939-02-21	2,148,399
Crocker, William O.	1872-09-24	131,600
Crocker, William O.	1874-06-09	151,761
Crocker, William W.	1923-12-18	1,477,943
Cross, Ranslar R.	1900-01-02	640,369
Crowe, John M.	1935-03-05	1,993,338
Cunningham, Andrew	1915-06-01	1,141,528
Dahnke, Marye	1949-10-25	2,486,126
Dailey, James W.	1920-12-07	1,361,368
Dalrymple, Hartwell	1896-06-30	563,139
Dane, John Jr.	1872-01-23	122,997
Danner, Samuel	1907-03-12	846,829
Davis, Arthur	1897-03-02	577,945
Davis, Della	1901-08-13	680,229
Davis, John E.	1948-02-24	D-148,770
Davis, Joshua	1866-07-17	56,382
Dazey, Nathan P.	1907-04-16	850,525
Dazey, Nathan P.	1917-12-18	1,250,810
Dazey, Nathan P.	1922-02-14	1,406,619
De Martino, Alice	1949-08-09	D-154,752
De Vault, Ralph P.	1950-03-07	2,499,371
De Vault, Ralph P.	1957.02/19	2,782,014
De Witt, Louis I.	1954-01-12	2,665,872

Inventor	Date	Pat. No.
Dearborn, Gilbert K.	1870-07-26	105,655
Dehuff, Walter F.	1911-11-07	1,007,930
Dehuff, Walter F.	1939-11-21	2,181,078
Deis, Charles	1882-03-07	254,540
Deis, Charles	1884-04-22	297,115
Dekin, Le Roy J.	1922-11-28	1,437,133
Dennis, Elmer L.	1929-11-12	1,735,236
Dennison, William H.	1891-06-16	454,165
Diehl, Philip Jacob	1923-09-18	1,468,560
Diell, John J.	1888-08-07	387,214
Dingle, Charles	1924-12-16	1,519,533
Djuvik, Carl	1974-03-12	3,796,512
Dodson, Wilson P.	1887-12-20	375,274
Doerb, George W.	1925-03-24	1,530,716
Doll, Arnold	1882-10-31	266,679
Doll, Arnold	1883-01-16	270,642
Donahoe, Michael	1936-04-07	2,036,262
Doner, Halbert C.	1944-05-23	D-137,946
Doty, William H.	1914-12-29	1,122,876
Douglas, Robert W.	1927-02-15	1,617,747
Downing, Elmer T.	1900-07-24	654,426
Downing, Elmer T.	1900-07-24	654,526
Drennan, Charles M.	1866-09-18	58,165
Drew, Clayton L.	1935-07-09	2,007,850
Drott, H. F.	1860-09-18	30,053
Drucker, Samuel B.	1931-09-01	1,820,909
Drucker, William J.	1917-09-18	1,240,688
Dudley, George D.	1888-07-17	386,424
Dudley, Walter J.	1904-11-15	775,102
Dulje, Eustache R.	1877-06-19	192,157
Duncan, Israel P.	1925-06-26	1,539,245
Dunlap, John S.	1906-05-15	820,405
Dunlap, John S.	1907-02-26	845,341
Dunlap, John S.	1916-09-26	1,199,455
Dunne, John J.	1936-06-30	2,046,109
Dunning, Warren H.	1918-02-12	1,255,993
Dunning, Warren H.	1918-02-12	1,255,994
Dupre, Wilfred	1911-05-02	991,432
Dutt, Roller E.	1932-06-14	1,862,590
Duty, Michael K.	1877-12-18	198,363
Duvall, Walter J.	1948-08-31	2,448,174
Earl, Francis	1883-06-26	280,019
Earle, Lee Edgar	1928-07-17	1,677,754
Earle, Timothy	1863-07-07	39,134
Earle, Timothy	1866-04-24	54,134
Earle, Timothy	1870-01-25	99,173
Earle, Timothy	1870-07-05	105,057
Earle, Timothy	1870-09-27	107,673
Earle, Timothy	1875-06-13	R-6,542
Earle, Timothy	1880-03-02	225,003
Eastman, Rufus M.	1885-11-17	330,829
Ebel, John V.	1895-03-19	536,136
Ebeling, Charles W.	1918-07-30	1,247,021
Eberhart, Lloyd	1877-07-24	193,493
Eck, Warren C.	1933-06-20	1,915,017
Edlund, Henry J.	1931-01-13	1,789,224
Edwards, Russell E.	1909-08-10	930,364
Egedal, Lawrence	1960-08-16	2,949,284
Eichenberg, Edouard	1892-01-19	467,328
Eickelmann, Rolf W.	1984-09-18	4,472,063
Eifert, Robert August	1903-08-04	735,353
Elliott, Clarence E.	1935-02-26	1,992,654
Elliott, Clarence E.	1951-07-31	2,562,380
Elliott, Clarence E.	1953-09-15	D-170,404
Ellis, Wilson R.	1899-01-10	617,416
Ellis, Wilson R.	1927-08-23	1,639,932
Ellis, Wilson R.	1928-07-24	1,678,425
Elward, John H.	1902-08-19	707,404
Emery, Benjiman F.	1899-02-21	619,739
Emery, Harry Le Roy	1926-03-23	1,577,615
Emmert, John	1880-03-23	225,693
Endorf, Charles	1913-07-29	1,068,994
Erhardt, Oscar P.	1922-02-28	1,407,789
Erwin, James R.	1908-06-16	890,629
Euler, Donald J.	1951-08-28	2,565,723
Eynon, Elizabeth J.	1896-01-14	553,027
Fahlberg, Ernest	1929-03-19	1,705,639
Farmer, Edwin T.	1905-10-24	802,923
Farrington, Richard	1917-01-09	1,211,426
Feeney, John M.	1921-12-06	1,399,296
Fell, Pearl F.	1901-02-19	D-34,098
Felthouse, H. D. & J. H.	1866-03-27	53,429
Fisher, Charles W.	1910-02-01	948,214
Fisler, Thomas	1866-04-17	53,965
Fitch, Charles G.	1912-05-07	1,025,798
Fitch, Gilbert M.	1899-01-17	618,029
Fitzgerald, Patrick J.	1933-04-04	D-89,565
Fitzgerald, Patrick J.	1934-08-21	1,971,257
Fitzgerald, Patrick J.	1936-11-24	2,061,868
Fitzpatrick, George J.	1922-05-30	1,417,982
Fitzpatrick, George J.	1929-04-02	1,707,789
Flaherty, James F.	1898-09-16	609,270
Flanders, William G.	1884-01-15	291,890
Fletcher, John J.	1890-12-09	442,429
Fletcher, Theodore	1885-05-12	317,755
Flink, Carl E.	1922-10-31	1,433,710
Flowers, George R.	1906-04-10	817,635
Flynt, Anthony I.	1923-06-19	1,459,148
Fontan, Le Roy H.	1935-09-03	2,013,615
Ford, George E.	1945-10-16	D-142,550
Forth, Charles	1912-01-09	1,014,382
Foss, L. Bacon	1880-09-07	232,018
Foster, George N.	1891-06-09	453,998
Fougen H. G. & A. C.	1869-11-30	97,397
Fowler, Benjamin F.	1910-08-09	966,738
Fowler, Benjamin F.	1919-07-22	1,310,861
Fowler, George F.	1882-04-11	256,310
Frame, John	1915-10-05	1,155,907
Frame, John	1917-11-27	1,247,655
Frank, Miles E.	1906-10-16	833,518
Frates, Thomas L.	1929-07-09	1,719,973
Free, John Sr.	1916-07-18	1,191,170
French, Mary E.	1907-07-02	858,970
Friedman, Goste	1899-11-07	636,400
Friedman, Goste	1903-10-06	740,751
Fritz, Arthur	1906-10-02	832,052
Fulton, Harmon	1888-08-14	387,634
Fulton, William H.	1914-02-03	1,085,858
Gaar, William J. C.	1910-02-22	950,152
Galatius, Louis M.	1903-09-22	739,488
Gamache, Homer	1944-09-12	2,357,886
Gambon, Emile	1929-05-21	1,714,359
Ganfolfo, John F.	1904-05-03	758,746
Genge, Felix	1908-04-07	884,085
George E. Alexander	1921-05-24	1,379,507
Gerard, John	1888-03-27	380,200
Gibbs, Howard W.	1913-06-10	1,064,070
Gibson, Hannah Z.	1884-02-19	293,648
Gienandt, Fritz L.	1909-12-28	944,781
Gilbert, Alfred C.	1922-11-14	1,435,289
Gilbert, Alfred C.	1929-01-08	1,698,363
Gilbert, Alfred C.	1930-06-10	1,763,301
Gilbert, Alfred C.	1930-11-11	1,781,381
Gilbert, Alfred C.	1931-06-23	1,811,499
Gilbert, Alfred C.	1933-05-30	1,912,350
Gilbert, Alfred C.	1935-05-28	2,003,259
Gilbert, Alfred C.	1935-06-04	2,003,829
Gilbert, Alfred C.	1935-06-04	2,003,931
Gilbert, Alfred C.	1935-07-09	2,007,299
Gilbert, Alfred C.	1935-07-09	2,007,300
Gilbert, Alfred C.	1936-01-07	2,027,036
Gilbert, Alfred C.	1936-02-25	2,031,769
Gilbert, Alfred C.	1936-02-25	2,031,770
Gilbert, Alfred C.	1936-03-03	2,032,571
Gilchrist, Raymond B.	1916-10-17	1,201,284
Gilchrist, Raymond B.	1923-08-21	1,465,629
Gilchrist, Raymond B.	1923-08-21	1,465,630
Gilchrist, Raymond B.	1923-08-21	1,465,631
Gilchrist, Raymond B.	1923-08-21	1,465,632
Gilchrist, Raymond B.	1923-08-21	1,465,633
Gilchrist, Raymond B.	1923-08-21	1,465,634
Gilchrist, Raymond B.	1923-08-21	1,465,635
Gill, George W.	1881-02-15	237,741
Gilmour, Hugh Kerr	1910-05-31	959,731
Gipple, Rebecca A.	1899-01-03	617,093
Glover, Julia, B	1901-06-04	675,475
Gluck, Henry	1942-08-04	2,291,708
Godward, Ernest	1907-03-12	846,661
Godward, Ernest	1907-03-12	846,662
Godward, Ernest R.	1900-07-10	653,233
Goetz, Joseph F.	1923-02-13	1,444,910
Goetz, Joseph F.	1926-12-28	1,612,281
Goldfarb, Adolph E.	1966-11-15	3,285,584
Goss, Daniel S.	1903-10-06	740,752
Goundry, William J.	1929-04-30	1,711,409
Gourlie, John H.	1914-06-30	1,101,693
Grant, Sidney, A.	1912-08-06	1,034,908
Graves, Scott S.	1928-04-10	1,665,879
Green, George G.	1948-02-10	D-148,620
Green, James A.	1923-11-27	1,475,767
Griswold, Harry J.	1908-05-19	887,790
Grommet, Katie Annie	1931-04-14	1,801,154
Gross, George E.	1964-05-19	3,133,976
Guhl, August C.	1928-11-13	1,691,282
Haak, Thomas E.	1885-09-08	325,674
Hacmac, Edward R.	1939-01-17	D-112,956
Hacmac, Edward R.	1939-06-13	2,162,348
Hacmac, Edward R.	1939-12-12	2,182,984
Hacmac, Edward R.	1940-01-02	2,185,846
Hadley, Ethan	1873-05-06	138,647
Hadley, Ethan	1888-04-03	380,564
Hadley, Ethan	1891-06-16	454,345
Hagley, William	1895-02-05	533,589
Haines, William H.	1870-02-15	99,883
Hall, Michael W.	1909-04-06	917,289
Hallam, Frank	1890-03-25	424,108
Hallenberg, Albert	1909-11-02	939,017
Halse, Edwin	1931-09-29	1,825,450
Hamble, Melvin D.	1878-07-09	205,859
Hamilton, Charles H.	1922-03-07	1,408,591
Hamilton, Charles R.	1901-01-22	666,269
Hamilton, Charles R.	1903-08-18	736,723
Hancock, Addison	1893-09-05	504,472
Hanna, William A.	1911-08-29	1,001,949
Hansen, Harry	1949-09-27	2,483,280
Hansen, Oliver	1943-04-20	2,316,861
Hanson, Walter	1925-05-26	1,539,731
Haring, Peter Paul	1889-04-02	400,674
Harper, Murry D.	1956-08-28	2,760,763
Harr, John L.	1914-03-17	1,090,148
Harris, Lottie J.	1929-07-09	1,720,361
Harris, Victoria P.	1959-09-29	2,906,510
Harrison, Reuben N.	1878-02-12	200,290
Harrison, Reuben N.	1882-10-31	R-10,228
Hart, William	1861-03-12	31,663
Harvey, Jennie	1893-10-10	506,635
Harvey, Jennie	1893-10-10	506,636
Hauck, Charles J. Jr.	1890-05-06	427,473
Haus, Roy A.	1958-02-04	2,822,009
Hausman, Frederick	1936-05-26	2,042,176
Hawes, Benjamin N.	1909-09-14	934,169
Hawkins, Elisha D.	1881-11-01	249,044
Hayward, Agnes, C.	1922-12-19	1,439,102
Hazzard, Paul	1923-08-28	1,465,940
Headley, Afton Rees	1925-10-13	1,557,364
Hegner, Stella B.	1901-04-09	671,516
Heich, John B.	1857-12-15	18,849
Heiser, Lucien	1922-09-26	1,430,012
Helken, Emil, W. H.	1912-10-01	1,039,735
Helmer, William	1904-06-07	D-36,957
Henderson, Frederick	1930-05-13	1,758,111
Henderson, William B.	1884-05-13	298,375
Henry, Frank	1880-09-14	232,125
Hensel, Otto A.	1894-12-04	530,268
Hensel, Otto A.	1895-08-13	D-24,545
Herron, George A.	1929-05-21	1,713,828
Herter, Clarence	1939-12-12	2,182,921
Hess, George F.	1911-10-03	1,004,786
Hessey, John L.	1920-08-17	1,350,098
Hetherington, John	1930-06-24	1,766,171
Hickey, James	1913-06-17	1,064,729
Hill, John E.	1901-11-05	685,986
Hill, John E.	1907-01-15	841,320
Hillman, Shimer B.	1904-12-20	777,675

Inventor	Date	Pat. No.
Hills, Sidney C.	1916-11-28	1,206,327
Hills, Sidney C.	1918-07-23	1,273,486
Hills, Sidney C.	1921-08-02	1,386,405
Hills, Sidney, C.	1922-10-24	1,433,508
Hindes, Howard W.	1940-08-06	2,210,810
Hindes, Howard W.	1940-09-06	2,210,810
Hirt, Clifford I.	1914-12-15	1,120,716
Hjert, Andrew G.	1932-03-01	1,847,563
Hobbs, Samuel T.	1930-06-24	1,767,454
Hoerburger, Alex	1917-11-27	1,248,327
Hoffer Ivan L.	1929-10-08	1,730,506
Hoffer, Ivan L.	1926-10-26	1,604,513
Hoffman, John A.	1908-01-14	876,549
Holden, Elbridge	1907-07-16	859,943
Holister, Frank O.	1939-06-20	D-115,335
Holister, Frank O.	1941-06-24	2,246,517
Holt, Edward E.	1922-08-15	1,426,080
Holt, Thomas	1899-08-22	631,715
Holt, Thomas	1900-04-03	646,736
Holt, Thomas	1913-11-04	1,077,832
Hommel, Susanna C.	1931-02-24	1,793,934
Hood, Harrison P.	1872-08-06	130,297
Hood, Thomas Hubert	1909-05-18	921,991
Hood, William L.	1927-11-29	1,651,276
Hooper, Beekman D.	1902-09-02	708,229
Hooper, Beekman D.	1902-12-23	716,840
Horner, John W.	1910-05-31	959,536
Hotchkiss, Clarence	1933-06-06	1,912,525
Houck, Frank A.	1886-12-28	355,170
Hough, Earl F.	1885-09-08	325,840
Howe, Emma Jane	1897-10-26	592,708
Howes, John	1875-07-13	165,585
Howie, Robert K.	1939-07-18	2,166,437
Howson, Henry Jr.	1881-03-01	238,393
Hoyle, Ella L. D.	1895-10-01	547,263
Huber, George W.	1893-09-26	505,766
Hudson, Frederick W.	1889-02-19	398,258
Hudson, James H.	1916-07-25	1,192,426
Hudson, Mahal	1912-05-14	1,026,355
Hughes, Dewey C.	1949-09-20	2,482,587
Hughes, James R.	1878-04-30	203,153
Hughes, James R.	1880-12-07	235,245
Hughes, John M.	1894-05-29	520,566
Hull, Henry M.	1921-12-27	1,401,408
Hulvorsen, Martin	1905-08-22	797,959
Humphrey, Ernest N.	1926-11-30	1,609,254
Humphrey, Ernest N.	1927-11-01	1,647,800
Humphrey, Ernest N.	1928-07-03	1,676,189
Hunkler, Benjamin	1909-09-07	933,646
Hunter, Rudolph M.	1887-09-20	370,335
Hunting, George H.	1877-11-13	197,135
Hunziker, James G.	1895-10-08	547,488
Husser, Jules	1907-02-05	843,461
Hutchinson, Job	1913-09-02	1,071,747
Hutton, Junius O.	1949-06-21	D-154,202
Hvale, James L.	1960/01/12	D-187,038
Hvale, James L.	1962/05/15	D-192,812
Illsche, Arthur	1939-06-13	2,162,017
Ives, George H.	1885-09-08	325,933
Jackson, David B.	1909-11-23	941,075
Jackson, Richard W.	1927-01-25	1,615,386
Jagow, Leroy J.	1947-02-18	D-146,363
Jaquette, Harry	1893-11-28	509,665
Jay, James M.	1860-02-07	27,054
Jay, James M.	1860-04-17	27,908
Jembrzcki, Stanley	1923-09-11	1,467,989
Jennings, Benjamin	1888-10-09	390,974
Jennings, Benjamin	1888-10-17	391,150
Jennings, Nancy G.	1913-09-16	1,073,133
Jensen, Christian E.	1923-05-22	1,456,448
Jeppsson, Ivar	1935-09-10	2,013,887
Johannes, Hubert G.	1931-07-28	1,816,046
Johnson, Albert H.	1956-06-05	2,749,098
Johnson, Andrew	1950-07-18	2,515,713
Johnson, Edward H.	1912-05-14	1,025,982
Johnson, Edward H.	1917-12-18	1,250,889
Johnson, Edward V.	1931-01-13	1,788,675
Johnson, Erich	1919-07-08	1,308,953

Inventor	Date	Pat. No.
Johnson, William H.	1985-09-03	4,538,922
Johnson, William J.	1887-03-22	359,976
Johnson, William J.	1897-08-10	588,112
Johnson, Willis	1884-02-05	292,821
Johnston, Arthur W.	1915-05-18	1,140,341
Joinette, Ernest A.	1917-11-13	1,246,103
Jones, George W.	1874-10-27	156,357
Jones, Harry C.	1950-04-04	2,502,571
Jones, J. M. C.	1900-10-23	660,513
Jones, Louis W.	1926-06-29	1,590,831
Jones, Samuel F.	1859-05-03	23,843
Jones, Thomas E.	1917-11-13	1,246,104
Jorgenson, Thorleif B.	1915-01-19	1,125,337
Juergens, Henry F.	1893-06-20	499,741
Julier, Camilla	1899-07-11	628,471
Kadel, Dottie	1906-01-23	810,417
Kail, Charles E.	1923-10-09	1,470,169
Kail, Charles E.	1923-10-09	1,470,170
Kail, Charles E.	1931-10-27	1,828,932
Kail, Charles E.	1934-07-10	1,965,650
Kamerrer, William C.	1908-08-25	896,919
Kapheim, Frederick	1907-06-11	856,469
Kaplan, Natham	1961-11-21	3,009,686
Karamanos, Demetrios	1920-12-14	1,362,164
Karp, Edward J.	1942-03-31	2,277,986
Keller, Graydon, M.	1928-10-02	1,686,280
Kelley, Albert	1935-07-09	2,007,249
Kelley, Albert	1939-08-15	2,169,607
Kelly, Guy W.	1917-03-27	1,220,426
Kelly, Roger L.	1973-07-10	D-227,646
Kelly, Roger L.	1973-07-10	D-227,647
Keppeler, Adolph	1916-02-08	1,171,054
Kesilman, Sol	1968-11-26	3,412,983
Kier, John M.	1909-02-23	913,398
Kilborn, Eugenia	1884-08-05	303,022
Killman, Thomas A.	1929-10-01	1,730,219
Killman, Thomas A.	1932-10-04	1,881,361
Killman, Thomas A.	1933-09-05	1,925,638
King, Francis L.	1866-01-02	51,839
King, Francis L.	1867-06-18	65,916
King, Guy	1938-08-16	D-110,899
Kirby, John L.	1889-07-09	406,653
Kirkpatrick, Orson	1949-08-30	2,480,482
Kirkpatrick, Orson F.	1916-05-02	1,181,142
Kitchell, Oscar	1884-12-09	308,901
Kitterman, George M.	1882-08-01	261,857
Klepper, P.	1867-07-16	66,855
Knapp, Edwin L.	1911-10-17	1,005,847
Knobel, Abraham	1916-11-07	1,204,363
Knoblauch, Edward	1925-09-29	1,555,502
Kohlenberg,Ferdinand	1896-11-03	570,668
Kopenhaver, Anna A.	1927-05-27	1,629,956
Kost, Alwin	1951-01-30	2,539,436
Krandelt, Frank	1870-02-22	100,155
Krasberg, Rudolf	1951-08-14	2,563,941
Kress, John	1914-12-15	1,121,107
Kreuzberger, Bartlett	1909-08-24	932,294
Kritikson, John H.	1964-05-12	3,132,849
Kuck, Henry G.	1930-06-03	1,761,634
Kuhn, Geroge	1933-10-31	1,933,439
Kunkle, Erastus B.	1871-09-05	118,727
Kyle, Hattie	1912-03-05	1,019,055
Kyseth, George	1937-09-07	2,092,353
Lacey, Robert	1930-09-09	1,775,566
Ladd, Earnest W.	1908-07-07	892,856
Ladd, Earnest W.	1915-12-28	1,165,423
Lahiere, Eugene A.	1915-06-08	1,142,331
Lamb, Joseph F.	1905-04-18	787,774
Lamb, Joseph F.	1905-11-07	803,833
Lambert Clara B.	1927-10-11	1,645,062
Lambert, Clara B.	1929-08-13	1,724,356
Lambert, Clara, B.	1924-03-11	1,486,255
Lampton, William R	1875-10-05	168,506
Landis, Jacob F.	1874-06-09	151,784
Landsberg, William	1915-06-22	1,144,215
Lange, William F.	1923-05-01	1,453,761
Larock, Frederick J.	1909-12-28	944,621
Larson, Glen M.	1951-12-04	2,576,947

Inventor	Date	Pat. No.
Latham, Ricahrd S.	1961/09/12	D-191,321
Latham, Richard S.	1959-08-25	D-185,970
Latshaw, Fred F.	1945-07-31	D-141,900
Laube, Godfried	1886-07-27	346,375
Laurick, Carl	1905-11-21	805,020
Laurick, Carl	1921-10-18	1,393,799
Laurie, Linn	1869-12-21	98,168
Lauterbur, Frank X.	1928-06-05	1,672,224
Lawrence, B.E.	1943-03-30	2,315,018
Lawrence, John R.	1941-12-09	2,265,533
Lawrence, John R.	1950-04-25	2,505,362
Lawton, Jason Lee	1918-06-04	1,268,586
Lebowitz, Sam	1980-03-18	4,193,697
Leger, Splandien	1912-07-16	1,032,551
Lehmann, Charles	1870-03-29	101,281
Lehmann, Charles	1872-09-10	131,283
Lehmann, Charles	1874-02-10	147,412
Leighty, Elroy Homer	1938-06-28	2,121,918
Leighty, Elroy Homer	1941-02-18	2,231,926
Leinan, Edwin S.	1923-07-03	1,460,493
Leu, Frederick	1901-12-10	688,657
Lewis, Samuel W.	1917-03-27	1,220,862
Leyburn, Edward J.	1893-01-10	489,821
Leyer, Amand	1918-10-15	1,281,603
Libbman, Louis	1905-07-04	793,843
Libbman, Louis	1905-07-04	793,844
Lienhard, Richard B.	1927-04-05	1,623,256
Lienhard, Richard B.	1937-08-31	2,091,786
Lienhard, Richard B.	1940-03-12	2,193,461
Little, Charles E.	1933-09-26	1,928,022
Little, John M.	1938-12-13	D-112,531
Lively, Elbert W.	1923-02-20	1,445,696
Livingood, Katherine	1883-08-07	282,738
Lockwood, Harry C.	1926-02-02	1,571,591
Loll, Frederick W.	1906-10-09	833,069
Long, Russell L.	1920-04-20	1,337,478
Louden, Henry W.	1868-02-25	74,837
Lower, Raymond S.	1922-08-08	1,425,026
Lozo, Martin	1875-10-05	168,510
Lum, James	1953-09-15	2,652,236
Lynch, John W.	1933-09-12	2,926,910
Lyon, Ray W.	1926-02-02	1,571,851
Mackay, D. D.	1868-12-29	85,460
Mackay, Donald D.	1874-08-18	154,263
Mackay, Donald D.	1874-12-08	157,456
MacMoran, Henrietta	1917-09-18	1,240,355
Madigan, Thomas J.	1929-11-19	1,736,542
Madigan, Thomas J.	1931-07-07	1,813,862
Madsen, Carl A.	1940-06-18	2,205,147
Maffel, Leo J.	1959-04-21	D-184,950
Magin, Anna M.	1892-03-01	470,005
Mahony, William J.	1934-07-10	1,966,352
Mahony, William Jay	1931-10-06	1,826,356
Maltby, Harriet S.	1870-10-18	108,498
Mamugh, John S.	1897-09-14	590,160
Mann, Harry C.	1878-08-06	206,742
Marchand, Henry E.	1879-04-29	214,936
Marie, Wallace R.	1905-09-05	798,613
Marsh, Edith A.	1886-07-20	345,709
Marsh, Thomas	1870-06-14	104,174
Marsh, Thomas	1870-08-09	106,182
Marsh, Thomas	1870-09-20	107,515
Marsh, Thomas	1871-06-13	115,862
Martinet, Eugene F.	1936-06-02	2,042,791
Maslow, Louis	1933-05-23	1,910,302
Maslow, Louis	1940-07-16	2,208,337
Mason, Herbert W.	1896-09-15	567,909
Mattern, August	1910-07-12	964,291
Maurer, Fred	1903-10-13	741,586
Maxson, William E.	1946-02-26	D-143,981
Maxwell, Robert G.	1927-02-08	1,616,817
Maynard, Mark	1933-05-23	1,910,303
Maynard, Mark K.	1942-12-22	D-134,612
Maynard, Mark K.	1958-12-09	2,863,332
McBean, Thomas	1859-05-24	24,134
McCool, Horace, B.	1880-09-21	232,358
McCord, King S.	1977-03-08	4,010,934
McDowell, Bartley D.	1893-12-26	511,637

Inventor	Date	Pat. No.
McDowell, John J.	1889-02-12	397,655
McKinlay, Alexander	1914-06-30	1,101,560
McLean, James P.	1860-06-19	28,760
McLean, William A	1938-08-02	2,125,455
McLoughlin, James E.	1935-09-10	2,013,783
McLoy, Jesse J.	1915-07-27	1,148,032
McRae, Kate Hatch	1901-06-02	677,421
Meyer, John W.	1889-12-03	416,636
Midorikawa, Edward	1923-02-13	1,445,342
Mihan, P.	1858-03-23	19,738
Milks, John H.	1916-04-04	1,178,255
Miller, C.J. Jr.	1869-11-09	96,604
Miller, Harvey	1857-12-01	18,759
Miller, Harvey	1872-02-06	123,353
Miller, Nathaniel C.	1870-02-01	99,337
Miller, Nathaniel C.	1873-04-22	138,094
Mills, George M.	1908-08-25	896,848
Minney, Arthur W.	1923-09-25	1,468,826
Minney, Arthur Wells	1924-04-22	1,490,980
Mitchell, Arobine C.	1891-12-29	466,178
Mitchell, Arobine C.	1894-05-08	519,584
Moeller, Arturo F.	1925-06-09	1,540,946
Mohr, Leopold	1894-03-13	516,214
Monroe, J. F. & E. P.	1874-08-25	154,411
Monroe, J. T. & E. P.	1860-10-16	R-1,062
Monroe, J.F. & E.P.	1859-04-19	23,694
Monroe, James F.	1877-05-01	190,238
Moody, Thomas A.	1896-09-15	567,684
Mooney, George	1878-06-04	204,498
Mooney, George	1879-06-03	216,053
Moore, Robert A.	1915-08-24	1,151,372
Moore, Robert A.	1925-08-18	1,549,889
Moore, Samuel C.	1866-05-01	54,388
Morgan, Edward	1904-12-06	776,791
Morgan, Edward M.	1910-11-01	974,586
Morgan, Edward M.	1929-05-07	1,712,156
Morgan, Edward M.	1947-07-29	2,424,703
Morgan, Francis E.	1942-05-05	2,281,985
Morse, Edward	1880-05-11	227,378
Moses, Albert	1916-08-22	1,195,839
Moses, Albert	1916-12-26	1,210,192
Muehlhaus, Frank R.	1951-06-05	2,555,756
Muir, Herbert H.	1935-01-15	1,987,700
Mulford, Charles J.	1891-09-29	460,265
Munn, George M.	1905-03-21	785,114
Munsing, George D.	1921-12-13	1,400,309
Munson, David	1872-03-05	124,375
Munson, David	1873-06-17	140,067
Munson, Samuel R.	1899-12-26	D-32,028
Munson, Samuel R.	1903-06-02	729,884
Musser, George R.	1918-08-13	1,275,587
Muth, Henry	1872-10-22	132,483
Myers, Frederick	1916-11-07	1,203,899
Myers, Thomas B.	1929-12-03	1,738,112
Nakamura, Mitsutaro	1921-02-08	1,368,180
Nash, Elizabeth F.	1934-11-27	1,982,531
Nastrom, Nels	1932-08-09	1,870,741
Nehr, Herman F.	1910-03-15	951,834
Nelleson, Lambert	1889-11-05	414,566
Nelson, John L.	1896-06-16	562,018
Nelson, John L.	1899-01-24	618,122
Neukirchen, Peter	1920-01-06	1,327,568
Newcomer, Jacob L.	1885-05-26	318,786
Newnham, Eugene	1931-01-27	1,790,242
Newton, Ann F.	1907-07-30	861,603
Nicholas, Stella A.	1909-04-27	919,625
Nichols, Charles A.	1910-01-11	946,521
Nichols, William B.	1876-10-24	183,589
Nicholson, William T.	1860-09-25	30,152
Nicholson, William T.	1861-07-23	32,886
Nicolai, John L.	1859-04-26	23,814
Nielsen, Rasmus	1910-04-19	955,672
Nilson, Oliver C.	1912-01-02	1,013,803
Nippert, Tessie M.	1929-04-30	1,710,836
Noakes, William	1911-01-03	980,824
Nordby, Julius E.	1934-07-31	1,968,502
Nordgarden, Ernest	1950-02-28	2,499,074
Nyberg, Albert F.	1921-12-06	1,399,513

Inventor	Date	Pat. No.
O'Neal & Favorite	1916-10-24	1,202,415
O'Neall, James M.	1905-08-01	796,083
O'Neill, John M.	1893-02-14	491,583
Oakley, Frederick	1867-01-29	61,679
Olander, Ernest V.	1918-07-16	1,272,506
Olsen, Mariues B.	1911-05-11	991,883
Opdahl, Carl	1911-09-05	1,002,434
Orzchovski, Stanley	1922-12-12	1,438,716
Osborn, William L.	1938-07-05	2,123,118
Osius, Frederick J.	1911-10-10	1,005,653
Osner, Charles	1911-01-03	980,827
Otten, Arthur H. Otten	1910-07-12	964,306
Overkamp, Charles H.	1908-01-21	877,468
Ovidi, Adolofo	1908-07-28	894,459
Owens, Wayne F.	1948-03-16	D-149,011
Paige, James H.	1919-08-12	1,312,569
Paine, Frances E.	1893-08-29	504,112
Paine, George H.	1887-06-28	365,624
Paley, William V.	1904-09-27	771,088
Palmieri, Cesare	1939-11-28	2,181,833
Pangborn, Samuel B.	1866-05-15	54,761
Pardini, Julian A.	1930-04-01	1,752,650
Parent, Ludger M.	1915-06-01	1,141,207
Parham, William J.	1913-09-02	1,072,251
Parish, Graham C.	1905-12-26	808,613
Park, Watson	1925-06-16	1,542,574
Parker, Frank H.	1929-12-24	1,740,709
Parker, Frank H.	1929-12-24	1,740,710
Parker, J. J.	1859-08-09	25,038
Pauline Koment	1933-06-20	1,915,190
Payne, William H.	1894-11-06	528,688
Pearson, James H.	1910-10-25	973,554
Peirce, Charles, R.	1872-08-20	130,591
Peirce, William H.	1868-03-24	75,787
Perez, Waldo F.	1910-08-16	967,232
Perrin, Thomas H.	1906-04-24	818,914
Perry, James A.	1889-11-26	415,733
Persons, Ernest Leon	1906-04-10	817,272
Peters, Daniel	1887-09-27	370,406
Peters, Daniel	1888-05-29	383,489
Peters, James	1930-07-01	1,768,926
Pfau, Christian F.	1889-04-09	401,058
Pickard, Frank	1931-10-13	1,827,608
Pickett, Sterling P.	1899-01-03	616,964
Pinder, Charles	1866-10-16	58,882
Pinkney, Bryan D.	1918-12-17	1,287,741
Piperi, Anthony J.	1939-05-15	2,158,912
Platner, Marshal D.	1887-03-22	359,887
Polcar, Marguerite	1945-05-01	2,374,831
Poore, Alfred C.	1910-01-11	945,983
Pottsgrove, Philip N.	1932-11-01	1,886,118
Pratt, E. L.	1866-11-06	59,449
Pratt, E. L.	1867-09-10	68,788
Preston, Henry C.	1909-09-07	933,580
Pribil, Frank J.	1948-05-25	2,442,326
Pritchard, William C.	1931-09-29	1,824,929
Pullen, Lester T.	1934-04-03	1,953,722
Purdin, Conn A.	1933-03-21	1,902,376
Purkapile, Emerson	1990-08-07	4,946,286
Pusey, Caroline S.	1887-10-25	372,043
Pyle, Virgil Matthew	1930-06-10	1,762,421
Pyne, John	1859-11-15	26,123
Rabb, Michael	1934-05-22	1,960,089
Rabiger, Robert G.	1900-12-25	664,779
Rabin, Samuel	1921-04-05	1,373,761
Rambeaud, Rene	1909-03-02	913,766
Ramstad, John N.	1910-05-31	959,606
Raymond, Frances V.	1886-12-28	354,934
Raymond, George L.	1907-10-15	868,124
Read, Ellis D.	1911-04-11	989,418
Read, Harry	1910-08-09	966,765
Read, Harry	1911-11-07	1,007,891
Redheffer, William	1874-01-20	146,710
Redheffer, William	1875-07-13	165,615
Redheffer, William	1875-07-27	166,143
Redheffer, William	1875-08-17	166,893
Reed, Frank	1907-09-17	866,067
Reedy, Edward E.	1897-07-06	585,703

Inventor	Date	Pat. No.
Renn, John F.	1894-02-20	515,249
Rettenmeyer, F. W.	1935-09-03	2,013,616
Rex, Alfred C	1884-05-13	298,503
Rice, David Hall	1887-10-25	371,976
Richardson, Gus W.	1882-01-24	252,800
Richardson, John	1889-08-20	409,616
Richardson, William	1904-04-12	757,144
Rider, John	1885-09-29	327,109
Riedel, Curtis	1934-02-06	1,945,915
Ringwald, Clarence	1932-03-01	1,847,226
Roberts, Emmett R.	1902-02-04	692,479
Roberts, Henry P.	1912-09-10	1,038,204
Roberts, Henry P.	1912-12-10	1,046,648
Roberts, Henry P.	1913-07-29	1,068,450
Roberts, Henry P.	1914-03-17	1,090,567
Roberts, Henry P.	1931-03-31	1,798,757
Roberts, John C.	1899-07-25	629,608
Roberts, Maurice H.	1918-12-31	1,289,545
Roberts, Maurice H.	1922-04-25	1,413,874
Robertson, William P.	1917-05-29	1,227,671
Robertson, William P.	1917-05-29	1,227,935
Robertson, William P.	1917-06-05	1,228,823
Robinson, Alexander	1866-05-15	54,776
Robinson, Richard	1899-11-07	636,559
Rochow, Arthur J.	1940-07-16	2,208,431
Rock, Daniel B.	1885-12-22	332,837
Rock, Peter J.	1899-01-17	D-30,015
Roeck, Emmanuel	1905-05-09	789,172
Rogers, Ivan	1936-06-16	2,044,331
Rogers, Ulysses J.	1911-11-07	1,007,798
Roles, Duane	1948-01-20	2,434,812
Rolph, William	1934-02-20	1,948,431
Rommel, Paul J.	1938-03-15	2,11,407
Roos, Axel H.	1941-12-23	2,267,424
Roos, Axel, H.	1936-01-28	2,028,921
Rosenberry, Christian	1867-07-30	67,218
Rosenbranz, Louis	1887-12-13	374,706
Ross, Antonio	1916-05-30	1,185,004
Ross, Ashton D.	1911-08-22	1,001,451
Rostocki, John M.	1921-06-14	1,381,665
Rote, John F.	1873-11-11	144,567
Rote, John F.	1875-08-03	166,412
Round, Albert W.	1930-04-15	1,755,132
Rowe, Robert M.	1909-09-14	934,217
Rowley, Charles A.	1933-03-21	1,902,525
Rowley, Charles A.	1937-01-26	D-102,959
Rowley, Charles A.	1938-05-10	D-109,647
Ruckstuhl, Frederick W.	1902-08-12	707,019
Ruggles, Wells G.	1924-11-25	1,516,792
Rupp, Laurente	1917-10-23	1,243,982
Ruppel, William	1907-10-29	869,736
Russell, Matthew C.	1877-02-13	187,417
Ryerson, Eugene H.	1918-06-04	1,268,284
Sabatella, Vincent	1949-09-06	2,481,352
Sack, Harry	1933-09-26	1,928,032
Saito, Kohei	1917-02-27	1,217,832
Sallade, William	1864-05-03	42,603
Saltsman, Aaron J.	1894-07-10	522,944
Saltsman, Aaron J.	1897-04-27	581,493
Saltsman, Aaron J.	1908-10-06	900,210
Samuels, Julius	1924-11-18	1,516,210
Sandall, Arthur	1906-10-02	832,504
Sari, Mary	1915-05-11	1,138,897
Sauer, Lena	1923-10-16	1,470,882
Savage, George E.	1907-11-26	871,895
Schaedler, John M.	1922-01-03	1,402,380
Scheidecker, Wayne	1951-11-20	2,575,978
Schenk, Charles	1911-10-03	1,004,821
Schenk, Charles	1912-01-16	1,014,909
Schiff, Sigmund	1930-12-16	1,785,563
Schildecker, Peter	1863-10-06	40,188
Schlageter, Frederick	1930-02-11	1,747,032
Schleicher, George	1930-06-03	1,762,081
Schlumbohm, Peter	1943-09-21	2,330,012
Schmidt, Ernst M.C.	1915-09-28	1,154,940
Schmidt, George A.	1880-10-12	233,287
Schmitz, Ernst	1909-06-15	925,038
Schneider, Lorenz	1913-03-04	1,054,797

Inventor	Date	Pat. No.
Schonmeyer, F. E.	1875-09-14	167,696
Schramm, William	1925-01-13	1,523,085
Schrebler, Charles	1883-04-24	276,290
Schubert, Edward	1917-08-21	1,237,707
Schuirmann, Ernst	1907-04-02	849,273
Schwager, Joseph W.	1921-09-20	1,391,013
Scofield, James H.	1877-05-08	190,628
Scollon, Richard	1919-03-04	1,296,326
Scopes, Edward John	1897-09-07	589,795
Scopes, Edward John	1898-02-22	599,661
Scopes, Edward John	1901-12-03	688,201
Seaman, John Albert	1906-10-30	834,876
Sears, Augustus H.	1916-06-06	1,186,526
Seifke, Herman A.	1912-07-09	1,032,029
Seitz, C. F. Augustus	1869-04-06	88,672
Seltzer, Uriah D.	1892-11-29	487,024
Sette, Frederick	1941-05-27	2,243,443
Sette, Frederick E.	1943-03-23	2,314,522
Seybert, Theodore	1943-05-04	2,318,534
Seymour, Frederick J.	1876-02-22	174,015
Seymour, Frederick J.	1876-05-15	177,574
Shailer, Philip B.	1932-12-06	1,890,307
Shapleigh, Marshall	1910-08-30	969,120
Shattuck, Burt E.	1915-06-01	1,141,420
Shaw, Edward Payne	1906-11-06	835,165
Sheaffer, John E.	1917-05-22	1,227,327
Shearer, John A.	1920-06-08	1,343,091
Shelton, William G.	1913-12-23	1,082,243
Shelton, William G.	1921-06-28	1,382,682
Shepherd, Francis H.	1889-06-18	405,683
Sherwood, Daniel	1882-06-06	259,056
Shinn, Luther E.	1903-06-30	732,661
Shinn, Thornton A.	1880-07-13	230,075
Shive, David	1862-07-29	36,030
Shores, William P.	1948-11-23	2,454,350
Short, Samuel	1883-02-27	273,173
Silver, William H.	1875-06-15	164,491
Silver, William H.	1878-04-30	203,081
Silver, William H.	1885-11-03	329,859
Silver, William H.	1886-05-11	341,697
Sinclair, Harry R.	1914-06-16	1,100,683
Sisson, George P.	1877-01-16	186,278
Smalley, Albert G.	1899-08-01	630,009
Smith, Charles F.	1897-08-24	588,663
Smith, Gertrude L.	1934-08-07	1,969,162
Smith, Harold B.	1936-03-17	2,034,214
Smith, Harry Arthur	1905-02-07	781,917
Smith, Morris	1903-08-11	736,161
Smith, Oliver, C.	1915-07-06	1,145,275
Smith, Ralston R.	1935-06-04	2,003,521
Smith, William B.	1865-12-26	51,758
Smith, William B.	1902-10-14	711,185
Snyder, Geroge H.	1908-11-10	903,515
Soukup, Wenzl	1924-09-02	1,506,951
Sowers, Ray V.	1931-11-10	1,831,040
Spanier, Waldemar	1900-05-15	649,683
Spear, Fannie G.	1912-03-05	1,019,546
Spear, Fannie G.	1914-06-23	1,101,347
Speer, Fannie Hoyt	1909-06-29	926,362
Sperry, Evelyn P.	1912-08-20	1,036,159
Spilker, Bernard J.	1897-12-14	595,354
Spruin, William	1898-02-15	599,268
Stambaugh, Charles	1887-05-10	362,858
Stansbury, Benjamin	1981-04-28	4,264,216
Steele, Arthur G.	1923-09-04	1,467,205
Steele, George H.	1896-12-22	D-26,438
Stewart, Alexander T.	1906-07-31	827,474
Stewart, Charles A.	1917-02-06	1,215,214
Stewart, Theron S.	1888-03-27	380,226
Stiles, Harry L.	1949-12-27	D-156,679
Stock, Harry A.	1896-07-21	564,345
Stone, Randolph	1930-06-24	1,768,012
Stough, Turnet H.	1915-03-30	1,133,413
Strange, Emerson C.	1866-08-28	57,596
Strief, Willie H.	1936-03-10	2,033,453
Stromer, Nicholas	1906-12-04	837,432

Inventor	Date	Pat. No.
Stubbs, Joel	1890-03-25	424,438
Stump, Ira E.	1916-03-21	1,176,409
Sturgis, Herbert M.	1900-10-09	659,558
Sturma, William	1904-08-23	768,086
Sturma, William	1906-12-04	837,750
Sturma, William	1907-02-05	843,309
Sturma, William	1910-01-11	946,169
Swanson, Ray	1945-10-23	D-142,680
Swartz, Daniel M.	1870-10-11	108,203
Sweeting, Harry W.	1916-02-01	1,170,358
Swift, Willis S.	1897-06-01	583,775
Swigert, Joseph O.	1919-01-21	1,292,141
Sydney, Minatojo	1929-07-02	1,718,989
Szerenyi, Andrew	1950-05-30	2,509,706
Szlemko, Katherine	1916-01-11	1,168,127
Taplin, Clarence A.	1903-04-14	725,507
Tarrant, Marion A.	1935-09-10	2,013,902
Tatum, Charles A.	1890-03-04	422,462
Taylor, Dorothy	1910-09-20	970,969
Taylor, Herbert M.	1927-11-22	1,649,874
Taylor, J.E. & T.G.	1910-01-4	945,639
Taylor, William	1916-09-05	1,197,565
Taylor, William J.	1928-03-27	1,663,961
Teetsell, Ulysses G.	1922-02-14	1,406,778
Theodoropulos, A. A.	1933-03-21	1,902,678
Thinglum, Albert E.	1940-08-06	2,210,608
Thomas, George H.	1885-12-01	331,662
Thomas, George H.	1886-09-28	350,023
Thomas, Louis R.	1940-07-09	2,207,335
Thompson, Andrew J.	1907-03-12	846,763
Thompson, Herbert L.	1924-04-29	1,492,229
Thompson, Herbert L.	1924-10-14	1,511,541
Thompson, Milton O.	1920-05-25	D-55,340
Tilden, Howard	1865-08-01	49,176
Tingley, Philo B.	1900-12-04	663,305
Toda, Sozaburo	1913-05-20	1,062,059
Tomlinson, Walter H.	1907-11-19	871,247
Tone, John W.	1964-05-12	3,132,851
Townsend, Harry E.	1911-04-18	989,733
Tripke, Paul	1917-08-21	1,237,585
Tripke, Paul	1917-08-28	1,238,461
Tripke, Paul	1918-08-06	1,274,634
Tripke, Paul	1918-10-22	1,282,148
Trust, Henry	1922-09-26	1,430,040
Trust, Henry	1923-07-10	1,461,468
Trust, Henry	1924-01-29	1,482,279
Trust, Henry	1924-12-23	1,520,375
Tucker, James D.	1932-09-06	1,876,264
Turner, Rose Rice	1912-06-25	1,030,796
Turner, William D.	1917-04-24	1,223,839
Tuson, Charles R.	1908-03-10	881,268
Tutt, John C.	1900-04-10	647,341
Ullman, Louis	1920-04-20	1,337,860
Ulmer, Sarah, A.	1880-02-03	224,117
Usher, Frederick S.	1917-02-06	1,214,975
Valy, Maximillian A.	1909-08-17	931,100
Van Deusen, W.A.	1894-03-13	516,415
Van Engelen, Lucy	1911-05-02	991,253
Van Guilder, Walter	1936-07-14	2,047,841
Van Houten, Frank H.	1909-12-07	942,116
Van Woert, Kenneth	1934-11-20	1,981,531
Van Woert, Kenneth B.	1939-01-17	D-112,953
Vasconcelles, Harvey	1907-09-10	865,620
Velissarides, V.	1916-12-19	1,208,862
Verbrugge, Henry A.	1946-03-19	2,396,975
Vickers, William	1886-10-12	350,708
Vidinghoff, Charles	1916-04-18	1,179,984
Viers, Burr D.	1920-11-16	1,359,208
Viner, John H.	1922-09-05	1,427,986
Vogel, Joseph M.	1925-02-10	1,525,967
Walker, Lena E.	1917-01-23	1,213,561
Walker, Sylvenus	1860-01-24	26,958
Walther, Henry S.	1920-09-28	1,354,230
Ward, James N.	1910-06-14	961,272
Ward, Paul S.	1925-08-11	1,548,919
Warner, Alonzo A.	1905-07-18	795,082

Inventor	Date	Pat. No.
Warner, Alonzo A.	1915-04-27	1,137,037
Warrington, Claude H.	1895-03-12	535,474
Washburn, Reginald	1910-02-08	948,750
Washburn, Reginald	1915-04-06	1,134,170
Washington, William	1905-01-31	781,247
Webber, Alexander	1897-09-28	590,782
Weber, Bertha E.	1903-10-27	742,264
Weber, Erwin	1921-03-22	1,372,578
Webster, Dudley	1867-12-10	72,136
Weed, Elisha L.	1902-06-03	701,432
Weeks, Charles D.	1894-11-27	529,764
Weidlich, Kunz	1923-05-08	1,454,199
Weimer, Philip G.	1940-12-17	2,224,941
Weisenback, A.	1901-10-22	684,966
Weissenborn, Oscar	1884-08-05	303,080
Welling, John Edward	1885-06-30	321,327
Wells, Harlan P.	1908-11-24	905,036
Wenk, Wilheim	1910-08-09	966,501
Werfel, Harry A.	1935-09-03	2,013,617
Werner, Charles	1934-12-18	1,984,557
Werner, Otto P.	1921-04-19	1,375,338
Werth, Reinhardt	1919-02-04	1,293,274
Wessell, George	1924-12-09	1,518,284
Wessell, George	1924-12-09	1,518,285
Westby, Adolph C	1911-12-19	1,012,489
Westby, Adolph C.	1913-09-30	1,074,397
Westerman, F.	1924-01-15	R-15,746
Westerman, Fred	1923-12-04	1,475,978
Westerman,Frederick	1922-12-12	1,438,281
Westover, George C.	1867-01-22	61,494
Wetzel, Hugo A.	1929-07-23	1,722,187
Wheeler, Levi E.	1934-04-10	1,954,507
Wheeler, William	1892-04-05	472,092
White, Albert	1891-03-31	449,187
White, Arthur S.	1927-11-29	1,650,777
Whitmann, Joseph H.	1937-10-19	2,096,442
Whitney, Edward H.	1891-11-24	463,818
Wickersham, William	1867-04-09	63,774
Wickstrom, Maurice	1915-01-12	1,124,567
Wiedersheim, John A.	1889-07-02	406,321
Wiegandt, Paul C.	1936-06-23	2,045,171
Wiester, William H.	1878-10-22	209,205
Wikidal, La Fayette	1887-08-02	367,569
Wikstedt, Frans F.	1917-05-15	1,225,907
Wiley, Frederick	1893-01-31	490,730
Wilkinson, David A.	1891-06-16	454,194
Williams, Harry S.	1950-08-22	2,520,075
Williams, Lewis	1870-01-04	98,533
Williams, Linus H.	1881-02-01	237,150
Williams, Marvin T.	1867-05-21	64,928
Williams, Nora	1921-09-20	1,391,439
Williams, Robert S.	1889-04-16	401,724
Williams, Turner	1870-05-31	103,811
Willing, John Edward	1884-06-03	299,884
Wilson, Robert Grout	1920-09-21	1,353,443
Wilson, Sylvanus C.	1868-03-10	75,340
Wilton, Ralph P.	1916-01-04	1,166,568
Wiltrout, Edgar I.	1924-05-27	1,495,367
Winter, David T.	1887-10-25	372,282
Wise, Clarence L.	1959-09-22	2,905,453
Wishart, Edward	1898-10-04	611,726
Witherbee, Mary	1917-12-18	1,250,539
Wittmann, Joseph H.	1942-03-31	2,278,398
Wittmann, Joseph H.	1954-03-02	2,670,938
Wolfe, Rowland H.	1922-03-14	1,409,209
Wood, Frances F.	1891-09-15	459,668
Woodruff, Oliver D.	1907-01-29	842,509
Wright, Horace C.	1936-04-21	2,038,256
Yerby, E.	1858-07-27	21,042
Yiakas, Esidoros	1915-12-14	1,164,443
Ziemba, John	1922-04-21	1,410,522
Zimmer, Myron	1936-08-04	2,049,727
Zimmer, Myron	1948-10-05	D-151,312
Zimmer, Myron J.	1940-05-28	D-120,771

Bibliography

Barlow, Ronald S. *Victorian Houseware Hardware & Kitchenware.* El Cajon, California: Windmill Publishing Company.

Burpee, Charles W. *History of Hartford County, Connecticut, 1633-1928.* Chicago: S.J. Clarke, 1928.

Celehar, Jane H. *Kitchens and Gadgets 1920 to 1950.* Des Moines, Iowa: Wallace-Homestead Book Company, 1982.

Celehar, Jane H. *Kitchens and Kitchenware.* Lombard, Illinois: Wallace-Homestead Book Company, 1985.

Directory of Manufacturers of Queens Borough New York City. New York: Chamber of Commerce of the Borough of Queens, 1918

Dover Stamping Company 1869. The American Historical Catalog Collection. Princeton, New Jersey: The Pyne Press, no date (reprint 1971).

Farmer, Fannie. *The Boston Cooking-School Cook Book.* Boston: Fannie Farmer, 1896

Florence, Gene. *Kitchen Glassware of the Depression Years.* Paducah, Kentucky: Collector Books, 1990.

Franklin, Linda Campbell. *From Hearth to Cookstove — Collectibles of the American Kitchen 1700-1930.* Florence, Alabama: House of Collectibles, 1975.

Franklin, Linda Campbell. *300 Years of Kitchen Collectibles.* Florence, Alabama: Books Americana, 1991.

Franklin, Linda Campbell. *300 Years of Kitchen Collectibles.* Iola, Wisconsin: Kruse Publications/Books Americana, 1997.

Franklin, Linda Campbell. *300 Years of Housekeeping Collectibles.* Florence, Alabama: Books Americana, 1992.

Griswold, B.J. *The Pictorial History of Fort Wayne, Indiana.* Fort Wayne, Indiana: B.J. Griswold, 1917.

Harland, Marion. *Breakfast, Lunch and Tea.* Part of *Common Sense in the Household* series. New York: Charles Scribner Sons, 1875.

Illustrated History of Lowell and Vicinity, Massachusetts. Lowell, Massachusetts: Courier-Citizen Company, 1897.

Lantz, Louise K. *Price Guide to Old Kitchenware.* Hydes, Maryland: Louise K. Lantz, 1965.

Lifshey, Earl. *The Housewares Story — A History of the American Housewares Industry.* Chicago: National Housewares Manufacturing Association, 1973.

Leavitt, Robert Keith. *Foundation for the Future: History of The Stanley Works.* New Britain, Connecticut: 1951.

Matranga, Victoria Kasuba. *America at Home: A Celebration of Twentieth-Century Housewares.* Rosemont, Illinois: National Housewares Manufacturers Association, 1997.

Orcutt, Samuel. *History of Torrington.* Albany, New York: J Munsell, 1878.

Practical Housekeeping, A Careful Compilation of Tried and Approved Recipes. Minneapolis, Minnesota: Buckeye Publishing Company, 1883.

Prize-Winning Recipes from Radio Contests. Star-Rite Magic Maid/Fitzgerald Mfg. Company, Torrington, Connecticut: 1932.

Seward, William Foote. *Binghamton and Broome County, New York: A History.* New York and Chicago: Lewis Historical Publishing Co., 1924.

Smith, Wayne. *Ice Cream Dippers.* Walkersville, Maryland: Wayne Smith, 1991.

Stone, Orra L. *History of Massachusetts Industries.* Boston-Chicago: The S. J. Clarke Publishing Co., 1930.

Thornton, Don. *The Eggbeater Book.* New York: Arbor House, 1983.

Thornton, Don. *Beat This! The Eggbeater Chronicles.* Sunnyvale, California: Off Beat Books, 1994.

Thornton, Don. *Apple Parers.* Sunnyvale, California: Off Beat Books, 1997.

Washburn, Charles G. *Industrial Worcester.* Worcester, Massachusetts: The Davis Press, 1917.

Wood, Oliver B. *Worcester: Its Past and Present.* Worcester, Massachusetts: Oliver B. Wood, 1888.

Index

Organizations

▶ **KOOKS, Kollectors Of Old Kitchen Stuff,** is dedicated to the collection, preservation and enjoyment of old kitchen tools. Information about KOOKS, its newsletter and very popular bi-annual conventions, is available by writing:

Dea Allen
KOOKS President
1605 Oscar
St. Joseph, MO 64505

▶ Information about membership in the **International Society of Apple Parer Enthusiasts,** which promotes interest in and appreciation of apple parers, can be obtained by writing:

John Gray
APEs President
Suite 1408
2180 Marine Drive
Oakville, Ont. L6L 5V2
CANADA

Order Information

You can order additional copies of this or any other Thornton House title directly from the author/ publisher. Save time and get an autographed copy to impress your friends!

The Eggbeater Chronicles, 2nd ed.
by Don Thornton
ISBN 0-9641243-4-3
352 pp. quality softcover
$44.95 + $5.50 shipping & handling

Apple Parers
by Don Thornton
ISBN 0-9641243-3-5
256 pp. quality softcover
  Comprehensive history, identification & price guide. Features 575 photos, 215 patents, catalog & advertising art, apple industry items, more…
$55 + $4.50 shipping & handling

Thornton House
1345 Poplar Avenue
Sunnyvale, CA 94087-3770

phone: (408) 737-0434
fax: (408) 737-0191
email: info@thorntonhouse.com

www.thorntonhouse.com/publishing.html

About the Author & Designer

Don and Diane Thornton, the chief executives and only employees of Thornton House, live in Sunnyvale, California with their dog Chico, and more than 900 eggbeaters.

About the Photographers

Don Simons was a nuclear physicist, but photography was his favorite pastime, winning him numerous awards. We all miss him greatly since his passing in 1996. This book was his final photography project.

Bob Arnold has been a freelance photographer for 25 years and lives in Sturbridge, Massachusetts with his wife Susan, their dog Chloe, and thousands of negatives.